An Introduction to

WAVES, RAYS AND RADIATION IN PLASMA MEDIA

An Introduction to

WAVES, RAYS AND RADIATION IN PLASMA MEDIA

J. J. BRANDSTATTER

Senior Mathematical Physicist,
Stanford Research Institute

McGRAW-HILL BOOK COMPANY, INC.

New York Toronto London

AN INTRODUCTION TO WAVES, RAYS AND RADIATION
IN PLASMA MEDIA

 Library of Congress Catalog Card Number 63-11104

07195

To the Memory of Dr. J. T. Bolljahn

PREFACE

This text, like many others, is the outgrowth of lecture notes on the theory and application of ray propagation in general media. These notes were prepared while the author was a lecturer at Stanford University and simultaneously conducting studies on the subject at Stanford Research Institute. Although the original intention was to prepare a short monograph on ray theory and its applications to the ionosphere with special emphasis on the anisotropic and inhomogeneous character of the medium, it soon became apparent that for a better understanding of both the theory and its applications it was necessary to introduce the wave theory background and thus establish the intimate connection between rays and waves.

There also existed numerous other factors which motivated the above decision. The recognition that the field of Plasma Physics was undergoing a rapid expansion in which the methods and concepts used in this field had much in common with those in others (*e.g.*, ionospheric research) was a strong influence. The understanding of propagation phenomena in magneto-elastic media, in semi-conductors, etc., provided some of the motivation. Radiation phenomena in anisotropic media is a continuing challenge. Besides these physical motivations the mathematical problems associated with them should provide a fruitful source of research.

It is inevitable that in order to understand propagation and radiation in plasma-like media, one must study those aspects of a plasma which influence or more generally affect the propagation of disturbances in such media. For such a study there are several alternative levels of approach. One of these is a purely mathematical one utilizing the theory of characteristics as a basis, another level of approach is a purely physical description where the so-called intuition provides the guidelines of thought and analysis. The choice adopted in this text lies somewhere between these two approaches, more in the spirit of mathematical physics which the author believes helps to bridge the gap between the abstract concepts and the applied nature of a variety of problems.

In the nine chapters that are presented the author has attempted to synthesize and unify the concepts and techniques which are considered as basic. Some of the chapters are self-contained, for example, Chapters I and II can be used to form an introduction to propagation in homogeneous unbounded anisotropic media. Chapter III which introduces the student to hydrodynamics should be combined with Chapters IV and V for a better understanding of magneto-hydrodynamics and those aspects of electrodynamics which utilizes hydrodynamic notions more fully than in a majority of elementary texts. Chapter VI is concerned with propagation in non-homogeneous media which are either plane or cylindrically stratified. In Chapter VII a self-contained treatment of the theory of ray propagation in an anisotropic medium is given in considerable detail. However, such topics as caustics, diffraction, etc., have been neglected since otherwise this chapter would become too voluminous. Chapter VIII introduces the reader to the microscopic approach of describing a low density plasma and finally, in Chapter IX, we give a formulation of radiation phenomena in homogeneous unbounded anisotropic media.

The text is aimed at the senior-graduate university student and its usefulness as a reference text for the scientist and engineer in government and industry will have to be judged on a separate basis. The source material for the main body of the text and the problems have been chosen from the basic papers in the literature of the field and from the author's own studies and interests. The mathematical level of maturity required to follow the development ranges from the elementary to the sophisticated. The problems have been selected to test the student's understanding of the material in each chapter, to enhance his physical intuition and mathematical skills, and to extend some of the theoretical aspects which were not considered in detail in the chapters. These problems are, in general, non-trivial. That is, they are not of the plug in-calculate answer type; in fact, the bulk of the problems are quite challenging.

Finally, the author wishes to acknowledge his gratitude to those persons who aided in bringing this text to fruition. In particular, to Prof. R. A. Helliwell of Stanford University and Dr. I. W. Yabroff of Stanford Research Institute for introducing the author to some of the important problems of their research interests; to Messrs. T. Morrin, G. Wiley and Dr. D. R. Scheuch for securing and continuing the support in the writing and preparation of the manuscript; to Charles Elkind for his excellent liaison with the publishers. I am especially grateful to Ronald Blum for his diligent and worthy contributions to the early chapters. Many thanks are due to Mary Armstrong and her co-workers for their efforts in bringing the manuscript to final form.

CONTENTS

AN INTRODUCTION TO WAVES, RAYS AND RADIATION IN PLASMA MEDIA

J. J. Brandstatter

CHAPTER I

BASIC MATHEMATICAL CONCEPTS OF WAVES AND RAYS IN PLASMAS

1. THE WAVE EQUATION

In many fields of physics and engineering, a phenomenon is often described by the propagation of some quantity of interest. For example, the description of sound in some medium can be given in terms of the propagation of a pressure distribution; in heat flow one is concerned with the propagation of temperature distributions, and so forth. We shall concern ourselves with those phenomena in which the quantity of interest is described by a wave equation. At first we shall consider a scalar wave equation of the form

$$\nabla^2\Psi(x_1, x_2, x_3, t) = \frac{\mu^2}{V_0^2}\frac{\partial^2\Psi(x_1, x_2, x_3, t)}{\partial t^2} . \tag{1.1}$$

The notation used indicates a right-handed rectangular cartesian coordinate system (x_1, x_2, x_3), and t is the time. The operator ∇^2 in this system is defined by

$$\nabla^2 = \frac{\partial^2}{\partial x_1^2} + \frac{\partial^2}{\partial x_2^2} + \frac{\partial^2}{\partial x_3^2} . \tag{1.2}$$

The significance of the other terms in (1.1), μ and V_0, will become clear in the subsequent discussion. The function Ψ represents the quantity which is being propagated (*e.g.*, pressure, temperature, electromagnetic field component, etc.). For convenience in writing we shall use the notation

$$\Psi(x_1, x_2, x_3, t) = \Psi(\mathbf{r}, t) , \tag{1.3}$$

the choice depending on what it is that we wish to emphasize. In (1.1) we imply that the medium is characterized by the parameters μ and V_0; in the propagation of light these represent, respectively, the phase refractive index and the speed of light in some reference medium. Any function which satisfies (1.1) is called a wave function, or simply a wave.

We may define a simple monochromatic wave by

$$\Psi(\mathbf{r}, t) = f(\mathbf{r}) e^{2\pi i \nu t} \tag{1.4}$$

where

$$f(\mathbf{r}) = A(\mathbf{r}) e^{-2\pi i \psi(\mathbf{r})} \tag{1.5}$$

The exponential form is very convenient to use, but it must always be understood that only the real part, $\mathrm{Re}(\Psi)$, of Ψ has physical significance.

It often happens that for a refracting medium, in which Ψ satisfies an equation of form (1.1), for example,

$$\nabla^2\Psi = \frac{1}{V^2}\frac{\partial^2\Psi}{\partial t^2} \quad ; \tag{1.6}$$

that the speed of propagation, V, is a function of position *and* frequency, ν. This dependence upon frequency is known as the *dispersion*. Furthermore, instead of defining V at each point of the medium, we can define an *index of refraction*, μ, with respect to some homogeneous reference medium in which the velocity of propagation V_0 is the same at all points. Then we define

$$\mu(\mathbf{r}) = \frac{V_0}{V(\mathbf{r})} \tag{1.7}$$

so that (1.6) is consistent with (1.1). Thus for a simple monochromatic wave

$$\frac{\partial^2\Psi}{\partial t^2} = -\omega^2\Psi \tag{1.8}$$

where $\omega = 2\pi\nu$ is the angular frequency.

Eq. (1.6) becomes

$$\nabla^2\Psi + \frac{\omega^2}{V^2}\,\Psi = \nabla^2\Psi + \frac{\omega^2\mu^2}{V_0^2}\,\Psi = 0 \tag{1.9}$$

or, after canceling $e^{2\pi i\nu t}$,

$$\nabla^2 f + \frac{\omega^2\mu^2}{V_0^2}\, f = 0 \quad . \tag{1.10}$$

2. HOMOGENEOUS ISOTROPIC MEDIA

In a homogeneous isotropic medium which is characterized by a constant index of refraction (μ is a function of frequency alone), we find the simple monochromatic solution of the wave equation:

$$\Psi(\mathbf{r}, t) = A \exp i\omega[t - (\mu/V_0)\mathbf{n}\cdot\mathbf{r}] \tag{2.1}$$

where A is a constant, and $\mathbf{n}$ a unit vector. This form of solution represents a plane monochromatic wave of amplitude A and angular frequency ω. The phase of the monochromatic wave is defined by

$$\phi = \omega[t - (\mu/V_0)\mathbf{n}\cdot\mathbf{r}] \quad , \tag{2.2}$$

and we note that at a given instant of time, the phase will be constant on the planes,

$$\mathbf{n}\cdot\mathbf{r} = \text{const.} \tag{2.3}$$

These are the *planes of equal phase*. The components of the unit vector, $\mathbf{n}$, are the direction cosines of the normal to these planes. As t increases, the values of the phase move in space by passing from one plane of equal phase to another. The phase is displaced in the direction $\mathbf{n}$, which is therefore known as the direction of propagation of the wave. The speed with which the phase is displaced in the direction $\mathbf{n}$ is easy to calculate: by definition this is the speed with which an observer must be displaced so as to always observe a fixed value of the phase. If ds is an element of length measured in the direction of propagation, then we can write

$$ds = \mathbf{n}\cdot d\mathbf{r} \quad . \tag{2.4}$$

Since the change in phase is due to changes in both time and position

$$d\phi = \omega dt - (\omega\mu/V_0)\mathbf{n} \cdot \mathbf{dr} \qquad (2.5)$$

and $d\phi = 0$ for an observer if he is displaced along $\mathbf{n}$ with speed

$$ds/dt = V_0/\mu \quad . \qquad (2.6)$$

This is the *phase speed*; $(ds/dt)\mathbf{n}$ is the *phase velocity*.

The *wavelength* , λ, of a plane wave is defined as the distance Δs traversed *in the direction* $\mathbf{n}$, *for fixed* t, during which the phase changes by 2π. This change is given by

$$2\pi = \Delta\phi = -(\mu\omega/V_0)\,\Delta s \qquad (2.7)$$

so that

$$\lambda = \Delta s = (2\pi V_0/\mu\omega) = V_0/\mu\nu \qquad (2.8)$$

is the wavelength . Thus, at any instant of time, wave surfaces of equal phase, $e^{i\phi}$, are separated by a normal distance λ.

If, instead of keeping t fixed, we fix a point in space and note the change in time required to produce a change in ϕ of amount 2π, we then define the *period* T of the oscillation

$$T = \Delta t = 2\pi/\omega \quad . \qquad (2.9)$$

Thus, after a time T the function (2.1) is restored to its original value. We may also note that

$$T = \mu\lambda/V_0 \quad . \qquad (2.10)$$

which results from using (2.8).

Dispersive Media— In the foregoing we tacitly assumed that μ was not a function of ν. If it is a function of ν, then we say the medium is *dispersive*, or that we have *dispersion*. The functional relation $\mu = \mu(\nu)$ is called the *law of dispersion*; one may also find dispersion laws given in the implicit form $F(\mu,\nu) = 0$.

In the dispersive case, Ψ satisfies a more general equation of the form

$$\nabla^2\Psi - \frac{1}{V_0^2}\frac{\partial^2\Psi}{\partial t^2} = K\Psi \tag{2.11}$$

with K constant. Such an equation can arise in a system undergoing forced oscillations. If we insert (2.1) into (2.11) we find

$$\left(-\frac{\omega^2}{V_0^2}\mu^2 + \frac{\omega^2}{V_0^2} - K\right)\Psi = 0 \tag{2.12}$$

so, if we put

$$\mu^2 = 1 - KV_0^2/\omega^2 \equiv [\mu(\nu)]^2 \tag{2.13}$$

then (2.11) has the same form as (1.9), although μ is now a function of ν.

We can achieve compactness in representing a plane wave if we introduce the wave (number) vector, or propagation vector, $\mathbf{k}$, defined by

$$\mathbf{k} = (2\pi/\lambda)\mathbf{n} = (\mu\omega/V_0)\mathbf{n} \quad . \tag{2.14}$$

With this notation the wave defined by (2.1) is now written as

$$\Psi(\mathbf{r}, t) = A \exp i(\omega t - \mathbf{k}\cdot\mathbf{r}) \quad . \tag{2.15}$$

We have thus far considered μ a real quantity, but now we will allow it to be complex. In this case the wave vector has complex components, $\mathbf{k} = \mathbf{k}_1 - i\mathbf{k}_2$, where $\mathbf{k}_1$ and $\mathbf{k}_2$ are real vectors in the $\mathbf{n}$ direction. Therefore, (2.15) becomes

$$\Psi(\mathbf{r}, t) = Ae^{-\mathbf{k}_2\cdot\mathbf{r}}\, e^{i(\omega t - \mathbf{k}_1\cdot\mathbf{r})} \tag{2.16}$$

and we have either a growing wave or a damped wave, depending upon whether $\mathbf{k}_2 \cdot \mathbf{r}$ is negative or positive. In the latter case we term the wave *attenuated*. Since $\mathbf{k}_2$ is parallel to $\mathbf{n}$, the wave either grows or is attenuated as it propagates in that direction.

If we replace μ by the *complex* index of refraction, M, in Eq. (1.9), then the *most general* plane wave solution still has the form of Eq. (2.16), but $\mathbf{k}_1$ and $\mathbf{k}_2$ are not necessarily parallel. The vector $\mathbf{k}_1$ is still in the direction normal to the planes of constant phase, but $\mathbf{k}_2$ is normal to the *planes of constant amplitude* defined by

$$\mathbf{k}_2 \cdot \mathbf{r} = \text{const.} \tag{2.17}$$

Thus the wave form in (2.16) now has two distinct families of surfaces, and the necessary relations between the complex index of refraction and the complex wave vector are obtained by substituting (2.16) into (1.9) with M in place of μ:

$$\nabla^2\Psi + \omega^2 M^2/V_0^2\Psi = (-\mathbf{k}\cdot\mathbf{k} + \omega^2 M^2/V_0^2)\Psi = 0 \quad . \tag{2.18}$$

A close look at Eq. (2.18) shows that it is possible to generalize the notion of index of refraction by defining the complex *vector*, $\mathbf{M} = \boldsymbol{\mu} - i\boldsymbol{\chi}$, where $\boldsymbol{\mu}$ and $\boldsymbol{\chi}$ are real vectors. Then we can say that (2.18) is equivalent to

$$\mathbf{k}\cdot\mathbf{k} = (\omega/V_0)^2\,\mathbf{M}\cdot\mathbf{M} \tag{2.19}$$

or

$$\mathbf{k}_1 = (\omega/V_0)\mu\,\mathbf{n}_1 \tag{2.20}$$

$$\mathbf{k}_2 = (\omega/V_0)\chi\,\mathbf{n}_2 \tag{2.21}$$

where $\mathbf{n}_1$, $\mathbf{n}_2$ are unit vectors in the directions of $\boldsymbol{\mu}$, $\boldsymbol{\chi}$, respectively.

A wave of the form shown in (2.16) and satisfying Eqs. (2.20), (2.21) is called an *inhomogeneous plane wave*. The term $(\omega\chi/V_0)$ is the factor measuring the attenuation in the direction of most rapid change of amplitude; viz., the *extinction coefficient*. The *true* phase velocity is in the direction $\mathbf{k}_1$ which thus defines the direction of phase propagation, whereas $\mathbf{k}_2$ gives the *direction of extinction* of the wave.

Situations of this sort occur frequently in nature, usually arising from the presence of a damping term in the wave equation as in Eq. (2.11). For example it is well known that an electromagnetic wave attenuates rapidly upon penetrating a metal due to ohmic heating within the conductor which takes energy away from the electric field. Another case, which will be investigated in later chapters, is the scattering of electromagnetic radiation by charged particles in a plasma, where some of the energy is dissipated in collisions between particles.

3. NON-HOMOGENEOUS ISOTROPIC MEDIA: THE GEOMETRICAL OPTICS APPROXIMATION AND THE EIKONAL EQUATION

The treatment in Section 2 of the scalar wave equation for homogeneous isotropic media is quite simple and well known. Complications arise when the medium is *non-homogeneous* and isotropic: this means that the refractive index and the speed of propagation are functions, not only of frequency, but of position as well. In seeking a solution for this case we naturally proceed by analogy with the homogeneous situation; *i.e.*, we want to consider monochromatic solutions of the scalar wave equation, while retaining the general forms of (1.4) and (1.5). This means that A and ψ must be functions of position.

If we assume that A and ψ are sufficiently differentiable then inserting (1.5) into (1.10) yields:

$$\nabla^2 A - 4i\pi\,\mathbf{grad}\,\psi \cdot \mathbf{grad}\,A - 2\pi i A \Delta^2 \psi - 4\pi^2 A(\mathbf{grad}\,\psi)^2 + \frac{\omega^2\mu^2}{V_0^2} A = 0 \qquad (3.1)$$

after canceling the factor $e^{-2\pi i\psi}$. This equation gives two real equations obtained by requiring that the real and imaginary parts of (3.1) vanish separately:

$$4\pi^2(\mathbf{grad}\,\psi)^2 = \frac{\omega^2\mu^2}{V_0^2} + (A^{-1})\nabla^2 A \qquad (3.2)$$

$$\mathbf{grad}\,\psi \cdot \mathbf{grad}\,A + \frac{1}{2}\nabla^2\psi = 0 \quad . \qquad (3.3)$$

By analogy with the homogeneous case given in (2.7), and (2.8), we define the *local wavelength as*

$$\lambda(\mathbf{r}) = \frac{V_0}{\mu(\mathbf{r})\nu} = \frac{V(\mathbf{r})}{\nu} \,, \qquad \text{since} \quad \mu = \frac{V_0}{V} \,; \qquad (3.4)$$

or, equivalently,, by

$$\frac{d\psi}{ds} = \frac{1}{\lambda} \tag{3.5a}$$

where ds is an element of length along the normal to the surface, $\psi(\mathbf{r})$ = constant, at a given point; so that λ now varies from point to point. The surfaces $\psi(\mathbf{r})$ = constant are still called the surfaces of constant phase, but are no longer plane surfaces. Only locally can we consider them as planes; if the medium is homogeneous, then A is constant and we find

$$|\mathbf{grad}\ \psi| = 1/\lambda \quad ; \tag{3.5b}$$

V is still the speed with which an observer must be displaced along the normal to $\psi(\mathbf{r})$ = const. in order to continue observing the same fixed value of ψ. As in the homogeneous case the phase is given by

$$\phi = 2\pi[\nu t - \psi(\mathbf{r})] \quad . \tag{3.6}$$

The phase speed is calculated as before; the change in phase due to changes in time and distance, dt and ds, along the normal $\mathbf{n}$ is

$$d\phi = 2\pi\nu dt - 2\pi \frac{d\psi}{ds} ds \quad , \tag{3.7}$$

which vanishes when

$$V = \frac{ds}{dt} = \nu \left(\frac{d\psi}{ds}\right)^{-1} \quad . \tag{3.8}$$

The right side of this equation is the expression for the phase speed. As we move normal to the surfaces of constant ψ, we have

$$d\psi = |\mathbf{grad}\ \psi|\ ds \tag{3.9}$$

and making use of (3.8), we find

$$d\psi = (\nu/V)ds = |\mathbf{grad}\ \psi|\ ds \quad . \tag{3.10}$$

Therefore, from (3.5b),

$$V(\mathbf{r}) = \nu\lambda(\mathbf{r}) \quad . \tag{3.11}$$

Rays—It will be convenient to introduce the concept of the *rays* associated with the wave surfaces: the rays are defined by the curves whose tangents are parallel to **grad** ψ. Thus we may represent ψ as an integral,

$$\psi = \int_{P_0}^{P} d\psi = \int_{P_0}^{P} \frac{\nu}{V}\, ds \quad , \tag{3.12}$$

taken along the ray, starting from some initial point P_0 on the surface $\psi(\mathbf{r}) = \psi_0$. The solution of the scalar wave equation can then be put in the form

$$\Psi(\mathbf{r}, t) = A(\mathbf{r}) \exp 2\pi i \left(\nu t - \nu \int_{P_0}^{P} \frac{ds}{V} \right) \quad . \tag{3.13}$$

P_0 is called the *origin of phases relative to P*; it is a construct whose physical significance will become apparent. The defining equation for P_0 is such that if we take t_0 as the time corresponding to $\psi = \psi_0$, then at $t > t_0$ the change in phase of expression (3.13) is 2π:

$$\frac{\Delta\phi}{2\pi} = 1 = \nu(t - t_0) - \nu \int_{P_0}^{P} \frac{ds}{V} \quad . \tag{3.14}$$

Nature of the Approximation—In general $V(\mathbf{r})$ is not known *a priori*, and its determination entails the solution of the partial differential equations (3.2) and (3.3) for the functions $A(\mathbf{r})$ and $\psi(\mathbf{r})$. We want to avoid this difficult task, so we will examine the conditions for which it is possible to do so. That is, under what circumstances does the relation, $|\mathbf{grad}\ \psi| = 1/\lambda$, remain approximately true in the neighborhood of a point in an inhomogeneous medium? Equation (3.2) shows that the second term must be negligible with respect to the first term. Let us then examine the function $A(\mathbf{r})$ and consider the change in it when we go from $\mathbf{r}$ to $\mathbf{r} + \Delta\mathbf{r}$. A Taylor expansion yields

$$A(x+\Delta x) - A(x) = \frac{\partial A}{\partial x_i}\Delta x_i + \frac{1}{2}\frac{\partial^2 A}{\partial x_i \partial x_j}\Delta x_i \Delta x_j + \ldots \tag{3.15}$$

where the repeated index in a term implies summation on that index from 1 to 3.

Let us now choose a sphere of radius ϵ defined by

$$\epsilon^2 = (\Delta \mathbf{r})^2 = \Delta x_i \Delta x_i \quad , \tag{3.16}$$

where the Δx_i are independent of each other, and therefore uncorrelated. If we consider (3.15) averaged over the sphere, denoting the averages by $< >$, then

$$<\Delta x_i> = 0 \quad ; \quad <\Delta x_i \Delta x_j> = 0 \quad , \quad i \neq j \quad . \tag{3.17}$$

But

$$<(\Delta x_1)^2> = <(\Delta x_2)^2> = <(\Delta x_3)^2> = \frac{1}{3}<\Delta x_i \Delta x_i> = \frac{\epsilon^2}{3} \tag{3.18}$$

and therefore

$$<A(x+\Delta x) - A(x)> = \frac{1}{2}\left[\frac{\partial^2 A}{\partial x_1^2}<(\Delta x_1)^2> + \frac{\partial^2 A}{\partial x_2^2}<(\Delta x_2)^2> + \frac{\partial^2 A}{\partial x_3^2}<(\Delta x_3)^2>\right]$$

$$= \frac{\epsilon^2}{6}\nabla^2 A \tag{3.19}$$

since $<\partial^2 A/\partial x_i^2> = \partial^2 A/\partial x_i^2$ (the derivatives evaluated at $P(x)$ are constants). If we choose $\epsilon = \lambda(x)$, then (3.19) becomes:

$$<A(x+\Delta x) - A(x)> = \frac{\lambda^2}{6}\nabla^2 A \quad . \tag{3.20}$$

Thus we see that if

$$\frac{\nabla^2 A}{A} << \frac{4\pi^2}{\lambda^2} \tag{3.21}$$

it must follow that

$$\langle A(x+\Delta x) - A(x)\rangle = \frac{\lambda^2}{6}\ \nabla^2 A \ll \frac{2\pi^2}{3} A \quad . \tag{3.22}$$

This inequality states that the average value of the fluctuations of A in the neighborhood of $P(x)$, in which the dimensions are of the order of $\lambda(x)$, is very much smaller than $A(x)$ itself. This, then, is the necessary and sufficient condition to be able to neglect the second term on the right side of (3.2).

If we examine (3.3), using the definition of wavelength in (3.5b) and multiplying by λ^2, then

$$\lambda\left(\frac{d\psi}{ds}\right)^{-1} \mathbf{grad}\ \psi \cdot \mathbf{grad}\ A + \frac{1}{2}\lambda^2 A\nabla^2\psi = 0 \quad . \tag{3.23}$$

However,

$$\frac{d\psi}{ds} = |\mathbf{grad}\ \psi| \tag{3.24}$$

$$\mathbf{grad}\ \psi \cdot \mathbf{grad}\ A = |\mathbf{grad}\ \psi|\ |\mathbf{grad}\ A|\ \cos\theta \tag{3.25}$$

where θ is the angle between $\mathbf{grad}\ \psi$ and $\mathbf{grad}\ A$. If we divide (3.24) by A and use (3.25), then

$$\frac{\lambda}{A}\ |\mathbf{grad}\ A|\ \cos\theta + \frac{1}{2}\lambda^2\nabla^2\psi = 0 \quad . \tag{3.26}$$

Since $|\mathbf{grad}\ A|\ \cos\theta = dA/ds$, we find

$$\frac{\lambda}{A}\ \frac{dA}{ds} + \frac{1}{2}\lambda^2\nabla^2\psi = 0 \tag{3.27a}$$

or,

$$\lambda\ \frac{d\ \log A}{ds} + \frac{1}{2}\lambda^2\nabla^2\psi = 0 \quad . \tag{3.27b}$$

Equation (3.22) implies the following inequalities:

$$|dA| = \left|\frac{\partial A}{\partial x_1}\right| |dx_1| < |\lambda| \left|\frac{\partial A}{\partial x_1}\right| << A \tag{3.28}$$

and similarly for x_2 and x_3. Applying this result to (3.27b) shows that the first term is negligible with respect to the second term; hence (3.2) and (3.3) reduce to

$$|\mathbf{grad}\ \psi|^2 = \frac{\mu^2\nu^2}{V_0^2} \quad , \tag{3.29}$$

$$\lambda^2\nabla^2\psi = 0 \quad . \tag{3.30}$$

Equation (3.29) is called the *Eikonal equation*, or the equation of geometrical optics. We note that only the *magnitude* of **grad** ψ is determined by this equation.

From (3.4) and (3.11) we can write

$$V(x) = \frac{\nu}{|\mathbf{grad}\ \psi|} = \frac{V_0}{\mu(x)} \quad , \tag{3.31a}$$

$$\lambda = \frac{V}{\nu} = \frac{V_0}{(\mu\nu)} \quad . \tag{3.31b}$$

Equation (3.31a) shows that if $\mu(x)$ is practically constant within a distance of the order of a wavelength , then so are V_0/μ and $|\mathbf{grad}\ \psi|$. Thus we can consider $|\mathbf{grad}\ \psi|$ as linear in the variables x_i, and therefore the second derivatives of ψ must vanish, which means that (3.30) is necessarily true. The expression (3.13) furnishes us with the approximate solution to the wave equation. Therefore, we have derived the phase $\psi(\mathbf{r})$ without having to find $A(\mathbf{r})$, since μ is assumed known. The method we have used in obtaining ψ is substantially the WKB approximation, which is, in essence, an asymptotic solution to the scalar wave equation. Qualitatively, the assumptions made in deriving the solution are equivalent to saying: we assume that the properties characterizing the medium are slowly varying within a distance of the order of a wavelength; therefore, we may treat μ as uniform over this distance. In other words, we consider the medium to be *locally homogeneous*, assuming also, that μ is continuous.

Amplitude Variations and the Fluid Analogue—It is now interesting to examine (3.3) on its own merits, and observe the manner in which the amplitude varies. If we multiply (3.3) by $2A$ we have

$$\mathbf{grad}\ \psi \cdot \mathbf{grad}\ A^2 + A^2 \operatorname{div} \mathbf{grad}\ \psi = 0 \tag{3.32}$$

or, more compactly,

$$\operatorname{div}\ (A^2\ \mathbf{grad}\ \psi) = 0 \quad . \tag{3.33}$$

This divergence expression suggests the conservation law (equation of continuity) as applied to a fluid. In our case, let us, by analogy, consider A^2 **grad** ψ proportional to the *current density* of a fictitious fluid, and take its integral over a closed surface, Σ, surrounding a region of volume R. The divergence theorem gives

$$0 = \int_R \operatorname{div}(A^2\ \mathbf{grad}\ \psi)\, dR = \int_\Sigma A^2\ \mathbf{grad}\ \psi \cdot \mathbf{n}\, d\Sigma \tag{3.34}$$

where **grad** $\psi \cdot$ **n** is the directional derivative of ψ normal to the surface Σ. If we consider this fictitious fluid to have (material) density proportional to A^2 and velocity proportional to **grad** ψ then (3.34) states that A^2 is conserved in time.

If we assume that $|A|^2 = |\Psi|^2$ is a measure of the energy localized in the wave at each point, that **grad** ψ is proportional to the velocity of the energy flux at each point, and that **grad** ψ is directed along the ray associated with the wave; then it appears as if the energy *is a fluid which is conserved as it flows along the rays*. Thus, the rays appear as trajectories of energy, a thin pencil of rays being analogous to a tube through which the energy flows.

4. THE FOURIER TRANSFORM AND WAVE PACKETS IN HOMOGENEOUS MEDIA

The concepts of energy propagation and group velocity are tied very closely with the notion of a *wave packet* or *group of waves*. In this section we will develop the ideas and formulas leading to the concept of a wave packet: first for a non-attenuating medium, and then, more generally, for the attenuating case. These formulas will then be used in conjunction with the appropriate assumptions to develop variational principles for the trajectories of energy, amplitude, and phase propagation. Thus, we shall also lead to a generalization or extension of Fermat's Principle for absorbing media. The simplest and most natural approach to the subject is through the ideas and tools of the Fourier Transform, and the Principle of Stationary Phase.

Plane Monochromatic Waves--The plane monochromatic wave must really be considered as an abstraction, since it occupies all space and time. If one considers the type of experiments in which the speed of light is actually measured—revolving mirrors, toothed wheels, etc.—one observes the results of an *interrupted wave train*. A wave always occupies a bounded region of space at a given instant and at a given point; it always has a beginning and an end. A wave defined in this way is called a *wave train*.

In order to represent a wave train, we do not consider a single plane monochromatic wave, but an ensemble of plane monochromatic waves. Such an ensemble is represented by

$$\Psi(\mathbf{r},t) = \Sigma_\nu A(\nu,\mathbf{n}) \exp 2\pi i \, [\nu t - (\nu\mu/V_0)\mathbf{n}\cdot\mathbf{r} + \delta(\nu,\mathbf{n})] \qquad (4.1)$$

the sum being either finite or infinite. The notation $A(\nu,\mathbf{n})$ means $A(\nu,n_1,n_2,n_3)$ with $\mathbf{n}\cdot\mathbf{n} = 1$; $\delta(\nu,\mathbf{n})$ indicates that each wave has a different phase. Clearly, Ψ satisfies a wave equation if each wave does so separately, at least for the case of a finite sum. For an infinite sum the usual questions of convergence arise.

Let us also consider an *integral* solution of the wave equation. In this case

$$\Psi(\mathbf{r},t) = \iiint A(\nu,n_1,n_2) \exp 2\pi i \left[\nu t - \frac{\nu\mu}{V_0}\mathbf{n}\cdot\mathbf{r} + \delta(\nu,n_1,n_2)\right] d\nu dn_1 dn_2 \qquad (4.2)$$

with no integration over n_3, since it is determined by the normalization condition, $\mathbf{n} \cdot \mathbf{n} = 1$.

If μ is a function of ν, then we replace μ everywhere by $\mu(\nu)$. As in the previous section, we introduce the wave vector $\mathbf{k}$, which we shall, at first, assume real; *i.e.*, $\mu(\nu)$ is real.

Wave Trains—To demonstrate that the representation of a wave train by an ensemble of plane waves is possible, consider the case of a wave train propagating in a given direction defined by the wave vector $\mathbf{k}_0$, $\mathbf{k}_0 = (2\pi\mu\nu_0/V_0)\mathbf{n}_0$, where ν_0 is some central frequency and $\mathbf{n}_0$ some average direction. We wish to represent the wave train in the form

$$\Psi(\mathbf{r}, t) = A(\mathbf{r}, t) \exp i(\omega t - \mathbf{k}_0 \cdot \mathbf{r}) \quad . \tag{4.3}$$

Let $A(\mathbf{r}, t)$ be symmetric about the direction of $\mathbf{k}_0$: then, since the wave train is bounded in space, the amplitude, A, for a fixed t, will be different from zero only for values of $\mathbf{r}$ such that

$$\bar{x}_i - \Delta x_i < x_i < \bar{x}_i + \Delta x_i \qquad (i = 1,2,3) \quad , \tag{4.4}$$

where the $\bar{x}_i$ are the coordinates of some fixed point $\bar{\mathbf{r}}$, and the Δx_i represent a three-dimensional interval about this fixed point. For convenience we will take the fixed point as the origin, $\bar{x}_i = 0$. This interval determines the region in which the wave train differs significantly from zero.

The analysis is further simplified if we assume that in the region occupied by the wave train A is practically uniform at some fixed instant of time, except near the boundaries of the region where it falls off rapidly to zero. Therefore, *inside the region the wave train coincides with a plane monochromatic wave*, but clearly differs from it on the boundaries.

Wave Packets—Thus we arrive at the following qualitative definition: a *wave packet or group of waves* is an ensemble of plane monochromatic waves whose frequencies and directions of propagation are arbitrarily close to each other.

We shall now show that the wave train can be represented by such a group of waves if we assume that the dimensions of the wave train are large compared to λ, and that its duration in time is large compared with the period T.

Because of its symmetry property, $\boldsymbol{A}(\mathbf{r},t)$ is an even function with respect to $\mathbf{k}_0$, so if we succeed in representing the wave train by a wave packet it will be of the form:

$$\Phi(\mathbf{r},t) = \int_{\mathbf{k}_0-\Delta\mathbf{k}}^{\mathbf{k}_0+\Delta\mathbf{k}} f(\mathbf{k},\mathbf{k}_0)\ \exp\ i\ [\omega t - \mathbf{k}\cdot\mathbf{r} + \delta(\mathbf{k})]d\mathbf{k} \qquad (4.5)$$

This, it should be understood, is just a compact way of expressing the multiple integral

$$\int_{n_{2_0}-\Delta n_2}^{n_{2_0}+\Delta n_2} dn_2 \int_{n_{1_0}-\Delta n_1}^{n_{1_0}+\Delta n_1} dn_1 \int_{\omega_0-\Delta\omega}^{\omega_0+\Delta\omega} d\omega f(\omega,\omega_0;n_1,n_2,n_{1_0},n_{2_0})\ \exp\ i[\omega t - \mathbf{k}\cdot\mathbf{r} + \delta(\omega,n_1,n_2)]$$

An integration over a range of frequencies $\Delta\omega$ about some center frequency ω_0; *i.e.*, $\omega_0 - \Delta\omega < \omega < \omega_0 + \Delta\omega$; and over a range of directions about $\mathbf{n}_0$. The function $f(\mathbf{k},\mathbf{k}_0)$ then weights each plane wave according to its direction and frequency, and the result is summed (integrated) over the band of wave vectors within $\Delta\mathbf{k}$ of $\mathbf{k}_0$. The function $f(\mathbf{k},\mathbf{k}_0)$ is a smooth function which is large near $\mathbf{k} = \mathbf{k}_0$ and symmetric about the direction of propagation, falling to zero rapidly outside of the interval $\pm|\Delta\mathbf{k}|$. We shall, however, expressly exclude functions which oscillate rapidly within the interval about $\mathbf{k}_0$.

Locally Plane Waves—Strictly speaking, it is only when the magnitude of $\Delta\mathbf{k}$ is sufficiently small that (4.5) is called a wave *packet*, and $\mathbf{k}_0$ characterizing its center. Since $\mu = \mu(\nu)$, then $\omega = [2\pi V_0/\lambda\mu(\nu)]$ is not a simple function of λ or of $|\mathbf{k}|$. Let us denote ω as a function of $\mathbf{k}$ by $\omega(\mathbf{k})$ and assume that it can be expanded about $\mathbf{k}_0$ as

$$\omega(\mathbf{k}) = \omega(\mathbf{k}_0) + (\mathbf{k} - \mathbf{k}_0)\cdot\left(\frac{\partial\omega}{\partial\mathbf{k}}\right)_0 + \ldots \qquad (4.7a)$$

retaining only the first order terms. The notation used here is equivalent to that employed in (3.15); that is,

$$(\mathbf{k} - \mathbf{k}_0) \cdot \left(\frac{\partial\omega}{\partial\mathbf{k}}\right)_0 = (\mathbf{k} - \mathbf{k}_0)_i \left(\frac{\partial\omega}{\partial\mathbf{k}}\right)_{i0} , \qquad (4.7b)$$

where the subscript (0) indicates that the derivatives are to be evaluated at $\mathbf{k} = \mathbf{k}_0$.

In the following treatment we shall retain the vector symbolism of (4.7), defining $\omega_0 = \omega(\mathbf{k}_0)$, and simplifying the analysis by taking all the phases $\delta(\mathbf{k}) = 0$. If we then add and subtract $i\mathbf{k}_0 \cdot \mathbf{r}$ to the exponent in (4.5) we have

$$\Phi(\mathbf{r}, t) \approx e^{i(\omega t - \mathbf{k}_0 \cdot \mathbf{r})} \int_{\mathbf{k}_0 - \Delta\mathbf{k}}^{\mathbf{k}_0 + \Delta\mathbf{k}} f(\mathbf{k}, \mathbf{k}_0) \exp i \left\{ (\mathbf{k} - \mathbf{k}_0) \cdot \left[\left(\frac{\partial\omega}{\partial\mathbf{k}}\right)_0 t - \mathbf{r} \right] \right\} d\mathbf{k} . \qquad (4.8)$$

We obtain a full identification of (4.8) with (4.3), if we set $\Phi(\mathbf{r}, t) = \Psi(\mathbf{r}, t)$; *i.e.*,

$$A(\mathbf{r}, t) = \int_{\mathbf{k}_0 - \Delta\mathbf{k}}^{\mathbf{k}_0 + \Delta\mathbf{k}} f(\mathbf{k}, \mathbf{k}_0) \exp i \left\{ (\mathbf{k} - \mathbf{k}_0) \cdot \left[\left(\frac{\partial\omega}{\partial\mathbf{k}}\right)_0 t - \mathbf{r} \right] \right\} d\mathbf{k} . \qquad (4.9)$$

This representation of A is required if we are to describe the wave train by a wave packet.

In a small neighborhood of $\mathbf{k}_0$ we can consider $f(\mathbf{k}, \mathbf{k}_0) = f(\mathbf{k} - \mathbf{k}_0)$, and if $f(\mathbf{k} - \mathbf{k}_0)$ is chosen so as to vanish outside of this small neighborhood, $\Delta\mathbf{k}$ of $\mathbf{k}_0$, then nothing is changed if we allow the limits of the integral in (4.9) to extend to infinity. If we make the substitutions:

$$\mathbf{u} = \mathbf{k} - \mathbf{k}_0 \quad ; \quad \mathbf{V}_g = \left(\frac{\partial\omega}{\partial\mathbf{k}}\right)_0 \quad ; \quad \mathbf{w} = \mathbf{V}_g t - \mathbf{r} \qquad (4.10)$$

then $A(\mathbf{r}, t)$ can be expressed in the following form

$$A(\mathbf{r}, t) = A(\mathbf{w}) = (2\pi)^{-3/2} \int_{-\infty}^{\infty} f(\mathbf{u}) e^{i\mathbf{u} \cdot \mathbf{w}} d\mathbf{u} \qquad (4.11)$$

where a triple integral over the ranges of u_1, u_2, u_3 is implied [the factor $(2\pi)^{-3/2}$ is introduced for symmetry].

The theory of the Fourier Integral tells us that (4.11) is simply the Fourier Transform of $A(\mathbf{w})$, and that it is possible in this case to represent $f(\mathbf{u})$ by the inverse transformation:

$$f(\mathbf{u}) = (2\pi)^{-3/2} \int_{-\infty}^{\infty} A(\mathbf{w}) e^{-i\mathbf{u}\cdot\mathbf{w}}\, d\mathbf{w} \quad . \tag{4.12}$$

From this we see that the process of representing a wave train by means of a wave packet simply means that we must be able to reduce the Fourier transformations to integrals over very small ranges $\Delta\mathbf{u}$, and for this reduction to be possible, $f(\mathbf{k},\mathbf{k}_0)$ must vanish outside of the interval. Since we are assuming A practically constant in the interval Δx_i and vanishing outside of it, this is necessarily true.

Propagation— If we write A as in (4.9) the wave train can be put in the form

$$\Psi(\mathbf{r},t) = \exp i(\omega t - \mathbf{k}_0 \cdot \mathbf{r}) \int_{\mathbf{k}_0-\Delta\mathbf{k}}^{\mathbf{k}_0+\Delta\mathbf{k}} f(\mathbf{k},\mathbf{k}_0) \exp i \left\{ (\mathbf{k}-\mathbf{k}_0) \cdot \left[\left(\frac{\partial\omega}{\partial\mathbf{k}}\right)_0 t - \mathbf{r} \right] \right\} d\mathbf{k} \quad . \tag{4.13}$$

The factor $\exp i(\omega t - \mathbf{k}_0 \cdot \mathbf{r})$ represents the *group phase* and the multiple integral represents the *group amplitude*. We define the *propagation of the group* by the propagation of the group amplitude, and we can obtain information about this propagation by examining the surfaces of constant amplitude. By this we mean the surfaces for which the integral in (4.9) is constant; *i.e.*,

$$A(\mathbf{r},t) = \text{const.} \tag{4.14}$$

For (4.14) to hold it is sufficient that $f(\mathbf{k},\mathbf{k}_0)$ be a slowly-varying function and that the phase satisfy

$$(\mathbf{k}-\mathbf{k}_0) \cdot \left[\left(\frac{\partial\omega}{\partial\mathbf{k}}\right)_0 t - \mathbf{r} \right] = \text{const.} \tag{4.15}$$

These surfaces are propagated with a velocity given by

$$\frac{d\mathbf{r}}{dt} = \left(\frac{\partial\omega}{\partial\mathbf{k}}\right)_0 = \mathbf{V}_g \tag{4.16}$$

which is the defining equation for the *group velocity*. To illuminate the significance of the group velocity consider the situation when the index is *not* a function of the frequency. Then we have,

$$\Phi(\mathbf{r}, t) = \int_{\mathbf{k}_0-\Delta\mathbf{k}}^{\mathbf{k}_0+\Delta\mathbf{k}} f(\mathbf{k},\mathbf{k}_0) \exp i(\omega t - \mathbf{k}\cdot\mathbf{r})\, d\mathbf{k} \tag{4.17}$$

and since,

$$|\mathbf{k}| = \frac{\omega}{V_0} \quad ; \quad \omega t - \mathbf{k}\cdot\mathbf{r} = |\mathbf{k}|\,(V_0 t - \mathbf{n}\cdot\mathbf{r}) \quad ,$$

$$\Phi(\mathbf{r}, t) = \int_{\mathbf{k}_0-\Delta\mathbf{k}}^{\mathbf{k}_0+\Delta\mathbf{k}} f(\mathbf{k},\mathbf{k}_0) \exp i\,[|\mathbf{k}|\,(V_0 t - \mathbf{n}\cdot\mathbf{r})]\, d\mathbf{k} \quad . \tag{4.18}$$

This shows that Φ is a function only of $V_0 t - \mathbf{n}\cdot\mathbf{r}$ and therefore the pulse travels with the speed V_0 *without altering its shape*. The motion of the pulse results from the change of phase of all the different wave lengths in the pulse which arise from multiplication by $\exp i\,|\mathbf{k}|\,V_0 t$. So, for $t \neq 0$, the waves do not add up in phase at $\mathbf{r} = 0$, but instead are all in phase at the point $\mathbf{r} = V_0 t\,\mathbf{n}$. The change of position of the wave packet is therefore caused by the change of conditions for constructive and destructive interference.

The Principle of Stationary Phase—In the dispersive case, the wave packet still changes with time but in a more complicated manner than when $\omega = V_0|\mathbf{k}|$, since now it is clear that Φ is not a function of $V_0 t - \mathbf{n}\cdot\mathbf{r}$ alone. Consequently, the position of the center of the wave packet as well as its shape changes with time. To see how the packet moves as a whole, we examine the position of the maximum of the packet. In the non-dispersive case there exists at each instant one point where waves of different $\mathbf{k}$ do not interfere destructively and this occurs wherever the phase $\phi = \omega t - \mathbf{k} \cdot \mathbf{r}$ is an extremum. At this point there will be a range of $\mathbf{k}$ where all the waves have nearly the same phase; hence there will be constructive interference. This point is obtained from the fact that a necessary condition for an extremum is

$$\frac{\partial \phi}{\partial \mathbf{k}} = \left(\frac{\partial \omega}{\partial \mathbf{k}}\right) t - \mathbf{r} = 0 \quad ; \tag{4.19}$$

which implies that the *maximum* of the wave packet moves through space with the "group velocity"

$$\mathbf{V}_g = \left(\frac{\partial \omega}{\partial \mathbf{k}}\right)_{\mathbf{k}=\mathbf{k}_0} , \tag{4.20}$$

because it is the velocity with which the group of waves collected in the form of a packet, moves. In other words, if an observer moves along the direction $\mathbf{n}$ with velocity $\mathbf{V}_g$ he will always observe any pair of waves in phase with respect to each other. It is clear then that $\mathbf{V}_g$ is different from the phase velocity which is the velocity with which a point on a surface of constant phase moves. If $\omega(\mathbf{k})$ is proportional to k, then the group velocity coincides with the phase velocity.

Bandwidth and Uncertainty Relations—We will now examine the conditions under which a non-trivial wave packet can be obtained. If we look at Eq. (4.12) and recall that A is practically constant in the spatial neighborhood $2|\Delta\mathbf{r}|$, then if $\exp(-i\mathbf{u} \cdot \mathbf{w})$ has a large number of oscillations (or periods) in this interval they will tend to cancel each other in the integral (4.12) and $f(\mathbf{u})$ will be practically zero. Therefore, in order for $f(\mathbf{u})$ to have a value significantly different from zero, it is necessary, for fixed t, that

$$\mathbf{u} \cdot 2\Delta\mathbf{r} = (\mathbf{k} - \mathbf{k}_0) \cdot 2\Delta\mathbf{r} \cong 2\pi \quad , \tag{4.21}$$

where the sign $\cong$ means "the order of."

Now, $\mathbf{k} - \mathbf{k}_0$ represents a small departure of the wave vector $\mathbf{k}$ from $\mathbf{k}_0 = 2\pi/\lambda_0 \cdot \mathbf{n}_0$; let us denote this departure by $d\mathbf{k}$. But since,

$$\mathbf{k} = \frac{1}{\lambda\!\!\!^{-}}\mathbf{n} \quad , \quad \left(\lambda\!\!\!^{-} = \frac{\lambda}{2\pi}\right) \tag{4.22a}$$

$$d\mathbf{k} = \frac{\partial \mathbf{k}}{\partial \mathbf{n}} \cdot d\mathbf{n} + \frac{\partial \mathbf{k}}{\partial \lambda\!\!\!^{-}} d\lambda\!\!\!^{-} \quad , \tag{4.22b}$$

since $\mathbf{k}$ varies with $\lambda\!\!\!^{-}$ and $\mathbf{n}$. In (4.22a), first hold λ fixed, and obtain,

$$\frac{d\mathbf{n}}{\lambda\!\!\!^{-}} \cdot 2\Delta\mathbf{r} \cong 1 \quad ; \tag{4.23}$$

in order that,

$$|d\mathbf{n}| << |\mathbf{n}_0| = 1 \qquad (\text{since } \mathbf{n}_0 \cdot \mathbf{n}_0 = 1) \tag{4.24}$$

we must have $\lambda\!\!\!^{-} << 2|\Delta\mathbf{r}|$. This last requirement says that the dimensions of the wave train are *much greater than a wavelength* (which was one of the hypotheses made at the outset). Now let us keep $\mathbf{n}$ fixed and consider the change due to $\lambda\!\!\!^{-}$ (or ν): we find, in the elementary case, that $\mathbf{V}_g$ and $d\mathbf{k}$ are parallel

$$\mathbf{V}_g \cdot d\mathbf{k} = V_g dk = \left(\frac{\partial \omega}{\partial \mathbf{k}}\right) \cdot d\mathbf{k} = d\omega \tag{4.25}$$

therefore,

$$V_g = \frac{d\nu}{d(\lambda)} \quad , \tag{4.26}$$

and

$$\frac{\partial \mathbf{k}}{\partial \nu} = \mathbf{n}\frac{d}{d\nu}\left(\frac{1}{\lambda\!\!\!^{-}}\right) = 2\pi\mathbf{n}\frac{1}{V_0}\frac{d}{d\nu}(\mu\nu) = \frac{2\pi\mathbf{n}}{V_g} \quad , \tag{4.27}$$

then, substituting

$$\mathbf{n}\frac{d\nu}{V_g} \cdot 2\Delta\mathbf{r} \cong 1 \quad , \tag{4.28a}$$

or,

$$V_g \cong \mathbf{n}\Delta\nu \cdot 2\Delta\mathbf{r} \quad , \tag{4.28b}$$

and in order that $d\nu << \nu_0$, we must have

$$V_g \cong |d\nu| \; |2\Delta\mathbf{r}| << \nu_0| \; |2\Delta\mathbf{r}| \quad , \tag{4.29a}$$

or,

$$2|\Delta\mathbf{r}| >> \frac{V_g}{\nu_0} = V_g T_0 \quad , \tag{4.29b}$$

so that the product $V_g T_0$ is not, in general, equal to the wave length VT_0, where V is the phase speed, although the two quantities are sometimes of the same order of magnitude. We can now conclude that the wave train can be represented by a wave packet when all of its dimensions are large with respect to a wave length.

If $\mathbf{r}_1$ and $\mathbf{r}_2$ represent respectively the beginning and the end of the wave train, the time required by the train to completely pass a fixed point is obviously given by

$$t_2 - t_1 = \frac{|\mathbf{r}_2 - \mathbf{r}_1|}{V_g} \quad , \tag{4.30}$$

and according to (4.29b) this time must be very long with respect to the period ν_0. This was our second hypothesis. By the same reasoning as above but applied to Eq. (4.21) we find, ($\kappa = k/2\pi$)

$$2\Delta\,\mathbf{k} \cdot \Delta\mathbf{r} \cong 1 \quad , \tag{4.31}$$

that is, it is at least of the order of unity. Now we write,

$$\kappa \equiv \frac{\mathbf{n}}{\lambda} \quad , \tag{4.32}$$

and denote by $\delta\,\mathbf{k}$ the change in $\mathbf{k}$ which produces the maximum change in each component of $\mathbf{k}$. This change is due to a change in $\mathbf{n}$, say $\delta\mathbf{n}$, and a change in ν, say $\delta\nu$, and therefore,

$$\delta\mathbf{k} = \frac{\delta\mathbf{n}}{\lambda} + \frac{\mathbf{n}\delta\nu}{V_g} \quad ; \tag{4.33}$$

the maximum change in $\delta\mathbf{k}$ is then due to the maximum change in each component of $\delta\mathbf{n}$, and the maximum change of frequency in the group. If $|\delta\mathbf{r}| = 2|\Delta\mathbf{r}|$ is the *maximum extent* of the wave train, due to the maximum range of each component Δx_i we obtain,

$$\delta\mathbf{k} \cdot \delta\mathbf{r} = \frac{\delta\mathbf{n}}{\lambda} \cdot \delta\mathbf{r} + \frac{\mathbf{n}\delta\nu}{V_g} \cdot \delta\mathbf{r} \quad . \tag{4.34}$$

Since each term, in magnitude is at least of the order of unity, we conclude that for each component,

$$\delta k_1 \delta x_1 \geq 1 \quad , \quad \delta k_2 \delta x_2 \geq 1 \quad , \quad \delta k_3 \delta x_3 \geq 1 \quad . \tag{4.35}$$

If we also denote by

$$\delta t = t_2 - t_1 = \frac{|\mathbf{r}_2 - \mathbf{r}_1|}{V_g} \quad , \tag{4.36}$$

the time required for the wave train to pass a fixed point in space and if $\delta\nu$ is defined as above, we have from (4.29) and (4.30) the following inequality,

$$\nu_0 \delta t >> \delta\nu\delta t > 1 \quad . \tag{4.37}$$

The relations (4.35) and (4.37) constitute the *uncertainty relations*.*

The relation (4.37) is already familiar in radio transmission, *i.e.*, the fact that a pulse requires a band of frequencies, that is, a given bandwidth. More specifically, for a radio wave to carry audio-frequency pulses, the frequency of the radio wave must be displaced by an amount of the order of magnitude of the audio frequencies to be carried. Therefore, if we are tuned to receive a bandwidth of amount $\delta\nu$, the shortest pulse length that can be received has a duration $\delta t \cong 1/\delta\nu$. We see then that

---

* In quantum mechanics particle energy, $E = h\nu$, momentum $p = kh$; thus (4.35) and (4.37) are equivalent to Heisenberg's Principle.

the smaller $\delta\nu$ is in the spectral resolution of a given wave, the more nearly monochromatic is the wave. Thus, if a wave is more nearly monochromatic the larger the value of δt, that is, the slower the variation of the amplitude at a given point in space.

The significance of the relations (4.35) is given by the following considerations. A given beam of light of finite width *cannot* have a fixed direction of propagation. If $\mathbf{n}_0$ is the average direction of light propagation in the beam (for convenience we take the x_1-axis as this direction), and if $\delta\theta$ is of the order of magnitude of the deviation of the beam from its average direction, say in the x_2-x_3 plane, we find from (4.35)

$$\delta\theta \approx \frac{|\mathbf{k}_2|}{|\mathbf{k}|} \geq \frac{1}{|\mathbf{k}|\,\delta x_2}, \tag{4.38}$$

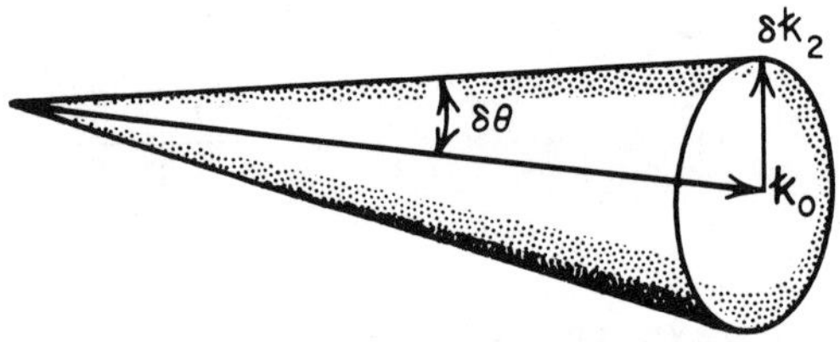

This relation also tells how sharp we can expect an optical image to be. For if we take a beam of light, all of whose rays theoretically would intersect in a point, it actually gives an image in the form of a spot, not a point. So, if δ denotes the maximum width of this spot, then by the above formula we have, $\delta \cong 1/k\theta \cong \lambda/\theta$, where θ is the opening angle of the beam. This relation holds for both image and object. Thus, in observing a beam of light emanating from a point, this point cannot be distinguished from a body of dimensions λ/θ. This determines the limit of resolution of a microscope. The smallest value of δ that is obtained say for $\theta \cong 1$ is λ, which agrees with the fact that the limit of geometrical optics is determined by the wavelength of light.

5. WAVE PACKETS IN NON-HOMOGENEOUS MEDIA

The concept of a wave packet or group of waves developed for homogeneous media can be carried over into a non-homogeneous medium which is also anisotropic and absorbing. First we consider the Eikonal equation (3.29):

$$(\mathbf{grad}\ \psi)^2 = \frac{\nu^2\mu^2}{V_0^2} . \tag{3.29}$$

The theory of partial differential equations teaches us that the surfaces of constant phase belong to a family of complete integrals of (3.29); indeed, it is a two-parameter family

$$\psi(\mathbf{r},\alpha,\beta) = \text{const.} \tag{5.1}$$

which comprises the solutions of (3.29). In the case of a homogeneous medium these are of the form

$$\psi = \left(\frac{\nu\mu}{V_0}\right) \mathbf{n} \cdot \mathbf{r} \tag{5.2}$$

with

$$n_3^2 = 1 - n_1^2 - n_2^2 \tag{5.3}$$

so that n_1, n_2 are the two parameters which in this case correspond to α,β in (5.1). A wave packet in a non-homogeneous medium then consists of an ensemble of simple sinusoidal waves whose frequencies lie in the small range $\omega_0 - \Delta\omega < \omega < \omega_0 + \Delta\omega$ for which the values of α,β lie within the small intervals $(\alpha - \Delta\alpha,\ \alpha + \Delta\alpha)$, $(\beta - \Delta\beta,\ \beta + \Delta\beta)$.

Absorbing Media— To treat absorbing media we utilize equation (1.10), but we must now replace μ by the *complex* index, M. By an argument exactly analogous to Section 3, we arrive at the corresponding Eikonal equation for the absorbing case:

$$(\mathbf{grad}\ \psi)^2 = \left(\frac{\nu^2}{V_0^2}\right) M^2 . \tag{5.4}$$

Hence, we put

$$\mathbf{grad}\ \psi = \left(\frac{\nu}{V_0}\right) \mathbf{M} \tag{5.5}$$

where $\mathbf{M}$ is now interpreted as a complex *wave normal* and ψ is a complex wave surface. We may define a unit wave normal, η, by

$$\eta = \frac{\mathbf{M}}{|\mathbf{M}|} = \frac{\mathbf{M}}{M} = \eta_1 + i\eta_2 \tag{5.6}$$

where $|\mathbf{M}| = (\mathbf{M} \cdot \mathbf{M})^{1/2}$; η_1 and η_2 are real vectors. And if we set

$$\psi = \psi_1 - i\psi_2 \quad ; \qquad \mathbf{M} = \mu - i\chi \tag{5. 7}$$

then, in general, $\mu = |\mu|$ and $\chi = |\chi|$ are also functions of the frequency.

The *complex phase* ψ is defined through the relation

$$\psi = \int_{P_0}^{P} \mathbf{grad}\ \psi \cdot d\mathbf{r} = \left(\frac{\nu}{V_0}\right) \int_{P_0}^{P} \mathbf{M} \cdot d\mathbf{r} \tag{5.8}$$

where $d\mathbf{r}$ is a real vector. The vector μ is normal to the family of surfaces ψ_1 = const. and χ is normal to the family ψ_2 = const. These surfaces are, in general, distinct; therefore,

$$2\pi\psi_1 = \left(\frac{\omega}{V_0}\right) \int_{P_0}^{P} \mu \cdot d\mathbf{r} \tag{5.9a}$$

$$2\pi\psi_2 = \left(\frac{\omega}{V_0}\right) \int_{P_0}^{P} \chi \cdot d\mathbf{r} \quad . \tag{5.9b}$$

Now we can write, substituting (5.6) into (5.9),

$$\left(\frac{\omega}{V_0}\right) \int \mu \cdot d\mathbf{r} = 2\pi \int [\mathrm{Re}(M)\eta_1 - \mathrm{Im}(M)\eta_2] \cdot d\mathbf{r} \tag{5.10a}$$

$$\left(\frac{\omega}{V_0}\right)\int \chi \cdot d\mathbf{r} = -2\pi \int [\mathrm{Im}(M)\eta_1 + \mathrm{Re}(M)\eta_2] \cdot d\mathbf{r} \tag{5.10b}$$

(Im = imaginary part; Re = real part). From (5.6) we also obtain the additional relations:

$$M^2 = (\mu - i\chi) \cdot (\mu - i\chi) = P - iQ \tag{5.11}$$

which is equivalent to

$$\mu^2 - \chi^2 = P \quad ; \qquad 2\mu\chi \cos\theta = Q \tag{5.12}$$

where θ is the angle between μ and χ,

$$\mu^2 = \frac{1}{2}\left\{P + \left[P^2 + \left(\frac{Q}{\cos\theta}\right)^2\right]^{1/2}\right\}, \tag{5.13a}$$

$$\chi^2 = \frac{1}{2}\left\{-P + \left[P^2 + \left(\frac{Q}{\cos\theta}\right)^2\right]^{1/2}\right\}. \tag{5.13b}$$

The first expression defines a *refractive index surface*, and the second, an *extinction index surface.*

We now define a *simple wave* in a non-homogeneous absorbing medium by

$$\Psi(\mathbf{r}, t) = A \exp(-2\pi\psi_2) \exp i(\omega t - 2\pi\psi_1) \tag{5.14}$$

with A a constant. The surfaces of constant phase are defined by

$$\phi = \omega t - 2\pi\psi_1 = \omega t - \left(\frac{\omega}{V_0}\right)\int \mu \cdot d\mathbf{r} = \text{const.} \tag{5.15a}$$

while those of constant amplitude are defined by ψ_2 = const., *i.e.*,

$$\left(\frac{\omega}{V_0}\right)\int \chi \cdot d\mathbf{r} = \text{const.} \tag{5.15b}$$

A group of waves in a non-homogeneous absorbing medium is defined by the multiple integral

$$\Phi(\mathbf{r}, t) = \int_{\eta_0-\Delta\eta}^{\eta_0+\Delta\eta} f_1(\eta,\eta_0,\Delta\eta)\, d\eta \int_{\omega_0-\Delta\omega}^{\omega_0+\Delta\omega} f_2(\omega,\omega_0,\Delta\omega) \exp(-2\pi\psi_2) \exp i(\omega - 2\pi\psi_1)\, d\omega \tag{5.16}$$

the function f_1 weighting the directions about η_0 and f_2 the frequencies about ω_0. Thus η_0 and ω_0 define the *center* of the group. The first integral is actually a triple integral over the components of η, but because of the constraint $\eta \cdot \eta = 1$, it can be reduced to a double integral. If ψ_{10} is the function ψ_1 corresponding to the center of the group, and we add and subtract $(\omega_0 t - 2\pi\psi_{10})$ from the exponent in the above integral, then

$$\Phi = e^{i(\omega_0 t - 2\pi\psi_{10})} \int f_1 d\eta \int f_2 \exp(-2\pi\psi_2) \exp i[(\omega-\omega_0)t - 2\pi(\psi_1 - \psi_{10})]\, d\omega \tag{5.17}$$

The phase of the group is

$$\phi_0 = \omega_0 t - 2\pi\psi_{10} \tag{5.18}$$

and the amplitude of the group is the integral in (5.17). A set of sufficient conditions for the amplitude of the group to be constant are:

(a) f_1 and f_2 must be slowly varying functions of their arguments;

(b) $|\psi_2| << |\psi_1|$ (5.19)

(c) the phase, defined by $\phi - \phi_0$ = const. is stationary (principle of stationary phase).

The number of terms in equation (5.15a) can be reduced by differentiation with respect to ω, which gives

$$t - 2\pi \frac{\partial\psi_1}{\partial\omega} = 0. \tag{5.20}$$

Under the same conditions as in (5.19) we can also apply the method of stationary phase to the expression (5.15a) and compare the results with [5.19(c)]. The surfaces of constant *wave phase* are obtained from (5.15a); those of constant *wave amplitude* are obtained from (5.15b) making use of (5.9); the surfaces of constant *group phase* by setting expression ϕ_0 equal to a constant; and the surfaces of constant *group amplitude* from (5.17). If all of these relations are expressed in integral form we have the following system of equations, which is now amenable to formulation as a variational problem:

$$V_0 \int dt - \int \boldsymbol{\mu} \cdot d\mathbf{r} = \text{const.} \quad , \qquad (5.15a')$$

$$\int \boldsymbol{\chi} \cdot d\mathbf{r} = \text{const.} \quad , \qquad (5.15b')$$

$$V_0 \int dt - \int \boldsymbol{\mu}_0 \cdot d\mathbf{r}_0 = \text{const.} \quad , \qquad (5.18')$$

$$V_0(\omega - \omega_0) \int dt + \omega_0 \int \boldsymbol{\mu}_0 \cdot d\mathbf{r}_0 - \omega \int \boldsymbol{\mu} \cdot d\mathbf{r} = \text{const.} \qquad (5.19c')$$

After differentiating the last equation with respect to ω we have

$$V_0 \int dt = \int d\mathbf{r} \cdot \frac{\partial}{\partial \omega} (\omega \boldsymbol{\mu}) \quad . \qquad (5.20')$$

6. FERMAT'S PRINCIPLE, AND ITS EXTENSION

The integral which appears in (3.13) is closely connected with the well known principle of Fermat, which states that the curves, if they exist, between two fixed points P_0 and P in the medium are such as to make the integral stationary. That is to say,

$$\delta \int_{P_0}^{P} \mu \, ds = 0 \quad . \qquad (6.1)$$

In general the index is a function of both position and *direction*, in which case the medium is *anisotropic*. The isotropic media lack the dependence upon direction; the differences between these two types of media will be discussed more fully in a subsequent chapter.

In a non-absorbing medium the ray paths are determined by the variational prescription $\delta\omega = 0$, $\delta t = 0$. If we apply this to the primed equations in Section 5, (5.18′) excepted, we find

$$\delta \int \boldsymbol{\mu} \cdot d\mathbf{r} = 0 \tag{6.2a}$$

$$\delta \int \boldsymbol{\chi} \cdot d\mathbf{r} = 0 \tag{6.2b}$$

$$\delta \int \mu \cdot d\mathbf{r} = 0 \tag{6.2c}$$

$$\delta \int \frac{\partial}{\partial\omega} (\omega\mu) \cdot d\mathbf{r} = 0 \quad . \tag{6.2d}$$

In the non-absorbing case (6.2a) gives the phase path which is always normal to the surfaces of constant phase. Similarly, the trajectory of the amplitude surfaces is also normal to the surfaces of constant amplitude.

Generalization Postulates—For the absorbing case we shall make the following postulates which will enable us to generalize Fermat's Principle:

(1) the phase paths are always normal to the surfaces of constant phase;

(2) the amplitude paths are always normal to the surfaces of constant amplitude.

This means that μ is tangent to a path element of the phase trajectory, and χ is tangent to an element of the amplitude trajectory. If we denote these elements by $d\mathbf{r}_p$ and $d\mathbf{r}_a$, respectively, then Figure 1 illustrates these relations.

FIG. 1

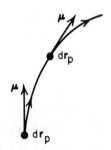

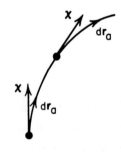

We note that although the expressions for these paths; *i.e,*, (6.2a) and (6.2c); appear to be identical, there is a difference in the path elements. *In an anisotropic medium the path of a ray is distinct from a phase path*; this fact will be derived in a later chapter.

If $d\mathbf{r}_g$ denotes an element of the path along which the group amplitude propagates, then the variational principle for this path is

$$\delta \int \mu \cdot d\mathbf{r}_g = \delta \int \frac{\partial}{\partial \omega}(\omega\mu) \cdot d\mathbf{r}_g = 0 \tag{6.3}$$

and we have the following Fig. 2 which is appropriate to this case in general:

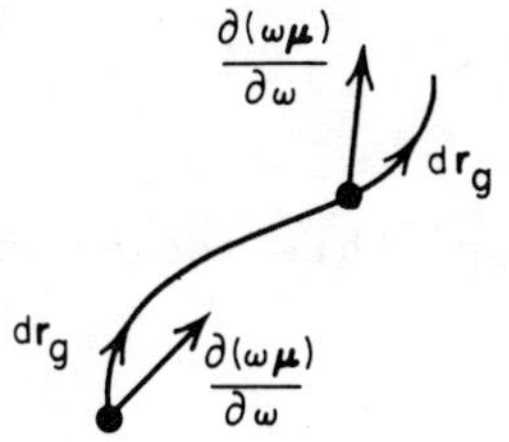

FIG. 2

If we denote the magnitude of $d\mathbf{r}$ by ds, the variational principles, equations (6.2), may be written:

$$\delta \int \mu \, ds_p = 0 \qquad \text{(wave phase)} \tag{6.4a}$$

$$\delta \int \chi \, ds_a = 0 \qquad \text{(wave amplitude)} \tag{6.4b}$$

$$\left.\begin{aligned} &\delta \int \mu \cos(\mu, d\mathbf{r}_g)\, ds_g = 0 && (6.4c) \\ &\delta \int \left| \frac{\partial}{\partial \omega}(\omega\mu) \right| \cos\left[\frac{\partial}{\partial \omega}(\omega\mu), d\mathbf{r}_g\right] ds_g = 0 && (6.4d) \end{aligned}\right\} \text{(group amplitude)}$$

where $\cos(\mu, d\mathbf{r}_g)$ is the cosine ot the angle between the vector μ and the element of group path; similarly for $\cos[\partial(\omega\mu)/\partial\omega, d\mathbf{r}_g]$. Equation (6.4a) constitutes the extension of Fermat's principle to an absorbing medium and from it we can see how absorption affects the phase trajectory. The remaining equations have similar interpretations. In a later chapter it will be demonstrated how to determine the group amplitude and wave phase trajectories explicitly.

The expression $\partial\omega\mu/\partial\omega$ is the basis for the definition of the *group velocity*. By definition, the displacement of (the center of) the wave group in a time dt is

$$d\mathbf{r}_g = \mathbf{V}_g dt \tag{6.5}$$

where $\mathbf{V}_g$ is the group velocity. Let us now define a vector, which we will indicate by $(\mathbf{V}_g)^{-1}$, such that

$$\mathbf{V}_g \cdot (\mathbf{V}_g)^{-1} = 1 \quad . \tag{6.6}$$

If we take the scalar product of this vector with both sides of (6,5) and integrate, we obtain

$$\int \mathbf{V}_g^{-1} \cdot d\mathbf{r}_g = \int dt \tag{6.7}$$

But from (5.20′) we see that

$$V_0 \int dt = \int \frac{\partial\omega\mu}{\partial\omega} \cdot d\mathbf{r}_g \tag{6.8}$$

and comparing these two equations we find

$$(\mathbf{V}_g)^{-1} = \left(\frac{1}{V_0}\right) \frac{\partial}{\partial\omega} (\omega\mu) \quad . \tag{6.9}$$

If $\mathbf{e}_1$, $\mathbf{e}_2$, $\mathbf{e}_3$ is an orthonormal set of vectors, we can consider $(\mathbf{V}_g)^{-1}$ as given by

$$(\mathbf{V}_g)^{-1} = \left(\frac{1}{V_{g1}}\right) \mathbf{e}_1 + \left(\frac{1}{V_{g2}}\right) \mathbf{e}_2 + \left(\frac{1}{V_{g3}}\right) \mathbf{e}_3 \quad . \tag{6.10}$$

It is important to realize that *the path of energy propagation is taken as the path of group amplitude.* This is certainly plausible when we consider that the energy of a field is usually proportional to the square of the amplitude of its oscillations, as we have already noted in Section 3 of this chapter.

In the case of an electromagnetic field it is not so clear that the group path is also the energy path. This question is closely tied up with the time-average Poynting vector, and a careful analysis is requisite to determining whether the Poynting vector is indeed parallel to the energy trajectory; *i.e.*, the group path.

7. THE POYNTING VECTOR AND ENERGY FLOW

Starting from Maxwell's equations (mks)

$$\mathbf{curl\ E} + \dot{\mathbf{B}} = 0 \tag{7.1a}$$

$$\mathbf{curl\ H} - \dot{\mathbf{D}} = \mathbf{J} \tag{7.1b}$$

$$\text{div}\ \mathbf{D} = \rho \tag{7.1c}$$

$$\text{div}\ \mathbf{B} = 0 \tag{7.1d}$$

with **E**, **H**, **B**, **D** the field vectors, **J** the current density and ρ the charge density. For a homogeneous absorbing medium we set $\rho = 0$, the current density **J** being uniform, whether due to conduction or convection.

For simplicity we shall consider a plane wave structure for the field **E** given by

$$\mathbf{E} = \mathbf{E}_0 \exp(-\mathbf{k}_2 \cdot \mathbf{r}) \exp i(\omega t - \mathbf{k}_1 \cdot \mathbf{r}) \tag{7.2}$$

where $\mathbf{E}_0$ may have complex components and $\mathbf{k}_1$, $\mathbf{k}_2$ are real vectors, the former giving the direction of phase propagation, the latter that of amplitude. As in Section 1 we have $\mathbf{k} = \mathbf{k}_1 - i\mathbf{k}_2$, so these vectors are identical with (2.16).

For an isotropic medium we have $\mathbf{B} = \mu_m \mathbf{H}$, where μ_m is the magnetic permeability of the medium. (Note: we shall adhere to the usual convention of taking μ_0 as the magnetic permeability *in vacuo*). In a rectangular cartesian frame for fields varying sinusoidally as $e^{i\omega t}$ equation (7.1a) yields the relation

$$\mathbf{k} \mathrm{x} \mathbf{E} = \mu_m \omega \mathbf{H} . \tag{7.3}$$

According to (2.16) this is equivalent to

$$\mu_m \omega \mathbf{H} = \left(\frac{\omega}{V_0}\right) (\mu \mathbf{n}_1 - i\chi \mathbf{n}_2) \,\mathbf{x}\mathbf{E} \quad . \tag{7.4}$$

The divergence relation (7.1c) with $\rho = 0$ and since $\mathbf{D} = \epsilon \mathbf{E}$, with ϵ a constant, yields

$$(\mu \mathbf{n}_1 - i\chi \mathbf{n}_2) \cdot \mathbf{E} = 0 \quad . \tag{7.5}$$

This implies

$$\mathbf{n}_1 \cdot \mathbf{E} \neq 0 \quad ; \qquad \mathbf{n}_1 \cdot \mathbf{H} \neq 0 \tag{7.6}$$

and we may conclude that neither $\mathbf{E}$ nor $\mathbf{H}$ is perpendicular to $\mathbf{n}_1$. However, they are both clearly **transverse** to $\mathbf{k}$, the *complex* wave normal. The relations (7.6) are not changed if $\mathbf{E}$ and $\mathbf{H}$ are replaced by real functions.

The time-average Poynting vector $\mathbf{s}$ is defined by

$$\mathbf{s} = \langle \mathrm{Re}(\mathbf{E}) \;\mathbf{x}\; \mathrm{Re}(\mathbf{H}) \rangle = \frac{1}{2} \mathrm{Re}(\mathbf{E}\mathbf{x}\mathbf{H}^*) \tag{7.7}$$

where $\mathbf{H}^*$ is the complex conjugate of $\mathbf{H}$. Using (7.3) we find

$$\begin{aligned} \mathbf{E}\mathbf{x}\mathbf{H}^* &= (\mu_m \omega)^{-1} \,\mathbf{E}\mathbf{x}\; (\mathbf{k}^* \mathbf{x} \mathbf{E}^*) \\ &= (\mu_m \omega)^{-1} \left[(\mathbf{E} \cdot \mathbf{E}^*)\mathbf{k}^* - (\mathbf{E} \cdot \mathbf{k}^*)\mathbf{E}^* \right] \quad ; \end{aligned} \tag{7.8}$$

since $\mathbf{E} \cdot \mathbf{E}^*$ is real and $\mathbf{k}^* = \mathbf{k}_1 + i\mathbf{k}_2$

$$\mathbf{s} = (2\mu_m \omega)^{-1} \left[(\mathbf{E} \cdot \mathbf{E}^*)\mathbf{k}_1 - \mathrm{Re}(\mathbf{E} \cdot \mathbf{k}^*)\mathbf{E}^* \right] \tag{7.9}$$

from which we conclude that

$$\mathbf{s}\mathbf{x}\mathbf{k}_1 \neq 0 \quad . \tag{7.10}$$

This significant relation states that $\mathbf{s}$ and $\mathbf{k}_1$ are linearly independent vectors since $\mathrm{Re}(\mathbf{E} \cdot \mathbf{k}^*)\mathbf{E}^*$ is in general not zero. Consequently, the direction of flow of electromagnetic energy, if measured by $\mathbf{s}$, is *not* in the direction of phase propagation in an absorbing medium, as prescribed by $\mathbf{k}_1$. This conclusion is not at all surprising when we consider that $\mathbf{s}$ measures the *total* energy flow, not just the optical portion of it. This is made more clear if we recall the classical derivation of the Poynting vector and its significance as given by the energy balance equation,

$$\dot{U} + Q + \int \mathbf{s} \cdot \mathbf{n} dA = 0 \tag{7.11}$$

where the energy density of the field is

$$U = U_{el} + U_{mag} \quad , \tag{7.12a}$$

$$U_{el} = \frac{1}{2} \mathbf{E} \cdot \mathbf{D}^* \quad , \tag{7.12b}$$

$$U_{mag} = \frac{1}{2} \mathbf{H} \cdot \mathbf{B}^* \quad , \tag{7.12c}$$

and Q is rate of energy dissipation per unit volume by means of non-ordered motion; analogous to ohmic heating.

BIBLIOGRAPHIES

1. Arzelies, H., On the calculation of the electromagnetic energy dissipated in a selective absorbing medium. Ann. de Physique, 12th Series, Vol. 2, pp. 536-554 (Sept.-Oct. 1947).
2. Arzelies, H., On the mean velocity of the energy in an absorbing heterogeneous ionized medium of slowly varying parameters. Comptes Rendus, 2nd Semestre, No. 6, Vol. 235, pp. 421-23 (1952).
3. Arzelies, H., Selective reflection and metallic reflection, Ann. de Physique, pp. 133-194, 12th Series, Vol. 2(March-April 1947). See also erratum.
4. Braun, G., On the method of stationary phase, Acta Physica Austriaca. Vol. 10, pp. 8-33 (1957).
5. Cap, F. and Rover, W., Lightpath in inhomogeneous, absorbing, isotropic media. Acta Physica Austriaca, Physik al. Verhandl. 6, 160, pp. 346-55 (1953).
6. Eckersley, T. L., On the connection between the ray theory of electric waves and dynamics. Proc. Roy. Soc. A, 132, 83 (1931).
7. Furutsu, K., On the group velocity, wave path and their relations to the Poynting vector of the electromagnetic field in an absorbing medium. J. Phys. Soc. Japan, 7, 458 (1952).
8. Gans, R., Propagation of light through an inhomogeneous medium. Ann. Phys., Lpg. 47,709 (1915).
9. Hines, C. O., Wavepackets, the Poynting Vector and energy flow. Part I. Non-dissipative anisotropic homogeneous media. Part II. Group propagation through dissipative isotropic media. Part IV. Poynting and Macdonald velocities in dissipative anisotropic media. J. Geophys. Res. 56, 63, 197, 207, 535.
10. Picht, J., Ann. der Physik, 3, 433 (1929).
11. Saxon, D. S., Modified WKB methods for the propagation and scattering of electromagnetic waves. IRE Trans. on Antennas and Propagation. Symposium on electromagnetic theory, Vol. AP-7 pp. 5320-23 (Dec. 1959)
12. Scott, J. C. W., The Poynting Vector in the Ionosphere, Proc. IRE, 38, p. 1057 (1950).
13. Suchy, K., Coupled wave equations for inhomogeneous anisotropic media, Z. Naturforschg., 9A, pp. 630-636 (24 April 1954).
14. Suchy, K., Stepwise transition from wave optics to ray optics in inhomogeneous anistropic absorbing media. I. Equations for the wave-normals, refractive index and polarization. Ann. Phys. 11, no. 2-3, pp. 113-30 (1952). See also corrections to the above.
15. Suchy, K., Stepwise transition .....II. Solution of the wave-normal equation and refractive index equation using the WKB approximation, ray-optical reflection and alternation. Ann. Phys. 13, No. 1-5, pp. 178-97 (1953).
16. Suchy, K., Stepwise transition .....III. Group Propagation. Ann. Phys. 14, No. 6-8, pp. 412-25 (1954).

GENERAL BIBLIOGRAPHIES

1.. Bateman, H., Partial Differential Eqs., Dover, (1944)
2. Bohm, D., Quantum Theory, Prentice-Hall, Inc., N.Y. (1951)
3. Born, M. and Wolf, E., Principles of Optics, Pergamon Press, N.Y. (1961).

4. Brekhovskikh, Leoned M., Waves in Layered Media, Academic Press, N.Y. (1960)

5. Bremmer, H., Terrestrial Radio Waves, Elsevier Pub. Co. Inc., N.Y. (1949)

6. Brillouin, L., Wave Propagation and Group Velocity, Academic Press, N.Y. (1960)

7. Budden, K. G., Radio Waves in the Ionosphere, Cambridge, (1961)

8. De Broglie, L., Non-Linear Wave Mechanics, Elsevier Pub. Co., Amsterdam, Holland (1960)

9. Landau and Lifshitz, Classical Theory of Fields, Addison-Wesley, Reading, Mass. (1951)

10. Landau and Lifshitz, Electrodynamics of Continuous Media, Addison-Wesley (1961)

11. Lindsay, R. B., Mechanical Radiation, McGraw-Hill Co., N.Y. (1960)

12. Panofsky and Philips, Classical Electricity and Magnetism, Addison-Wesley Pub. Co., Reading, Mass. (1955)

13. Petrovsky, I. G., Lectures on Partial Diff. Eqs., Interscience Pub. Inc., N.Y. (1954)

14. Sommerfed, A., Optics, Academic Press Inc., N.Y. (1954)

15. Stratton, J. A., Electromagnetic Theory, McGraw-Hill, N.Y. (1941)

CHAPTER II

THE HOMOGENEOUS ELECTRON PLASMA IN A UNIFORM MAGNETIC FIELD

8. THE LORENTZ THEORY

In the problems with which electromagnetic theory is concerned, two different viewpoints can be adopted; these viewpoints are:

(a) the macroscopic phenomenological theory of Maxwell;

(b) the exhaustive microscopic theory of Lorentz.

In the Maxwell theory the description of the actual phenomena is given on a macroscopic scale (*i.e.*, compared to the atomic particles of the medium). This avoids giving an explanation of what happens to the individual charged particles which constitute the medium in which the phenomena are taking place. In this theory the influence of the medium—that is, the subatomic particles comprising the medium—is accounted for by means of factors called *constitutive parameters*.

The effect on the electric field of equal numbers of oppositely charged particles comprising the medium is accounted for by the relative capacitivity, ϵ. The effects on the fields due to the *motions* of the charges comprising the medium are taken into account in the following manner:

(1) the motion of the unbound charges is subsumed under the *conduction current* by means of a *conductivity*, σ;

(2) the *translational motion* of the bound charges is subsumed in the *electric displacement* field by means of the *relative* capacitivity, ϵ;

(3) the *rotational motion* of the constituent charges is subsumed in the *magnetic* field by means of the *relative permeability*, μ_m.

This representation of the dynamical behavior of the constituent charges by means of the parameters ϵ, μ_m, σ, is of great practical importance. This importance lies in the advantage of being able to separate the investigation of the macroscopic behavior of the fields from that of the microscopic behavior of the constituents of the medium in which the fields are present. In many media the constitutive parameters can be determined by empirical means much more easily than by theoretical considerations. For such media the macroscopic theory is eminently most suitable.

In an isotropic dielectric medium $(\epsilon\mu_m)^{-1/2}$ is the speed of a wave propagating through it, and σ is the factor of proportionality between the conduction current density at any point in the medium and the electric intensity, **E**, at that point. Of course, these parameters will also depend on the temperature, frequency of the oscillation, etc. In macroscopic theory the total displacement current is the sum of the free space displacement current and the displacement current due to the dielectric.

In plasma-like media (ionized gases) it is difficult to measure the constitutive parameters; this is in contrast to media made up of neutral molecules. The difficulty arises from the fact that the space charges present and the boundary condition imposed by the measuring apparatus affect each other significantly. Thus, in order to determine these parameters a knowledge of the dynamical behavior of the microscopic constituents is required.

The Lorentz theory attempts to describe all electrical phenomena in terms of the elementary positive and negative charges comprising the medium. This microscopic theory dispenses with the concept of the material medium and considers only the ensemble of negative and positive charges (which actually constitute the medium) in free space. More specifically, this theory postulates that in all permeable bodies there exists a large number of charged particles of very small size which are separated from each other by free space. Conducting bodies are imagined to be constituted of a large number of free particles capable of being moved through the body under the action of an electric force. Non-conducting or weakly conducting bodies are considered to be made up of particles bound to their positions of equilibrium by an elastic force. Even though they are displaced from their equilibrium positions this displacement is not very large (small oscillations). It is also postulated that the medium has no net charge, that the positive and negative charges balance exactly. When particles are displaced from their equilibrium positions, the medium becomes polarized.

The Lorentz theory further assumes that the free space displacement current exists not only in the empty space between the particles but also within the particles themselves. The action of the material medium participates in this theory if we consider the motions of the charged particles under the influence of the electromagnetic forces as a fundamental concept. If each particle has a charge q, and a mass, m, then under the action of the electric force the particle will be displaced from its equilibrium position, and at time t it will have a velocity of magnitude v. However, the moving charge produces a current $q\mathbf{v}$, and if there are N such particles per unit volume, this gives rise to a convection current density $Nq\mathbf{v}$ (by $\mathbf{v}$ we understand the *time-average* value of the charge velocity). The average convection current density can be written as $Nq\mathbf{v} = \rho\mathbf{v}, = \mathbf{J}$ regardless of whether the charges are free or bound.

For varying fields, it is not clear *a priori* whether this total current is a conduction current proportional to the electric intensity and in phase with it, or a displacement current proportional to $\dot{\mathbf{E}}$ and out of phase with $\mathbf{E}$, the electric intensity, by $\pi/2$. Consequently, the total current density must be written as the sum of the free space displacement current and the material convection current.

Let us summarize the two views: the Maxwell theory describes the phenomena in terms of the equations

$$\mathbf{curl}\ \mathbf{E} + \dot{\mathbf{B}} = 0 , \tag{8.1a}$$

$$\mathbf{curl}\ \mathbf{H} = \mathbf{J} + \dot{\mathbf{D}} , \tag{8.1b}$$

$$\text{div}\ \mathbf{D} = \rho , \tag{8.1c}$$

$$\text{div}\ \mathbf{B} = 0 , \tag{8.1d}$$

supplemented by the relations

$$\mathbf{B} = \mu_m \mathbf{H} , \tag{8.1e}$$

$$\mathbf{D} = \epsilon \mathbf{E} , \tag{8.1f}$$

$$\mathbf{J} = \sigma \mathbf{E} . \tag{8.1g}$$

The Lorentz microscopic theory describes the electromagnetic phenomena by the same set of Maxwell's equations as given above, but since there is no medium in this point of view, the relations (8.1e, f, g) must be given *in vacuo*,

$$\mu_m = \mu_0; \qquad \epsilon = \epsilon_0, \tag{8.2}$$

and the current density is given directly in terms of the moving charges:

$$J = \sum_k q_k \mathbf{v}_k / \text{Volume of region containing charges} \tag{8.3}$$

Maxwell's equations relate the fields to the charges and their motions, but since these are not known, it is necessary to supplement them with the dynamical equations of motion for the charges. These equations have the form, for each particle, q_k:

$$\frac{d(m_k \mathbf{v}_k)}{dt} = q_k (\mathbf{E} + \mathbf{v}_k \mathbf{x} \mathbf{B}) \tag{8.4}$$

where $\mathbf{B}$ is the *total* magnetic induction field evaluated at the position, $\mathbf{r}_k$, of the kth particle; $\mathbf{E}$ is the *total* electric field evaluated at $\mathbf{r}_k$. These fields can consist in part of external fields, and in part of fields due to the q_k themselves.

The set of equations (8.1, 2, 3, 4) must be solved simultaneously for the dynamical behavior of the charges, and from this behavior we can derive the constitutive parameters for the macroscopic model of the medium.

In the Lorentz theory, the motion of the electrical charges is described in terms of the polarization vector (dipole moment per unit volume) rather than in terms of the convection current. In this case the polarization vector is $\mathbf{P} = Nq\mathbf{r}$, $\mathbf{r}$ being the average displacement of the charged particle. Consequently, $\mathbf{J} = \dot{\mathbf{P}}$.

9. PROPAGATION IN AN ISOTROPIC CONDUCTING MEDIUM

We will now consider the propagation of a plane electromagnetic wave in a conducting medium of infinite extent. The structure of the electric field is taken to be:

$$\mathbf{E} = \mathbf{E}_0 \exp i(\omega t - \mathbf{k} \cdot \mathbf{r}), \tag{9.1a}$$

$$\mathbf{H} = \mathbf{H}_0 \exp i(\omega t - \mathbf{k} \cdot \mathbf{r}), \tag{9.1b}$$

where $\mathbf{E}_0$, $\mathbf{H}_0$ are constant complex vectors, and $\mathbf{k}$ is a vector with complex components; thus,

$$\mathbf{k} = (k_1 - ik_2)\mathbf{n} \tag{9.2}$$

and $\mathbf{n}$ is a real unit vector in the direction of phase propagation. The equations describing the fields are given by (8.1), but here we put $\rho = 0$, assuming no net charge. These relations then become

$$\mathbf{curl\ E} = -i\mathbf{k}\mathrm{x}\mathbf{E} = -i\mu_m\omega\,\mathbf{H} \tag{9.3a}$$

$$\mathbf{curl\ H} = -i\mathbf{k}\mathrm{x}\mathbf{H} = (\sigma + i\epsilon\omega)\mathbf{E} \tag{9.3b}$$

$$\mathrm{div}\,\mathbf{D} = -i\mathbf{k}\cdot\mathbf{D} = 0 \tag{9.3c}$$

$$\mathrm{div}\,\mathbf{B} = -i\mathbf{k}\cdot\mathbf{B} = 0 \tag{9.3d}$$

Note that the last two relations imply that $\mathbf{E}$ and $\mathbf{H}$ are perpendicular to the direction of propagation. Substituting for $\mathbf{H}$ in (9.3b) using (9.3a) gives

$$\mathbf{k}\mathrm{x}(\mathbf{k}\,\mathrm{x}\,\mathbf{E}) = (\mathbf{k}\cdot\mathbf{E})\mathbf{k} - (\mathbf{k}\cdot\mathbf{k})\mathbf{E} = (i\omega\sigma\mu_m - \epsilon\mu_m\omega^2)\mathbf{E} \quad . \tag{9.4}$$

and since (9.3c) implies $\mathbf{k}\cdot\mathbf{E} = 0$ we have

$$(\mathbf{k}\cdot\mathbf{k})\mathbf{E} = (\epsilon\mu_m\omega^2 - i\omega\sigma\mu_m)\mathbf{E} \tag{9.5}$$

Therefore, the condition for propagation is that

$$\mathbf{k}\cdot\mathbf{k} = \epsilon\mu_m\omega^2 - i\omega\sigma\mu_m \tag{9.6}$$

which requires, by (9.2),

$$k_1^2 - k_2^2 = \epsilon\mu_m\omega^2 \tag{9.7a}$$

$$2k_1k_2 = \omega\sigma\mu_m \tag{9.7b}$$

These equations imply $|k_1| > |k_2|$ and that both must have the same sign. If k_1, k_2 were negative, then we would find a damped oscillatory field propagating in the $-\mathbf{n}$ direction; when they are positive the field propagates in the $\mathbf{n}$ direction. Let us consider the positive solutions. Solving (9.7)

$$k_1 = \omega(\mu_m \epsilon)^{1/2} \left\{ \frac{1 + [1 + (\sigma/\epsilon\omega)^2]^{1/2}}{2} \right\}^{1/2} \tag{9.8a}$$

$$k_2 = \omega(\mu_m \epsilon)^{1/2} \left\{ \frac{-1 + [1 + (\sigma/\epsilon\omega)^2]^{1/2}}{2} \right\}^{1/2} \tag{9.8b}$$

Refraction and Extinction Indices—Since, from (2.20) and (2.21)

$$k_1 = (\omega/V_0)\mu \tag{9.9a}$$

$$k_2 = (\omega/V_0)\chi \tag{9.9b}$$

we have the result that the speed of propagation is

$$|V| = V = (\eta^2 \mu_m \epsilon)^{-1/2} \tag{9.10}$$

with

$$\eta = \left\{ \frac{1 + [1 + (\sigma/\epsilon\omega)^2]^{1/2}}{2} \right\}^{1/2} > 1 \tag{9.11}$$

in which we define η to be the coefficient of reduction, and shows that the speed of propagation of an electromagnetic wave in an absorbing medium is less than the speed it would have in a medium whose conductivity was zero but which was otherwise identical to the first in its constitutive parameters, ϵ and μ. Such a medium would be non-absorbing, since (9.8b) clearly shows that k_2 vanishes.

The real index of refraction in the absorbing case is

$$\eta V_0 (\mu_m \epsilon)^{1/2} = \mu \tag{9.12a}$$

and the coefficient of extinction is

$$\chi = V_0(\mu_m \epsilon)^{1/2} \left\{ \frac{-1 + [1 + (\sigma/\epsilon\omega)^2]^{1/2}}{2} \right\}^{1/2} \tag{9.12b}$$

The absorption coefficient is defined by

$$k = \frac{k_2}{k_1} = \frac{\epsilon\omega}{\sigma} \left\{ -1 + [1 + (\sigma/\epsilon\omega)^2]^{1/2} \right\} \tag{9.13}$$

Cases for Limiting Frequencies—If one lets the frequency become very large, it can be seen that the extinction and absorption coefficients become vanishingly small, and the reduction coefficient goes to unity. Thus, for high enough frequencies an isotropic absorbing medium behaves like an isotropic transparent (non-absorbing) medium. This is physically reasonable, since at high enough frequencies the inertial masses of the particles composing the medium prevent them from following appreciably the rapid changes in the electromagnetic forces being exerted upon them. Thus, the conductivity, which is a measure of the effect of the electromagnetic forces upon the motion of charged particles, is essentially zero, and one has a formal identity with the non-conducting dielectric medium.

For low frequency (long wave-length), when $\sigma/\epsilon\omega >> 1$, the speed of propagation, V, approaches zero as $(\epsilon\omega/\sigma)^{1/2}$; therefore, the medium will not transmit waves of low frequency. In this case

$$k_2 \approx (\mu\omega\sigma)^{1/2} \tag{9.14}$$

a formula derived by J. J. Thompson.

If we define a quantity

$$\xi = \left\{ \frac{-1 + [1 + (\sigma/\epsilon\omega)^2]^{1/2}}{2} \right\}^{1/2} \tag{9.15}$$

then we have

$$\xi^2 + \eta^2 = [1 + (\sigma/\epsilon\omega)^2]^{1/2} \tag{9.16}$$

so, in the transparent medium, $\sigma = 0$,

$$\xi = 0, \qquad \eta = 1 \quad . \tag{9.17}$$

Relations Between the Electric and Magnetic Field Vectors—We know from (9.3c, d) that $\mathbf{E}_0$ and $\mathbf{H}_0$ are perpendicular to the direction of propagation, and we also know, from (9.3a) that $\mathbf{k}\mathbf{x}\mathbf{E} = \mu_m\omega\,\mathbf{H}$, which yields, when canceling the exponential factor common to both quantities, the complex scalar equation:

$$(k_1 - ik_2)\mathbf{E}_0 = \mu_m\omega\,\mathbf{H}_0 \quad . \tag{9.18}$$

Using Euler's form of the complex k:

$$(k_1^2 + k_2^2)^{1/2}e^{-i\delta}\mathbf{E}_0 = \mu_m\omega\,\mathbf{H}_0 \tag{9.19a}$$

where

$$\delta = \tan^{-1}(k_2/k_1) \quad . \tag{9.19b}$$

Thus we find that the magnitudes of electric and magnetic fields are related by:

$$\sqrt{\mu}|\mathbf{H}_0| = \sqrt{\epsilon}(\eta^2 + \xi^2)^{1/2}|\mathbf{E}_0| = \sqrt{\epsilon}[1 + (\sigma/\epsilon\omega)^2]^{1/4}\mathbf{E}_0 \quad . \tag{9.20}$$

This means that the ratio of energy stored in the magnetic field to that in the electric field is

$$U_{mag}/U_{el} = [1 + (\sigma/\epsilon\omega)^2]^{1/2} \quad . \tag{9.21}$$

The presence of δ in (9.19) also indicates that the magnetic field lags the electric field by a phase difference δ. In the limit of $\sigma/\epsilon\omega >> 1$, we find

$$U_{mag}/U_{el} = (\sigma/\epsilon\omega) >> 1, \tag{9.22}$$

indicating that almost all of the energy is stored in the magnetic field, and $\delta \rightarrow \pi/4$. The significance of δ is apparent from (7.7), where it appears in the Poynting vector as a factor $\cos\delta = (2)^{-1/2}$.

Note that $k_2 \approx \sqrt{\mu_m \omega\sigma/2}$ provides a damping factor exp $[-\mathbf{n} \cdot \mathbf{r}(\mu_m \omega\sigma/2)^{1/2}]$ exactly analogous to that in the case of skin effect in a metallic conductor where skin depth is defined as

$$d = \sqrt{\frac{2}{\mu_m \omega\sigma}} \quad . \tag{9.23}$$

10. PROPAGATION IN A HOMOGENEOUS ANISOTROPIC MEDIUM

In this section we shall consider the propagation of plane electromagnetic waves in an unbounded anisotropic medium. We shall assume the medium is non-magnetic, so that $\mu_m = \mu_0$, a constant which is the permeability of some reference medium (*e.g.*, free space). It will be convenient, in the discussion to follow, to consider two coordinate systems: the original Cartesian frame of reference, (x_1, x_2, x_3), and a system $(\bar{x}_1, \bar{x}_2, \bar{x}_3)$ obtained from it by a linear transformation, **A**.

In a dielectric we assume no free currents so the equations which will describe the fields are

$$\mathbf{curl\ E} = -\mu_0 \dot{\mathbf{H}} \quad , \tag{10.1a}$$

$$\mathbf{curl\ H} = \dot{\mathbf{D}} \quad , \tag{10.1b}$$

$$\operatorname{div} \mathbf{D} = 0 \quad , \tag{10.1c}$$

$$\operatorname{div} \mathbf{B} = 0 \quad , \tag{10.1d}$$

$$\mathbf{B} = \mu_0 \mathbf{H} \quad . \tag{10.1e}$$

We also assume a plane-wave structure for **E** and **H**:

$$\mathbf{E} = \mathbf{E}_0 \exp(i\omega t - i\mathbf{k} \cdot \mathbf{r}) \quad , \tag{10.2a}$$

$$\mathbf{H} = \mathbf{H}_0 \exp(i\omega t - i\mathbf{k} \cdot \mathbf{r}) \quad . \tag{10.2b}$$

Anisotropy— If we now recall the definition of **D** in terms of **P**, the polarization per unit volume,

$$\mathbf{D} = \epsilon_0 \mathbf{E} + \mathbf{P} \tag{10.3}$$

we can introduce the anisotropy of the medium by assuming that **E** and **P** are related through a *tensor*, **S**, such that:

$$\mathbf{P} = \epsilon_0 \mathbf{SE} \quad , \tag{10.4}$$

therefore, in matrix notation

$$\mathbf{D} = \epsilon_0(\mathbf{I} + \mathbf{S})\mathbf{E} = \epsilon_0 \epsilon \mathbf{E} \quad , \tag{10.5}$$

where **I** is the identity matrix. Thus we have defined the dielectric *tensor*, ϵ.

Replacing the operators curl in (10.1) we have

$$\mathbf{kxE} = \omega\mu_0 \mathbf{H} \quad , \tag{10.6a}$$

$$-\mathbf{kxH} = \dot{\mathbf{D}} \quad , \tag{10.6b}$$

$$\mathbf{k} \cdot \mathbf{D} = 0 \quad , \tag{10.6c}$$

$$\mathbf{k} \cdot \mathbf{B} = 0 \quad . \tag{10.6d}$$

Substituting for **H** in (10.6b) we find

$$(\mathbf{k} \cdot \mathbf{k})\mathbf{E} - (\mathbf{k} \cdot \mathbf{E})\mathbf{k} = \epsilon_0 \mu_0 \omega^2 (\mathbf{I} + \mathbf{S})\mathbf{E} \quad . \tag{10.7}$$

Let us examine the consequences of assuming that

$$\mathbf{k} = (\omega/V)\mathbf{n} \quad , \tag{10.8}$$

then (10.7) becomes

$$\mathbf{E} - (\mathbf{E} \cdot \mathbf{n})\mathbf{n} = \epsilon_0 \mu_0 V^2 \epsilon \mathbf{E} \quad . \tag{10.9}$$

If we assume, as part of our hypothesis, that the dielectric tensor is nonsingular, then we know that it is possible to find eigen-values of such a tensor and to diagonalize is by means of a suitable transformation, **A**, to the space spanned by the eigen-vectors of ϵ. Of course, it is possible that the eigen-values we will find for a given dielectric tensor will be complex; however, this does not detract from the validity of the transformation. Thus, transforming coordinates by $\mathbf{X} = \mathbf{A}\overline{\mathbf{X}}$,

$$\overline{\epsilon} = \mathbf{A}^{-1}\epsilon\mathbf{A} = \begin{pmatrix} \overline{\epsilon}_1 & 0 & 0 \\ 0 & \overline{\epsilon}_2 & 0 \\ 0 & 0 & \overline{\epsilon}_3 \end{pmatrix} \qquad (10.10)$$

(It should be clear from its definition that **A** must also be non-singular, and have left- and right-inverses.)

Dispersion Equation—Writing (10.9) in the transformed system in matrix notation, where $\mathbf{A}'$ is the transpose of $\mathbf{A}$:

$$\overline{\mathbf{E}} - (\overline{\mathbf{E}}'\mathbf{A}'\mathbf{A}\overline{\mathbf{n}})\overline{\mathbf{n}} = \epsilon_0\mu_0 V^2 \overline{\boldsymbol{\epsilon}}\,\overline{\mathbf{E}} \qquad (10.11)$$

Writing (10.11) out in tensor notation (repeated indices indicate a summation over that index):

$$\overline{E}_i - \overline{E}_j a_{kj} a_{kp} \overline{n}_p \overline{n}_i = \epsilon_0\mu_0 V^2 \overline{\epsilon}_{ij} \overline{E}_j \ . \qquad (10.12)$$

If we simply note that $\overline{E}_i$ is equivalent to $\delta_{ij}\overline{E}_j$, then we obtain the following determinantal equation:

$$|\delta_{ij} - a_{kj} a_{kp} \overline{n}_p \overline{n}_i - \epsilon_0\mu_0 V^2 \overline{\epsilon}_{ij}| = 0 \ , \qquad (10.13)$$

which, if **A** represents an orthogonal transformation, reduces to

$$|\delta_{ij} - \overline{n}_i \overline{n}_j - \epsilon_0\mu_0 V^2 \overline{\epsilon}_{ij}| = 0 \qquad (10.14)$$

(i denotes row; j column). This equation is the necessary and sufficient condition for the system of equations in (10.12) to have a non-trivial solution. And it results in a *quadratic* equation in the quantity $M^2 = (\epsilon_0\mu_0 V^2)^{-1}$, the *index of refraction*, which, in general, is complex.

The treatment and solution of this equation, both in the case of a non-conducting crystal and for a plasma in a magnetic field will be discussed in greater detail in the next section of this chapter, in which we shall also derive expressions for the electromagnetic field and current density.

Conductivity Tensor—If we write (10.5), separating the real and imaginary parts of $\mathbf{D}$, then

$$\mathbf{D} = \epsilon_0 \mathrm{Re}(\epsilon)\mathbf{E} + i\epsilon_0 Im(\epsilon)\mathbf{E} \quad , \tag{10.15}$$

and find its first partial derivative with respect to time, recalling that this is equivalent to multiplication by $i\omega$:

$$\dot{\mathbf{D}} = \epsilon_0 \mathrm{Re}(\epsilon)\dot{\mathbf{E}} - \omega\epsilon_0 Im(\epsilon)\mathbf{E} \quad , \tag{10.16}$$

Then, comparing the quantity in (10.6b) with the right-hand side of (9.3b) we see that if we take our actual dielectric constant as $\epsilon_0\mathrm{Re}(\epsilon)$, we may by analogy define an effective conductivity tensor by

$$\boldsymbol{\sigma} = -\omega\epsilon_0 Im(\epsilon) \quad . \tag{10.17a}$$

Thus we can write (10.16) as

$$\mathbf{curl\ H} = \sigma\mathbf{E} + \epsilon_0 \mathrm{Re}(\epsilon)\dot{\mathbf{E}} \quad , \tag{10.17b}$$

where $\boldsymbol{\sigma}\mathbf{E}$ is the equivalent current density; since $\boldsymbol{\sigma}$ is a tensor we also have the generalized Ohm's Law.

In the case that (10.8) holds for $\mathbf{k}$, as well as (9.2) we have

$$\mathbf{k} \cdot \mathbf{k} = (\omega/V_0)^2 M^2 = (\omega/V_0)^2 (P - iQ)^2 \tag{10.18}$$

since M^2 is in general, complex. Or, in other words; for the wave traveling in the $\mathbf{n}$-direction:

$$k_1 = \frac{\omega}{V_0}\left(\frac{P}{2} + \frac{1}{2}\sqrt{P^2 + Q^2}\right)^{1/2} \tag{10.19a}$$

$$k_2 = \frac{\omega}{V_0}\left(\frac{-P}{2} + \frac{1}{2}\sqrt{P^2 + Q^2}\right)^{1/2} \tag{10.19b}$$

Since (10.14) is quadratic there are two solutions in M^2, *i.e.*, two speeds of propagation, two absorption coefficients, and two different fields associated with these speeds, each of which satisfies Maxwell's equations and are propagated by plane waves. In this situation we term the medium "doubly refracting."

Propagation in an Ionized Medium—In order to discuss propagation in a plasma the relationship between the polarizations (or the current density) and the electric intensity must be added to Maxwell's equations; this completed set we shall call the Maxwell-Lorentz equations.

We shall consider the interesting and important case of propagation in an unbounded homogeneous plasma in the presence of an externally applied uniform magnetic field.

In the plasma the electrons and ions are detached completely from their parent molecules; there are no elastic forces binding them as in the case of a solid body such as a crystal. These particles therefore, have no free period of oscillation of their own. However, under the influence of an applied force, they will be disturbed by collisions with the neutral molecules. In the collision process some of the energy of motion of the electrons and ions is converted into energy of random motion of particles; *i.e.*, heat energy. The charged particles are therefore losing energy continually and this loss can be represented as a resistance to their motions. This simple model of a resistive mechanism is incorporated into the equations of motion of the charged particles as a damping force.

Mechanism of Propagation of the Electromagnetic Wave—The electron theory of Lorentz gives some idea of the mechanism by which the charged particles alter the phase velocity of a propagating wave field.

The electromagnetic wave traveling through the free space between the particles excites the charged particles and causes them to oscillate so that they essentially become small dipole oscillators, the wave field governing their phase of oscillation.

At each point either in or external to the region in which the particles are contained (we refer to a semi-infinite medium) the secondary waves which are radiated by the oscillators interfere with the original wave field and with the other radiated waves; this gives rise to a resultant field at the point. Moreover, it is the resultant field that acts on the particles at the given point which causes them to vibrate. The total intensity at any point is the vector sum of the intensity of the original wave field and the resultant intensity due to all the oscillating particles. According to this picture, in general, the emerging wave has its phase velocity altered.

The Plasma Crystal-Optics Analogy—Propagation in a homogeneous unbounded plasma has several features analogous to that in a crystal, but although some of these features parallel each other, there are some subtle differences which will be revealed in the following exposition. It is believed that propagation in a plasma could be more closely compared with propagation in optically active anisotropic media (*i.e.*, media which rotate the plane of polarization of light when it passes through them), because elliptical polarization is always associated with each of the two modes of propagation in the latter. However, the interpretation of the physical characteristics of propagation in an optically inactive anisotropic medium is simpler than that for the active medium.

We assume for the present that the only species of charged particles which affect propagation in the plasma are the electrons because of their small mass relative to the other ionic constituents. An analysis including all species of charged particles with some further assumptions leads to a medium which is more than doubly refracting.

In constructing the analogy we will list the relations which hold in the crystal and in the plasma.

11. THE PLASMA IN AN APPLIED MAGNETIC FIELD

In order to describe the propagation in a plasma in an external magnetic field, we will first establish the relation between the convection current density $\mathbf{J}$ and the electric field intensity $\mathbf{E}$ in the presence of a uniform external magnetic field, $\mathbf{B}_0$.

The equations of motion of an electron are given by

$$m\ddot{\mathbf{r}} = e\mathbf{E} - g\dot{\mathbf{r}} + e(\dot{\mathbf{r}}\mathbf{x}\mathbf{B}_t) \tag{11.1}$$

where $\mathbf{B}_t$ is the resultant magnetic induction composed of (a) the external field $\mathbf{B}_0$, which is stationary, and (b) a much smaller wave field $\mathbf{B}$.

Then we can replace $\mathbf{B}_t$ in (11.1) by $\mathbf{B}_0$. The remaining terms are the electron mass, m, and charge e (a negative quantity), and the damping constant g, which defines the collision frequency, $\nu = g/m$.

If we assume all time-dependent quantities to vary sinusoidally with the same circular frequency, ω, then

$$\dot{\mathbf{r}} = i\omega r \tag{11.2a}$$

$$\ddot{\mathbf{r}} = -\omega^2\mathbf{r} \tag{11.2b}$$

and Eq. (11.1) becomes

$$-(m\omega^2/e)\left(\beta\mathbf{r} - \frac{ie}{m\omega}\mathbf{B}_0\mathbf{x}\mathbf{r}\right) = \mathbf{E} \tag{11.3}$$

with

$$\beta = 1 - i\nu/\omega \tag{11.4}$$

Gyrotensor Ω—Let us choose, for our coordinates, a Cartesian system in which the x_3-axis is parallel to $\mathbf{B}_0$. If we define the tensor Ω to be

$$\Omega = (e/m\omega)|\mathbf{B}_0| \begin{pmatrix} 0 & 1 & 0 \\ -1 & 0 & 0 \\ 0 & 0 & 0 \end{pmatrix} , \tag{11.5}$$

and define $\Omega = (e/m\omega)|\mathbf{B}_0|$ then the vector cross-product in (11.3) can be expressed in an equivalent manner as the product of the skew-symmetric tensor, $\boldsymbol{\Omega}$, and the position vector, $\mathbf{r}$; *i.e.*,

$$(e/m\omega)\mathbf{B}_0\mathbf{x}\mathbf{r} \longleftrightarrow -\boldsymbol{\Omega}\,\mathbf{r} \quad . \tag{11.6}$$

Then, (11.3) takes the form

$$\left(-\frac{m\omega^2}{e}\right)[\beta\mathbf{I} + i\boldsymbol{\Omega}]\mathbf{r} = \mathbf{E} \tag{11.7}$$

where I is the identity matrix.

If N is the number of electrons per unit volume, and we neglect the motions of the heavy ions as a negligibly small contribution to the total convection current, we may then define an effective polarization, $\mathbf{P} = Ne\mathbf{r}$ such that

$$\mathbf{J} = \dot{\mathbf{P}} = Ne\dot{\mathbf{r}} = i\omega Ne\mathbf{r} \quad . \tag{11.8}$$

If we solve (11.8) for $\mathbf{r}$, using the inverse matrix of $\beta\mathbf{I} + i\mathbf{\Omega}$, we have

$$\mathbf{r} = \left(\frac{-e}{m\omega^2}\right)(\beta\mathbf{I} + i\mathbf{\Omega})^{-1}\mathbf{E} \tag{11.9}$$

which when substituted into (11.8) yields

$$\mathbf{J} = \boldsymbol{\sigma}\cdot\mathbf{E} \quad , \tag{11.10a}$$

$$\boldsymbol{\sigma} = \left(\frac{-iNe^2}{m\omega}\right)(\beta\mathbf{I} + i\mathbf{\Omega})^{-1} \quad . \tag{11.10b}$$

Thus we have defined the conductivity tensor, $\boldsymbol{\sigma}$, which relates the convectio current density to the electric field. We can now write the relations that hold for the plasma:

$$\mathbf{B} = \mu_0\mathbf{H} \quad , \tag{11.11a}$$

$$\mathbf{J} = \boldsymbol{\sigma}\mathbf{E} \quad , \tag{11.11b}$$

$$\mathbf{D} = \epsilon_0\mathbf{E} \quad . \tag{11.11c}$$

Effective Displacement—Let us define an *effective* displacement vector, $\mathbf{D}_e$, by the equation

$$\frac{\partial\mathbf{D}_e}{\partial t} = \mathbf{J} + \frac{\partial\mathbf{D}}{\partial t} \tag{11.12}$$

This is suggested by way of analogy with the displacement in a dielectric, which is $\mathbf{D}_e = \mathbf{D} = \mathbf{P} + \epsilon_0\mathbf{E}$. Then we find that, for *both* a plasma and a non-conducting crystal (no free charge), Maxwell's Equations take the form:

$$\mathbf{curl\ E} = -\frac{\partial\mathbf{B}}{\partial t} \tag{11.13a}$$

$$\mathbf{curl\ H} = \frac{\partial \mathbf{D}_e}{\partial t} \qquad (11.13b)$$

and since, for any vector, div **curl** ≡ 0,

$$\text{div}\ \mathbf{curl\ H} = 0 \quad , \qquad (11.13c)$$

therefore, in the non-stationary case

$$\text{div}\ \mathbf{D}_e = 0 \quad . \qquad (11.13d)$$

Clearly, (11.13a, b, c, d) hold for both media.

For harmonic time variation $e^{i\omega t}$, the field equations become

$$\mathbf{curl\ E} = -i\omega \mathbf{B} = -i\omega\mu_0 \mathbf{H} \quad , \qquad (11.14a)$$

$$\mathbf{curl\ H} = i\omega \mathbf{D}_e \quad , \qquad (11.14b)$$

$$\text{div}\ \mathbf{D}_e = 0 \quad , \qquad (11.14c)$$

the last relation following from (11.13b, c).

For the crystal case we know that

$$\mathbf{D}_e = \epsilon_0 \epsilon \mathbf{E} \qquad (11.15)$$

with ϵ a tensor; for the plasma

$$\mathbf{D}_e = \mathbf{J}/i\omega + \mathbf{D} = (\sigma/i\omega + \epsilon_0 \mathbf{I})\mathbf{E} \qquad (11.16)$$

Therefore, we see by analogy that $(\sigma/i\omega\epsilon_0 + \mathbf{I})$ is the *effective dielectric tensor of the plasma*, ϵ_e.

If we assume that the field is propagated in such a way that each of the vector components contain the factor

$$e^{i(\omega t - \mathbf{k}\cdot\mathbf{r})} \qquad (11.17)$$

where $\mathbf{r}$ is the position vector from the origin to a point in the field and $\mathbf{k}$ is the wave vector. We find from (11.14a, b, c)

$$\mathbf{k} \times \mathbf{E} = \omega\mu_0 \mathbf{H} \quad , \tag{11.18a}$$

$$-\mathbf{k} \times \mathbf{H} = \omega \mathbf{D}_e \quad , \tag{11.18b}$$

$$\mathbf{k} \cdot \mathbf{D}_e = 0 \quad . \tag{11.18c}$$

If we eliminate $\mathbf{H}$ from (11.18a, b) we obtain

$$\mathbf{D}_e = -(1/\mu_0\omega^2)[\mathbf{k} \times (\mathbf{k} \times \mathbf{E})] = (1/\mu_0\omega^2)[(\mathbf{k} \cdot \mathbf{k})\mathbf{E} - (\mathbf{k} \cdot \mathbf{E})\mathbf{k}] \tag{11.19}$$

Since $\mathbf{k} \cdot \mathbf{k}$ is a scalar invariant, we define k^2 by $k^2 = \mathbf{k} \cdot \mathbf{k}$, and write (11.19) in the form

$$(\mathbf{k} \cdot \mathbf{E})\mathbf{k} = k^2\mathbf{E} - \mu_0\omega^2\mathbf{D}_e \quad . \tag{11.20}$$

Since $\mathbf{D}_e$ is derivable from $\mathbf{E}$ by means of the dielectric tensor [see Eqs. (11.15)(11.16)], then for any assumed $\mathbf{k}$ and ω (11.20) constitutes the set of equations that determines $\mathbf{E}$. These equations are not always soluble; they can be solved only when the parameters involved are such that the appropriate dispersion equation is satisfied. However, we are now in a position to derive a dispersion relation from (11.20).

In the case of the plasma, we have shown the effective dielectric tensor, ϵ_e to be

$$\epsilon_e = \sigma/i\omega\epsilon_0 + \mathbf{I} \quad . \tag{11.21}$$

Thus, for the plasma, (11.20) becomes

$$(\mathbf{k} \cdot \mathbf{E})\mathbf{k} = k^2\mathbf{E} - \mu_0\omega^2\epsilon_0\epsilon_e\mathbf{E} \quad ; \tag{11.22}$$

and if we make the substitution $\epsilon_e = \epsilon$ in (11.22) we have the corresponding equation for propagation in a crystal.

Dispersion Equation—If we write (11.22) in the tensor formalism, we have

$$(k_i E_i)k_j + \mu_0\epsilon_0\omega^2(\epsilon_e)_{ji}E_i - k^2\delta_{ji}E_i = 0 \tag{11.23}$$

where i and j range from 1 to 3, and we sum over i. The Kronecker delta, δ_{ji}, takes the place of the unit tensor, **I**. If we isolate the E_i factor, we have what amounts to a system of three homogeneous linear equations in three unknowns, E_i:

$$[k_j k_i + \mu_0 \epsilon_0 \omega^2 (\epsilon_e)_{ji} - k^2 \delta_{ji}] E_i = 0 \; , \quad (j = 1, 2, 3) \; . \tag{11.24}$$

The necessary and sufficient condition for a non-trivial solution is that the determinant of the system vanish. If, by analogy with the conventional expression for index of refraction relative to free space, we make a purely formal substitution:

$$\frac{1}{M^2} = \frac{\mu_0 \epsilon_0 \omega^2}{k^2} \; , \tag{11.25}$$

then the *condition for propagation* is that the determinant be zero:

$$\left| \frac{k_j k_i}{k^2} - \delta_{ji} + \frac{1}{M^2} (\epsilon_e)_{ji} \right| = 0 \; . \tag{11.26}$$

Although it might seem at first that this is a cubic equation in M^2, it follows from the definition of **k** and k^2 that

$$\left| \frac{k_j k_i}{k^2} - \delta_{ji} \right| = 0 \tag{11.27}$$

and therefore, that $M^2 = \infty$ is a root of (11.26). However, since this corresponds to a zero phase velocity we shall not consider it as a mode of propagation.

Due to (11.27), expansion of the determinant in (11.26) yields a characteristic equation which is *quadratic* in M^2. *Equation (11.26) is the dispersion equation.* Since the dielectric tensor is known, there can be propagation only for those values of **k** and M^2 which are consistent with (11.26)

Up to this point we have made *no assumptions* concerning the nature of **k**: its components may be real or complex, and may be completely independent of each other; the preceding development is valid in any case.

Now let us assume that **k** is of the form

$$\mathbf{k} = (\omega/V)\mathbf{n} \qquad (11.28)$$

where **n** is the unit vector in the direction of propagation and V is the phase speed, which may be complex. The circular frequency is real and positive. We shall see subsequently that V depends upon the direction of propagation as a result of the dispersion relation.

Eq. (11.20) now becomes

$$\mathbf{n}(\mathbf{n} \cdot \mathbf{E}) = \mathbf{E} - \mu_0 V^2 \mathbf{D}_e \quad . \qquad (11.29)$$

It is evident from the above equation that **n**, **E**, and $\mathbf{D}_e$ are coplanar, and from (11.18a) we see that **H** is perpendicular to this plane. In addition, we see from (11.18c) that **n** and $\mathbf{D}_e$ are mutually perpendicular. This is represented in Fig. 3, from which it can be seen that the Poynting vector, **ExH**, is not parallel to **n**, as it is in the familiar case of propagation in transparent isotropic media.

12. THE ELECTROMAGNETIC FIELDS IN THE NON-CONDUCTING CRYSTAL

In the case of the *non-conducting crystal* examined in Section 10, the matrix ϵ is real and symmetric; consequently, there exists a real, right-handed orthogonal system of axes, the eigenvectors of ϵ, in which ϵ is diagonal, with components $\epsilon_i (i = 1, 2, 3)$. In this system we can write

$$(\mathbf{D}_e)_i = \epsilon_0 \epsilon_i E_i \; , \; (i = 1,2,3) \quad . \qquad (12.1)$$

If we choose this system as our original frame of reference, and n_i are the components of **n** relative to this system, we may write (11.29) in component form (i = 1, 2, 3; *no* sum on i)

$$n_i (\mathbf{n} \cdot \mathbf{E}) = \left(\frac{1}{\epsilon_0 \epsilon_i} - \mu_0 V^2 \right) (\mathbf{D}_e)_i \quad . \qquad (12.2)$$

Since, for the crystal case (11.18c) holds, and, in general $\mathbf{n} \cdot \mathbf{E} \neq 0$, if we multiply both sides of (12.2) by n_i and sum over i, we obtain

$$\frac{n_i n_i}{\dfrac{1}{\epsilon_0 \epsilon_i} - \mu_0 V^2} = \frac{n_i D_{ei}}{\mathbf{n} \cdot \mathbf{E}} = 0 \quad . \qquad (12.3a)$$

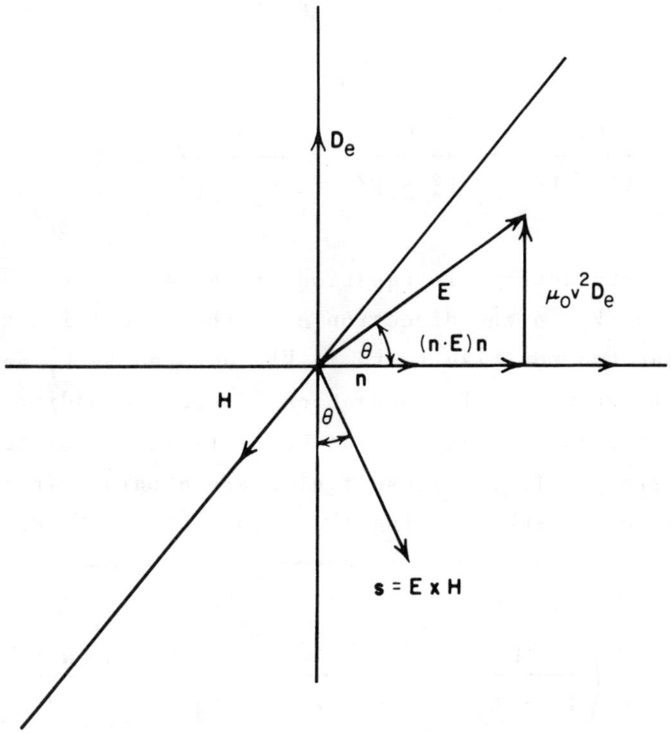

FIG. 3

or

$$\frac{n_1^2}{\dfrac{1}{\epsilon_0\epsilon_1} - \mu_0 V^2} + \frac{n_2^2}{\dfrac{1}{\epsilon_0\epsilon_2} - \mu_0 V^2} + \frac{n_3^2}{\dfrac{1}{\epsilon_0\epsilon_3} - \mu_0 V^2} = 0 \quad . \qquad (12.3b)$$

If we define

$$V_i^2 = (1/\epsilon_0\epsilon_i\mu_0), \qquad (i = 1, 2, 3) \quad , \qquad (12.4)$$

then (12.3) becomes

$$\frac{n_1^2}{V_1^2 - V^2} + \frac{n_2^2}{V_2^2 - V^2} + \frac{n_3^2}{V_3^2 - V^2} = 0 \qquad (12.5)*$$

This is the characteristic equation which relates the velocity of phase propagation, V, in the direction $\mathbf{n}$ to the velocities V_1, V_2, and V_3. In general it has two positive roots in V^2, denoted by $V_{,1}^2$ and $V_{,2}^2$; showing that there exist two modes of propagation; *i.e.*, the medium is doubly refracting (birefringence). Each mode has a field associated with it, $(\mathbf{D}_e, \mathbf{E}, \mathbf{H})_j$, where $j = 1, 2$. These fields are obtained from (12.2), (12.1), (11.18a) after substituting the values V_1^2 and V_2^2 obtained from (12.5).

$$(\mathbf{D}_e)_j = \left(\frac{n_1}{V_1^2 - V_{,j}^2}, \frac{n_2}{V_2^2 - V_{,j}^2}, \frac{n_3}{V_3^2 - V_{,j}^2}\right)\left(\frac{\mathbf{n}\cdot\mathbf{E}_j}{\mu_0}\right) \qquad (12.6a)$$

$$(\mathbf{E})_j = \left(\frac{n_1 V_1^2}{V_1^2 - V_{,j}^2}, \frac{n_2 V_2^2}{V_2^2 - V_{,j}^2}, \frac{n_3 V_3^2}{V_3^2 - V_{,j}^2}\right)(\mathbf{n}\cdot\mathbf{E}_j) \qquad (12.6b)$$

$$(\mathbf{H})_j = \left[n_2 n_3\left(\frac{V_3^2}{V_3^2 - V_{,j}^2} - \frac{V_2^2}{V_2^2 - V_{,j}^2}\right), n_1 n_3\left(\frac{V_1^2}{V_1^2 - V_{,j}^2} - \frac{V_3^2}{V_3^2 - V_{,j}^2}\right), \right.$$
$$\left. n_1 n_2\left(\frac{V_2^2}{V_2^2 - V_{,j}^2} - \frac{V_1^2}{V_1^2 - V_{,j}^2}\right)\right](\mathbf{n}\cdot\mathbf{E}_j/\mu_0 V_{,j}) \qquad (12.6c)$$

* This can also be obtained directly from (11.26).

These equations show that since the vector components are in phase, all the field vectors are linearly polarized. It can also be shown that $\mathbf{D}_{e_1}$ and $\mathbf{D}_{e_2}$ are mutually orthogonal; this is also true for $\mathbf{H}_1$ and $\mathbf{H}_2$. This follows immediately from the scalar product of $\mathbf{D}_{e_1}$ and $\mathbf{D}_{e_2}$ and the definition of $V_{,j}^2$:

$$\mathbf{D}_{e_1} \cdot \mathbf{D}_{e_2} = \left(\frac{\mathbf{n} \cdot \mathbf{E}_1}{\mu_0}\right) \left[\frac{n_1^2}{(V_1^2 - V_{,1}^2)(V_1^2 - V_{,2}^2)} + \frac{n_2^2}{(V_2^2 - V_{,1}^2)(V_2^2 - V_{,2}^2)} + \frac{n_3^2}{(V_3^2 - V_{,1}^2)(V_3^2 - V_{,2}^2)} \right] \left(\frac{\mathbf{n} \cdot \mathbf{E}_2}{\mu_0}\right) \qquad (12.7a)$$

which becomes, by virtue of a decomposition in partial fractions;

$$\mathbf{D}_{e_1} \cdot \mathbf{D}_{e_2} = \left(\frac{\mathbf{n} \cdot \mathbf{E}_1}{\mu_0}\right) \left(\frac{\mathbf{n} \cdot \mathbf{E}_2}{\mu_0}\right) (V_2^2 - V_1^2)^{-1} \left[\left(\frac{n_1^2}{V_1^2 - V_{,2}^2} - \frac{n_1^2}{V_1^2 - V_{,1}^2} \right) + \left(\frac{n_2^2}{V_2^2 - V_{,2}^2} - \frac{n_2^2}{V_2^2 - V_{,1}^2} \right) + \left(\frac{n_3^2}{V_3^2 - V_{,2}^2} - \frac{n_3^2}{V_3^2 - V_{,1}^2} \right) \right] = 0 \qquad (12.7b)$$

the positive and negative terms of which separately total zero according to our definition of $V_{,j}^2$ as the roots of (12.5). That the same is true of $\mathbf{H}_1$ and $\mathbf{H}_2$ must be immediately obvious from Fig. 3, , since the vector $\mathbf{n}$ is common to both modes.

13. ELECTROMAGNETIC FIELDS IN THE BIREFRINGENT PLASMA

The analysis for a plasma is not as simple as for a non-conducting crystal; we have already indicated that the relation between the effective displacement vector and the electric field $\mathbf{E}$ is given by:

$$\mathbf{D}_e = \epsilon_0 \left(\frac{1}{i\omega\epsilon_0} \sigma + \mathbf{I} \right) \mathbf{E} \quad . \qquad (13.1)$$

Canonical Transformation to a Mathematical System—Since we have chosen one of the coordinate axes to be in the direction of the impressed magnetic field, we shall see that the structure of the effective dielectric tensor ϵ_e is somewhat simplified. The reason for this becomes evident if we seek the eigenvectors of the matrix $(\beta\mathbf{I} + i\Omega)$.

First we must solve its characteristic equation

$$|(\beta - \lambda)\mathbf{I} + i\Omega| = \begin{vmatrix} \beta - \lambda & i\Omega & 0 \\ -i\Omega & \beta - \lambda & 0 \\ 0 & 0 & \beta - \lambda \end{vmatrix} = 0 \tag{13.2}$$

which yields the possible eigen-values

$$\lambda_1 = \beta + \Omega; \quad \lambda_2 = \beta - \Omega; \quad \lambda_3 = \beta \quad . \tag{13.3}$$

When these values are substituted into the equation

$$(\beta\mathbf{I} + i\Omega)\mathbf{r} = \lambda\mathbf{r} \quad , \tag{13.4}$$

we find the corresponding normalized eigenvectors to be

$$\bar{\mathbf{e}}_1 = (2)^{-1/2}(\mathbf{e}_1 - i\mathbf{e}_2); \quad \bar{\mathbf{e}}_2 = (2)^{-1/2}(\mathbf{e}_1 + i\mathbf{e}_2); \quad \bar{\mathbf{e}}_3 = \mathbf{e}_3 \quad , \tag{13.5}$$

where $\mathbf{e}_i$ is the unit vector in the x_i-direction in our original Cartesian system of coordinates.

Thus we have defined the matrix $\mathbf{A}$,

$$\mathbf{A} = (2)^{-1/2} \begin{pmatrix} 1 & 1 & 0 \\ -i & i & 0 \\ 0 & 0 & \sqrt{2} \end{pmatrix} \tag{13.6}$$

which gives the transformation from our original, or *physical system*, into a new *mathematical system* (barred) as follows:

$$\mathbf{F} = \mathbf{A}\bar{\mathbf{F}} \quad . \tag{13.7a}$$

Where $\mathbf{F} = x_i \mathbf{e}_i$ is a vector expressed in the physical system, and $\overline{\mathbf{F}} = \overline{x}_i \overline{\mathbf{e}}_i$ is the same vector expressed in the mathematical system. Furthermore, it is clear from the relation

$$\mathbf{A}^{*\prime}\mathbf{A} = \mathbf{I} \quad ; \tag{13.7b}$$

that $\mathbf{A}$ represents a *unitary* transformation where ($'$) denotes transposed matrix, and (*) denotes complex conjugate;

We see by (13.5) that the third eigenvector is parallel to the uniform magnetic field $\mathbf{B}_0$; therefore, our choice of this axis was indeed a judicious one, and under the transformation $\mathbf{A}$, this axis is *invariant*. However, the mathematical system has two *non-real* axes, $\overline{x}_1$ and $\overline{x}_2$: this simply means that in the mathematical system components transverse to the magnetic field are described by means of the *complex* x_1, x_2 - plane rather than the customary real plane. It should be noted that *scalar* products are not affected by the transformation, so that the exponential factor of (11.17) *remains the same* for both physical and mathematical systems.

Since the set of orthogonal transformations is just a subgroup of the set of unitary transformations, and $\mathbf{n}$ is real, we may express the divergence condition (11.18c) in the real system as

$$\mathbf{n} \cdot \mathbf{D}_e = \mathbf{n}^* \cdot \mathbf{D}_e = 0 \quad , \tag{13.8}$$

and since a unitary transformation preserves the complex inner product we also have

$$\mathbf{n}^* \cdot \mathbf{D}_e = \overline{\mathbf{n}}^* \cdot \mathbf{D}_e = 0 \quad . \tag{13.9}$$

If we transform (11.15) to the barred system by (13.7a) we find: (in matrix notation)

$$\mathbf{A}\overline{\mathbf{D}}_e = \epsilon_0 \epsilon_e \mathbf{A}\overline{\mathbf{E}} \quad , \tag{13.10a}$$

and when both sides are multiplied by $\mathbf{A}^{*\prime}$,

$$\overline{\mathbf{D}}_e = \epsilon_0 (\mathbf{A}^{*\prime} \epsilon_e \mathbf{A})\overline{\mathbf{E}} = \epsilon_0 \overline{\epsilon}_e \overline{\mathbf{E}} \tag{13.10b}$$

where we can identify the quantity in parenthesis as the transformed dielectric tensor, $\overline{\epsilon}_e$.

Principal Dielectric Constants of the Plasma—To see what this tensor really is, we must return to our original definition of the dielectric tensor. But first let us define some quantities for convenience in the discussion to follow:

$$\omega_c^2 = \frac{Ne^2}{\epsilon_0 m} \qquad (13.11)$$

where ω_c is the plasma frequency; as will be shown later, this is the resonant frequency for a free electron under the influence of an impressed electric field;

$$a = \omega_c^2/\omega^2 \quad , \qquad (13.12)$$

the ratio of plasma and applied frequencies;

$$\mathbf{S} = -a(\beta\mathbf{I} + i\Omega)^{-1} \quad . \qquad (13.13)$$

From equations (11.10) and (11.16) we see that

$$\epsilon_e = (\mathbf{I} + \mathbf{S}) \qquad (13.14)$$

and

$$\overline{\epsilon}_e = \mathbf{A}^{*\prime}(\mathbf{I} + \mathbf{S})\mathbf{A} = \mathbf{I} + \overline{\mathbf{S}} \quad . \qquad (13.15)$$

The matrix $\mathbf{S}$ is most easily found by first considering the transformation of its inverse. From (13.13) it is clear that

$$-a\mathbf{S}^{-1} = \beta\mathbf{I} + i\Omega \quad , \qquad (13.16a)$$

and transforming the above equation to diagonalize Ω,

$$-a\mathbf{A}^{*\prime}(\mathbf{S}^{-1})\mathbf{A} = -a(\overline{\mathbf{S}})^{-1} = \mathbf{A}^{*\prime}(\beta\mathbf{I} + i\Omega)\mathbf{A} \quad . \qquad (13.16b)$$

When we carry out the indicated matrix multiplication, we find

$$-\begin{pmatrix} \beta + \Omega & 0 & 0 \\ 0 & \beta - \Omega & 0 \\ 0 & 0 & \beta \end{pmatrix} = a(\overline{\mathbf{S}})^{-1} \qquad (13.16c)$$

Once we have a diagonalized matrix, inversion is simple:

$$\bar{\mathbf{S}} = -a \begin{pmatrix} \dfrac{1}{\beta + \Omega} & 0 & 0 \\ 0 & \dfrac{1}{\beta - \Omega} & 0 \\ 0 & 0 & \dfrac{1}{\beta} \end{pmatrix} \tag{13.17a}$$

To find $\mathbf{S}$ we just make the inverse transformation from the mathematical back to the physical system:

$$\mathbf{S} = \mathbf{A}\bar{\mathbf{S}}\mathbf{A}^{*\prime} = -\frac{a}{\beta(\beta^2 - \Omega^2)} \begin{pmatrix} \beta^2 & -i\beta\Omega & 0 \\ i\beta\Omega & \beta^2 & 0 \\ 0 & 0 & \beta^2 - \Omega^2 \end{pmatrix}, \tag{13.17b}$$

and substituting this result into (13.14) yields

$$\epsilon_e = \mathbf{I} - \frac{a}{\beta(\beta^2 - \Omega^2)} \begin{pmatrix} \beta^2 & -i\beta\Omega & 0 \\ i\beta\Omega & \beta^2 & 0 \\ 0 & 0 & \beta^2 - \Omega^2 \end{pmatrix}, \tag{13.17c}$$

and

$$\bar{\epsilon}_e = \mathbf{I} + \bar{\mathbf{S}} = \begin{pmatrix} 1 - \dfrac{a}{\beta + \Omega} & 0 & 0 \\ 0 & 1 - \dfrac{a}{\beta - \Omega} & 0 \\ 0 & 0 & 1 - \dfrac{a}{\beta} \end{pmatrix}. \tag{13.17d}$$

Now, by analogy with a crystal we can define the principal dielectric constants for a plasma,

$$\bar{\epsilon}_{e_1} = 1 - \frac{a}{\beta + \Omega}, \tag{13.18a}$$

$$\bar{\epsilon}_{e_2} = 1 - \frac{a}{\beta - \Omega}, \tag{13.18b}$$

$$\bar{\epsilon}_{e_3} = 1 - \frac{a}{\beta}, \tag{13.18c}$$

Dispersion Equation for the Plasma—We are now in a position to derive a dispersion equation for propagation of electromagnetic waves in a plasma, in a way that is formally identical to the method used in the non-conducting crystal. If we take **k** as defined by (11.28), and transform (11.29) to the mathematical system by means of (13.7a), then

$$\bar{\mathbf{n}}(\mathbf{n}\cdot\mathbf{E}) = \bar{\mathbf{E}} - \mu_0 V^2 \bar{\mathbf{D}}_e \quad , \tag{13.19a}$$

and substituting for $\bar{\mathbf{E}}$ from (13.10b),

$$\bar{\mathbf{n}}(\mathbf{n}\cdot\mathbf{E}) = \left[\frac{1}{\epsilon_0}(\bar{\epsilon}_e)^{-1} - \mu_0 V^2\right]\bar{\mathbf{D}}_e \quad , \tag{13.19b}$$

we need not transform $\mathbf{n}\cdot\mathbf{E}$ since it is a scalar, and generally not equal to zero. If we express (13.19b) in component form we may write:

$$\frac{\bar{n}_i}{\left(\dfrac{1}{\epsilon_0\bar{\epsilon}_{ei}} - \mu_0 V^2\right)} = \frac{\bar{\mathbf{D}}_{e\,i}}{\mathbf{n}\cdot\mathbf{E}} \quad ; \tag{13.20a}$$

if $\mathbf{n}\cdot\mathbf{E}$ is zero, then the dispersion relation for V^2 are trivial. Generally, $\mathbf{n}\cdot\mathbf{E}$ is not zero, then if we multiply (13.20a) by $\bar{n}_i^*$ and sum on i, we see from (13.9) that the right side is zero; so we have the corresponding dispersion relation for a plasma,

$$\frac{\bar{n}_1^*\bar{n}_1}{\dfrac{1}{\epsilon_0\bar{\epsilon}_{e1}} - \mu_0 V^2} + \frac{\bar{n}_2^*\bar{n}_2}{\dfrac{1}{\epsilon_0\bar{\epsilon}_{e2}} - \mu_0 V^2} + \frac{\bar{n}_3^*\bar{n}_3}{\dfrac{1}{\epsilon_0\bar{\epsilon}_{e3}} - \mu_0 V^2} = 0 \ . \tag{13.20b*}$$

The formal similarity to (12.3b) is readily apparent.

If we transform back to our physical system by means of (13.7a) we have $\bar{\mathbf{n}} = \mathbf{A}^{*\prime}\mathbf{n}$, or

$$\frac{\frac{1}{2}(n_1^2 + n_2^2)}{\bar{V}_1^2 - V^2} + \frac{\frac{1}{2}(n_1^2 + n_2^2)}{\bar{V}_2^2 - V^2} + \frac{n_3^2}{\bar{V}_3^2 - V^2} = 0 \quad , \tag{13.21*}$$

* In agreement with (11.26).

in which we have defined

$$\overline{V}_i^2 = (\epsilon_0 \mu_0 \overline{\epsilon}_{ei})^{-1} \quad , \tag{13.22}$$

by analogy with (12.4).

The Electromagnetic Field in the Plasma—This dispersion equation (13.21) relates the (complex) velocity of phase propagation V in the direction $\mathbf{n} = (n_1, n_2, n_3)$ to the constant complex velocities, $\overline{V}_i$, $(i = 1, 2, 3)$. It is quadratic in V^2, having two roots, $\overline{V}_{,1}^2$ and $\overline{V}_{,2}^2$, which implies the existence of two modes of propagation. In other words, the plasma medium is "doubly refracting." The fields associated with each mode, $(\overline{\mathbf{D}}_e, \overline{\mathbf{E}}, \overline{\mathbf{H}})_j$, $(j = 1, 2)$ will first be expressed in the mathematical system, and can be derived from (11.29), (13.10), and (11.18) in exactly the same way as we obtained (12.6) in the crystal case. Thus we find expressions for the electric fields in the mathematical system which are formally identical with (12.6a) and (12.6b). When we substitute n_i in place of the components of $\overline{\mathbf{n}}$ then

$$(\overline{\mathbf{D}}_e)_j = \left[\frac{1}{\sqrt{2}}\left(\frac{n_1 + in_2}{\overline{V}_1^2 - \overline{V}_{,j}^2}\right), \frac{1}{\sqrt{2}}\left(\frac{n_1 - in_2}{\overline{V}_2^2 - \overline{V}_{,j}^2}\right), \frac{n_3}{\overline{V}_3^2 - \overline{V}_{,j}^2}\right]\left(\frac{\mathbf{n}\cdot\mathbf{E}_j}{\mu_0}\right) \tag{13.23a}$$

$$(\overline{\mathbf{E}})_j = \left[\frac{1}{\sqrt{2}}\left(\frac{n_1 + in_2}{\overline{V}_1^2 - \overline{V}_{,j}^2}\right)\overline{V}_1^2, \frac{1}{\sqrt{2}}\left(\frac{n_1 - in_2}{\overline{V}_2^2 - \overline{V}_{,j}^2}\right)\overline{V}_2^2, \frac{n_3\overline{V}_3^2}{\overline{V}_3^2 - \overline{V}_{,j}^2}\right](\mathbf{n}\cdot\mathbf{E}_j) \tag{13.23b}$$

In the case of a plasma, we also wish to determine $\overline{\mathbf{J}}$, the current density, and from (11.12) $\overline{\mathbf{J}} = i\omega\overline{\mathbf{D}}_e - i\omega\epsilon_0\overline{\mathbf{E}}$, so

$$(\overline{\mathbf{J}})_j = \left[\frac{(n_1 + in_2)}{\sqrt{2}}\left(\frac{\frac{1}{\epsilon_0\mu_0} - \overline{V}_1^2}{\overline{V}_1^2 - \overline{V}_{,j}^2}\right), \frac{(n_1 - in_2)}{\sqrt{2}}\left(\frac{\frac{1}{\epsilon_0\gamma_0} - \overline{V}_2^2}{\overline{V}_2^2 - \overline{V}_{,j}^2}\right), n_3\left(\frac{\frac{1}{\epsilon_0\gamma_0} - \overline{V}_3^2}{\overline{V}_3^2 - \overline{V}_{,j}^2}\right)\right](i\omega\epsilon_0\mathbf{n}\cdot\mathbf{E}_j) \tag{13.23c}$$

The expression for the magnetic field is somewhat more complicated: from (11.18a) we have

$$\mathbf{n}\mathrm{x}(\mathbf{E})_j = \overline{V}_{,j}\mu_0(\mathbf{H})_j \tag{13.24a}$$

and substituting by (13.7a)

$$\mathbf{A}\bar{\mathbf{n}}\mathrm{x}\mathbf{A}(\overline{\mathbf{E}})_j = \overline{V}_{,j}\mu_0\mathbf{A}(\overline{\mathbf{H}})_j \tag{13.24b}$$

multiplying both sides by $\mathbf{A}^{-1}$ and performing the indicated operations we find $(\overline{\mathbf{H}})_j$ to be

$$(\overline{\mathbf{H}})_j = \left[\frac{n_3(n_1 + in_2)}{\sqrt{2}}\left(\frac{\overline{V}_1^2}{\overline{V}_1^2 - \overline{V}_{,j}^2} - \frac{\overline{V}_3^2}{\overline{V}_3^2 - \overline{V}_{,j}^2}\right);\ \frac{n_3(n_1 - in_2)}{\sqrt{2}}\left(\frac{\overline{V}_3^2}{\overline{V}_3^2 - \overline{V}_{,j}^2} - \frac{\overline{V}_2^2}{\overline{V}_2^2 - \overline{V}_{,j}^2}\right);\right.$$

$$\left.\frac{1}{2}(n_1^2 + n_2^2)\left(\frac{\overline{V}_2^2}{\overline{V}_2^{\,2} - \overline{V}_{,j}^{\,2}} - \frac{\overline{V}_1^2}{\overline{V}_1^2 - \overline{V}_{,j}^2}\right)\right]\frac{i(\mathbf{n}\cdot\mathbf{E}_j)}{\mu_0 V_{,j}} \quad . \tag{13.24c}$$

If we now desire to express the field quantities in the physical system, we find upon transforming the effective displacement vector by $\mathbf{A}$:

$$(\mathbf{D}_e)_j = \frac{\mathbf{n}\cdot\mathbf{E}_j}{2\mu_0}\left[\left(\frac{n_1 + in_2}{\overline{V}_1^2 - \overline{V}_{,j}^2} + \frac{n_1 - in_2}{\overline{V}_2^2 - \overline{V}_{,j}^2}\right),\ i\left(\frac{n_1 - in_2}{\overline{V}_2^2 - \overline{V}_{,j}^2} - \frac{n_1 + in_2}{\overline{V}_1^2 - \overline{V}_{,j}^2}\right),\ \frac{2n_3}{\overline{V}_3^2 - \overline{V}_{,j}^2}\right] \quad . \tag{13.25}$$

The other field quantities are most easily found by

$$\mathbf{E}_j = \mathbf{n}(\mathbf{n}\cdot\mathbf{E}_j) + \mu_0\overline{V}_{,j}^2\mathbf{D}_{ej} \quad , \tag{11.29'}$$

$$\mathbf{H}_j = (\mu_0\overline{V}_{,j})^{-1}\mathbf{n}\mathrm{x}\mathbf{E}_j = \overline{V}_{,j}\mathbf{n}\mathrm{x}\mathbf{D}_{ej} \tag{11.18a'}$$

$$\mathbf{J}_j = i\omega(\mathbf{D}_{ej} - \epsilon_0\mathbf{E}_j) \tag{11.12'}$$

$$= i\omega[(1 - \epsilon_0\mu_0\overline{V}_{,j}^2)\mathbf{D}_{ej} - \epsilon_0(\mathbf{n}\cdot\mathbf{E})\mathbf{n}] \quad .$$

Thus, for a given frequency, ω, direction of propagation, $\mathbf{n}$, and angle, $\theta' = \arccos(\mathbf{n} \cdot \mathbf{E})/|\mathbf{E}|$, which the electric field makes with $\mathbf{n}$, we have completely specified the directions, relative magnitudes, and mode of propagation of the electromagnetic fields. The *exact* magnitude of any quantity depends upon the physical boundary conditions, and need not concern us here.

14. THE APPLETON-HARTREE FORMULA

The Appleton-Hartree dispersion relation for the two modes of propagation in a plasma under the influence of a uniform, external magnetic field is customarily given in the following way: the (complex) index of refraction is

$$M_j^2 = 1 - x(1 - iz - iyQ_j \cos\theta)^{-1} \quad (j = 1, 2) \tag{14.1a}$$

where Q_j are the roots of

$$Q^2 + 2iGQ + 1 = 0 \tag{14.1b}$$

and

$$G = g(1 - iz - x)^{-1} \tag{14.1c}$$

$$g = (1/2)y \sin\theta \tan\theta \quad , \tag{14.1d}$$

where θ is the angle between $\mathbf{n}$ and the external magnetic field $\mathbf{B}_0$.

The parameters x, z, and y are just the customary notation* for the physical parameters of the problem:

$$x = a \; ; \; y = \Omega \; ; \; 1 - iz = \beta \quad . \tag{14.2}$$

If we denote the roots of (14.1b) by Q_1 and Q_2 then

$$Q^2 + 2iGQ + 1 = (Q - Q_1)(Q - Q_2) \quad , \tag{14.3a}$$

therefore,

$$Q_1 Q_2 = 1 \; ; \quad \text{and} \quad Q_1 + Q_2 = -2iG \quad . \tag{14.3b}$$

---

* Used by workers in Ionospheric Physics.

It is interesting to show that we can obtain the same results from the dispersion equation (13.21). If we set $\mathbf{k} = \omega\mathbf{n}/V$ and express $\mathbf{n}$ in spherical polar coordinates,

$$\mathbf{n} = (\sin\theta\cos\phi \; , \; \sin\theta\sin\phi \; , \; \cos\theta) \tag{14.4}$$

then (13.21) can be written

$$\frac{\sin^2\theta}{\dfrac{1}{\epsilon_{e1}} - \dfrac{1}{M^2}} + \frac{\sin^2\theta}{\dfrac{1}{\epsilon_{e2}} - \dfrac{1}{M^2}} + \frac{2\cos^2\theta}{\dfrac{1}{\epsilon_{e3}} - \dfrac{1}{M^2}} = 0 \; , \tag{14.5}$$

or in the usual quadratic form

$$M^4[(\bar{\epsilon}_{e1} + \bar{\epsilon}_{e2})\sin^2\theta + 2\bar{\epsilon}_{e3}\cos^2\theta] - M^2[2\bar{\epsilon}_{e1}\bar{\epsilon}_{e2}\sin^2\theta + \bar{\epsilon}_{e3}(\bar{\epsilon}_{e1} + \bar{\epsilon}_{e2})(1 + \cos^2\theta)] + 2\bar{\epsilon}_{e1}\bar{\epsilon}_{e2}\bar{\epsilon}_{e3} = 0 \; . \tag{14.6}$$

The corresponding quadratic in M^2 whose roots are given by (14.1a) is

$$(M^2 - M_1^2)(M^2 - M_2^2) = 0 \tag{14.7}$$

which yields, after multiplying by $(1 - iz - iyQ_1\cos\theta)(1 - iz - iyQ_2\cos\theta)$ and making use of (14.3b)

$$\begin{aligned} &M^4[(1 - iz)^2 - 2y(1 - iz)G\cos\theta - y^2\cos^2\theta] \\ &\quad - 2M^2[(1 - iz)^2 + yG(x - 2 + 2iz)\cos\theta - x(1 - iz) - y^2\cos^2\theta] \\ &\quad + [(1 - iz)^2 + 2yG[x - (1 - iz)]\cos\theta - 2x(1 - iz) - y^2\cos^2\theta + x^2] = 0 \; . \end{aligned} \tag{14.8}$$

If we now substitute for x, y, z, and G, and multiply the left side of (14.8) by $2(\beta - a)/\beta(\beta^2 - \Omega^2)$ we get

$$M^4\left\{\frac{2[\beta(\beta - a) - \Omega^2]}{\beta^2 - \Omega^2}\sin^2\theta + \frac{2(\beta - a)\cos^2\theta}{\beta}\right\}$$

$$- 2M^2\left\{\left[\frac{2(\beta - a)^2 - 2\Omega^2}{\beta^2 - \Omega^2} + \frac{a\Omega^2}{\beta(\beta^2 - \Omega^2)}\right]\sin^2\theta\right.$$

$$\left. + \left[2\left(\frac{\beta - a}{\beta}\right)\left(\frac{\beta^2 - \Omega^2 - a\beta}{\beta^2 - \Omega^2}\right)\right]\cos^2\theta\right\} + 2\left(\frac{\beta - a}{\beta}\right)\left[\frac{(\beta - a)^2 - \Omega^2}{\beta^2 - \Omega^2}\right] = 0$$

(14.9)

and (13.18) shows that this is identical with (14.6).

Ordinary and Extraordinary Modes of Propagation—If propagation is along the direction of the field, $\mathbf{B}_0$, (*longitudinal*) then $\theta = 0$ or π, $g = 0$, and $Q = \pm i$. Therefore, from (14.1), in our notation,

$$\bar{\epsilon}_{e1} = M_1^2 = 1 - a(\beta + \Omega)^{-1} \quad ; \qquad (14.10a)$$

$$M_2^2 = 1 - a(\beta - \Omega)^{-1} = \bar{\epsilon}_{e2} \quad . \qquad (14.10b)$$

If the propagation is *transverse* to the magnetic field, then in the limit as $\cos\theta$ approaches zero,

$$Q_1 \cos\theta = 0 \quad ; \quad Q_2 \cos\theta = -i\Omega/(\beta - a) \qquad (14.11)$$

and

$$\bar{\epsilon}_{e3} = M_1^2 = 1 - a/\beta \quad ; \qquad (14.12a)$$

$$M_2^2 = 1 - a\left(\beta - \frac{\Omega^2}{\beta - a}\right)^{-1} = \frac{2\bar{\epsilon}_{e1}\bar{\epsilon}_{e2}}{\bar{\epsilon}_{e1} + \bar{\epsilon}_{e2}} = \bar{\epsilon}_{e4} \quad . \qquad (14.12b)$$

In (14.12a) M_1 is the complex refractive index for the *ordinary* wave of transverse propagation, which is unaffected by the magnetic field. The index, M_2 is for the *extraordinary* wave of transverse propagation.

15. POLARIZATION OF LIGHT IN THE PLASMA

Let us consider a second system of coordinates as shown in Fig. 4; here we take **n**, ζ, and ξ as our unit base vectors. They are all mutually orthogonal, and we *define* them in the following way:

$$\xi = \mathbf{n} \mathrm{x} \mathbf{e}_3 / \sin\theta \qquad (15.1a)$$

$$\zeta = \xi \mathrm{x} \mathbf{n} \qquad (15.1b)$$

where **n** is unit propagation vector of (14.4). Since ξ is perpendicular to **n**, $\mathbf{e}_3$ and ζ, it follows that these three vectors are coplanar, as shown in the figure.

We now define a new quantity,

$$Q' = H_\zeta / H_\xi \quad , \qquad (15.2)$$

known as the (complex) polarization of the field. We have seen (Fig. 4). that **H** lies entirely in the $\xi\zeta$-plane, so that if we determine Q' we can interpret it in terms of the elliptic locus of the variable magnetic vector. Because $\mathbf{E} \cdot \mathbf{H} = 0$, we have

$$Q' = -E_\xi / E_\zeta \quad , \qquad (15.3)$$

which gives us the elliptic locus of the transverse part of the electric vector as well.

To find Q' explicitly we note that

$$\mathbf{H} = \overline{V}\, \mathbf{n} \mathrm{x} \mathbf{D}_e \quad , \qquad (11.18a')$$

(for convenience we shall drop the subscript $j = 1, 2$ but it should be understood in the equations which follow). Performing the indicated vector operations, we then find

$$Q' = \frac{n_1 D_{e2} - n_2 D_{e1}}{D_{e3}} \quad . \qquad (15.4)$$

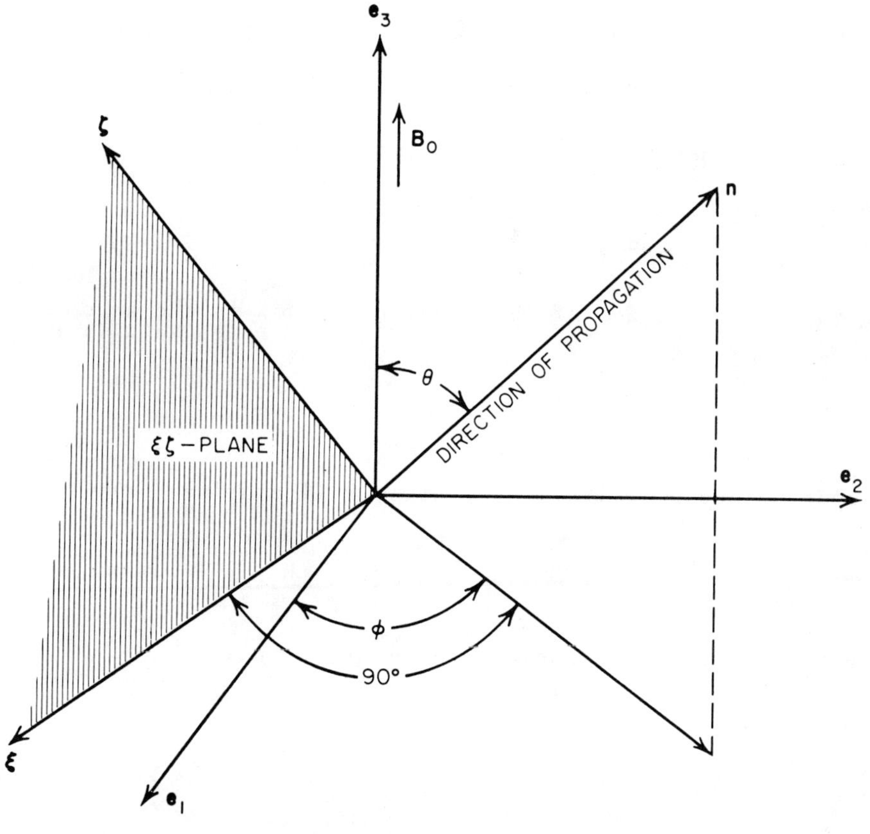

e_3
B_0
ζ
n
DIRECTION OF PROPAGATION
θ
$\xi\zeta$ – PLANE
e_2
ϕ
90°
ξ
e_1

FIG. 4

If we now find Q' in terms of M^2 and $\overline{\epsilon}_{e\,i}$ by means of (13.25), (13.22), (11.25); and (13.21):

$$iQ' = \frac{M^2 (\cos\theta)(\overline{\epsilon}_{e\,2} - \overline{\epsilon}_{e\,3})}{M^2(\overline{\epsilon}_{e\,1} + \overline{\epsilon}_{e\,2}) - 2\overline{\epsilon}_{e\,1}\overline{\epsilon}_{e\,2}} \tag{15.5}$$

and if we substitute for M^2 from (14.1a) and for $\overline{\epsilon}_{e\,i}$ from (13.18)

$$iQ' = \frac{(\cos\theta)(\beta - a - iQ\,\Omega\cos\theta)}{iQ(\beta - a)\cos\theta - \Omega(\sin^2\theta + \cos^2\theta)} \quad . \tag{15.6}$$

Recalling that equation (14.1b) can also be written

$$Q = -2iG - 1/Q \quad , \tag{15.7}$$

and substituting in place of the Q which appears in the *denominator* of (15.6), we find that

$$Q' = Q \quad . \tag{15.8}$$

If we separate the polarization, Q, into real and imaginary parts, then

$$Q = qe^{i\delta} = U + iV \quad . \tag{15.9}$$

The Polarization Ellipse—Since we are actually concerned with the real parts of the magnetic field in the $\xi\zeta$-plane as defined above,

$$H_\xi = \cos\omega t \quad ; \quad H_\zeta = q\cos(\omega t + \delta) \tag{15.10}$$

(neglecting a real multiplicative constant), so that the locus traced out by the tip of the vector $\mathbf{H} = \boldsymbol{\zeta}\, q\cos(\omega t + \delta) + \boldsymbol{\xi}\cos\omega t$, is an ellipse whose equation is found by expanding $\cos(\omega t + \delta)$ and substituting for $\cos\omega t = H_\xi$:

$$H_\zeta^2 - 2H_\zeta H_\xi q\cos\delta + H_\xi^2 q^2 = q^2\sin^2\delta \quad . \tag{15.11}$$

This is recognizable as a simple quadratic form which becomes, in matrix notation:

$$\mathbf{H}'\mathbf{A}\mathbf{H} = q^2 \sin^2 \delta \qquad (15.12)$$

where $\mathbf{H}$ is the magnetic vector in column notation, $\mathbf{H}'$ is its transpose, and

$$\mathbf{A} = \begin{pmatrix} 1 & -q \cos \\ -q \cos & q^2 \end{pmatrix}, \text{ a positive definite form.} \qquad (15.13)$$

If we solve its characteristic equation $|\mathbf{A} - \lambda\mathbf{I}| = 0$ we find its eigenvalues to be;

$$\lambda_1 = \frac{1}{2}(q^2 + 1) + \frac{1}{2}[q^4 + 1 + 2(U^2 - V^2)]^{1/2} , \qquad (15.14a)$$

$$\lambda_2 = \frac{1}{2}(q^2 + 1) - \frac{1}{2}[q^4 + 1 + 2(U^2 - V^2)]^{1/2} . \qquad (15.14b)$$

Since $\mathbf{A}$ is real and symmetric we know that the eigenvalues indicate an orthogonal transformation which diagonalizes $\mathbf{A}$, but preserves the value of (15.12). This takes the form

$$\lambda_1 H_1^2 + \lambda_2 H_2^2 = q^2 \sin^2 \delta , \qquad (15.13')$$

which clearly gives an ellipse, whose axes are in the ratio,

$$R^2 = \frac{\lambda_1}{\lambda_2} = \frac{\lambda_1^2}{\lambda_1 \lambda_2} = \frac{1 + 2U^2 + q^2 + (1 + q^2)[1 + 2(U^2 - V^2) + q^4]}{2V^2} \geqq 0 .$$

(15.14c)

Furthermore, if we also consider the equation

$$\mathbf{A}\mathbf{H} = \lambda\mathbf{H} , \qquad (15.15)$$

we find,

$$H_\zeta - q\delta H_\xi \cos = \lambda H_\zeta , \qquad (15.16)$$

or

$$\tan \psi = H_\xi / H_\zeta = (1 - \lambda)/U \quad , \tag{15.17}$$

where ψ is the angle the axis appropriate to λ makes with the projection of $\mathbf{B}_0$ on the $\xi\zeta$-plane. The sense of description of the ellipse is right-handed with respect to the direction of propagation if V is greater than zero, and left-handed if V is less than zero. Those waves which propagate such that $H_\zeta/H_\xi = -E_\xi/E_\zeta$ are called *characteristic waves.*

From the foregoing considerations it can be seen that the polarization is circular for longitudinal propagation and linear for transverse propagation. If we take $M = \mu - i\chi$, where μ is the usual refractive index and $(\omega/V_0)\chi = k$ the absorption coefficient, explicit expressions can be derived for μ and χ. Their behavior can be explored in detail by varying a, β, and Ω.

Representation and Interpretation of Transformed Fields—Let us now return to a consideration of the relations for the transformed electric field $\overline{\mathbf{E}}$. Still taking $\mathbf{k} = (\omega/V)\mathbf{n}$, we find $\overline{\mathbf{E}}$ by solving the indicated equations of (13.19a) after making the substitution for $\overline{\mathbf{D}}_e$ from (13.10). The resulting system of equations is

$$[M^2(1 + \cos^2\theta) - 2\overline{\epsilon}_{e1}]\overline{E}_1 - M^2\sin^2\theta e^{2i\phi}\overline{E}_2 - \sqrt{2}\, M^2\sin\theta\cos\theta e^{i\phi}\overline{E}_3 = 0$$

$$-M^2\sin^2\theta e^{-2i\phi}\overline{E}_1 + [M^2(1 + \cos^2\theta) - 2\overline{\epsilon}_{e2}]\overline{E}_2 - \sqrt{2}\, M^2\sin\theta\cos\theta e^{-i\phi}\overline{E}_3 = 0$$

$$-M^2\sin\theta\cos\theta e^{-i\phi}\overline{E}_1 - M^2\sin\theta\cos\theta e^{i\phi}\overline{E}_2 + \sqrt{2}\,[M^2\sin^2\theta - \overline{\epsilon}_{e3}]\overline{E}_3 = 0 \tag{15.18}$$

which yield

$$\frac{\overline{E}_1}{M^2(M^2 - \overline{\epsilon}_{e2})e^{i\phi}\cos\theta\sin\theta} = \frac{\overline{E}_2}{M^2(M^2 - \overline{\epsilon}_{e1})e^{i\phi}\cos\theta\sin\theta}$$

$$= \frac{\sqrt{2}\,\overline{E}_3}{2M^4\cos^2\theta - M^2(\overline{\epsilon}_{e1} + \overline{\epsilon}_{e2})(1 + \cos^2\theta) + 2\overline{\epsilon}_{e1}\overline{\epsilon}_{e2}} \tag{15.19}$$

These can also be written in terms of the physical components **E** by transforming back to the original system.

Since the real part of any complex quantity, Z, can be expressed by $\mathrm{Re}(Z) = (1/2)(Z + Z^*)$, we find

$$\mathrm{Re}(E_1) + i\,\mathrm{Re}(E_2) = (2)^{-\frac{1}{2}}\,(\overline{E}_1 + \overline{E}_2^*) \quad . \tag{15.20}$$

Now let us consider the behavior of the **E**-vector's projection onto the $\xi\zeta$-plane by examining its representation in the complex E_1E_2-plane.

In general, when **k** is completely unspecified, one may assume that ω can be complex. Therefore, if $\omega = \alpha + i\gamma$:†

$$\overline{E}_1 = \overline{E}_{01}e^{i\omega t} \quad ; \quad \overline{E}_2 = \overline{E}_{02}e^{i\omega t} \quad ; \tag{15.21}$$

therefore

$$\overline{E}_1 = |\overline{E}_{01}| \exp\,[-\gamma t + i(\alpha t + \gamma_1)] \quad ; \tag{15.22a}$$

$$\overline{E}_2^* = |\overline{E}_{02}| \exp\,(-i\omega^* t - i\gamma_2)$$

$$= |\overline{E}_{02}| \exp\,[-\gamma t - i(\alpha t + \gamma_2)] \quad , \tag{15.22b}$$

where γ is the phase angle of the complex $\overline{E}_0$-term. Thus we see that in general the field component perpendicular to the externally applied uniform magnetic field $\mathbf{B}_0$ can be analyzed into two opposite rotating fields of equal angular velocity and damping.

From Eqs. (13.21), (13.23) and (13.24) we can draw some important conclusions:

(a) the plasma in a uniform magnetic field is always doubly refracting, since there exist two possible values of the phase velocity of plane waves, each value corresponding to a mode of propagation;

(b) the fields associated with each mode of propagation can be resolved into a linearly polarized component parallel to the uniform magnetic field and two oppositely rotating circularly polarized components whose plane of rotation is perpendicular to the

† Note: If $\mathbf{k} = (\omega/V)\mathbf{n}$, then ω *must* be real, to avoid contradicting conservation laws.

direction of the applied magnetic field. In general, these circularly polarized components are not equal in amplitude, although they may degenerate into one linearly polarized component under special conditions;

(c) the two fields associated with the different modes of propagation are completely independent (no coupling in the case of the uniform plasma);

(d) if we fix n_3, then we define a cone which makes a fixed angle θ with the uniform magnetic field. This cone contains all directions of propagation $\mathbf{n}$ which are at angle θ to the $\mathbf{B}_0$ field. Since $n^2 = 1$, the dispersion relation (13.21) shows that $\overline{V}_1$ and $\overline{V}_2$ are constant. Thus, for a given mode of propagation the components parallel to the magnetic field $\mathbf{B}_0$ must remain unchanged, but the two circularly polarized components $(\overline{x}_1, \overline{x}_2)$ may change in phase, traversing the rim of the cone.

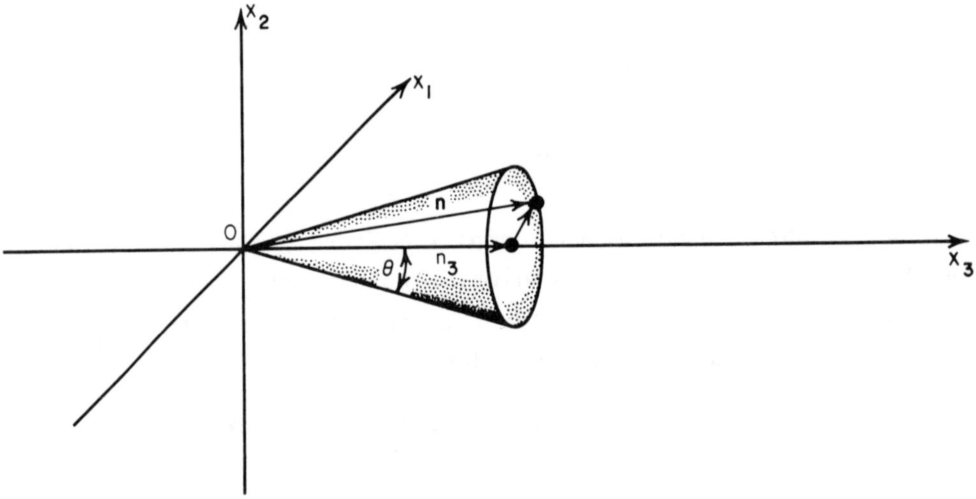

16. PLASMA OSCILLATIONS

In this section we will explore the possible types of oscillations of an electron plasma of a given density and collision frequency in the presence of a uniform magnetic field.

A pure oscillatory field is characterized by the fact that its partial derivative with respect to time is independent of position. Clearly, this is equivalent to saying that the components of **k** are all zero; implying, of course, that $\overline{\mathbf{k}}$ also vanishes. We will consider the nature of such fields in three special cases: (a) $\overline{E}_2 = \overline{E}_3 = 0$; (b) $\overline{E}_1 = \overline{E}_3 = 0$; (c) $\overline{E}_1 = \overline{E}_2 = 0$. The condition, $\mathbf{k} = 0$, implies that in Eq. (11.22) all terms in **k** vanish, and

$$\boldsymbol{\epsilon}_e \mathbf{E} = \overline{\epsilon}_e \overline{\mathbf{E}} = 0 \quad , \tag{16.1}$$

thus, we have that in situation (a), $\overline{\epsilon}_{e1} = 0$; in (b), $\overline{\epsilon}_{e2} = 0$; in (c), $\overline{\epsilon}_{e3} = 0$. We will now examine separately the consequences of these three situations.

In case (a), if one makes use of (13.18a), this implies:

$$\beta + \Omega = a \quad , \tag{16.2}$$

or, inserting (11.4), (13.12), and $\Omega = e|\mathbf{B}_0|/(m\omega) = \omega_H/\omega$ in (16.2) and solving for ω:

$$\omega = -\frac{1}{2}(\omega_H - i\nu) \pm \left[\omega_c^2 + \frac{1}{4}(\omega_H - i\nu)^2\right]^{1/2} . \tag{16.3}$$

If we set $\omega = \alpha + i\gamma$, then γ must be positive according to the energy conservation principle, and we shall require α to be positive also, so that our sinusoidal dependence is represented by a right-handed rotation in the complex plane. Therefore, we shall use the alternative,

$$\omega = \omega_1 = -\left(\frac{1}{2}\right)(\omega_H - i\nu) + \left[\omega_c^2 + \left(\frac{1}{4}\right)(\omega_H - i\nu)^2\right]^{1/2} . \tag{16.4}$$

If ν is much less than ω_H or ω_c in absolute magnitude ($\omega_H < 0$ for electrons), then we can approximate (16.4) by

$$a = \alpha_1 \approx -\frac{\omega_H}{2} + \left[\omega_c^2 + \left(\frac{1}{4}\right)\omega_H^2\right]^{1/2} \tag{16.5a}$$

$$\gamma = \gamma_1 \approx \frac{1}{2}\nu\left\{1 - \frac{\dfrac{\omega_H}{2}}{\left[\omega_c^2 + \left(\dfrac{1}{4}\right)\omega_H^2\right]^{1/2}}\right\} . \tag{16.5b}$$

The nature of the oscillation carried out by $\overline{E}_1$ is obtained by considering the real physical components corresponding to

$$\overline{E}_1 = \overline{E}_{01} e^{i\omega t} = (\overline{E}_{01}) e^{i\alpha_1 t - \gamma_1 t} , \tag{16.6a}$$

$$\overline{E}_2 = \overline{E}_3 = 0 . \tag{16.6b}$$

We find from (15.20) that

$$\mathrm{Re}\,(E_1) + i\,\mathrm{Re}\,(E_2) = (2)^{-\frac{1}{2}}\,\overline{E}_1 , \tag{16.7a}$$

$$\mathrm{Re}\,(E_3) = 0 , \tag{16.7b}$$

which shows that the real electric vector rotates in a positive (right-handed) sense about the direction of $\mathbf{B}_0$ with angular velocity α_1 and damping constant γ_1 given by (16.5). The other field quantities, $\mathbf{D}_e$, etc., do the same.

The next type of oscillation (b) yields

$$a = \beta - \Omega , \tag{16.8}$$

$$\omega = \omega_2 = \left(\frac{1}{2}\right)(\omega_H + i\nu) + \left[\omega_c^2 + \frac{1}{4}(\omega_H + i\nu)^2\right]^{\frac{1}{2}} , \tag{16.9}$$

$$\alpha = \alpha_2 \approx \left[\omega_c^2 + \left(\frac{1}{4}\right)\omega_H^2\right]^{\frac{1}{2}} + \frac{\omega_H}{2} , \tag{16.10a}$$

$$\gamma = \gamma_2 \approx \left(\frac{1}{2}\right)\nu\left\{1 + \frac{\dfrac{\omega_H}{2}}{\left[\omega_c^2 + \left(\frac{1}{4}\right)\omega_H^2\right]^{\frac{1}{2}}}\right\} , \tag{16.10b}$$

$$\mathrm{Re}\,(E_1) + i\,\mathrm{Re}\,(E_2) = (2)^{-\frac{1}{2}}\,\overline{E}_2^* , \tag{16.11a}$$

$$\mathrm{Re}\,(E_3) = 0 . \tag{16.11b}$$

So, if we write

$$\overline{E}_2 = \overline{E}_{02}e^{i\omega t} = (\overline{E}_{02})e^{i\alpha_2 t-\gamma_2 t} , \quad (16.12)$$

and

$$\overline{E}_2^* = (\overline{E}_{02}^*)e^{-i\alpha_2 t-\gamma_2 t} , \quad (16.13)$$

$$\overline{E}_1 = \overline{E}_3 = 0 , \quad (16.14)$$

we see that in this case the field rotates about the direction of $\mathbf{B}_0$ in the negative (left-handed) sense, with angular velocity α_2 and damping constant γ_2.

The last case (c) implies $\alpha = \beta$,

$$\omega = \omega_3 = \left(\frac{1}{2}\right)i\nu + \left(\omega_c^2 - \frac{\nu^2}{4}\right)^{1/2} , \quad (16.15)$$

$$\alpha = \alpha_3 \approx \omega_c \; ; \; \gamma_3 = \gamma \approx \frac{\nu}{2} . \quad (16.16)$$

Note: In this case the oscillation is linear in the direction of $\mathbf{B}_0$ with a circular frequency α_3 and damping constant γ_3.

Zeeman Effect—It is clear from the above analysis that there exists three types of oscillation of an electron plasma; the effect of collisions is not to alter the oscillatory character of the electromagnetic field but to damp the oscillations and reduce the natural frequencies. One may also note that in the case of no collisions, $\nu = 0$, and a very weak field $\mathbf{B}_0$, so that $\omega_H \ll \omega_c$,

$$\omega_1 \approx -\left(\frac{1}{2}\right)\omega_H + \omega_c \quad (16.17a)$$

$$\omega_2 \approx \left(\frac{1}{2}\right)\omega_H + \omega_c \quad (16.17b)$$

$$\omega_3 = \omega_c \quad (16.17c)$$

and we can see that the plasma frequency, ω_c is changed by $\pm(1/2)\omega_H$, depending upon the direction of rotation of the circularly polarized components. This result is in complete agreement with the classical Zeeman effect.

17. A GENERALIZED DISPERSION EQUATION FOR PROPAGATION OF WAVES IN AN ELECTRON PLASMA

We have previously derived the general relation for electromagnetic waves in a plasma:

$$(\mathbf{k}\cdot\mathbf{E})\mathbf{k} = (\mathbf{k}\cdot\mathbf{k})\mathbf{E} - \mu_0\epsilon_0\omega^2\epsilon_e\mathbf{E} \qquad (11.22)$$

where we have assumed space-time dependence of the field quantities to be expressed by the factor exp $(i\omega t - i\mathbf{k}\cdot\mathbf{r})$. We also derived an expression (11.16) for the effective dielectric tensor of the plasma, ϵ_e, and the matrix

$$\mathbf{A} = (2)^{-\frac{1}{2}}\begin{pmatrix} 1 & 1 & 0 \\ -i & i & 0 \\ 0 & 0 & \sqrt{2} \end{pmatrix} \qquad (13.5)$$

which transforms ϵ_e into the diagonal matrix $\overline{\epsilon}_e$:

$$\overline{\epsilon}_e = \mathbf{A}^{*\prime}\epsilon_e\mathbf{A} \quad . \qquad (13.10b)$$

We shall now obtain the dispersion relation valid for *any* **k**, real or complex. To this end, it is most convenient to use (11.26) directly. This expression can be recognized as the determinant of the matrix sum; $\mathbf{K} - \mathbf{I} + M^{-2}\epsilon_e$. In this case **I** is the identity matrix, ϵ_e the dielectric tensor in the *physical* system, M is defined exactly as in (11.25) (where by k^2 we mean $k_1k_1 + k_2k_2 + k_3k_3$), and a new matrix is defined:

$$\mathbf{K} = \left(\frac{1}{k^2}\right)(k_ik_j) \qquad (i = \text{row}\ ,\ j = \text{column}) \quad . \qquad (17.1)$$

Since the determinant of a matrix product is the product of the separate determinants, we can transform the determinant so that,

$$|\mathbf{K} - \mathbf{I} + M^{-2}\epsilon_e| \, | = |\mathbf{A}^{*\prime}\mathbf{K}\mathbf{A} - \mathbf{A}^{*\prime}\mathbf{I}\mathbf{A} + M^{-2}\mathbf{A}^{*\prime}\epsilon_e\mathbf{A}| \quad , \tag{17.2}$$

or

$$|\overline{\mathbf{K}} - \mathbf{I} + M^{-2}\overline{\epsilon}_e| = 0 \quad , \tag{17.3}$$

where

$$\mathbf{A}^{*\prime}\mathbf{K}\mathbf{A} = \overline{\mathbf{K}} = \frac{1}{\mathbf{k}\cdot\mathbf{k}}\begin{bmatrix} \dfrac{k_1^2 + k_2^2}{2} & \dfrac{(k_1 + ik_2)^2}{2} & k_3\left(\dfrac{k_1 + ik_2}{\sqrt{2}}\right) \\ \dfrac{(k_1 - ik_2)^2}{2} & \dfrac{k_1^2 + k_2^2}{2} & k_3\left(\dfrac{k_1 - ik_2}{\sqrt{2}}\right) \\ k_3\left(\dfrac{k_1 - ik_2}{\sqrt{2}}\right) & k_3\left(\dfrac{k_1 + ik_2}{\sqrt{2}}\right) & k_3^2 \end{bmatrix} \tag{17.4}$$

We now, for convenience, introduce the following notation:

$$\eta_i = k_i(\mathbf{k}\cdot\mathbf{k})^{-1/2} \quad ; \quad \overline{\eta}_i = \overline{k}_i(\mathbf{k}\cdot\mathbf{k})^{-1/2} \quad , \tag{17.5}$$

which may be considered as a generalized (complex) direction cosine. In this case our determinant becomes:

$$\begin{vmatrix} \dfrac{\overline{\epsilon}_{e1}}{M^2} - \overline{\eta}_1\overline{\eta}_2 - \overline{\eta}_3^2 & \overline{\eta}_1^2 & \overline{\eta}_1\overline{\eta}_3 \\ \overline{\eta}_2^2 & \dfrac{\overline{\epsilon}_{e2}}{M^2} - \overline{\eta}_1\overline{\eta}_2 - \overline{\eta}_3^2 & \overline{\eta}_2\overline{\eta}_3 \\ \overline{\eta}_2\overline{\eta}_3 & \overline{\eta}_1\overline{\eta}_3 & \dfrac{\overline{\epsilon}_{e3}}{M^2} - 2\overline{\eta}_1\overline{\eta}_2 \end{vmatrix} = 0 \; . \tag{17.6}$$

Algebraically, this equation reads:

$$\frac{1}{M^6}\,\bar{\epsilon}_{e1}\bar{\epsilon}_{e2}\bar{\epsilon}_{e3} - \frac{1}{M^4}\,[(\bar{\eta}_1\bar{\eta}_2 + \bar{\eta}_3^2)\bar{\epsilon}_{e3}(\bar{\epsilon}_{e1} + \bar{\epsilon}_{e2}) + 2\bar{\eta}_1\bar{\eta}_2\bar{\epsilon}_{e1}\bar{\epsilon}_{e2}]$$

$$+ \frac{1}{M^2}\,[(2\bar{\eta}_1\bar{\eta}_2 + \bar{\eta}_3^2)(\bar{\eta}_1\bar{\eta}_2\bar{\epsilon}_{e1} + \bar{\eta}_1\bar{\eta}_2\bar{\epsilon}_{e2} + \bar{\eta}_3^2\bar{\epsilon}_{e3})] = 0 \;. \tag{17.7}$$

This can also be cast into a form analogous to the well-known Fresnel equation of crystal optics:

$$\frac{\bar{\eta}_1\bar{\eta}_2}{\left(\dfrac{1}{M^2} - \dfrac{2\bar{\eta}_1\bar{\eta}_2 + \bar{\eta}_3^2}{\bar{\epsilon}_{e1}}\right)} + \frac{\bar{\eta}_1\bar{\eta}_2}{\left(\dfrac{1}{M^2} - \dfrac{2\bar{\eta}_1\bar{\eta}_2 + \bar{\eta}_3^2}{\bar{\epsilon}_{e2}}\right)} + \frac{\bar{\eta}_3^2}{\left(\dfrac{1}{M^2} - \dfrac{2\bar{\eta}_1\bar{\eta}_2 + \bar{\eta}_3^2}{\bar{\epsilon}_{e3}}\right)} = 0 \tag{17.8}$$

or, in the *physical* system, since

$$\bar{\eta}_1 = \frac{\eta_1 + i\eta_2}{2} \quad ; \quad \bar{\eta}_2 = \frac{\eta_2 - i\eta_2}{2} \quad ; \quad \bar{\eta}_3 = \eta_3 \tag{17.9}$$

and

$$2\bar{\eta}_1\bar{\eta}_2 + \bar{\eta}_3^2 = \eta_1^2 + \eta_2^2 + \eta_3^2 = \frac{\mathbf{k}\cdot\mathbf{k}}{\mathbf{k}\cdot\mathbf{k}} = 1 \tag{17.10}$$

we see that

$$\frac{\left(\dfrac{1}{2}\right)(\eta_1^2 + \eta_2^2)}{\left(\dfrac{1}{M^2} - \dfrac{1}{\bar{\epsilon}_{e1}}\right)} + \frac{\left(\dfrac{1}{2}\right)(\eta_1^2 + \eta_2^2)}{\left(\dfrac{1}{M^2} - \dfrac{1}{\bar{\epsilon}_{e2}}\right)} + \frac{\eta_3^2}{\left(\dfrac{1}{M^2} - \dfrac{1}{\bar{\epsilon}_{e3}}\right)} = 0 \;. \tag{17.11}$$

If we define a (complex) velocity, $V = \omega/|\mathbf{k}|$, then (17.11) corresponds exactly to (13.21).

18. FARADAY ROTATION

When linearly polarized light propagates through an electron plasma in a magnetic field there is a rotation of the *plane of polarization*;

viz., that plane which contains the $\mathbf{D}_e$, $\mathbf{E}$, and $\mathbf{n}$ vectors (see Fig. 3). This effect arises from the magnetic term $\mathbf{v} \times \mathbf{B}_0$ in the Lorentz force equation, and becomes more pronounced as the temperature of the plasma increases or the magnetic field gets stronger. Making use of the theoretical development in Sections 11, 13, 14, and 15, we are now able to make a precise calculation of this effect.

We have already shown that there are only two possible modes of propagation in the unbounded plasma, the ordinary and the extraordinary wave. In general, any electromagnetic radiation propagating through the plasma can do so only in the form of a linear superposition of these two modes. We are at liberty, however, to express this superposition in either the physical or mathematical system, whichever is most convenient. Thus,

$$\mathbf{E} = \sum_j (E)_j = \sum_j (\overline{E})_j \quad (j = 1,2). \tag{18.1}$$

A similar representation holds for all the other vector quantities.

We shall first examine the consequences of this representation in two elementary cases: (a) longitudinal propagation, and (b) transverse propagation. Assuming that $\mathbf{k} = (\omega/V)\mathbf{n}$, we shall make use of the Appleton-Hartree formulas (14.1a, b, c, d).

In Section 15 we demonstrated that

$$Q = H_\zeta/H_\xi = - E_\xi/H_\zeta \quad , \tag{18.2}$$

which gives us the direction of the $\mathbf{E}$-vector projected upon the plane perpendicular to the direction of propagation. Since this projection, $\mathbf{E}_\perp$, is just the intersection of the $\zeta\xi$-plane with the plane of polarization, we know the orientation of the latter when we know Q.

Circular Polarization—It must be remembered that thus far we have employed the complex representation of the field quantities as a convenient way of solving the differential equations and expressing the phase differences between *real* sinusoidal quantities. We must be careful to distinguish between this mode of representation and the one in which $r = x + iy$; *i.e.*, a vector's direction and magnitude are expressed by considering its x- and y-components as the real and imaginary part of a complex number and mapping it onto the complex plane.

Let us recall the result of (15.20) which says that when the *real* projection of the electric vector on the $\zeta\xi$-plane is represented as a complex number we have, in *either* mode

$$E_{\perp} = Re(E_1) + iRe(E_2) = (2)^{-\frac{1}{2}}(\overline{E}_1 + \overline{E}_2^*) \qquad (15.20)$$

Restating this more completely, according to (18.1):

$$E_{\perp} = Re(E_1) + iRe(E_2) = (2)^{-\frac{1}{2}} \sum_j [(\overline{E}_1)_j + (\overline{E}_2^*)_j] \quad . \qquad (18.3)$$

That is, the components of *any* field quantity perpendicular to $\mathbf{B}_0$ may be decomposed into right- and left-circularly polarized components in *each* mode. The exact values of the components in the decomposition depends upon boundary conditions, such as direction of propagation, $\mathbf{n}$, initial values of the field, and so forth. This will be demonstrated in the cases treated below.

Longitudinal Propagation. This is the case shown in Fig. 5,

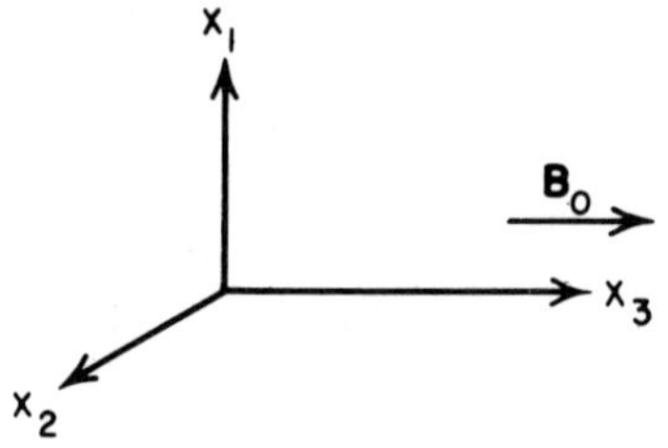

FIG. 5

for which $Q_1 = i$, and $Q_2 = -i$ (see Eq. 14.10). The corresponding modes of propagation are $M_1^2 = \overline{\epsilon}_{e1}$, $M_2^2 = \overline{\epsilon}_{e2}$.

We are at liberty to choose the ζ-axis as the x_1-direction, and the ξ-axis as the x_2-direction. Therefore,

$$Q = -E_2/E_1$$

which implies that in the first mode

$$(E_1 - iE_2)_1 = (\overline{E}_2)_1 = 0 \qquad (18.4a)$$

and in the second mode

$$(E_1 + iE_2)_2 = (\overline{E}_1)_2 = 0 \qquad (18.4b)$$

We can interpret these results in view of (15.20) to mean that for longitudinal propagation the right-circularly polarized component of the ordinary wave, $(\overline{E}_2^*)_1$, and the left-circularly polarized component of the extraordinary, $(\overline{E}_1)_2$, wave both vanish.

Suppose that we have a linearly polarized longitudinal wave in the plasma at $x_3 = 0$, then according to (18.1) and (18.4):

$$E_\perp = Re(E_1) + iRe(E_2) = (2)^{-1/2}[(\overline{E}_1)_1 + (\overline{E}_2^*)_2] \qquad (18.5)$$

Since the factor $e^{i(\omega t - k_j z)}$ must occur in every term in either the physical or mathematical system we may take:

$$(2)^{-1/2}(\overline{E}_1)_1 = Be^{i(\omega t - k_1 x_3)} \quad ; \quad (2)^{-1/2}(\overline{E}_2^*)_2 = C^* e^{-i(\omega t - k_2^* x_3)} \qquad (18.6)$$

where B and C are complex quantities:

$$B = be^{i\gamma_1} \quad ; \qquad C = ce^{i\gamma_2} \qquad (18.7)$$

At $x_3 = 0$ we require a linearly polarized wave, which we may choose to be $\mathbf{E}_\perp = \mathbf{e}_1 A \cos \omega t$, A real. Therefore, at any time t, and $x_3 = 0$

$$b \cos (\omega t + \gamma_1) + C \cos (\omega t + \gamma_2) = A \cos \omega t \qquad (18.8a)$$

$$b \sin (\omega t - \gamma_1) - C \sin (\omega t - \gamma_2) = 0 \qquad (18.8b)$$

Equating coefficients of $\sin \omega t$, $\cos \omega t$ in (18.8) we find that

$$\gamma_1 = \gamma_2 = \gamma; \qquad b = c = A/(2 \cos \gamma); \qquad \gamma = 0 \qquad (18.9)$$

$$E_{\perp} = (A/2)\left[e^{i(\omega t - k_1 x_3)} + e^{-i(\omega t - k_2^* x_3)}\right] \qquad (18.10)$$

where

$$k_1^2 = \mu_0 \epsilon_0 \omega^2 M_1^2, \quad k_2^2 = \mu_0 \epsilon_0 \omega^2 M_2^2 \quad . \qquad (18.11)$$

Thus, at $x_3 = d$

$$E_{\perp} = (A/2)\{C' \exp i[\omega t - dRe(k_1)] + D' \exp - i[\omega t - dRe(k_2)]\} \qquad (18.12)$$

where

$$C' = \exp[dIm(k_1)]; \quad D' = \exp[dIm(k_2)] \qquad (18.13)$$

(note: $Im(k_1) < 0$; $Im(k_2) < 0$ for damped wave)

To add two complex numbers of different magnitude and phase we use the following relations:

$$\left(\frac{A}{2}\right)(C'e^{i\theta'} + D'e^{i\phi'}) = (a/2)e^{i(\theta'+\phi'/2)}[C'e^{i(\theta'-\phi'/2)} + D'e^{-i(\theta'-\phi'/2)}] \qquad (18.14a)$$

$$= (A/2)e^{i(\theta'+\phi'/2)}e^{i\psi}[C'^2 + D'^2 + 2C'D'\cos(\theta' - \phi')]^{1/2} \qquad (18.14b)$$

where

$$\psi = \tan^{-1}\left[\frac{C' - D'}{C' + D'}\tan\left(\frac{\theta' - \phi'}{2}\right)\right] \qquad (18.14c)$$

Making use of Eqs. 18.14 in our expression for E (18.12) we have

$$\frac{\theta' + \phi'}{2} = \frac{d}{2}[Re(k_2) - Re(k_1)] \qquad (18.15a)$$

$$\frac{\theta' + \phi'}{2} = \omega t - \frac{d}{2}[Re(k_1) + Re(k_2)] \qquad (18.15b)$$

To find k_1 and k_2 most easily we may rewrite Eqs. (14.10):

$$M_{1,2}^2 = 1 - \frac{a}{\beta \pm \Omega} = \frac{(\beta \pm \Omega - a)(\beta^* \pm \Omega)}{(\beta \pm \Omega)(\beta^* \pm \Omega)} \qquad (18.16a)$$

or since $\beta = 1 - i\nu/\omega$

$$M_{1,2}^2 = \frac{(1 \pm \Omega)(1 \pm \Omega - a) + \nu^2/\omega^2 - ai\nu/\omega}{(1 \pm \Omega)^2 + \nu^2/\omega^2} \tag{18.16b}$$

and in complex notation:

$$M_{1,2}^2 = A_\pm e^{i\phi_\pm} \tag{18.17a}$$

where

$$A_\pm = [(1 \pm \Omega)^2 + \nu^2/\omega^2]^{-1}\{[(1 \pm \Omega)(1 \pm \Omega - a) + \nu^2/\omega^2]^2 + a^2\nu^2/\omega^2\}^{1/2} \tag{18.17b}$$

$$\phi_\pm = \tan^{-1} \frac{-a\nu/\omega}{(1 \pm \Omega)(1 \pm \Omega - a) + \nu^2/\omega^2} \tag{18.17c}$$

$$k_{1,2} = \frac{\omega}{V_0} \sqrt{A_\pm} e^{i\phi_\pm/2} \tag{18.18}$$

Substituting (18.18) into (18.15):

$$\frac{1}{2}(\theta' + \phi') = \frac{\omega d}{2V_0}\left[\sqrt{A_-} \cos\left(\frac{1}{2}\phi_-\right) - \sqrt{A_+} \cos\left(\frac{1}{2}\phi_+\right)\right] \tag{18.19a}$$

$$\frac{1}{2}(\theta' + \phi') = \omega t - \frac{\omega d}{2V_0}\left[\sqrt{A_+} \cos\left(\frac{1}{2}\phi_+\right) + \sqrt{A_-} \cos\left(\frac{1}{2}\phi_-\right)\right] \tag{18.19b}$$

Let us now examine Eq. (18.14b) more closely and discuss the origin and significance of its different factors. Making the appropriate substitutions for θ', ϕ', and ψ, (18.14b) represents the $\mathbf{E}_\perp$ mapped onto the complex E_1E_2-plane. *If* we fix t and compare $E_\perp$ at $x_3 = 0$ to E at $x_3 = d$ we can see that the plane of polarization, as previously defined in this section, has rotated through an angle equal to $1/2\ (\theta' + \phi') + \psi$ and the magnitude of $E_\perp$ has changed due to the factor in the brackets.

Collision Effects—If we look at the expression in brackets in Eq. (18.14a), neglecting $\exp[i(\theta' + \phi')/2]$ for the moment, we see that in the plane $x_3 = d$, the $E_\perp$-vector traces an ellipse whose parametric equations are

$$E_1 = \frac{A}{2}(C' + D') \cos [\omega t - d\overline{Re(k)}] \tag{18.20a}$$

$$E_2 = \frac{A}{2}(C' - D') \sin [\omega t - d\overline{Re(k)}] \tag{18.20b}$$

where

$$\overline{Re(k)} = \frac{1}{2}[Re(k_1) + Re(k_2)] \tag{18.21}$$

if $C' > D'$ the direction of rotation of the E-vector with time t will be positive; if $C' < D'$, it will be negative. The major and minor axes of the ellipse will be $A/2\ (C' + D')$ and $A/2\ |C' - D'|$, respectively.

It is clear that this effect is due to the unequal damping for the ordinary and extraordinary modes. In the special case where there is no damping ($\nu = 0$), or equal damping ($C' = D'$) then $E_2 = 0$ and the wave remains linearly polarized.

It is interesting to note that both E_1 and E_2 propagate with the same phase velocity $V = \omega/\overline{Re(k)}$, the effective wave number, $\overline{Re(k)}$, being the average of the ordinary and extraordinary wave numbers.

Magnetic Effects—The effect of $e^{i(\theta'+\phi')/2)}$ is just to rotate the ellipse of Eq. (18.20) by an amount $(\theta' + \phi')/2$. It is this rotation which Faraday discovered, and in the case of no magnetic field then $\Omega = 0$, $k_1 = k_2$, and $1/2\ (\theta' + \phi') = 0$.

Thus, the over-all effect is that the radiation propagates as an elliptically polarized wave of phase velocity $V = \omega/\overline{Re(k)}$ and that there is an additional rotation due to the magnetic field. This may be visualized (see Fig. 6) as a precession of the ellipse, which, at the same time is shrinking and changing its eccentricity due to damping.

If we consider a wave propagating in the $\theta = \pi$ direction, *antiparallel* to the field we find that $M_1^2 = \overline{\epsilon}_{e2}$; $M_2^2 = \overline{\epsilon}_{e1}$; so the situation is now reversed: k_1 is now the wave-number of the left-circular component, k_2 the wave-number of the right-circular component.

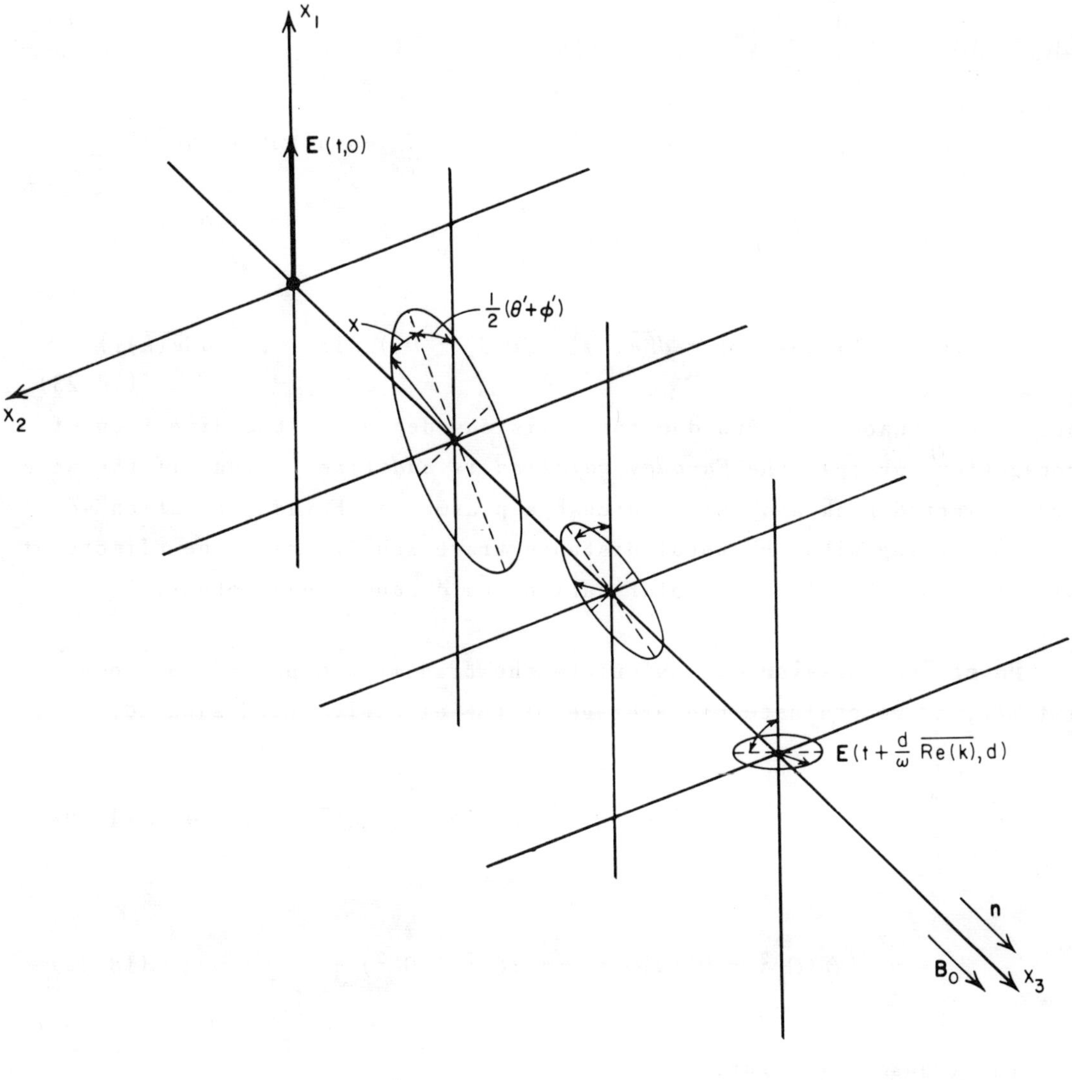

x_1
$\mathbf{E}(t,0)$
x_2
χ
$\frac{1}{2}(\theta'+\phi')$
ι
$\mathbf{E}(t+\frac{d}{\omega}\overline{Re(k)},d)$
$\mathbf{n}$
$\mathbf{B}_0$
x_3

FIG. 6

Thus

$$E_\perp = (A/2)[e^{i(\omega t - k_2 x_3)} + e^{-i(\omega t - k_1^* x_3)}] \quad ; \qquad (18.22)$$

and if we observe the wave in the plane $x_3 = -d$,

$$E_\perp = (A/2)\exp\left\{\frac{-id}{2}[Re(k_1) - Re(k_2)]\right\}$$

$$\{(D' + C')\cos[\omega t + d\overline{Re(k)}] + i(D' - C')\sin[\omega t + d\overline{Re(k)}]\}$$

$$= (A/2)\exp\left\{\frac{id}{2}[Re(k_2) - Re(k_1)]\right\}$$

$$\{(D' + C')\cos[\omega t + d\overline{Re(k)}] - i(C' - D')\sin[\omega t + d\overline{Re(k)}]\} \qquad (18.23)$$

Thus we see that rotations due to collisions depend on the direction of propagation, whereas the *Faraday rotation is additive*. Thus, if the wave were reflected back and forth through a plasma the Faraday rotation would keep increasing with the total distance traversed, whereas the effects of collisions on the plane of polarization would cancel each other.

Power Transmission—To calculate the transmitted power over some distance, d, we evaluate the average of the electric field squared:

$$\overline{E^2} = \frac{A^2}{8\pi}\int_0^{2\pi}\{C'^2 + D'^2 + 2C'D'\cos[2\omega t - 2d\overline{Re(k)}]\}d(\omega t) \qquad (18.24)$$

$$= \frac{A^2}{8\pi}[2\pi(C'^2 + D'^2)] = \frac{A^2}{4}(C'^2 + D'^2) \qquad (18.25)$$

Thus the transmission ratio is

$$\frac{P_{out}}{P_{in}} = \frac{\frac{A^2}{4}(C'^2 + D'^2)}{\frac{1}{2}A^2} = \frac{1}{2}(C'^2 + D'^2) \qquad (18.26)$$

Special Cases—

$$f_p = \frac{\omega_p}{2\pi} = 8.97 \times 10^3\ N^{1/2} \tag{18.27}$$

is the plasma frequency where N is the density of *free* electrons per cm^3. Let us consider an important case; the terrestrial atmosphere at 100 kilometers above the earth. Using the formula

$$\nu = 3.5 \times 10^9\ PT^{-1/2} \quad * \tag{18.28}$$

(P = total pressure in mm. Hg, T = temperature in degrees Kelvin) we find $\nu \approx 10^5\ sec^{-1}$. At 100 kilometers $N \approx 10^5$ electrons/cm^3; then $\omega_p \approx 20 \times 10^7\ sec^{-1}$. At latitude 45°N the earth's magnetic field has been found to be $B_0 \approx 6 \times 10^{-5}$ webers/m^2 or 0.6 gauss. Thus we may take the cyclotron frequency to be $\omega_H \approx 10^7\ sec^{-1}$.

Taking these values as our guide, let us investigate the effect of the magnetic field upon a linearly-polarized oscillation, $e^{i\omega t}$, propagating through an electron plasma, when

$$\nu << \omega_H << \omega_p \tag{18.29}$$

I) $\omega^2 << \omega_H^2$

$$M_{1,2}^2 = 1 - a(\beta \pm \Omega) \approx \frac{-a}{\Omega^2 \pm 2\Omega}\left[1 \pm \Omega + i\nu/\omega\right] \tag{18.30}$$

$$\approx \frac{\mp a}{\Omega^2 \pm 2\Omega}(\Omega + 1)e^{i\phi_\pm}, \qquad \tan\phi_\pm = \frac{\nu/\omega}{1 \pm \Omega} \approx \phi_\pm \tag{18.31}$$

In the limit of very low $\omega << \omega_H$

$$M_{1,2}^2 = \mp \frac{\omega_p{}^2}{\omega\omega_H}\ e^{\pm i\nu/\omega_H} \tag{18.32}$$

---

* Nicolet, Collision Frequency of Electrons in the Terrestrial Atmosphere, *Physics of Fluids*, **2**, 95 (1959).

Finding k_1, k_2, from (18.11)

$$k_1 = -i(\omega/V_0)\left[\frac{a(\Omega + 1)}{\Omega^2 + 2\Omega}\right]^{1/2} e^{(i\nu/2\omega)/(1+\Omega)} \tag{18.33a}$$

$$k_2 = (\omega/V_0)\left[\frac{a(\Omega - 1)}{\Omega^2 - 2\Omega}\right]^{1/2} e^{(i\nu/2\omega)/(1-\Omega)} \tag{18.33b}$$

where we have chosen the signs so that the imaginary part of each k is negative.

Let us now calculate these effects over a distance, $d = 2\pi V_0/\omega$, *i.e.*, one wavelength in vacuo, for two cases $\omega = 10^4$ sec^{-1}, and 2×10^6 sec^{-1}.

$\omega = 10^4$ sec^{-1}	$\omega = 2 \times 10^6$ sec^{-1}
$\lvert\phi_\pm\rvert = 10^{-2}$ radians	$\phi_+ = 8.3 \times 10^{-3}$,
	$\phi_- = -12.5 \times 10^{-3}$ radians
$\lambda_0 k_1 = 2\pi\left(630 \sin\frac{\phi_+}{2} - 630 \cos\frac{\phi_+}{2}\right)$	$\lambda_0 k_1 = 2\pi\left(576 \sin\frac{\phi_+}{2} - 576 \cos\frac{\phi_+}{2}\right)$
$\lambda_0 k_2 = 2\pi\left(630 \cos\frac{\phi_-}{2} + 630 \sin\frac{\phi_-}{2}\right)$	$\lambda_0 k_2 = 2\pi\left(720 \cos\frac{\phi_-}{2} + 720 \sin\frac{\phi_-}{2}\right)$
$\lambda_0 = 188$ km	$\lambda_0 = 0.94$ km.

Faraday Rotation;

$\frac{1}{2}(\theta + \phi)$: $2\pi(313.4)$ radians $(358.8)2\pi$ radians

Collision Effects

$C' = e^{\lambda_0 Im(k_1)}$: $e^{-2\pi(630)} \approx 0$ $e^{-2\pi(576)} \approx 0$

$D' = e^{\lambda_0 Im(k_2)}$: $e^{-2\pi(3.15)} \approx 0$ $e^{-2\pi(4.5)} \approx 0$

Comparing the two cases it can be seen that the plane of polarization rotates several hundred times in one wave length, however, both frequencies are completely damped out long before they have travelled that far, due to collisions. The effect can be seen to increase with frequency. So, if we had examined the first case at a distance of about 1 kilometer from the source we would have found a rotation through about 1½ revolutions, and although C' would be very nearly zero, D' would be around 0.91 so that the extraordinary wave (in both cases) suffers much less damping, and would have about 80% of its power transmitted through the plasma in one kilometer.

II) $\omega = \omega_H + \Delta \qquad |\Delta| << \omega_H$

$$M_1^2 = -\left(\frac{1}{2}\right)\left(\frac{a}{\Omega}\right) e^{i\nu/2\omega_H} \qquad (18.34)$$

$$M_2^2 = -\left(\frac{a\omega}{\sqrt{\Delta^2 + \nu^2}}\right) e^{i\phi}; \qquad \phi = \tan^{-1}(\nu/\Delta) \qquad (18.35)$$

Thus,

$$\lambda_0 k_1 = -2\pi i \sqrt{\frac{a}{2\Omega}}\, e^{i\nu/4\omega_H} \qquad (18.36)$$

$$\lambda_0 k_2 = -2\pi i \left(\frac{a\omega}{\sqrt{\Delta^2 + \nu^2}}\right)^{1/2} e^{i\phi/2} \qquad (18.37)$$

Note that the sign of Δ only affects the phase of k_2 and as Δ goes to zero the absolute value of k_2 is a maximum. Thus we would expect a strong resonance effect upon the extraordinary wave at $\omega = \omega_H$. We calculate the results for this case:

$$\lambda_0 k_1 = 2\pi(14.1 \sin \nu/4\omega_H - 14.1 i \cos \nu/4\omega_H)$$

$$\lambda_0 k_2 = 2\pi(211 \sin \pi/4 - 211\, i \cos \pi/4)$$

$$\frac{1}{2}(\theta + \phi) = 2\pi(71) \text{ radians}; \quad C' = e^{-88.8} \approx 0,$$

$$D' = e^{-888.0}, \quad \lambda_0 \approx 190 \text{ meters}$$

Once again we have a very strong damping effect; however, in this case the extraordinary wave is most quickly absorbed. The Faraday rotation is now very pronounced: approximately 135° per *meter*.

III) $\omega = \omega_p + \Delta, \quad |\Delta| \ll \omega_p$

$$M_{1,2}^2 = \frac{2\Delta \pm \omega_H - i\nu}{\omega_p + 2(\Delta \pm\pm\omega_H)} \tag{18.38}$$

If we examine the case $\omega = \omega_p$, then $\Delta = 0$

$$M_{1,2}^2 \approx \pm\left(\frac{\omega_H}{\omega_p}\right) e^{\mp i\nu/\omega_H} \tag{18.39}$$

$$\lambda_0 k_1 = 2\pi\left(\frac{\omega_H}{\omega_p}\right)^{1/2} e^{-i\nu/(2\omega_H)} \tag{18.40a}$$

$$\lambda_0 k_2 = -2\pi i\left(\frac{\omega_H}{\omega_p}\right)^{1/2} e^{i\nu/(2\omega_H)} \tag{18.40b}$$

$$\lambda_0 k_1 = 2\pi(0.22 \cos \nu/2\omega_H - 0.22i \sin \nu/2\omega_H) \tag{18.41a}$$

$$\lambda_0 k_2 = 2\pi(0.22 \sin \nu/2\omega_H - 0.22i \cos \nu/2\omega_H) \tag{18.41b}$$

$$\frac{1}{2}(\theta + \phi) = 2\pi(-0.11) \text{ radians}$$

$$C' \approx e^{-0.007}, \quad D' \approx e^{-1.4} = 0.25 \tag{18.42}$$

$$= 0.993$$

We can see that as we move away from the cyclotron frequency the damping effect decreases; it may also be noted that the sense of the rotation is reversed above this frequency. This is in agreement with (18.27) which shows that the argument of k_2 changes sign as we pass through the resonant frequency. Using the formula (18.26) we find the power transmission to be 52%.

As the frequency increases beyond the plasma frequency these effects become smaller and smaller as $M \to 1$.

Transverse Propagation—In this case $\theta = \pi/2$ (see Fig. 7) and from (14.1b, c, d) we have

$$Q = iG \pm i\sqrt{G^2 + 1} \tag{18.43}$$

$$G(\theta) = \frac{\Omega}{2} \frac{\sin\theta \tan\theta}{\beta - a} \tag{18.44}$$

$$\lim_{\theta \to (\pi/2)} G(\theta) = \infty \tag{18.45}$$

therefore

$$\lim_{\theta \to (\pi/2)} Q(\theta) = \lim_{G \to \infty} \left[-iG \pm \left(G + \frac{1}{2G} + \ldots \right) \right] \tag{18.46}$$

$$Q_1\left(\frac{\pi}{2}\right) = 0; \quad Q_2\left(\frac{\pi}{2}\right) = -i\infty \tag{18.47}$$

Thus we see that in mode No. 1

$$\frac{-E_\xi}{E_\zeta} = 0 \text{ or } E_\xi = E_1 = 0; \quad M_1^2 = \bar{\epsilon}_{e3} \tag{18.48}$$

and in mode No. 2,

$$\frac{-E_\zeta}{E_\xi} = 0 \text{ or } E_\zeta = E_3 = 0; \quad M_2^2 = \bar{\epsilon}_{e4} \tag{18.49}$$

Thus, if one starts with a linearly polarized wave at the plane $x_2 = 0$ it will split into two linear components, the one parallel and one perpendicular to B_0 travelling with velocities $V_0/\sqrt{\bar{\epsilon}_{e3}}$, and $V_0/\sqrt{\bar{\epsilon}_{e4}}$, respectively, in the x_2-direction.

As defined previously in Section 14 we shall consider the first wave, $(E_3)_1$, to be the *ordinary* wave, and the second, $(E_1)_2$, to be the *extraordinary* wave. These distinctions are largely semantic, and for the sake

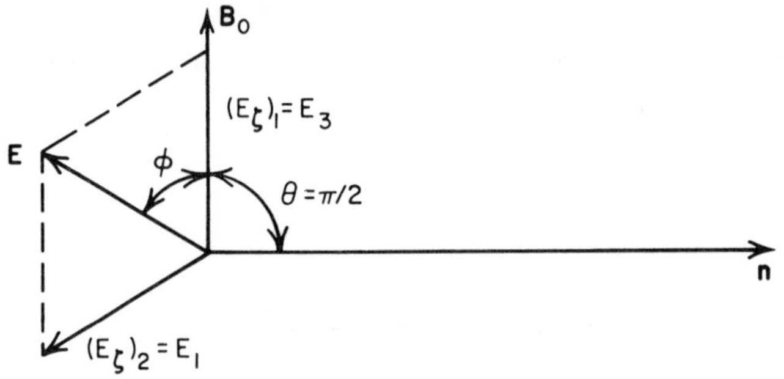

FIG. 7

of convenience, since the wave velocities will change depending upon ν, φ, B_0, and N. Thus the comparison to crystal optics, where the extra-ordinary wave is usually faster is not complete. However, there is a close phenomenological analogy to the effect of a uniaxial crystal upon light propagating through it transverse to its optic axis. That is, any light which enters is split into a component parallel and a component perpendicular to the optic axis, the two components propagating with different velocities. This can give rise to many useful polarization devices such as quarter-wave plates, half-wave plates, etc.

This would suggest a similar employment for a rarefied gas in an applied magnetic field as a polarizer for electromagnetic radiation and also as a spectrum analyzer, since M^2 is a function of frequency, ω.

19. FARADAY ROTATION: GENERAL CASE

Let us now consider the more general case of rotational and collisional effects for a wave propagating through the plasma at an angle, θ, to the uniform magnetic field, $\mathbf{B}_0$ (see Fig. 8).

First let us recall the definition of Q, the polarization, in detail:

$$Q^2 + 2iGQ + 1 = 0; \tag{19.1a}$$

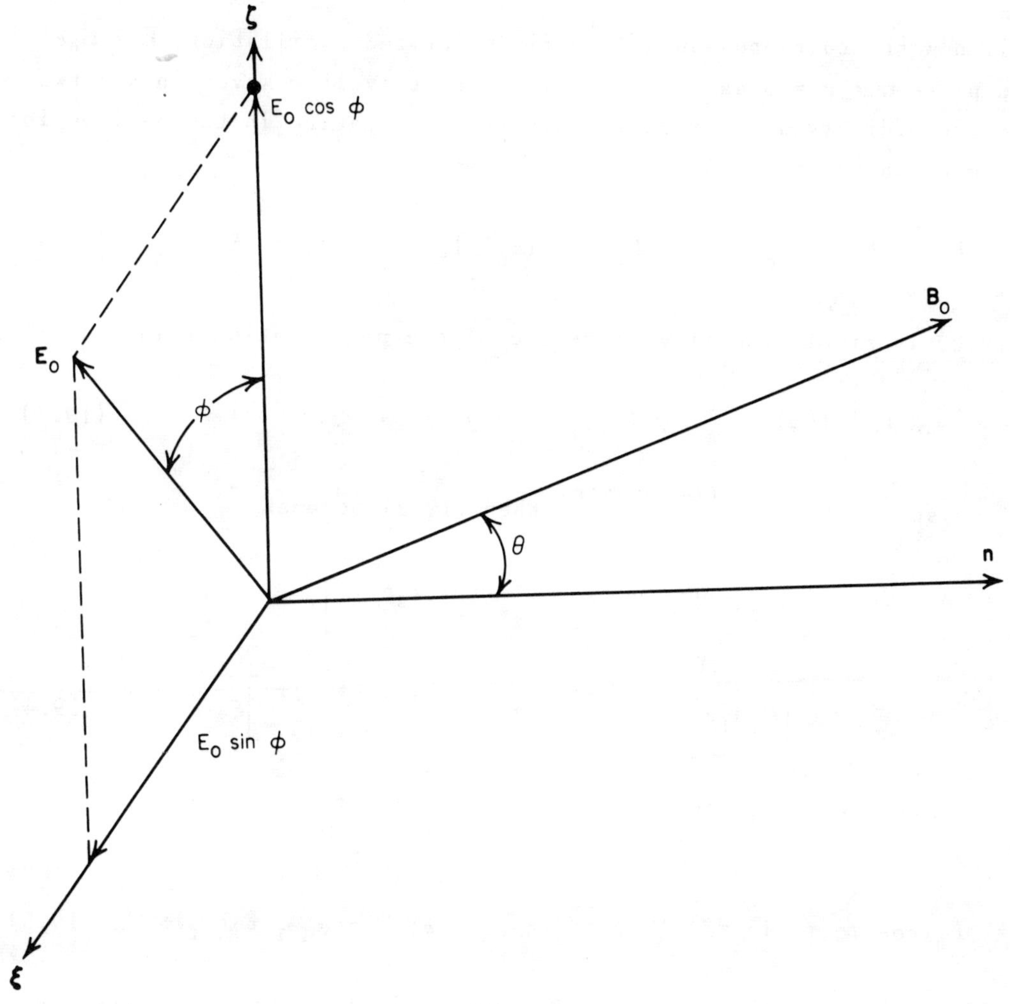

FIG. 8

$$G = \frac{1}{2} \frac{\Omega \sin^2 \theta}{(\beta - a) \cos \theta} \tag{19.1b}$$

$$Q_{1,2} = -iG \pm i\sqrt{G^2 + 1} \tag{19.1c}$$

$$Q_1 Q_2 = 1 \tag{19.1d}$$

We will now try to represent a linearly-polarized oscillation, $\mathbf{E} = \mathbf{E}_0 e^{i\omega t}$, in the plane $\mathbf{n} \cdot \mathbf{r} = 0$ as a superposition of traveling waves in the two modes, the ordinary and the extraordinary, propagating in the $\mathbf{n}$-direction. To do so we therefore assume

$$E = E_\zeta \zeta + E_\xi \xi = [(E_\zeta)_1 + (E_\zeta)_2]\zeta + [(E_\xi)_1 + (E_\xi)_2]\xi \tag{19.2}$$

Eq. (19.2) is simplified if we make use of the polarization relation, (15.3);

$$(E_\xi)_j = -Q_j (E_\zeta)_j \qquad (j = 1,\ 2) \tag{19.3}$$

And if we set $(E_\zeta)_j = A_j e^{i(\omega t - k_j \mathbf{n} \cdot \mathbf{r})}$ then (19.2) becomes

$$E = \left[A_1 e^{i(\omega t - k_1 \mathbf{n} \cdot \mathbf{r})} + A_2 e^{i(\omega t - k_2 \mathbf{n} \cdot \mathbf{r})}\right]\zeta$$

$$-\left[Q_1 A_1 e^{i(\omega t - k_1 \mathbf{n} \cdot \mathbf{r})} + Q_2 A_2 e^{i(\omega t - k_2 \mathbf{n} \cdot \mathbf{r})}\right]\xi \tag{19.4}$$

We can now determine A_1 and A_2 from the condition that in the plane $\mathbf{n} \cdot \mathbf{r} = 0$

$$\mathbf{E} = E_0(\cos \phi \boldsymbol{\zeta} + \sin \phi \boldsymbol{\xi}) e^{i\omega t} = (A_1 + A_2) e^{i\omega t} \zeta - (Q_1 A_1 + Q_2 A_2) e^{i\omega t} \xi \tag{19.5}$$

Cancelling $e^{i\omega t}$ on both sides and equating real and imaginary parts, we obtain the following system of four simultaneous equations in the unknowns A_1, A_1^*, A_2, A_2^*.

$$2E_0 \cos \phi = A_1 + A_2 + A_1^* + A_2^* \tag{19.6a}$$

$$0 = A_1 + A_2 - (A_1^* + A_2^*) \tag{19.6b}$$

$$-2E_0 \sin\phi = Q_1A_1 + Q_2A_2 + Q_1^*A_1^* + Q_2^*A_2^* \tag{19.6c}$$

$$0 = Q_1A_1 + Q_2A_2 - (Q_1^*A_1^* + Q_2^*A_2^*) \tag{19.6d}$$

The solutions are

$$A_1 = E_0\left(\frac{Q_2 \cos\phi + \sin\phi}{Q_2 - Q_1}\right) \tag{19.7a}$$

$$A_2 = E_0\left(\frac{Q_1 \cos\phi + \sin\phi}{Q_1 - Q_2}\right). \tag{19.7b}$$

Substituting these results in (19.4) we have

$$\mathbf{E} = E_0\left[\left(\frac{Q_2 \cos\phi + \sin\phi}{Q_2 - Q_1}\right)e^{i(\omega t - k_1\mathbf{n}\cdot\mathbf{r})} + \left(\frac{Q_1 \cos\phi + \sin\phi}{Q_1 - Q_2}\right)e^{i(\omega t - k_2\mathbf{n}\cdot\mathbf{r})}\right]\zeta$$

$$-E_0\left[\left(\frac{\cos\phi + Q_1 \sin\phi}{Q_2 - Q_1}\right)e^{i(\omega t - k_1\mathbf{n}\cdot\mathbf{r})} + \left(\frac{\cos\phi + Q_2 \sin\phi}{Q_1 - Q_2}\right)e^{i(\omega t - k_2\mathbf{n}\cdot\mathbf{r})}\right]\xi \tag{19.8}$$

(Note: we have made use of $Q_1Q_2 = 1$ in the ξ-component.)
If we write out the damping terms more explicitly:

$$C' = \exp\left[\mathbf{n}\cdot\mathbf{r}\ Im(k_1)\right]; \qquad D' = \exp\left[\mathbf{n}\cdot\mathbf{r}\ Im(k_2)\right] \tag{19.9}$$

then

$$\mathbf{E} = E_0\left[\left(\frac{Q_2 \cos\phi + \sin\phi}{Q_2 - Q_1}\right)\zeta - \left(\frac{\cos\phi + Q_1 \sin\phi}{Q_2 - Q_1}\right)\xi\right]C' e^{i[\omega t - Re(k_1)\mathbf{n}\cdot\mathbf{r}]}$$

$$+E_0\left[\left(\frac{Q_1 \cos\phi + \sin\phi}{Q_1 - Q_2}\right)\zeta - \left(\frac{\cos\phi + Q_2 \sin\phi}{Q_1 - Q_2}\right)\xi\right]D' e^{i[\omega t - Re(k_2)\mathbf{n}\cdot\mathbf{r}]} \tag{19.10}$$

Although conceptually simple, any attempt to compose $\mathbf{E}$ into a complex number $\mathbf{E} = Re(E_\zeta) + iRe(E_\xi)$ as was done in the longitudinal case would be extremely tedious. However, the rotations and amplitude changes in any specific case may be calculated from (19.10) above, by first determining Q_j and A_j.

BIBLIOGRAPHIES

1. Akhiezer, A. I., Prokhoda, I. G., and Sitenko, A. G., On the scattering of electromagnetic waves in a plasma. Zh. eksper. teor. Fiz. Vol. 33, p. 750 (1957).

2. Anderson, J. M. and Goldstein, L., Interaction of Electromagnetic Waves of Radio-Frequency in Isothermal Plasmas. Phys. Rev. 100, pp. 1037-1046 (1955).

3. Appleton, Sir E. V. and Builder, G., The Ionosphere as a Doubly Refracting Medium. Proc. Phys. Soc. 45, 208 (1933).

4. Argence, E., Rawer, K., and Suchy, K., Influence of the earth's magnetic field on the absorption of short waves in the ionosphere (normal incidence) Comptes Rendus, pp. 190-192 (12 Jan. 1953) (In French).

5. Argence, E., Rawer, K., and Suchy, K., The Theorems of Equivalence in Ionospheric Absorption. Comptes Rendus, pp. 505-507, 241 (1 August 1955).

6. Arzelies, H., On a matrix and tensor form of the fundamental relations of the magneto-ionic theory. Compte Rendus, Vol. 234, pp. 2430-2432 (1952).

7. Bailey, V. A., Study of the Magneto-Ionic Theory of Wave-Propagation by Means of Conformal Representation. Cambridge Phil. Soc. (1934).

8. Banerjea, B. K., On the propagation of electromagnetic waves through the atmosphere. Proc. Roy. Soc. A, Vol. 190, pp. 67-81 (1947).

9. Booker, H. G., Some general properties of the formulae of the magneto-ionic theory. Proc. Roy. Soc. A, 147, p. 352 (1934).

10. Budden, K. G., Effects of small irregularities on the constitutive relations for the ionosphere. J. Res. Nat. Bur. Stand. 63D, p. 135 (1959).

11. Burkhardt, G., Dispersive Power and Characteristic Oscillations of an Ionized Gas. Annalen der Physik, series 6, Vol. 5, pp. 373-80 (1950).

12. Daniels, F. B. and Bauer, S. J., The Ionospheric Faraday Effect and Its Applications, J. Franklin Inst. 267, pp. 187-200 (1959).

13. Darwin, C. G., The Refractive Index of an Ionized Medium. Proc. Roy. Soc. A, 146, pp. 17-46 (1934).

14. Darwin, C. G., The Refractive Index of an Ionized Medium. II. Proc. Roy. Soc. A, 182, pp. 152-66 (1943).

15. Gerson, N. C. and Seaton, S. L., Generalized Magneto-Ionic Theory. J. Franklin Inst. 246, 483 (1948).

16. Hatanaka, T., The Faraday Effect in the Earth's Ionosphere with Special Reference to Polarization Measurement of the Solar Radio Emmission. Publications of the Astronomical Society of Japan, Vol. 8, No. 2, pp. 73-86 (1956).

17. Hibberd, F. H., The Faraday Fading of Radio Waves from an Artificial Satellite. J. Geo. Res., 64, pp. 45-48 (1959).

18. Huxley, L. G. H., The Propagation of Electromagnetic Waves in an Ionized Atmosphere. Phil. Mag. 25, p. 148 (1938).

19. Huxley, L. G. H., The Propagation of Electromagnetic Waves in an Atmosphere Containing Free Electrons. Phil. Mag. 29, p. 313 (1940).

20. Lange-Hesse, G., A comparison of the birefringence in a crystal and in the ionosphere. Arch. Electr. Ubertr. 6, 149 (1952).

21. Lorentz, H. A., Theory of Electrons, Dover Pub., N.Y. (1909).

22. Nichols, H. W. and Schelling, J. R., Propagation of Electric Waves over the Earth, Bell Syst. Tech. Journal, Vol. 4, pp. 215-34 (1925).

23. Northover, F. H., The Propagation of Electromagnetic Waves in Ionized Gases, IRE Trans. Vol. AP-7 (Special Supplement) pp. 5340-5360 (Dec. 1959).

24. Poeverlein, H., Peculiar Wave Propagation Characteristics of a Plasma with Magnetic Field. Paper presented at the symposium on the Plasma Sheath. Boston, Mass. (Dec. 7, 1959).

25. Rawer, K., Electric Waves in a Stratified Medium. Ann. Phys. Lpz. 35, 385 (1939).

26. Rawer, K., and Suchy, K., Equivalence theorem on wave absorption in a plasma. Ann der Phys., Series 7, Vol. 1, pp. 255-60 (1958).

27. Rawer, K., and Suchy, K., The fourth reflection condition of electromagnetic waves. Comptes Rendus, Vol. 246, p. 3428 (1958).

28. Schumann, W. O., On the propagation of long electric waves in a magnetized plasma and their transmission through plasma layers. Zeit. fur Angew. Phys. Vol. 10, No. 9, pp. 428-433 (Sept. 1958).

29. Silver, S., Microwave Antenna Theory and Design, McGraw-Hill Co., N.Y. (1949).

30. Turner, C. H. M., Birefringence in Crystals and in the Ionosphere. Canadian Journal of Physics, Vol. 32, pp. 16-34 (1954).

31. Van Mieghem, J., Propagation of Electromagnetic Waves in Homogeneous Media, Institut Belge De Recherches Radioscientifique, Vol. IX, Gauthier-Villans and Co., Paris (1944)

32. Westfold, K. C., New analysis of the polarization of radiation and the Faraday effect in terms of complex vectors. Jour. of the Optical Soc. of America, Vol. 49, No. pp. 717-23 (July, 1959).

33. Westfold, K. C., The Interpretation of the Magneto-Ionic Theory. Journ. of Atmos. and Terrest. Physics., Vol. 1, pp. 152-86 (1951).

34. Westfold, K. C., The wave equations for electromagnetic radiation in an ionized medium in a magnetic field. Australian Journal of Scientific Res. Series A, Physical Sciences, Vol. 1, 194B, pp. 170-183 (1949).

GENERAL BIBLIOGRAPHIES

1. Bellman, R., Introduction to Matrix Analysis, McGraw-Hill Co., N.Y. (1960).

2. Bremmer, H.,

3. Budden, K. G.,

4. Chandrasekhar, S., Plasma Physics, Univ. of Chicago Press, Chicago, Ill. (1960).

5. Collin, R. E., Field Theory of Guided Waves, McGraw-Hill Co., N.Y. (1960).

6. Delcroix, J. L., Introduction to the Theory of Ionized Gases, Interscience Pub. Inc., N.Y. (1960).

7. Gershman, B. N., Ginzburg, V. L., and Denisov, N. G., Propagation of Electromagnetic Waves in a Plasma (Ionosphere), Translated from Uspekhi Fiz. Nauk. 61, 561-612 (1957), AEC-tr-3493.

8. Joos, G., Theoretical Physics, 2d ed., Blackie & Sons, Ltd. Glasgow (1951).

9. Massey, H. S. W., and Boyd, R. L. F., The Upper Atmosphere, Hutchinson & Co., London (1958).

10. Mitra, S. K., The Upper Atmosphere (2nd Ed.). The Royal Asiatic Society of Bengal, Calcutta (1952).

11. Ratcliffe, J. A., The Magneto-Ionic Theory and Its Applications to the Ionosphere. Cambridge Univ. Press, Cambridge (1959).

12. Rawer, K., The Ionosphere, F. Ungar Pub. Co., N.Y. (1956).

13. Shubnikov, A. V., Principles of Optical Crystallography (Translated from Russian) Consultants Bureau, N.Y. (1960).

14. Sommerfeld, A.,

15. Stratton, J. A.,

16. Valasek, J., Introduction to Theoretical and Experimental Optics, John Wiley & Sons, N.Y. (1949).

CHAPTER III

A RÉSUMÉ OF THE HYDRODYNAMICAL EQUATIONS AND SHOCK CONDITIONS FOR GASES

In this chapter we give a coherent and self contained treatment of classical hydrodynamics in which we shall derive the fundamental equations. We then apply the results to derive the shock conditions for gases. The purpose in giving this exposition is multifold. First, we want the overall treatment of propagation to be as self contained as possible. That is, we do not want the reader to have to refer to so many outside references that he will lose the trend of thought already established in the preceding chapters. Second, since hydrodynamic methods and views are utilized so frequently in the various models of ionized gas mixtures we feel that the separate exposition will be an aid in the understanding of such mixtures. Third, in the chapters which follow, the understanding of the phenomenon of propagation of magnetohydrodynamic waves is clearly based on the concepts and equations of hydrodynamics. The idea of shock waves, either ordinary or magnetohydrodynamic, and the study of the propagation of discontinuities which arise in ionized gases presupposes the hydrodynamic equations. Finally, the study of transport phenomena which result from an approach via the Boltzmann equation has its interpretation macroscopically speaking, in the language of hydrodynamics.

We could expound further and give many more reasons for the inclusion of the exposition, but the ones given above should suffice for our main purposes. Consequently, we shall start from simple first principles and derive accordingly the basic working equations.

20. BASIC CONSIDERATIONS AND NOMENCLATURE. VISCOUS AND COMPRESSIBLE FLUIDS

The study of hydrodynamics can essentially proceed from two distinct points of view, both of which are useful according to the nature of the problem under consideration. The first view is due to Lagrange and is therefore called the Lagrangian or particle description of fluid flow. By a fluid we mean either a liquid or gas or mixtures of either. In the

Lagrangian view we consider a fluid to consist of particles having a separate identity and postulate its description according to the labeling of the particles. That is, each particle is labeled by the formula

$$x_i = x_i(\alpha_1, \alpha_2, \alpha_3, t) \equiv x_i(\alpha, t) \quad , \qquad (i = 1,2,3) \quad . \qquad (20.1)$$

The set of numbers x_i, identifies each particle. The numbers α_i, are the coordinates of the particle at time $t = 0$, or they can represent arbitrary functions of these initial coordinates. The velocity of the particle is defined by

$$v_i = \frac{\partial x_i}{\partial t} \,, \quad \text{with the } \alpha_i \text{ held fixed,} \qquad (i = 1,2,3) \quad . \qquad (20.2)$$

The determination of v_i and hence x_i constitutes the complete description of the fluid at any time t.

The other point of view is attributed to Euler, and is called the Eulerian or field description of the fluid. In this view the labeling of the individual particles is discarded.

The Eulerian description starts with the fact that at each point x_i in the fluid and at time t, there exists in the fluid a definite velocity which is a function of position and time. That is, the velocity is defined (in a rectangular cartesian reference frame) by

$$v_i = v_i(x_1, x_2, x_3, t) \quad , \qquad (i = 1,2,3) \quad , \qquad (20.3)$$

$$v_i = \frac{dx_i}{dt} \quad . \qquad (20.4)$$

The acceleration is defined (following a definite particle) by,

$$a_i = \frac{dv_i}{dt} = \frac{\partial v_i}{\partial t} + \frac{\partial v_i}{\partial x_j}\frac{dx_j}{dt} \quad , \qquad (i = 1,2,3) \quad , \qquad (20.5)$$

repeated indices implies summation over that index as in the previous chapters. This derivative is called the comoving-time derivative; it is the rate of change moving with the fluid. Equation (20.5) can also be written in standard vector language as

$$\mathbf{a} = \dot{\mathbf{v}} = \frac{\partial \mathbf{v}}{\partial t} + (\mathbf{v} \cdot \nabla)\mathbf{v} \tag{20.6}$$

and we shall use a mixed vector and tensor description wherever it appears useful to emphasize an equation or for other conveniences. A fluid particle in the Eulerian description is therefore not a point in the mathematical sense, but rather a small (differential element) volume of matter to which is assigned a definite velocity at some point inside this volume element. For our purposes in any of the descriptions, a fluid is considered to be a continuous medium.

21. BASIC DYNAMICAL ASSUMPTIONS

For the present development it will be more convenient to utilize a Lagrangian description of the fluid. This means, more precisely, that the motion of the fluid is represented by equations of the form

$$x_i = x_i(\bar{x}_1, \bar{x}_2, \bar{x}_3, t) \quad , \quad (i = 1,2,3) \quad , \tag{21.1}$$

where the x_i and $\bar{x}_i$ are coordinates of the same rectangular cartesian system and t is the time. A particle, which is initially at the point $\bar{x}_i$, will at the time t be located at the point x_i in accordance with eqs. (21.1). We shall suppose that the functions $x_i(\bar{x}, t)$ have a unique inverse for any value of t; and for this it is sufficient that the $x_i(\bar{x}, t)$ are continuous functions and that the partials of x_i with respect to the $\bar{x}_j$ and t are continuous through the third order.

The velocity components $v_i(x, t)$ which are defined by $v_i = \partial x_i/\partial t$ are then continuous in x_i and t and have continuous derivatives through the second order with respect to x_i and t. Let V denote a finite volume of the fluid and let Σ denote its bounding surface. From the assumptions made about the functions $x_i(\bar{x}, t)$, if V is initially a continuum then it will remain a continuum under the motions of the fluid particles which comprise V and Σ. In what follows we assume that all volumes together with their boundaries are of the above stated type. The basic dynamical assumptions are:

(A) The rate of change of the momentum of the fluid in V parallel to any fixed direction is equal to the component parallel to this direction of the total external forces which act on V.

(B) The rate of change of the angular momentum of the fluid in V about any fixed line is equal to the moment of the external forces acting on V about this line.

These assumptions are clearly nothing more than Newton's second law.

The law of conservation of mass is also assumed and this states that the mass of the moving fluid volume V remains constant in time. This is expressed mathematically by the formula,

$$\frac{d}{dt}\int_V \rho dV = 0 , \tag{21.2}$$

where ρ is the density, *i.e.*, mass per unit volume at points of the fluid. In a compressible fluid for which ρ is not constant, we must assume besides the above assumption (21.2) an equation of state. This is ordinarily a relation between the density and the pressure acting on the fluid. The concept of pressure will be defined subsequently.

Let F_i denote the components of the external or applied force per unit mass acting in V. These components are parallel to the axes of the rectangular coordinate system x to which the position of the fluid particles are referred. We denote by T_i the components of a surface force per unit area over the surface Σ. The momentum per unit volume is defined by $\rho\mathbf{v}$ or ρv_i. The moment of the force about any axis, say x_i, will be denoted by M_i, or $M_i = (\mathbf{r x F})_i$. A more convenient expression for M_i in terms of the x_i and F_i is obtained by introducing the permutation symbol e_{ijk} which is defined by the two conditions; $e_{123} = 1$, and e_{ijk} is skew-symmetric. Thus, $e_{213} = -1$, $e_{112} = 0$, etc., if any two indices are alike, it vanishes. Therefore, with these designations, the dynamical assumptions (A) and (B) take the following respective forms.

$$\frac{d}{dt}\int_V \rho v_i dV = \int_\Sigma T_i d\Sigma + \int_V \rho F_i dV , \tag{21.3}$$

$$\frac{d}{dt}\int_V (\mathbf{r}\mathbf{x}\rho\mathbf{v})_i dV \equiv \frac{d}{dt}\int_V (e_{ijk}x_j\rho v_k)dV$$

$$= \int_\Sigma e_{ijk}x_jT_k d\Sigma + \int_V (e_{ijk}x_j\rho F_k)dV \quad , \quad (i = 1,2,3) \quad . \qquad (21.4)$$

We shall now suppose that no applied forces act on the fluid, that is, $\mathbf{F} \equiv 0$. In what follows, we also assume that all functions of x_i and t are continuous together with their partial derivatives for all values of x_i and t considered. The summation convention is also retained, unless otherwise stated.

22. VARIABLE BOUNDARIES AND DIFFERENTIATION OF INTEGRALS

Before we can carry through the time differentiations indicated in eqs. (21.3) and (21.4) we must understand clearly the meaning of such an operation. To this end consider a volume $V(t)$ in the space defined by the x_i, which may vary with the time and also let Σ denote the surface of $V(t)$. Now if u_n is the component of the velocity of the surface Σ along the outward drawn normal to Σ and if $f(x,t)$ is any function of $x \equiv (x_1,x_2,x_3)$ and t, then the change in the integral $\int_V f(x,t)dV$ with respect to the time t consists of two parts: first, the change in $f(x,t)$ for fixed x; second, the change due to the fact that the surface Σ is changing. The first change is $\int_V \partial f(x,t)/\partial t \, dV$ and the second is $\int_\Sigma f u_n d\Sigma$ and hence we can write,

$$\frac{d}{dt}\int_V f(x,t)dV = \int_V \frac{\partial f}{\partial t} dV + \int_\Sigma f u_n d\Sigma \quad . \qquad (22.1)$$

If, in the special case, the change in V is determined by the motion of the fluid particles themselves, that is, the surface Σ is composed of the fluid particles, we can then write $u_n = v_i n_i = \mathbf{v} \cdot \mathbf{n}$, where $\mathbf{n}$ is the outward drawn unit normal vector to Σ.

23. THE EQUATION OF CONTINUITY

The formula given by eq. (22.1) is now applied to eq. (21.2) by putting $f \equiv \rho$ and $u_n = v_i n_i$ from which we obtain,

$$\int_V \frac{\partial \rho}{\partial t}\, dV + \int_\Sigma \rho\, \mathbf{v} \cdot \mathbf{n}\, d\Sigma = 0 \ ,$$

and using Green's theorem to transform the surface integral into a volume integral, we have

$$\int_V \left[\frac{\partial \rho}{\partial t} + \text{div}\ (\rho \mathbf{v}) \right] dV = 0 \ . \tag{23.1}$$

It follows from the continuity of the integrand and the arbitrariness of V that,

$$\frac{\partial \rho}{\partial t} + \text{div}\ (\rho \mathbf{v}) = 0 \ , \tag{23.2}$$

which is the equation of continuity, and is the equivalent of eq. (21.2). Let us go back to the general expression (22.1) with $u_n = \mathbf{v} \cdot \mathbf{n}$ and use the equation of continuity, then by Green's theorem we first obtain,

$$\int_\Sigma f\, \mathbf{v} \cdot \mathbf{n}\, d\Sigma = \int_V \text{div}\ (f\mathbf{v})\ dV = \int_V \textbf{grad}\ f \cdot \mathbf{v}\ dV + \int_V f\ \text{div}\ (\mathbf{v})\ dV$$

and if $\rho = \rho(t)$ alone, we find, since $\partial\rho/\partial t = d\rho/dt$,

$$\int_\Sigma f\, \mathbf{v} \cdot \mathbf{n}\, d\Sigma = \int_V \textbf{grad}\ f \cdot \mathbf{v}\ dV - \int_V \frac{f}{\rho} \frac{d\rho}{dt}\, dV \ .$$

Therefore,

$$\frac{d}{dt} \int_V f dV = \int_V \frac{df}{dt}\, dV - \int_V \frac{f'}{\rho} \frac{d\rho}{dt} \ .$$

Now if we replace f by ρf, we have,

$$\frac{d}{dt} \int_V \rho f dV = \int_V \rho \frac{df}{dt}\, dV \ , \tag{23.3}$$

which is the equation satisfied in a fluid when the change in the volume V is produced by the motion of the fluid particles.

24. THE STRESS VECTOR AND STRESS TENSOR

In eq. (21.3) we have introduced the stress vector $\mathbf{T} \equiv (T_i)$ which represents the force per unit area or as we say, the stress over the surface Σ. By examining the equilibrium of a small regular tetrahedron three of whose faces are perpendicular to the coordinate axes, it can be shown that the stress vector is of the form,

$$T_i = \tau_{ij} n_j , \qquad (i = 1,2,3) , \tag{24.1}$$

where the τ_{ij} are functions of position and time. There are in general nine nonvanishing such functions. The functions τ_{ij} are called the components of the stress tensor. For indices, $i \neq j$, τ_{ij} are called the shear components and for $i = j$, say τ_{11}, etc., are called the normal components. The shear components are clearly parallel to the surface and the normal components are perpendicular to the surface.

From equation (23.3), equations (21.3) and (21.4) take the forms respectively, by using Green's theorem again,

$$\int_V \rho \frac{dv_i}{dt} dV = \int_\Sigma \tau_{ij} n_j d\Sigma = \int_V \frac{\partial \tau_{ij}}{\partial x_j} dV ,$$

and

$$\int_V \rho e_{ijk} \frac{d}{dt} (x_j v_k) \, dV = \int_\Sigma e_{ijk} x_j \tau_{kl} n_l d\Sigma = \int_V \frac{\partial}{\partial x_l} (e_{ijk} x_j \tau_{kl}) \, dV .$$

For notational convenience we shall indicate partial derivatives by the rule,

$$\tau_{ij,l} \equiv \frac{\partial \tau_{ij}}{\partial x_l} .$$

After carrying out the differentiations indicated in the last equation we have for both equations respectively,

$$\int_V \left(\rho \frac{dv_i}{dt} - \tau_{ij,j} \right) dV = 0 , \tag{24.2}$$

$$\int_V e_{ijk} x_j \left(\rho \frac{dv_k}{dt} - \tau_{kl,l} \right) dV + \int_V e_{ijk} \tau_{jk} dV = 0 . \tag{24.3}$$

From (24.2) and the arbitrariness of V, we deduce

$$\rho \frac{dv_i}{dt} = \tau_{kl,l} , \quad (i = 1,2,3) , \tag{24.4}$$

which represents the equilbrium between the inertial forces and the stresses acting on the surfaces in the fluid, in the absence of body forces. From eq. (24.3) we infer that $e_{ijk}\tau_{jk} = 0$, which implies the symmetry of the τ_{ij}. Consequently, there are in general six independent functions τ_{ij} Sometimes we use the symbol div $(\tau) = (\tau_{ij,j})$ to denote the divergence of the tensor $\tau \equiv (\tau_{ij})$. From the foregoing, both eqs. (21.3) and (21.4) can be replaced by the single equation (24.4). If we had taken into consideration the body forces acting on the fluid, we would have to add this force to the right side of eq. (24.4).

25. THE DISTORTION TENSOR

In order to introduce the notion of a distortion tensor we must consider first the displacement of a fluid particle. Consider a particle which is initially at the position defined by $\bar{x}_i$, and after a small time interval dt is displaced to point x_i. Then to a first order approximation we can write

$$x_i = \bar{x}_i + v_i(\bar{x}, t)dt . \tag{25.1}$$

In general, in the neighborhood of the point $\bar{x}$, the displacement can be decomposed into a stretching and a rotational motion about $\bar{x}$. The latter part constitutes a rigid motion and so contributes nothing to the deformation or distortion of the fluid. The distortion, or rather the rate of distortion, is defined by the set of nine functions

$$e_{ij} = \frac{1}{2}(v_{i,j} + v_{j,i}) , \qquad (i,j = 1,2,3) . \tag{25.2}$$

These functions define the strain rate tensor or briefly the strain tensor. They are clearly symmetric in the indices, and as in the case of the stress tensor, they are six independent functions of position and time. For $i \neq j$, we call them shear components and for $i = j$, the normal strains. The rate of dilatation of the fluid is defined by

$$\theta = e_{11} + e_{22} + e_{33} \equiv e_{ii} \tag{25.3}$$

or in terms of $\mathbf{v}$,

$$\theta = v_{i,i} = \operatorname{div} \mathbf{v} \tag{25.4}$$

which clearly characterizes the dilatation of the fluid. The distortion tensor designated by D_{ij} is now defined by

$$D_{ij} = e_{ij} - \frac{\theta}{3}\delta_{ij} . \tag{25.5}$$

It can be shown that the necessary and sufficient condition for the displacement to be without distortion is that $D_{ij} = 0$ for all i,j. These statements apply to the first order approximation assumed in defining (25.1). The distortion tensor is therefore considered to give a measure of the "rate of distortion," due to the flow, of any configuration of the fluid in the immediate neighborhood of the point $\bar{x}$.

26. PRESSURE AND VISCOSITY TENSOR

The pressure p which is a scalar function is defined in terms of the normal components of the stress tensor $\boldsymbol{\tau}$. That is,

$$p = -\frac{1}{3}\left(\tau_{11} + \tau_{22} + \tau_{33}\right) \equiv -\frac{\tau_{ii}}{3} , \tag{26.1}$$

the minus sign indicating that the pressure has a sense opposite to that of the tension. The viscosity tensor with components designated by σ_{ij} is also defined in terms of the stress tensor by

$$\sigma_{ij} = \tau_{ij} + p\delta_{ij} \quad . \tag{26.2}$$

These concepts permit us to define in a quantitative way the notion of an ideal or perfect fluid. A fluid is ideal if and only if the viscosity tensor vanishes, that is, $\sigma_{ij} \equiv 0$, for all i, j. In this case then $\tau_{ij} = -p\delta_{ij}$ and therefore the stress vector becomes $T_i = -pn_i$; which states that the surface force $\mathbf{T}$ is normal to every surface element. For ideal fluids then, it follows that the shearing force vanishes over arbitrary surface elements. The converse of this statement implies the vanishing of the viscosity tensor σ_{ij}. Alternatively, an ideal fluid can also be defined as one for which the shear force vanishes over any surface element independently of its orientation.

27. THE RELATION BETWEEN THE DISTORTION AND VISCOSITY TENSORS

As in the theory of elasticity of solid bodies, where Hooke's Law is used to define a relation between the stress and strain tensors, we seek an analogue of this for fluids. We assume that the components of the viscosity tensor are linear homogeneous functions (independent of the time) of the components of the distortion tensor. This assumption takes the following form,

$$\sigma_{ij} = C_{ijkl}(x)D_{kl} \quad , \qquad (i, j, k, l = 1,2,3) \tag{27.1}$$

where C_{ijkl} is a four index function of position. It is a tensor* of the fourth order, that is, since both σ_{ij} and D_{ij} are tensors then so is C_{ijkl}. This symbol is symmetric in both the i, j and k, l pairs of indices as is clear from the symmetry of σ_{ij} and D_{kl}.

28. HOMOGENEOUS AND ISOTROPIC FLUIDS

If we assume further that the fluid is homogeneous then we can simplify eqs. (27.1). By a homogeneous fluid we mean that the set of

* The rigorous tensor concept or definition is reserved for a later chapter. Even though we have used the word frequently till now, the understanding of the ideas involved should not be nullified because of a lack of precise definition of this term.

functions C_{ijkl} are invariant (*i.e.*, unchanged) when the coordinate system in which the C_{ijkl} are originally defined undergoes an arbitrary translation of axes. Consider then the translation

$$y_i = x_i + c_i \ , \qquad (i = 1,2,3) \ , \tag{28.1}$$

to obtain the invariant relation

$$C_{ijkl}(y) = C_{ijkl}(x) = C_{ijkl}(y - c) \ . \tag{28.2}$$

Because the c_i are arbitrary, it follows from the equality of the first and last members of (28.2) that C_{ijkl} must be independent of the coordinates. Conversely, if the C_{ijkl} are constants relative to a rectangular cartesian reference frame, the fluid is homogeneous. Therefore, homogeneity of a fluid means that the coefficients C_{ijkl} are constants in a rectangular cartesian system.

A fluid is isotropic if the value of the C_{ijkl} at any point remains unchanged under a rotation of axes about this point. By definition, any tensor which has this property is called an isotropic tensor. The most general symmetric isotropic tensor of the type C_{ijkl} can be represented in the form*

$$C_{ijkl} = \lambda\delta_{ij}\delta_{kl} + \mu(\delta_{ik}\delta_{jl} + \delta_{jk}\delta_{il}) \tag{28.3}$$

relative to rectangular coordinates and where λ and μ are scalars. If the fluid is both homogeneous and isotropic, λ and μ are constants. If we put C_{ijkl} as represented by eq. (28.3) into eq. (27.1) we obtain,

$$\sigma_{ij} = \lambda D_{kk}\delta_{ij} + 2\mu D_{ij} \ . \tag{28.4}$$

By using further eqs. (25.2) and (26.2), eq. (28.4) becomes,

$$\tau_{ij} = -p\delta_{ij} - \frac{2}{3}\mu\theta\delta_{ij} + \mu(v_{i,j} + v_{j,i}) \tag{28.5}$$

---

* H. and B. S. Jeffreys. Mathematical Physics, pp 87-89, Cambridge Univ. Press (1950)

which represents the most general expression for the stress tensor in a fluid which is both homogeneous and isotropic and for which eq. (27.1) holds. In eq. (28.5) the constant μ is called the viscosity constant of the fluid. The constants λ and μ clearly characterize the fluid. If we set $i = j$ and sum in accordance with the summation convention we find from (28.5) that $\tau_{ii} + 3p = 0$, which is consistent with the definition of pressure as we have defined it in the foregoing.

29. THE NAVIER-STOKES EQUATIONS

Let us return to the equations of equilibrium (24.4) and first calculate the div ($\boldsymbol{\tau}$) with $\boldsymbol{\tau}$ given by eq. (28.5). This yields

$$\tau_{ij,j} = \frac{\partial p}{\partial x_i} + \frac{\mu}{3}\frac{\partial \theta}{\partial x_i} + \mu v_{i,jj}$$

$$\tau_{ij,j} = p,_i + \frac{\mu}{3}\theta,_i + \mu v_{i,jj} , \tag{29.1}$$

which upon substitution into eq. (24.4) gives

$$\mu v_{i,jj} = p,_i + \rho\frac{\partial v_i}{\partial t} + \rho v_j v_{i,j} - \frac{\mu}{3}\theta,_i , \quad (i = 1,2,3) , \tag{29.2}$$

in which the viscosity constant is assumed to be non-negative. This system of equations (29.2) therefore describes the motion of a homogeneous, isotropic and viscous fluid. They are called the Stokes-Navier or Navier-Stokes equations after the men who first derived them. These equations supplemented by the equation of continuity and an equation of state provide the theoretical means of solving a class of problems of fluid motion. In certain applications it is often necessary to make more simplifying assumptions and thus find solutions to a smaller class of problems. This is accomplished by either assuming the density to be constant or the viscosity to be zero or both. Another assumption which is useful is to take the velocity vector equal to the gradient of a scalar function, *i.e.*, the velocity admits a potential. A further restriction is to consider only the so-called steady problems in which we consider fluid motions for which the velocity, pressure and density are independent of time. For example, the equations for the steady motion of a compressible fluid, *i.e.*, a gas, with no viscosity, are given by

$$p_{,i} + \rho v_{j,i} v_j = 0 \; ; \qquad (\rho v_j)_{,j} = 0 \; . \tag{29.3}$$

Now take ρ = constant and assume $\mathbf{v} = \mathbf{grad}\ \phi$, then we obtain

$$p_{,i} + \frac{1}{2}(\rho v_j v_j)_{,i} = 0 \; , \qquad \phi_{,jj} \equiv \nabla^2\phi = 0 \; . \tag{29.4}$$

These equations which were known a long time ago are considered to be the partial differential equations of classical hydrodynamics. The first group of equations of (29.4) is immediately integrable and therefore are used to define the pressure p when the density and velocity are known. It can be seen from eqs. (29.4) that in the preceding case the problem of determining the fluid motion is therefore equivalent to finding a solution of Laplace's equation $\nabla^2\phi = 0$ with ϕ subject to the boundary conditions of the problem under consideration.

30. PERFECT OR IDEAL GASES—THE EQUATION OF ENERGY

We shall consider in the following, the thermodynamic principles which enter into the discussion of the motion of gases. Let us calculate the work done per unit time on a moving volume V of the fluid by the forces acting on its surface Σ. The work done by these stresses is obtained from the formula,

$$W = \int_\Sigma \mathbf{T} \cdot \mathbf{v}\, d\Sigma = \int_\Sigma \tau_{ij} v_i n_j\, d\Sigma = \int_V (\tau_{ij} v_i)_{,j}\, dV$$

$$= \int_V \tau_{ij,j} v_i\, dV + \int_V \tau_{ij} v_{i,j}\, dV \; . \tag{30.1}$$

By utilizing the eqs. (24.4), (28.5) and (23.3), the equation above becomes

$$W = \frac{d}{dt}\int_V \frac{1}{2}\rho v_j v_j\, dV - \int_V p v_{j,j}\, dV + \int_V 2\mu (D_{ij})^2\, dV \; , \tag{30.2}$$

for convenience we shall put

$$\psi = 2\mu (D_{ij})^2 \; . \tag{30.3}$$

Equation (30.2) is the energy equation and the function ψ is the viscosity dissipation function. The physical interpretation of each term on the right side of (30.2) is as follows. The first integral gives the rate of increase of the kinetic energy of the moving volume V, the second integral represents the rate of work done by the pressure in changing the volume of V and the third integral gives the rate at which work is done on the volume against the viscous forces. The latter is work that is lost as mechanical energy and consequently must appear as disordered motion (*i.e.*, heat) developed in V.

We turn now to an ideal gas which by definition is one which satisfies the equation

$$p = \frac{\rho R}{m} T \tag{30.4}$$

where m is the molecular weight, T the absolute temperature and R the universal or absolute constant, it is the same for all gases. We denote, as is customary by C_p and C_V, the specific heats respectively, of the gas at constant pressure and volume. Elementary physics teaches us that between the quantities C_p, C_V, R and m there exists the following relation

$$\frac{R}{m} = J(C_p - C_V) \quad , \tag{30.5}$$

where J denotes the mechanical equivalent of heat. For an ideal gas it is assumed that both C_p and C_V are constants. Putting $\gamma = C_p/C_V$ eqs. (30.4) and (30.5) are rewritten in the form,

$$p = \rho J C_V(\gamma - 1) \quad , \qquad R = mJC_V(\gamma - 1) \quad . \tag{30.6}$$

31. THE THERMAL CONDUCTIVITY

Thermodynamic arguments show that the internal energy per unit mass of an ideal gas is given by JC_VT + constant, where the constant is determined by the choice of zero point of energy. The total energy of a gas is the sum of its kinetic and internal energies. If E is the total energy, we write

$$E = \frac{1}{2} v_j v_j + JC_VT + \text{constant} \quad . \tag{31.1}$$

With this expression, we transform eq. (30'.2) into

$$W = \frac{d}{dt}\int \rho E \, dV - JC_V \int_V \rho \frac{dT}{dt} \, dV - \int_V p v_{j,j} \, dV + \int_V \psi \, dV \qquad (31.2)$$

where we have also used (30.3). The constant appearing in (31.1) does not enter in eq. (31.2) as a consequence of the continuity equation.

If W' is rate at which heat is conducted into the moving volume V through its surface Σ, we can determine the value of W' quite simply. We assume that the rate of conduction of heat into V through an element of surface area $d\Sigma$ is given according to Fourier's law by $Jk(dT/dn)d\Sigma$. Here, k is the thermal conductivity of the gas, a constant, and n measures the distance in the direction of the outward drawn normal $\mathbf{n}$ of Σ. Therefore,

$$W' = Jk \int_\Sigma \textbf{grad}\ T \cdot \mathbf{n} \, d\Sigma = Jk \int_V \mathrm{div}\,(\textbf{grad}\ T) \, dV$$

$$= Jk \int_V \nabla^2 T \, dV \quad . \qquad (31.3)$$

The total energy of the gas is $W + W'$ and is equal to the rate of change of the total energy of the volume V. Hence, we can write

$$\frac{d}{dt}\int_V \rho E \, dV = W + W' \quad . \qquad (31.4)$$

From eqs. (31.2) and (31.3) together with eq. (31.4) there results,

$$JC_V \int_V \rho \frac{dT}{dt} \, dV + \int_V p v_{j,j} \, dV - \int_V \psi \, dV - Jk \int_V \nabla^2 T \, dV = 0 \quad ,$$

and from the arbitrariness of V, we obtain

$$JC_V \rho \frac{dT}{dt} + p v_{j,j} = Jk \nabla^2 T + \psi \quad . \qquad (31.5)$$

This equation governs the distribution of temperature in an ideal gas. It follows from eqs. (30.4) and (30.5) that

$$JC_V T = JC_p T - \frac{RT}{m} = JC_p T - \frac{p}{\rho} ;$$

differentiating this expression with respect to t and substituting the result into the left side of eq. (31.5) and using the equation of continuity gives

$$JC_p \rho \frac{dT}{dt} - \frac{dp}{dt} = Jk\nabla^2 T + \psi . \qquad (31.6)$$

This equation is an alternative form for eq. (31.5). If we set the viscosity μ and the thermal conductivity k equal to zero, both eqs. (31.5) and (31.6) become

$$JC_V \rho \frac{dT}{dt} + pv_{j,j} = 0 , \qquad JC_p \rho \frac{dT}{dt} - \frac{dp}{dt} = 0 . \qquad (31.7)$$

32. ENTROPY CONSIDERATIONS

The preceding discussion shows that the rate of increase of the heat content of the moving volume is given by the formula

$$Q = \int_\Sigma Jk \, \mathbf{grad} \, T \cdot \mathbf{n} \, d\Sigma + \int_V \psi \, dV = Jk \int_V \nabla^2 T \, dV + \int_V \psi \, dV .$$

The integrand on the right side, $(Jk\nabla^2 T + \psi)$ is therefore interpreted as giving the rate of increase of heat per unit volume at points in the gas. But this integrand is equal to the left hand side of eq. (31.5). By dividing the left member of (31.5) by ρ we derive an expression for the rate of increase of heat per unit mass. We have then

$$JC_V \frac{dT}{dt} + \frac{p}{\rho} v_{j,j} = JC_V \left[\frac{dT}{dt} + (\gamma - 1)\, T v_{j,j} \right]$$

$$= JC_V \left[\frac{dT}{dt} - (\gamma - 1) \frac{T}{\rho} \frac{d\rho}{dt} \right]$$

$$= JC_V T \left[\frac{d \log T}{dt} - (\gamma - 1) \frac{d \log \rho}{dt} \right]$$

$$= JC_V T \left[\frac{d}{dt} \log \left(\frac{p}{\rho} \right) - (\gamma - 1) \frac{d \log \rho}{dt} \right]$$

$$= JC_V T \frac{d}{dt} \log \left(\frac{p}{\rho^\gamma} \right) \quad . \tag{32.1}$$

Now define a function,

$$S = JC_V \log \left(\frac{p}{\rho^\gamma} \right) + \text{constant} \tag{32.2}$$

where the constant is an absolute constant, that is, independent of position and time. The product $T(dS/dt)$ is the rate of increase of heat per unit mass. The function S is the entropy per unit mass or the entropy of the gas. For any particular gas, the entropy is defined to within an additive constant. Eq. (32.2) is solved for p to obtain

$$p = \left[C \exp \left(\frac{S}{JC_V} \right) \right] \rho^\gamma \tag{32.3}$$

where C is an absolute constant for any gas. If the thermal conductivity and viscosity both vanish, then eq. (31.5) shows that $dS/dt = 0$. Therefore in an ideal gas with vanishing conductivity and viscosity, the entropy is constant along the path of a particle. If, in particular, the motion is steady, the entropy is constant along each stream line (which are curves whose tangents at all points have the same direction as $\mathbf{v}$). From this it follows that $C \exp (S/JC_V)$ in eq. (32.2) is constant along each stream line even though this function can vary from stream line to stream line. If the motion is such that $C \exp (S/JC_V)$ is constant throughout the gas then the gas is said to satisfy the adiabatic condition or that the flow is adiabatic.

An alternative formulation of the entropy condition proceeds as follow If $k = \mu = 0$ so that $dS/dt = 0$, we then differentiate eq. (32.3) totally with respect to t; and use the equation of continuity (23.2) together with the equations of motion (29.2) with $\mu = 0$ and obtain the result

$$\frac{\partial p}{\partial t} - \rho v_i \frac{\partial v_i}{\partial t} - \rho v_{i,j} v_i v_j + \gamma p v_{i,i} = 0 \quad . \tag{32.4}$$

Conversely, from this equation, the equation of continuity, and the equations of motion with $\mu = 0$, we can derive $dS/dt = 0$ in eq. (32.3). Therefo in an ideal gas with $k = \mu = 0$, the condition $dS/dt = 0$ is completely contained in eq. (32.4). If, further, the motion is a steady one, the conditi $dS/dt = 0$ is derived from

$$\rho v_{i,j} v_i v_j - \gamma p v_{j,j} = 0 \quad . \tag{32.5}$$

33. THE EQUATIONS FOR IDEAL GASES

A complete description of the motion of an ideal gas is obtained from the equation of continuity (23.2), the equations of motion (29.2) and eq. (31.5) for the temperature distribution in the gas. Besides these equations, there is an equation of state (30.4), which was at first introduced as the defining condition of the ideal gas. If we eliminate the temperature between eqs. (30.4) and (31.5), we obtain, instead of eq. (31.5 a differential equation in the variables p, ρ, and v_i and the relation (30.4) will then appear as an extra equation defining the temperature T. For the steady motion of an ideal gas with $\mu = k = 0$, we have

$$\text{div}\,(\rho \mathbf{v}) = 0 \quad , \tag{33.1}$$

$$(\mathbf{grad}\; p)_i + \rho v_{i,j} v_j = 0 \quad , \qquad (i = 1,2,3) \quad , \tag{33.2}$$

$$\rho v_{i,j} v_i v_j - \gamma p v_{j,j} = 0 \quad . \tag{33.3}$$

The preceding section has shown that eq. (33.3) is equivalent to $dS/dt = 0$ and is therefore equivalent to eq. (31.5) with $k = \mu = 0$ or to either equation of (31.7).

34. BERNOULLI'S EQUATION

If we multiply eq. (33.2) by v_i and sum on i, we find

$$\frac{dp}{dt} + \frac{1}{2}\rho\frac{d}{dt}(v_i v_i) = 0 ,$$

now divide by ρ and use eq. (32.3) in which S = constant along the stream lines; therefore

$$\frac{\gamma}{\gamma - 1}\frac{p}{\rho} + \frac{1}{2}v_i v_i = \text{constant} , \tag{34.1}$$

where the constant depends on the stream line. Eq. (34.1) is called the Bernoulli equation and is valid for the steady motion of an ideal gas for which $k = \mu = 0$. If the velocity admits a potential, eqs. (33.2) take the form

$$\frac{1}{\rho}(\textbf{grad}\ p)_i + \frac{1}{2}(\textbf{grad}\ v^2)_i = 0 , \quad (i = 1,2,3) . \tag{34.2}$$

For adiabatic flow, two considerations arise. The pressure p in the above equations can be eliminated by using eq. (32.3) and integrating the resulting equation. This leads to an equation of the form (34.1) in which the constant on the right side is independent of the stream line. In this case we call it a "strong" Bernoulli equation. When the constant does depend on the stream line we call it a "weak" equation.

35. SHOCK WAVES IN AN IDEAL GAS---THE CONCEPT OF SINGULAR SURFACES

In order to understand the concept of a shock wave, it is useful at first to define the notion of a singular surface. Therefore, let $\Sigma'(t)$ denote a moving surface which is such that each point of $\Sigma'(t)$ for fixed t lies in a surface element which has a well defined normal. Also, let $f(x,t)$ denote a function which is discontinuous in the variables x_i at all points of $\Sigma'(t)$. For those points $x \equiv (x_i)$ which do not lie on Σ' at any time we assume that $f(x,t)$ is continuously differentiable in all variables; it is assumed that $f(x,t)$ and its derivatives exist and are continuous on each side of Σ'. The surface $\Sigma'(t)$ is said to be singular relative to the function $f(x,t)$.

Let, now, V be any moving volume in the fluid which is divided by the surface Σ' above into two volumes designated by V_1 and V_2. Let Σ be the surface of V; Σ_1 and Σ_2 denote the portions of Σ which form parts of the boundaries of V_1 and V_2 respectively. The remaining part of the boundary of V_1 and V_2 is completed by the surface Σ'. We assume that the change in the volume V is produced by the moving fluid particles themselves. Hence, the normal component of the velocity of V at points of its surface Σ is $\mathbf{v} \cdot \mathbf{n}$ where $\mathbf{n}$ is the outward drawn unit normal vector to Σ. If u_n denotes the normal velocity of $\Sigma'(t)$ along the outward drawn normal to Σ' considered as part of the boundary of V_1 then $-u_n$ will be the corresponding normal velocity when Σ' is considered as a part of the boundary of V_2. We have then

$$\frac{d}{dt}\int_V f(x,t)\, dV = \frac{d}{dt}\int_{V_1} f(x,t)\, dV + \frac{d}{dt}\int_{V_2} f(x,t)\, dV \,, \qquad (35.1)$$

but each term on the right side is evaluated according to formula (22.1), that is,

$$\frac{d}{dt}\int_{V_1} f(x,t)\, dV = \int_{V_1} \frac{\partial f}{\partial t}\, dV + \int_{\Sigma_1} f\, \mathbf{v} \cdot \mathbf{n}\, d\Sigma + \int_{\Sigma'} f_1 u_n d\Sigma \,, \qquad (35.2)$$

$$\frac{d}{dt}\int_{V_2} f(x,t)\, dV = \int_{V_2} \frac{\partial f}{\partial t}\, dV + \int_{\Sigma_2} f\, \mathbf{v} \cdot \mathbf{n}\, d\Sigma - \int_{\Sigma'} f_1 u_n d\Sigma \,, \qquad (35.3)$$

where f_1 is the value of f on the side of Σ' bordering V_1 and f_2 the value of f on the side Σ' bordering V_2. The use of Σ as a designation as the area of integration in the above integrals as well as in the corresponding integrals in the following equations, refers, of course, to the part of the surface Σ bounding the volumes V_1 and V_2. Eqs. (35.2) and (35.3) when substituted into eq. (35.1) gives

$$\frac{d}{dt}\int_V f(x,t)\, dV = \int_V \frac{\partial f}{\partial t}\, dV + \int_\Sigma f\, \mathbf{v} \cdot \mathbf{n}\, d\Sigma + \int_{\Sigma'} (f_1 - f_2) u\, d\Sigma \,. \qquad (35.4)$$

Let us assume now that Σ' is a singular surface relative to the function p, the pressure. We assume that the density ρ and the velocity $\mathbf{v}$ are continuous and differentiable functions for points x which do not lie on $\Sigma'(t)$; moreover we shall also assume that ρ and $\mathbf{v}$ and their derivatives are continuous on each side of $\Sigma'(t)$. The moving volume V, which is divided into the volumes V_1 and V_2, must satisfy all of the integral conditions previously imposed and which have resulted in the differential equations for the motion of the gas under the assumptions of complete continuity. Let us state these integral conditions in the following order.

The Law of Conservation of Mass, eq. (21.2).
The Assumptions (A) and (B) of section 21.
The Assumption contained in eq. (31.4) from which we derived the differential equation governing the temperature distribution in the ideal gas.

If we now let the volume V shrink down to zero volume we obtain the relations, called "shock conditions," between the values of the quantities p, ρ and v_i on the two sides of the surface $\Sigma'(t)$. A surface $\Sigma'(t)$, which is singular relative to the pressure p, over which these shock conditions are satisfied is called a "shock wave." We shall treat the simple situation in which the viscosity and thermal conductivity vanish and hence derive the shock conditions for ideal gases.

36. THE FIRST SHOCK CONDITION

We refer to the side of Σ' which borders V_1 as the side 1 and to the side bordering V_2 as side 2 of Σ'. From eqs. (21.2) and (35.4) and with $f = \rho(x, t)$ we have

$$\int_V \frac{\partial \rho}{\partial t}\, dV + \int_{\Sigma_1} \rho\, \mathbf{v} \cdot \mathbf{n}\, d\Sigma + \int_{\Sigma_2} \rho\, \mathbf{v} \cdot \mathbf{n}\, d\Sigma + \int_{\Sigma'} (\rho_1 - \rho_2) u_n d\Sigma = 0 , \tag{36.1}$$

where ρ_1 and ρ_2 are the values of the density along the sides 1 and 2 of Σ'. Now fix t, and let V shrink to zero in such a way that in the limit it goes into a finite part Σ_0' of the surface Σ'. Now the volume integral in eq. (36.1) is of higher order than the surface integrals, *i.e.*, it tends to zero more rapidly than the surface integrals, hence it can be neglected with respect to the surface integrals. Thus under the conditions of differentiability and continuity assumed, we can write

$$\int_{V_1} \operatorname{div}(\rho \mathbf{v})\, dV = \int_{\Sigma_1} \rho\, \mathbf{v} \cdot \mathbf{n}\, d\Sigma + \int_{\Sigma'} \rho_1\, (\mathbf{v} \cdot \mathbf{n})_1\, d\Sigma \quad ; \tag{36.2}$$

by letting V shrink into the area Σ_0', the left side of (36.2) approaches zero and hence the limit in question is obtained, that is,

$$\int_{\Sigma_1} \rho\, \mathbf{v} \cdot \mathbf{n}\, d\Sigma \rightarrow -\int_{\Sigma_0'} \rho_1\, (\mathbf{v} \cdot \mathbf{n})_1\, d\Sigma \quad , \tag{36.3}$$

and in a similar way,

$$\int_{\Sigma_2} \rho\, \mathbf{v} \cdot \mathbf{n}\, d\Sigma \rightarrow \int_{\Sigma_0'} \rho_2\, (\mathbf{v} \cdot \mathbf{n})_2\, d\Sigma \quad , \tag{36.4}$$

where $(\mathbf{v} \cdot \mathbf{n})_1$ and $(\mathbf{v} \cdot \mathbf{n})_2$ denote the normal components of the fluid velocities on the sides 1 and 2 along the normal direction from the side 1 to the side 2. We obtain, therefore,

$$\int_{\Sigma_0'} [\rho_1\, (\mathbf{v} \cdot \mathbf{n})_1 - (u_n)_1 \rho_1]\, d\Sigma - \int_{\Sigma_0'} [\rho_2\, (\mathbf{v} \cdot \mathbf{n})_2 - (u_n)_2 \rho_2]\, d\Sigma = 0 \quad . \tag{36.5}$$

Because this condition holds independently of the extent of the surface of integration Σ_0', we have the "first shock condition," namely

$$\boxed{\rho_1[(\mathbf{v} \cdot \mathbf{n})_1 - (u_n)_1] = \rho_2[(\mathbf{v} \cdot \mathbf{n})_2 - (u_n)_2]} \tag{36.6}$$

over the surface $\Sigma'(t)$. This shock condition originates entirely from the principle of the conservation of mass.

The second shock condition is obtained according to assumption (A) which is expressed mathematically by eq. (21.3). For our case we put $\mathbf{F} = 0$ and also take the viscosity, $\mu = 0$, therefore the stress vector takes the form, $T_i = -pn_i$ and eq. (21.3) reduces to

$$\frac{d}{dt} \int_V \rho v_i\, dV + \int_\Sigma p n_i\, d\Sigma = 0 \quad , \qquad (i = 1,2,3) \quad . \tag{36.7}$$

As in the derivation of the first shock condition we let V tend to zero in the same way; we see that

$$\int_{\Sigma} pn_i \, d\Sigma \to \int_{\Sigma'_0} (p_2 - p_1) n_i \, d\Sigma \tag{36.8}$$

where n_i in the limit integral are the components of the unit normal directed from the side 1 to the side 2 of Σ'. By applying eq. (35.4) with $f = \rho v_i$, the first term in eq. (36.7) becomes

$$\int_V \frac{\partial}{\partial t} (\rho v_i) \, dV + \int_{\Sigma_1} \rho v_i (\mathbf{v} \cdot \mathbf{n}) \, d\Sigma + \int_{\Sigma_2} \rho v_i (\mathbf{v} \cdot \mathbf{n}) \, d\Sigma + \int_{\Sigma'} [\rho_1 (v_i)_1 - \rho_2 (v_i)_2] u_n \, d\Sigma$$

and in the limit, this expression yields

$$\int_{\Sigma'_0} \rho_1 (v_i)_1 \, [u_n - (\mathbf{v} \cdot \mathbf{n})_1] \, d\Sigma - \int_{\Sigma'_0} \rho_2 (v_i)_2 \, [u_n - (\mathbf{v} \cdot \mathbf{n})_2] \, d\Sigma \ . \tag{36.9}$$

Now substituting the expressions (36.8) and (36.9) for the two terms comprising the left member of (36.7), making use of the first shock condition (36.6), we finally obtain the "second shock condition"

$$\boxed{\begin{aligned} (p_2 - p_1) n_i \equiv [\Delta p] n_i &= \rho_1 [u_n - (\mathbf{v} \cdot \mathbf{n})_1][(v_i)_2 - (v_i)_1] \\ &\equiv \rho_1 [u_n - (\mathbf{v} \cdot \mathbf{n})_1][\Delta v_i] \ , \qquad (i = 1,2,3) \end{aligned}} \ . \tag{36.10}$$

In what follows we shall use the symbol Δ to denote the change in a quantity in crossing the surface Σ'.

By examining assumption (B) which is expressed mathematically by eq. (21.4) it can be shown that no new relations are obtained other than eqs. (36.6) and (36.10). We remind ourselves that these "shock conditions" are derived on the basis of vanishing viscosity.

We note that in (36.10) the product $\rho_1 [u_n - (\mathbf{v} \cdot \mathbf{n})_1]$ can not vanish at any point of Σ'. For if it did, the left side of (36.10) vanishes implying that $p_2 - p_1 = 0$. But this would contradict the condition for the surface Σ' to be a shock wave. The fact that the product $\rho_1[u_n - (\mathbf{v} \cdot \mathbf{n})_1]$ does not vanish, and hence that $\rho_2[u_n - (\mathbf{v} \cdot \mathbf{n})_2]$ does not vanish by the first shock condition, will be used presently.

Let us multiply eq. (36.10) by n_i and sum on i, to obtain

$$\rho_1[u_n - (\mathbf{v} \cdot \mathbf{n})_1](\Delta v_i)n_i = (\Delta p) = p_2 - p_1 \tag{36.11}$$

and defining

$$(\Delta v_i)n_i \equiv (\Delta v)_n , \tag{36.12}$$

we express both (Δv_i) and (Δp) in terms of $(\Delta v)_n$, therefore (36.11) becomes

$$(\Delta p) = \rho_1[u_n - (\mathbf{v} \cdot \mathbf{n})_1](\Delta v)_n . \tag{36.13}$$

Conversely, eqs. (36.13) and (36.12) imply eq. (36.10), and therefore eq. (36.13) is equivalent to the "second shock condition." It follows from eq. (36.13) and the condition $(\Delta p) \neq 0$ that $(\Delta v)_n$ can not vanish at points of a shock wave Σ'. Therefore by using this result, we see that eq. (36.12) implies that not all of the quantities (Δv_i), $(i = 1,2,3)$ can be equal to zero at any point of Σ' if this surface is a shock wave.

Using eqs. (36.6) and (36.10) again, we deduce

$$(\Delta v_i) = \frac{[u_n - (\mathbf{v} \cdot \mathbf{n})_1](\Delta \rho)n_i}{\rho_2} , \quad (i = 1,2,3) , \tag{36.14}$$

and,

$$(\Delta p) = \frac{\rho_1[u_n - (\mathbf{v} \cdot \mathbf{n})_1]^2(\Delta \rho)}{\rho_2} , \tag{36.15}$$

from which eqs. (36.6) and (36.10) can be recovered. Thus, eqs. (36.14) and (36.15), which express (Δv_i) and (Δp) in terms of $(\Delta \rho)$ are equivalent to the first and second shock conditions. All of these statements in the foregoing express conditions normal to Σ', but from them we can infer some properties of the fluid velocity tangent to the shock wave. If we multiply eq. (36.10) by a unit vector tangent to Σ', say α_i, and sum on i, we obtain

$$[\Delta(v_i\alpha_i)] = 0 , \tag{36.16}$$

which expresses the fact that the tangential components of the fluid velocity are continuous across a shock wave.

37. THE RANKINE-HUGONIOT RELATION

In this section we assume that both the viscosity and the thermal conductivity vanish. It follows that the quantity W' defined in eq. (31.1) now vanishes. Also, the stress tensor becomes $\tau_{ij} = -p\delta_{ij}$ as a consequence of vanishing viscosity. Substituting for W in eq. (31.4), this equation becomes

$$\frac{d}{dt}\int_V \rho E \, dV + \int_\Sigma \rho v_i n_i \, d\Sigma = 0 . \tag{37.1}$$

But from eq. (35.4) with $f = \rho E$, the first term can be written as

$$\int_V \frac{\partial}{\partial t}(\rho E)\, dV + \int_\Sigma \rho E(\mathbf{v}\cdot\mathbf{n})\, d\Sigma + \int_{\Sigma'} \{(\rho E)_1 - (\rho E)_2\} u_n \, d\Sigma . \tag{37.2}$$

We now put this expression for the first term in eq. (37.1) and then let V approach zero as in the preceding section; making use of the first shock condition, eq. (36.6), leads to the condition

$$[\Delta(p\,\mathbf{v}\cdot\mathbf{n})] = \rho_1[u_n - (\mathbf{v}\cdot\mathbf{n})_1](\Delta E) . \tag{37.3}$$

From eqs. (30.4) and (30.5) we obtain $JC_V T = JC_p T - p/\rho$ and substituting this into eq. (31.1) for E, we can write eq. (37.3) as

$$[\Delta(p\,\mathbf{v}\cdot\mathbf{n})] + \rho_1[u_n - (\mathbf{v}\cdot\mathbf{n})_1]\left[\Delta\left(\frac{p}{\rho}\right)\right] - \rho_1[u_n - (\mathbf{v}\cdot\mathbf{n})_1]\left[\Delta\left(JC_p T + \frac{1}{2}v^2\right)\right] = 0 . \tag{37.4}$$

Now using eqs. (36.6), (36.13) and (36.15) it can be shown that

$$[\Delta(p\,\mathbf{v}\cdot\mathbf{n})] = \{\rho_1[u_n - (\mathbf{v}\cdot\mathbf{n})_1](\mathbf{v}\cdot\mathbf{n})_2 + p_1\}(\Delta v)_n ,$$

$$\left[\Delta\left(\frac{p}{\rho}\right)\right] = [u_n - (\mathbf{v}\cdot\mathbf{n})_2](\Delta v)_n - \frac{p_1(\Delta v)_n}{\rho_1[u_n - (\mathbf{v}\cdot\mathbf{n})_1]} . \tag{37.5}$$

Upon substituting these expressions for $[\Delta(p\,\mathbf{v}\cdot\mathbf{n})]$ and $[\Delta(p/\rho)]$ into eq. (37.4), we obtain

$$\boxed{\left[\Delta\left(JC_pT+\frac{1}{2}v^2\right)\right] = u_n(\Delta v)_n \quad .} \tag{37.6}$$

This relation is one of the forms of the "third shock condition." From eqs. (30.4) - (30.6) and the conditions (36.14), (36.15) it follows that

$$[\Delta(JC_pT)] = \frac{\gamma}{\gamma-1}\left[\Delta\left(\frac{p}{\rho}\right)\right] \quad ,$$

$$\frac{1}{2}[\Delta(v^2)] = u_n(\Delta v)_n - \left(\frac{\rho_1+\rho_2}{2\rho_1\rho_2}\right)(\Delta p) \quad . \tag{37.7}$$

Substituting these relations in eq. (37.6), the resulting equations can be written

$$\boxed{\frac{p_2}{p_1} = \frac{(\gamma+1)\rho_2-(\gamma-1)\rho_1}{(\gamma+1)\rho_1-(\gamma-1)\rho_2} \quad .} \tag{37.8}$$

This form of the "third shock condition" is called the Rankine-Hugoniot relation, and is valid for an ideal gas in which the viscosity and thermal conductivity vanish. We note that this form of the third shock condition does not contain the wave velocity u_n even though the relation is not confined to steady shock waves.

An equivalent form of eq. (37.8) is the following

$$\frac{\rho_2}{\rho_1} = \frac{(\gamma+1)p_2+(\gamma-1)p_1}{(\gamma-1)p_2+(\gamma+1)p_1} \tag{37.9}$$

which results from eq. (37.8). By setting $x = \rho_2/\rho_1$ and $y = p_2/p_1$, the latter equation becomes

$$x = \frac{(\gamma+1)y+(\gamma-1)}{(\gamma-1)y+(\gamma+1)} = \frac{(\gamma+1)}{(\gamma-1)} - \frac{4\gamma}{(\gamma-1)^2y+(\gamma^2-1)} \quad . \tag{37.10}$$

From this form, we see that the maximum value of x occurs for $y = \infty$, since $\gamma > 1$. The maximum value of x is $(\gamma + 1)/(\gamma - 1)$. The smallest value of x is when $y = 0$ and is $(\gamma - 1)/(\gamma + 1)$. Therefore,

$$\frac{\gamma - 1}{\gamma + 1} \leqq x \leqq \frac{\gamma + 1}{\gamma - 1} . \tag{37.11}$$

38. THE COMBINED SHOCK CONDITIONS

We have deduced the three shock conditions which are completely expressed by eqs. (36.14), (36.15) and (37.8). By purely algebraic manipulations, these conditions can be cast in the respective forms,

$$(\Delta v_i) = \frac{2\{\rho_1[u_n - (\mathbf{v}\cdot\mathbf{n})_1]^2 - \gamma p_1\}n_i}{(\gamma + 1)\rho_1[u_n - (\mathbf{v}\cdot\mathbf{n})_1]} , \qquad (i = 1,2,3) \tag{38.1}$$

$$(\Delta p) = \frac{2\{\rho_1[u_n - (\mathbf{v}\cdot\mathbf{n})_1]^2 - \gamma p_1\}}{\gamma + 1} \tag{38.2}$$

$$(\Delta\rho) = \frac{2\rho_1\{\rho_1[u_n - (\mathbf{v}\cdot\mathbf{n})_1]^2 - \gamma p_1\}}{2\gamma p_1 + (\gamma - 1)\rho_1[u_n - (\mathbf{v}\cdot\mathbf{n})_1]^2} , \tag{38.3}$$

which express the values of v_i, p and ρ on side 2 of the wave surface Σ' directly in terms of the values v_i, p and ρ on side 1 of Σ', the unit normal $\mathbf{n}$ to Σ' (directed from side 1 to side 2) and the velocity of propagation u_n of the wave surface. For a stationary wave front we have $u_n = 0$, and the preceding relations reduce to

$$(\Delta v_i) = \frac{2[\rho_1(\mathbf{v}\cdot\mathbf{n})_1^2 - \gamma p_1]n_i}{-(\gamma + 1)\rho_1(\mathbf{v}\cdot\mathbf{n})_1} , \qquad (i = 1,2,3) , \tag{38.4}$$

$$(\Delta p) = \frac{2\rho_1[\rho_1(\mathbf{v}\cdot\mathbf{n})_1^2 - \gamma p_1]}{\gamma + 1} , \tag{38.5}$$

$$(\Delta\rho) = \frac{2\rho_1[\rho\ (\mathbf{v}\cdot\mathbf{n})_1^2 - \gamma p_1]}{2\gamma p_1 + (\gamma - 1)\rho_1(\mathbf{v}\cdot\mathbf{n})_1^2} . \tag{38.6}$$

It follows from the remarks made following eq. (36.10), that the denominator of eq. (38.1) can not vanish at points of a shock wave. The numerator of eq. (38.2) can not vanish either, for if it did, then we would have $(\Delta p) = 0$, which would contradict the condition that Σ' is a shock wave. Also, the denominator of eq. (38.3) can not vanish since if it were to vanish then $(\Delta \rho) = \infty$ which is impossible according to the assumptions made following eq. (35.4).

39. THE DENSITY AND ENTHROPY CHANGES IN PASSAGE THROUGH A SHOCK WAVE

The thermodynamic condition $dS/dt \geqq 0$ for continuous flow without thermal conductivity leads to the requirement that the entropy per unit mass S associated with a moving particle does not decrease in the passage with a moving particle through a shock wave (considered as representative of the rapid variations in a flow which is actually continuous). Hence, if a particle moves from side 1 to side 2 of a shock wave Σ' we have of necessity $S_2 \geqq S_1$ which implies $p_2/\rho_2^\gamma \geqq p_1/\rho_1^\gamma$ which results from eq. (32.2) for S. Therefore,

$$\frac{p_2}{p_1} \geqq \left(\frac{\rho_2}{\rho_1}\right)^\gamma , \tag{39.1}$$

now put $x = \rho_2/\rho_1$ and use the Rankine-Hugoniot relation (37.8) for the left side of (39.1) which becomes

$$\frac{(\gamma + 1)x - (\gamma - 1)}{(\gamma + 1) - (\gamma - 1)x} \geqq x^\gamma . \tag{39.2}$$

Define the function y by the equation

$$y = \frac{(\gamma + 1)x - (\gamma - 1)}{(\gamma + 1) - (\gamma - 1)x} - x^\gamma . \tag{39.3}$$

Then for $x = 1$, $y = 0$; also both dy/dx and d^2y/dx^2 vanish for $x = 1$, while

$$\frac{d^3y}{dx^3} = \frac{1}{2}(\gamma - 1)(2\gamma - 1)(3 - \gamma) .$$

If we take $\gamma = 1.4$ we see that $d^3y/dx^3 > 0$ for $x = 1$ so that y has a point of inflection at $x = 1$. A graph of y shows that the condition (39.2) is satisfied only for values of x for which $y \geqq 0$. Hence we must have $\rho_2/\rho_1 \geqq 1$. If $\rho_2 = \rho_1$ the relation (36.15) gives $(\Delta p) = 0$ which contradicts the hypothesis that Σ' is a shock wave. It follows that $\rho_2 > \rho_1$. But $x > 1$ means that $y > 0$ and hence the inequality sign holds in (39.2). This implies $S_2 > S_1$. Therefore, when a fluid particle traverses a shock surface the density and the entropy per unit mass associated with the particle are increased.

If a gas increases in density when it passes through a shock wave, the wave is called a compression wave. Hence shock waves, as here defined and treated, are compression waves in view of the above thermodynamic condition.

BIBLIOGRAPHIES

1. Coburn, N., Discontinuities in Compressible Fluid Flow. Mathematics Magazine, Vol. 27, No. 5, pp. 245-264 (June 1954).
2. Goldstein, S., Lectures on Fluid Mechanics, Interscience Publishers, Inc., N.Y. (1960).
3. Thomas, T. Y., The Fundamental Equations and Shock Conditions for Gases. Mathematics Magazine, Vol. XXII, No. 4, pp. 169-189 (March-April, 1949).

GENERAL BIBLIOGRAPHIES

1. Courant, R. and Friedrichs, K. O., Supersonic Flow and Shock Waves, Interscience Pub. N.Y. (1948).
2. Jeffreys, H. and Jeffreys, B. S., Methods of Mathematical Physics, Cambridge Univ. Press (1956).
3. Landau & Lifshitz, Fluid Mechanics, Addison-Wesley Pub. Co., Reading, Mass. (1959).
4. Prager, W., Introduction to Mechanics of Continua, Ginn, Boston, Mass. (1961).
5. Synge, J. L. and Schild, A., Tensor Calculus, Univ. of Toronto Press, Toronto (1949).

CHAPTER IV

THE HOMOGENEOUS IONIC PLASMA IN A MAGNETIC FIELD

In this chapter we shall be concerned with the derivation of the basic equations governing the propagation of waves in an ionic plasma. We shall be concerned with a low density plasma which is assumed to be unbounded in extent and homogeneous. The plasma constituents are positive and negative ions including electrons, and neutrals pervaded by a uniform externally applied magnetic field constant in time, and over-all electrically neutral. In contrast to the electron plasma treated in Chapter II, the motion of the ions now contributes to the convection current density. Besides this contribution we also take into account the temperature effects of the different species of particles. This temperature effect enters through the relation with the pressure through the gas laws. Thus we are generalizing our description of the plasma by generalizing the equations of motion of the particles. This means that we are introducing a macroscopic hydrodynamic treatment together with Maxwell's equations in order to examine the kind of waves that such a medium can support.

Our present state of knowledge of the motion of fluids acted upon by forces of nonelectromagnetic origin indicates that for gases and liquids the motion can be described by the macroscopic equations of hydrodynamics except at very low pressures. The fluid is accordingly treated as a continuum and the Eulerian or Lagrangian description can be used. In a very dilute gas where the mean free path of the molecules between interactions is of the same order of magnitude as the characteristic length of the system the continuum theory is no longer valid and must be replaced by kinetic theory methods. Even for not very dilute plasmas a microscopic gas kinetic approach is preferable. Here, one uses the Boltzmann equation together with Maxwell's equations to investigate the various general modes of oscillation. The mathematical difficulties that arise in using this approach are numerous and therefore one uses the simpler hydrodynamic description.

The fusing of the two subjects, hydrodynamics and electrodynamics in a systematic way is attributed to Alfvén and is presently known as magnetohydrodynamics or hydromagnetics. Besides Alfvén, there have been many detailed theoretical and experimental investigations of this important and interesting field of endeavor, notably by Lundquist, Piddington, Elsasser, Herlofson, Walén, Hartmann, *et al.* The continuum or hydrodynamic approach to the motion of conduction currents in a magnetic field has also been used in the magneto-ionic theory by Bailey and others. A systematic comprehensive investigation of the modes of oscillation in magneto-elastic media has been given by Banos and co-workers. The continuum theory is considered to be valid for systems in which the characteristic interaction length and time are small on a macroscopic scale and if the radius of curvature of the gyration particles is large on this scale. Although the hydrodynamic approach is simpler than the more rigorous gas kinetic one, it is not without difficulty. This difficulty stems from the fact that the hydrodynamic equations are basically non-linear even though the electrodynamic equations are linear. The coupling of the two systems of equations, hydrodynamic and electrodynamic by means of the Lorentz force causes the non linear aspects to be carried over into the resulting magneto-hydrodynamic equations. The new phenomena which arise are very interesting. Hydrodynamics yields for example, longitudinal fields, while electrodynamics yields transverse fields, so we can expect a coupling of the two fields, and hence the possibility of energy transfer between the longitudinal and transverse oscillations. This is of interest in astrophysical applications and for technology itself.

Because of the non-linear nature of the basic equations and its inherent difficulties we are led to study these fundamental equations by first linearizing them. The linearization is achieved by a perturbation procedure which is so common in the treatment of many non-linear problems. A further simplification obtains when we restrict ourselves to plane wave perturbations in unbounded homogeneous media. Although it is often argued that such simplifications are not close to physical reality, nevertheless it provides valuable insights and guides to the solution of non-linear problems. The linearized theory has been quite successful for example in explaining ionospheric phenomena and it is interesting to point out here that the existence of Alfvén type waves can be demonstrated from the linear theory. This type of wave also shows the significance of the presence of an externally applied magnetic field on an electrically conducting incompressible fluid. As is well known an incompressible fluid when described only by hydrodynamics shows that energy propagation at a velocity exceeding the average fluid velocity is not possible. But such a conducting fluid in the presence of the magnetic field now permits a new mode of energy propagation, called an

Alfvén wave, after Alfvén, who investigated this phenomena for astrophysical applications.

In the present chapter we treat first the derivation of the linearized equations taking into account pressure gradients and hence temperature effects. Here the process is assumed to be adiabatic rather than isothermal, the difference amounting to an order of magnitude effect, which is not serious considering the other simplifying assumptions.* By assuming plane wave perturbations, we arrive at a dispersion equation whose structure is quite complex but which reveals the coupling of the electron and ion motions. This dispersion equation contains as a special case that of ionospheric physics, *i.e.*, the Appleton-Hartree formula among other things. In this derivation we neglect damping by collisions since the salient features of the modes of oscillation are obtained without this assumption. By further specialization we study the various modes and their coupling. We include Astrom's basic work on waves in an ionized gas as a special case of the above development. It is interesting to point out here that in the case in which the impressed wave frequency is well below the gyrofrequency of all the ions and for an incompressible fluid we obtain the Alfvén waves from the magneto-ionic theory alone. This result is due to Astrom and shows clearly the effect of an applied magnetic field in yielding new modes of energy propagation as mentioned before.

Following this we derive anew the equations which describe the currents and forces in weakly ionized media where the reference background neutral particles are in motion. The average velocities and forces are operative as in the simple magneto-ionic theory, but the forces have their origin in the macroscopic electromagnetic effects on the charges and from the collisions between the free charges and neutral particles. In this treatment which is due to Hines, the friction like forces due to collisions between the charged particles and the neutral background is of the action and reaction type, that is, equal in magnitude but opposite in direction.†

---

* See for example, L. Oster, "Linearized Theory of Plasma Oscillations," Rev. Modern Physics, Vol. 32, No. 1, pp. 141-168, January 1960.

† C. O. Hines, "Generalized Magneto-Hydrodynamic Formulae." Proc. Cambridge Philosophical Society, 49, 299, (1953). See also same author, "Heavy-ion Effects in Audio-Frequency Radio Propagation," Jour. Atmos. and Terrest. Physics, 1957, Vol. 11, pp. 36-42. Pergamon Press Ltd., London.

Because of the mobile background, which is lacking in the usual magneto-ionic treatments, the resulting formulae are magneto-hydrodynamic in aspect. In all of the foregoing treatments we have gone into considerable detail so that the reader can follow the reasonings almost step by step. This is accomplished by using a mixed vector-matrix formalism which lends itself well to discussion and analysis. In this way it is possible to study a great variety of special circumstances in a unified manner.

Finally we sketch the comprehensive work of Baños and co-workers whose investigations are closely related to those above and a brief treatment on the reflection and refraction of hydromagnetic waves concludes the chapter.

40. THE BASIC EQUATIONS

The equations which describe the phenomena are a momentum balance or equation of motion, an equation of continuity, and the electromagnetic (Maxwell's) field equations. We write this system of equations for a typical constituent of a tenuous plasma as follows, neglecting interparticle collisions:

$$\frac{\partial \mathbf{V}}{\partial t} + (\mathbf{V} \cdot \nabla)\,\mathbf{V} + \frac{1}{Nm}\nabla P = \left(\frac{e}{m}\right)[\mathbf{E} + \mathbf{V}\mathbf{x}\mathbf{B}] \quad , \tag{40.1}$$

$$(\nabla \cdot N\mathbf{V}) + \frac{\partial N}{\partial t} = 0 \quad , \tag{40.2}$$

$$\nabla\mathbf{x}\mathbf{E} + \frac{\partial \mathbf{B}}{\partial t} = 0 \quad , \tag{40.3}$$

$$\nabla\mathbf{x}\mathbf{H} = \frac{\partial \mathbf{D}_e}{\partial t} \quad , \tag{40.4}$$

$$\nabla \cdot \mathbf{D}_e = 0 \quad . \tag{40.5}$$

(Note: e = *total* charge on a particle)

We shall linearize the above system by a perturbation technique. Denoting steady-state values by subscript zero, and perturbation quantities by lower case letters, we may write:

$$N = N_0 + n \; ; \quad \mathbf{V} = \mathbf{V}_0 + \mathbf{v} \; ; \quad \mathbf{B} = \mathbf{B}_0 + \mathbf{b} \; ; \quad \mu_0\mathbf{H} = \mathbf{B} \; ; \quad \mu_0\mathbf{h} = \mathbf{b}$$

where N is the number density of particles, $\mathbf{V}$ is their average velocity, and $\mathbf{B}$ is the total magnetic field. After substituting these quantities into the above equations we find for the momentum equation, (40.1)

$$\frac{\partial}{\partial t}(\mathbf{V}_0 + \mathbf{v}) + [(\mathbf{V}_0 + \mathbf{v}) \cdot \nabla](\mathbf{V}_0 + \mathbf{v}) + \frac{1}{(N_0 + n)m}\nabla P = \frac{e}{m}[\mathbf{E} + \mu_0(\mathbf{V}_0 + \mathbf{v})\,\mathbf{x}(\mathbf{H}_0 + \mathbf{h})] \quad . \tag{40.6}$$

We neglect the terms involving products of the perturbation quantities, e.g., $\mathbf{v} \cdot \nabla\mathbf{v}$, etc., and note that the term $[1/(N_0 + n)m\,\nabla P]$ is approximately

$(1/N_0 m)\ \nabla P$, ignoring the terms of order n/N_0 in the series expansion of the denominator. The resulting equations now read,

$$\frac{\partial}{\partial t}\mathbf{v} + (\mathbf{V}_0 \cdot \nabla)\mathbf{v} + \frac{1}{N_0 m}\nabla P = \frac{e}{m}\{\mathbf{E} + \mu_0[(\mathbf{V}_0 \mathbf{x} \mathbf{h}) + (\mathbf{v} \mathbf{x} \mathbf{H}_0) + (\mathbf{V}_0 \mathbf{x} \mathbf{H}_0)]\} \tag{40.7}$$

$$N_0 \nabla \cdot \mathbf{v} + \mathbf{V}_0 \cdot \nabla n + \frac{\partial n}{\partial t} = 0 \tag{40.8}$$

$$\nabla \mathbf{x} \mathbf{E} + \mu_0 \frac{\partial \mathbf{h}}{\partial t} = 0 \tag{40.9}$$

$$\nabla \mathbf{x} \mathbf{h} = \mathbf{J} + \epsilon_0 \frac{\partial \mathbf{E}}{\partial t} \equiv \frac{\partial \mathbf{D}_e}{\partial t} \tag{40.10}$$

$$\nabla \cdot \mathbf{D}_\epsilon = 0 \quad . \tag{40.11}$$

If we assume the processes within the plasma to take place adiabatically, and that the perfect gas laws are obeyed, we then find that $\nabla P = \gamma k T \nabla n$ where P is the partial pressure of the constituent, as in the momentum equation, γ is the ratio of its specific heats, T its temperature, and k is Boltzmann's constant. We shall represent this in terms of the speed of sound in the constituent as a medium; *i.e.*, $U^2 = \gamma kT/m$. If we **assume the** traveling-wave solution and take $\mathbf{V}_0 = 0$ (medium initially at rest), Eq. (40.7) becomes

$$i\omega\mathbf{v} - i\frac{U^2 n}{N_0}\mathbf{k} = \left(\frac{e}{m}\right)\mathbf{E} - \mu_0\left(\frac{e}{m}\right)\mathbf{H}_0 \mathbf{x} \mathbf{v} \quad . \tag{40.12}$$

This can be put into the equivalent matrix form,

$$(i\omega\mathbf{I} - \omega\mathbf{\Omega})\mathbf{v} = i\frac{U^2 n}{N_0}\mathbf{k} + \left(\frac{e}{m}\right)\mathbf{E} \tag{40.13}$$

where $\mathbf{\Omega}$ is as defined in Chapter 2. From eq. (40.8)

$$\mathbf{k} \cdot N_0 \mathbf{v} = \omega n \quad , \tag{40.14}$$

$$(\mathbf{k} : \mathbf{k})\mathbf{E} - (\mathbf{k} \cdot \mathbf{E})\mathbf{k} = \mu_0 \omega^2 \mathbf{D}_e \quad , \tag{40.15}$$

$$\mathbf{k} \cdot \mathbf{D}_e = 0 \quad , \tag{40.16}$$

where Eq. (40.15) combines both (40.9) and (40.10). Let us now denote each constituent by subscript r, then Eqs. (40.13) and (40.14) combine to give,

$$(i\omega^2 \mathbf{I} - \omega^2 \Omega_r)\mathbf{v}_r = iU_r^2(\mathbf{k} \cdot \mathbf{v}_r)\mathbf{k} + \frac{\omega e_r}{m_r}\mathbf{E} \quad . \tag{40.17}$$

We introduce the following notations:

$\mathbf{J}_r = N_{0r} e_r \mathbf{v}_r$, the current density of the rth constituent,

$\Omega_r = \dfrac{e_r B_0}{m_r \omega}\begin{pmatrix} 0 & 1 & 0 \\ -1 & 0 & 0 \\ 0 & 0 & 0 \end{pmatrix}$, the gyromagnetic tensor of the rth constituent,

$\omega_r^2 = \dfrac{N_{0r} e_r^2}{\epsilon_0 m_r}$

$a_r = \dfrac{\omega_r^2}{\omega^2}$, and U_r^2 is just the speed of sound in the rth constituent.

Multiply Eq. (40.17) by $(N_{0r} e_r / i\omega^2)$ and use the above definitions to obtain

$$[\mathbf{I} + i\Omega_r]\mathbf{J}_r = -ia_r \omega \epsilon_0 \mathbf{E} + \frac{U_r^2}{\omega^2}(\mathbf{J}_r \cdot \mathbf{k})\mathbf{k} \tag{40.18}$$

With $\mathbf{D}_e = (1/i\omega)\mathbf{J} + \epsilon_0 \mathbf{E}$, Eq. (40.15) takes the form,

$$[(\mathbf{k} \cdot \mathbf{k}) - \mu_0 \epsilon_0 \omega^2]\mathbf{E} = -\mu_0 \omega \mathbf{J} + (\mathbf{k} \cdot \mathbf{E})\mathbf{k} \quad . \tag{40.19}$$

The scalar product of both sides of this equation with $\mathbf{k}$ yields the relation,

$$\epsilon_0 \omega (\mathbf{E} \cdot \mathbf{k}) = i\mathbf{J} \cdot \mathbf{k} \quad , \tag{40.20}$$

and therefore Eq. (40.19) can be rewritten in the form,

$$\left(k^2 - \frac{\omega^2}{V_0^2}\right)\omega \epsilon_0 \mathbf{E} = -i\mu_0 \epsilon_0 \omega^2 \mathbf{J} + i(\mathbf{J} \cdot \mathbf{k})\mathbf{k} \tag{40.21}$$

where

$$k^2 = \mathbf{k} \cdot \mathbf{k}$$

and

$$\mu_0 \epsilon_0 = \frac{1}{V_0^2} \quad .$$

We now substitute $\omega \epsilon_0 \mathbf{E}$ from Eq. (40.19) into Eq. (40.18) and obtain,

$$(\mathbf{I} + i\Omega_r)\mathbf{J}_r = -ia_r \left[-\frac{i\mu_0\epsilon_0\omega^2}{\left(k^2 - \frac{\omega^2}{V_0^2}\right)} \mathbf{J} + \frac{i}{\left(k^2 - \frac{\omega^2}{V_0^2}\right)} (\mathbf{J} \cdot \mathbf{k})\mathbf{k} \right] + \frac{U_r^2}{\omega^2} (\mathbf{J}_r \cdot \mathbf{k})\mathbf{k} \tag{40.22}$$

or,

$$\omega^2(\omega^2 - k^2V_0^2)\,[\mathbf{I} + i\Omega_r]\mathbf{J}_r = \omega_r^2\omega^2\mathbf{J} - \omega_r^2V_0^2(\mathbf{J} \cdot \mathbf{k})\mathbf{k} + U_r^2(\omega^2 - k^2V_0^2)\,(\mathbf{J}_r \cdot \mathbf{k})\mathbf{k} \quad . \tag{40.23}$$

In this last equation if we replace $\mathbf{J}$ by its equivalent $\sum_s \mathbf{J}_s$ we find

$$\omega^2(\omega^2 - k^2V_0^2)\,[\mathbf{I} + i\Omega_r]\mathbf{J}_r = \omega_r^2\omega^2\sum_s\mathbf{J}_s - \omega_r^2V_0^2(\sum_s\mathbf{J}_s \cdot \mathbf{k})\mathbf{k} + U_r^2(\omega^2 - k^2V_0^2)\,(\mathbf{J}_r \cdot \mathbf{k})\mathbf{k} \tag{40.24}$$

or

$$\omega^2[(\omega^2 - k^2V_0^2) - \omega_r^2]\mathbf{I}\,\mathbf{J}_r + [\omega_r^2V_0^2 - U_r^2(\omega^2 - k^2V_0^2)]\,(\mathbf{J}_r \cdot \mathbf{k})\mathbf{k}$$
$$+ i\omega^2(\omega^2 - k^2V_0^2)\Omega_r\mathbf{J}_r = \omega_r^2 \sum_{s \neq r} [\omega^2\mathbf{J}_s - V_0^2(\mathbf{J}_s \cdot \mathbf{k})\mathbf{k}] \quad . \tag{40.25}$$

If we write this relation in tensor notation, putting $\mathbf{K} \equiv k_i k_j \equiv k_{ij}$, for p different constituents, then we have

$$\{\omega^2[(\omega^2 - k^2V_0^2) - \omega_r^2]\delta_{ij} + [\omega_r^2V_0^2 - U_r^2(\omega^2 - k^2V_0^2)]k_{ij} + i\omega^2(\omega^2 - k^2V_0^2)\Omega_{r,ij}\}J_{r,j}$$
$$- \omega_r^2 \sum_{s \neq r} (\omega^2\delta_{ij} - V_0^2k_{ij})J_{s,j} = 0 \,, \quad (i = 1,2,3) \,, \quad (r = 1,2,\ldots,p) \quad . \tag{40.26}$$

This represents a complete system of linear homogeneous equations for the $3p$ unknowns$(J_{1,1}, J_{1,2}, J_{1,3}, J_{2,1}, \ldots, J_{p,3})$. The vanishing determinant is the necessary and sufficient condition for non-trivial solutions, and provides an additional relation between ω and k; the so-called dispersion relation. The structure of the matrix of this system of equations, multiplying through by -1, becomes

$$\begin{pmatrix} \mathbf{M}_1 & \mathbf{A}_1 & \mathbf{A}_1 & \mathbf{A}_1 & \cdots & \mathbf{A}_1 \\ \mathbf{A}_2 & \mathbf{M}_2 & \mathbf{A}_2 & \mathbf{A}_2 & \cdots & \mathbf{A}_2 \\ \cdot & \cdot & \cdot & \cdot & \cdots & \cdot \\ \mathbf{A}_p & \mathbf{A}_p & & \cdots & \mathbf{A}_p & \mathbf{M}_p \end{pmatrix} \equiv \mathbf{M} \quad , \qquad (40.27)$$

where the $\mathbf{M}_i$ and $\mathbf{A}_i$ are *each* 3×3 matrices given by:

$$M_{r,ij} = \omega^2(k^2V_0^2 - \omega^2 + \omega_r^2)\delta_{ij} - [U_r^2(k^2V_0^2 - \omega^2) + \omega_r^2V_0^2]k_ik_j$$

$$+ i\omega^2(k^2V_0^2 - \omega^2)\Omega_{r,ij} \quad , \qquad (40.28)$$

$$A_{r,ij} = \omega_r^2(\omega^2\delta_{ij} - V_0^2k_ik_j) \quad . \qquad (40.29)$$

We see from Eq. (40.27) that the matrices A_r represent the coupling of the constituents to each other. The vanishing of the determinant of $\mathbf{M}$ contains the Appleton-Hartree equations as a special case (in the absence of collisions). The system described by $\mathbf{M}$ contains classical ionosphere physics of homogeneous media. This is easily seen from Eqs. (40.7) to (40.11) by considering only the effects of one constituent, the electrons, by neglecting the effects of electron pressure, and by assuming the medium to be incompressible, *i.e.*, div $\mathbf{v} = 0$. Consequently, $U_1^2 = 0$, $\mathbf{A}_r = \mathbf{0}$, $(r = 1, 2, \ldots, p)$ and $\mathbf{M}$ reduces to $\mathbf{M}_1$ for arbitrary orientation of the magnetic field. *If* the uniform magnetic field is chosen to be parallel with the x_3-axis then we can identify $|\mathbf{M}|$ with the expression in Eq. (11.26) of Chapter II.

In each $\mathbf{M}_r$ we observe the factors $(k^2V_0^2 - \omega^2 + \omega_r^2)$, $[U_r^2(k^2V_0^2 - \omega^2) + \omega_r^2V_0^2]$, $(k^2V_0^2 - \omega^2)$, and it suggests that we seek the meaning of these factors. To do so, we choose $\mathbf{k}$ along the x_1 direction, hence $k_2 = k_3 = 0$; further, let us consider only two constituents, electrons and positive ions.

We will also, in this case, choose the orientation of the uniform magnetic field to be in the x_1x_2 plane, then $\mathbf{B}_0 = (B_{0L}, B_{0T}, 0)$, with a longitudinal and transverse component. The dispersion equation is a 6×6 determinant, which, cancelling the factor $\omega^2 - k^2V_0^2$ in columns 1 and 4, and ω^2 in columns 2, 3, 5 and 6, is given by:

$$0 = \left| \begin{pmatrix} \mathbf{M}_e & \omega_e^2\mathbf{I} \\ \omega_i^2\mathbf{I} & \mathbf{M}_i \end{pmatrix} \right| \tag{40.30a}$$

where $\mathbf{I}$ is the usual identity matrix, and

$$\mathbf{M}_e = \begin{pmatrix} \omega^2 - \omega_e^2 - k^2U_e^2 & 0 & i\Omega_{e,T}(\omega^2 - k^2V_0^2) \\ 0 & \omega^2 - \omega_e^2 - k^2V_0^2 & -i\Omega_{e,L}(\omega^2 - k^2V_0^2) \\ -i\omega^2\Omega_{e,T} & i\Omega_{e,L}(\omega^2 - k^2V_0^2) & \omega^2 - \omega_e^2 - k^2V_0^2 \end{pmatrix} \tag{40.30b}$$

and

$$\mathbf{M}_i = \begin{pmatrix} \omega^2 - \omega_i^2 - k^2U_i^2 & 0 & -i\Omega_{i,L}(\omega^2 - k^2V_0^2) \\ 0 & \omega^2 - \omega_i^2 - k^2V_0^2 & i\Omega_{i,L}(\omega^2 - k^2V_0^2) \\ i\omega^2\Omega_{i,T} & -i\Omega_{i,L}(\omega^2 - k^2V_0^2) & \omega^2 - \omega_i^2 - k^2V_0^2 \end{pmatrix} \tag{40.30c}$$

where subscript e stands for electron, subscript i for ion, and

$$\left.\begin{aligned} \Omega_{e,L} &= \frac{eB_{0,L}}{m_e\omega}, & \Omega_{e,T} &= \frac{eB_{0,T}}{m_e\omega} \\ \Omega_{i,L} &= \frac{eB_{0,L}}{m_i\omega} & \Omega_{i,T} &= \frac{eB_{0,T}}{m_i\omega}\,. \end{aligned}\right\} \tag{40.31}$$

The determinant (40.30) consists of four distinct groups: the upper left hand group involves only the electrons, the lower right hand group involves only the ions, and the remaining groups provide the coupling between the electron and ion motions. The $\mathbf{M}_e$ and $\mathbf{M}_i$ matrices are the physically significant ones and contain two wave pairs which correspond to a longitudinal wave resulting from

$$\left.\begin{array}{l} \omega^2 - \omega_e^2 - k^2U_e^2 \\ \\ \omega^2 - \omega_i^2 - k^2U_i^2 \end{array}\right\} \qquad (40.32)$$

and two wave pairs,

$$\left.\begin{array}{l} \omega^2 - \omega_e^2 - k^2V_0^2 \\ \\ \omega^2 - \omega_i^2 - k^2V_0^2 \end{array}\right\} \qquad (40.33)$$

corresponding to a transverse type of oscillation. It is not surprising to associate the pair (40.32) with a longitudinal type of oscillation since it contains the factors U_e^2 and U_i^2. These thermal speeds are associated with the speeds of propagation of sound and we already know that sound oscillations are of a longitudinal nature. The other pair, (40.33), contains V_0, the phase velocity of an electromagnetic wave which is clearly of a transverse nature. The coupling of the two types of oscillations, longitudinal and transverse, is effected by the off-diagonal terms, some of which are zero due to the special choice of orientation of the uniform magnetic field. The non-vanishing off-diagonal terms contain the magnetic field and the factor $\omega^2 - k^2V_0^2$. The principal consequence of the uniform magnetic field is to couple the characteristic phase velocities and frequencies of both types of waves, *i.e.*, the longitudinal and transverse waves. The magnetic field also causes the multiple refraction of the waves, that is, the splitting of the two transverse waves. We note in the matrix, (40.30), that the coupling elements take the form of light waves, which are represented by

$$\omega^2 - k^2V_0^2 = 0 \quad . \qquad (40.34)$$

We see then, that in the presence of a uniform magnetic field there exists in general four pairs of waves. For a mixed frequency there can exist different phase velocities corresponding to the number of real solutions of the dispersion equation. The two transverse modes of oscillation appear separately, which correspond to the ordinary and extraordinary rays in a crystal.

Oscillations of an Electron Plasma in a Uniform Magnetic Field—In Chapter 2 we examined the propagation characteristics of an electron plasma without taking into account the pressure effects of the electrons. The formalism developed in the foregoing provides a convenient basis from which we can examine the influence of pressure gradients on the electron oscillations.

If we neglect the motions of the ions, we have only to consider the submatrix $\mathbf{M}_1 \equiv \mathbf{M}_e$ in (40.27). The dispersion equation is obtained by setting the determinant of $\mathbf{M}_e$ equal to zero. Thus

$$(\omega^2 - \omega_e^2 - k^2U_e^2)\,[(\omega^2 - \omega_e^2 - k^2V_0^2)^2 - (\omega_L^2/\omega^2)(\omega^2 - k^2V_0^2)^2]$$

$$- (\omega^2 - k^2V_0^2)\,\omega_T^2\,(\omega^2 - \omega_e^2 - k^2V_0^2) = 0 \quad , \qquad (40.35)$$

where

$$\begin{aligned} \omega_L &= \omega\Omega_{e,L} \\ \omega_T &= \omega\Omega_{e,T} \end{aligned} \qquad (40.36)$$

and we have dropped the subscript e where it is unnecessary. Equation (40.35) is cubic in k^2, and in the absence of the magnetic field $\omega_L = \omega_T = 0$, the coupling between the transverse and longitudinal waves disappears. In this case there exists only one dispersion relation for the longitudinal waves which involves the x_1 components E_1 and v_1, and only one common dispersion equation for both of the transverse modes of oscillation. These results obtain at once from Eq. (40.35).

Rather than treat the general case for Eq. (40.35), we shall extract the salient features from a consideration of some limiting situations.

Longitudinal Magnetic Field $\omega_T = 0$—In this case there is no coupling between the longitudinal oscillations defined by the vector (E_1, v_1) which are not affected by the magnetic field, and the two transverse modes of oscillation defined by (v_2, E_2, h_2) and (v_3, E_3, h_3) which are coupled together by the magnetic field. The dispersion equation for the longitudinal oscillations is,

$$\omega^2 - \omega_e^2 - k^2U_e^2 = 0 \tag{40.37}$$

and for the two transverse oscillations:

$$\omega^2(\omega^2 - \omega_e^2 - k^2V_0^2)^2 - (\omega^2 - k^2V_0^2)^2\omega_L^2 = 0 \quad . \tag{40.38}$$

Eq. (40.38) shows no pressure dependence and consequently will coincide with the results obtained in Chapter 2 by proper identification of terms. Eq. (40.38) gives the two roots for the index of refraction,

$$M_1^2 = \frac{V_0^2}{\left(\frac{\omega}{k}\right)^2} = 1 - \frac{\omega_e}{\omega}\frac{\omega_e}{\omega + \omega_L} , \tag{40.39}$$

which defines the "ordinary wave", and

$$M_2^2 = \frac{V_0^2}{\left(\frac{\omega}{k}\right)^2} = 1 - \frac{\omega_e}{\omega}\frac{\omega_e}{\omega - \omega_L} , \tag{40.40}$$

which defines the "extraordinary wave". We mention in passing that only these latter two waves occur in the ordinary ionospheric theory. The longitudinal mode does not occur in this theory because the electron pressure is not taken into consideration.

In the absence of a magnetic field, we would find

$$M^2 = 1 - \frac{\omega_e^2}{\omega^2} . \tag{40.41}$$

and clearly both (40.39) and (40.40) converge to (40.41) as $\omega_L \to 0$. The Zeeman effect is already inherent in both Eqs. (40.39) and (40.40): there is a spectral shift on both sides of ω to $\omega + \omega_L$ and $\omega - \omega_L$. This effect has been discussed already in Chapter 2.

Conditions for Propagation—Wave propagation is possible only when $M_2^2 > 0$. For the "ordinary ray," this occurs when,

$$\omega > -\left(\frac{\omega_L}{2}\right) + \left[\left(\frac{\omega_L^2}{4}\right) + \omega_e^2\right]^{1/2} \equiv \omega_1 \tag{40.42}$$

and for the "extraordinary wave" when,

$$\omega > +\left(\frac{\omega_L}{2}\right) + \left[\left(\frac{\omega_L^2}{4}\right) + \omega_e^2\right]^{1/2} \equiv \omega_2 \quad . \tag{40.43}$$

In both cases we exclude the negative square root. The effect of the magnetic field is to cause a shift of the lowest frequency able to propagate through the plasma as compared with the unshifted case defined by (40.41). For the extraordinary wave there exists another range of frequencies for which wave propagation is permissible. This results from the fact that for $\omega = \omega_L$, the refractive index becomes positive again, consequently for all frequencies such that

$$\omega < \omega_L \quad , \tag{40.44}$$

propagation is possible, which is already a well known fact in radio-wave propagation. It is obvious that as B_0 increases the band defined by

$$\omega_L < \omega < \left(\frac{\omega_L}{2}\right) + \left[\left(\frac{\omega_L^2}{4}\right) + \omega_e^2\right]^{1/2} \tag{40.45}$$

gets narrower and terminates for $\omega_L >> \omega_e$, in a "forbidden line" at ω_L, but there is no way of obtaining a continuous frequency range of propagation. If the magnetic field vanishes, the forbidden region of Eq. (40.45) cancels out and all frequencies $\omega^2 > \omega_e^2$ will propagate. Eqs. (40.39) and (40.40) also show that in both cases the phase velocity is greater than V_0. However, the phase velocities in the range of frequencies defined by $\omega \lessgtr \omega_L$ is always less than V_0 since $M > 1$. At the boundaries of the transmission region defined by $\omega = 0$ and $\omega = \omega_L$, the phase velocity goes to zero, and at $\omega = \omega_L/2$ the phase velocity is a maximum whose value is

$$\text{Max}\left(\frac{\omega^2}{k^2}\right) = \frac{V_0^2\omega_L^2}{\omega_L^2 + 4\omega_e^2} . \tag{40:46}$$

Let us now examine the relations between the field components **E**, **h** and **v**. From the curl relation (40.9) we find

$$h_2 = -\frac{k}{\mu_0\omega}E_3 \tag{40.47a}$$

$$h_3 = \frac{k}{\mu_0\omega}E_2 \tag{40.47b}$$

which are the only two relations between **h** and **E**. On the other hand, the **E** field is related to the **v** field through (40.41) and this yields

$$\frac{e}{m}E_1 = -i\frac{\omega_e^2}{\omega}v_1 \tag{40.48a}$$

$$\frac{e}{m}E_2 = -i\frac{\omega_e^2\omega}{\omega^2 - k^2V_0^2}v_2 \tag{40.48b}$$

$$\frac{e}{m}E_3 = -i\frac{\omega_e^2\omega}{\omega^2 - k^2V_0^2}v_3 \tag{40.48c}$$

These field relations must be compatible with the dispersion relations. We see from (40.48) that there exists only one relation for the longitudinal components v_1 and E_1, regardless of the existence of a magnetic field. But for the transverse components E_2 and v_2, and E_3 and v_3 this is not the case. The relations embodied in (40.48) contain the wave number k and therefore also the refractive index. By utilizing Eqs. (40.39) and (40.40) we obtain the explicit relations between E_2 and v_2, and E_3 and v_3. The two modes of oscillation which result correspond to the ordinary and extraordinary waves, which according to our preceding analysis do not exist at all frequencies.

Pure Transverse Magnetic Field, $\omega_L = 0$—From Eq. (40.35) one of the transverse modes separates out and gives the ordinary wave defined by

$$\omega^2 - \omega_e^2 - k^2 V_0^2 = 0 \quad . \tag{40.49}$$

By solving this equation for the phase velocity in the form

$$\left(\frac{\omega}{k}\right)^2 = \frac{V_0^2 \omega^2}{\omega^2 - \omega_e^2} \tag{40.50}$$

we see that there is no pressure dependence for the transverse waves (*i.e.*, U_e^2 does not appear) as there was in the case of a purely longitudinal magnetic field. The relation between **h**, **E** and **v** is,

$$h_3 = -\frac{1}{\omega}(\omega^2 - \omega_e^2)^{\frac{1}{2}} E_2 = i\frac{m}{e}(\omega^2 - \omega_e^2)\, v_2 \tag{40.51}$$

$$\frac{e}{m} E_2 = -i\omega v_2 \quad . \tag{40.52}$$

The remaining factor in the dispersion relation (40.35) is,

$$(\omega^2 - \omega_e^2 - k^2 U_e^2)(\omega^2 - \omega_e^2 - k^2 V_0^2) - \omega_T^2(\omega^2 - k^2 V_0^2) = 0 \quad . \tag{40.53}$$

For the pure transverse magnetic field the frequencies and phase velocities of the longitudinal pair (v_1, E_1) and one of the transverse waves (v_3, E_3, h_2) are coupled together. This suggests the possibility of an energy transfer between the longitudinal and transverse oscillations.

If in Eq. (40.53) we define

$$y = \frac{V_0 U_e}{\left(\frac{\omega}{k}\right)^2} \tag{40.54}$$

then we can write

$$y = -\frac{1}{2}B \pm \left[\frac{1}{4}B^2 - \left(\frac{\omega_e^2}{\omega^2} - 1\right)^2 + \frac{\omega_T^2}{\omega^2}\right]^{½} \tag{40.55}$$

where,

$$B \equiv \frac{V_0}{U_e}\left(\frac{\omega_e^2 + \omega_T^2}{\omega^2} - 1\right) + \frac{U_e}{V_0}\left(\frac{\omega_e^2}{\omega^2} - 1\right) .$$

The **relation** (40.53) holds for the longitudinal mode (v_1, E_1) as well as for the transverse mode (v_3, E_3, h_2). Consequently these two solutions are the same for both kinds of oscillations.

Now if $U_e^2 << V_0^2$, then the second factor in B is small compared with the first factor and we can write in this case;

$$B \approx \frac{V_0}{U_e}\frac{1}{\omega^2}(\omega_e^2 + \omega_T^2 - \omega^2) \tag{40.56}$$

and, since we are interested in $\omega^2 << \omega_e^2$, then

$$\frac{1}{4}B^2 >> \left(\frac{\omega_e^2}{\omega^2} - 1\right)^2 + \frac{\omega_T^2}{\omega^2} \tag{40.57}$$

is always valid. Using the above relations we can expand the square root term of y and obtain,

$$y \approx -\frac{1}{2}B \pm \frac{1}{2}B \pm B^{-1}\left[-\left(\frac{\omega_e^2}{\omega^2} - 1\right)^2 + \frac{\omega_T^2}{\omega^2}\right] . \tag{40.58}$$

For the oscillation corresponding to the negative alternative we obtain

$$y \approx -\frac{V_0}{U_e}\frac{1}{\omega^2}(\omega_e^2 + \omega_T^2 - \omega^2) = -B \tag{40.59}$$

which yields for the phase velocity,

$$\left(\frac{\omega}{k}\right)^2 = U_e^2 \frac{\omega^2}{\omega^2 - \omega_e^2 - \omega_T^2} \tag{40.60}$$

This value of the phase velocity corresponds closely to the phase velocity for longitudinal oscillations with zero magnetic field. But, here, this velocity applies to both waves. The waves propagate for ω such that

$$\omega^2 > \omega_e^2 + \omega_T^2 \equiv \omega_0^2 \tag{40.61}$$

For $\omega_T \to 0$, the coupling between longitudinal and transverse vector components vanishes.

If we now consider the positive alternative in (40.58) we find, for the phase velocity,

$$\left(\frac{\omega}{k}\right)^2 = + V_0^2 \left[\frac{\omega^2 \left(\omega_e^2 + \omega_T^2 - \omega^2\right)}{\omega^2\omega_T^2 - \left(\omega_e^2 - \omega^2\right)^2}\right] \tag{40.62}$$

By an analysis similar to that for the pure longitudinal case we obtain the transmission behavior of the plasma. Propagation is possible when the expression in brackets, [ ], is positive, *i.e.*,

$$\omega_2^2 < \omega^2 < \omega_0^2 < \omega_1^2 \tag{40.63}$$

and for

$$\omega^2 > \omega_1^2 \tag{40.64}$$

where $\omega_{1,2}$ are determined from,

$$\omega_{1,2}^2 \equiv \omega_e^2 + \frac{1}{2}\omega_T^2 \pm \left(\omega_e^2\omega_T^2 + \frac{1}{4}\omega_T^4\right)^{1/2} \tag{40.65}$$

As $\omega_T \to 0$, the critical frequency becomes ω_e^2, as it should. In the region of ω determined by (40.63) all phase velocities between ∞ ($\omega = \omega_2$) and zero ($\omega = \omega_0$) exist with

$$\omega/k = V_0 \qquad \text{for} \qquad \omega = \omega_e \; . \tag{40.66}$$

In the region defined by (40.64) the phase velocity varies from ∞ ($\omega = \omega_1$) to V_0 ($\omega \to \infty$). Note that

$$\Delta\omega = \omega_T^2 \left[\left(\frac{1}{4} + \frac{\omega_e^2}{\omega_T^2}\right)^{1/2} - \frac{1}{2}\right] \tag{40.67}$$

is the width of the frequency interval which is not allowed, and that

$$\lim_{\omega_T \to \infty} \Delta\omega \to \omega_e^2 \tag{40.68}$$

The relations between the vector components again yield Eq. (40.48) for the longitudinal terms (v_1, E_1); the amplitude relations are identical for both solutions, (40.60) and (40.62). However, these solutions give different relations between v_3, h_2, and E_3; v_2, E_2 and h_3 are unaffected by the magnetic field. If we consider only terms up to order (U_e^2/V_0^2) in (40.55), we can find the relations between v_3 and E_3 for the two solutions.

In both cases we begin with Eq. (40.48);

$$\frac{ieE_3}{m} = \frac{\omega\omega_e^2 v_3}{(\omega^2 - k^2 V_0^2)} \tag{40.69}$$

and from Eq. (40.54), $V_0^2 k^2/\omega^2 = yV_0/U_e$, and substituting in the above, and solving for v_3:

$$v_3 = \left(\frac{ie\omega E_3}{m\omega_e^2}\right)\left(1 - \frac{yV_0}{U_e}\right) \tag{40.70}$$

If we now replace y by its solutions in the two cases, we find that for $y = -B$:

$$v_3 = \frac{ieE_3 V_0^2}{m\omega\omega_e^2 U_e^2} (\omega_0^2 - \omega^2) \tag{40.71}$$

and in the second case:

$$v_3 = (ieE_3/m\omega)\,\frac{(\omega_e^2 - \omega^2)}{(\omega_0^2 - \omega^2)} \tag{40.72}$$

From the foregoing we can conclude that there exists transverse waves in the plasma which propagate with a phase velocity *almost equal to the speed of sound*, and with non-negligible amplitudes. We note that as $\omega_T \to 0$, both solutions of (40.70) tend toward the ordinary case of transverse waves.

41. ELECTROMAGNETIC WAVES IN THE PLASMA

In the previous section we formulated the basis of an extended magneto-ionic theory which takes into consideration the effects of pressure gradients on the propagation characteristics of the plasma. We specialized the theory to a single species, namely the electrons, in order to obtain the salient features of these effects. This was done by "freezing" the ion motions, the resulting dispersion relation contained the effects of the temperature of the electrons through the term U_e^2, the Newtonian sound velocity. The appearance of this term is in sharp contrast with the dispersion relation obtained for the electron plasma in Chapter 2. The existence of waves other than the usual "radio waves" occurs as we have already demonstrated.

In this section we will show how Alfvén's "magneto hydrodynamic waves" arise by using only the simple magneto ionic theory but considering the ionic motions, *i.e.* we do not "freeze" the ions. Alfvén's theory is contained in the dispersion equation, as long as the damping process is neglected, and could be developed by setting $U_e^2 = U_i^2 = 0$ in accordance with the concept of complete incompressibility. By neglecting the displacement current as compared with the conduction current, the usual magneto hydrodynamical equations result. We shall not follow Alfvén's development, but rather proceed from the general equations for the constituents of the plasma as have already been set down in Section 40. We shall again neglect the damping processes since here too, we wish to obtain only the salient features.

If we take the applied uniform magnetic field in the direction of the positive x_3-axis, then Eq. (40.18) with $U_r^2 = 0$ serves as our starting point. This equation is repeated here for convenience, but now the B field is the *total* field: *i.e.*, the uniform field plus the alternating field, the form of the resulting equation remains the same.

$$(\mathbf{I} + i\Omega_r)\mathbf{J}_r = - i a_r \omega \epsilon_0 \mathbf{E} \quad . \qquad (41.1)$$

Here, $\mathbf{\Omega}_r = (e_r\mathbf{B}/m_r\omega)$ with $\mathbf{B}$ the tensor utilizing the *total* field in its definition. We invert the matrix $\mathbf{I} + i\mathbf{\Omega}_r$, which is non-singular, and write:

$$\mathbf{J}_r = - i\omega a_r (\mathbf{I} + i\Omega_r)^{-1}\epsilon_0 \mathbf{E} \quad . \qquad (41.2)$$

As in the case of the electron plasma, we set

$$\mathbf{S}_r = a_r(\mathbf{I} + i\boldsymbol{\Omega}_r)^{-1} \quad , \tag{41.3}$$

we recall in the case of the electron plasma we inverted the matrix $(\beta\mathbf{I} + i\boldsymbol{\Omega})$, with the β term arising from collisions, [see Eq. (13.13)]. For no collisions $\beta = 1$, and we can therefore carry over the results of the inversion of this matrix directly. But first we require an expression for the total convection current $\mathbf{J}$ and for the effective displacement vector $\mathbf{D}_e$.

$$\mathbf{J} = \sum_r{}' \mathbf{J}_r = i\omega(\sum_r \mathbf{S}_r)\epsilon_0\mathbf{E} = i\omega\mathbf{S}\epsilon_0\mathbf{E} \tag{41.4}$$

where,

$$\sum_r \mathbf{S}_r = \mathbf{S} \quad , \tag{41.5}$$

with the sum taken over *all* types of charged particles. Since,

$$\mathbf{D}_e = (1/i\omega)\mathbf{J} + \epsilon_0\mathbf{E} \tag{41.6}$$

we obtain,

$$\mathbf{D}_e = (\sum_r \mathbf{S}_r + \mathbf{I})\epsilon_0\mathbf{E} = (\mathbf{S} + \mathbf{I})\epsilon_0\mathbf{E} \quad . \tag{41.7}$$

From Chapter 2, Eq. (13.17b), it follows that

$$\mathbf{S}_r = \frac{-a_r}{(1 - \Omega_r^2)} \begin{bmatrix} 1 & -i\Omega_r & 0 \\ i\Omega_r & 1 & 0 \\ 0 & 0 & 1-\Omega_r^2 \end{bmatrix} \quad , \tag{41.8}$$

and

$$\mathbf{S} = \begin{bmatrix} \sum_r \dfrac{-a_r}{1 - \Omega_r^2} & i\sum_r \dfrac{a_r\Omega_r}{1 - \Omega_r^2} & 0 \\ -i\sum_r \dfrac{a_r\Omega_r}{1 - \Omega_r^2} & -\sum_r \dfrac{a_r}{1 - \Omega_r^2} & 0 \\ 0 & 0 & -\sum_r a_r \end{bmatrix} \quad . \tag{41.9}$$

Therefore,

$$\mathbf{D}_e = \epsilon_0(\mathbf{S} + \mathbf{I})\mathbf{E} = \epsilon_0 \epsilon_e \mathbf{E} \quad , \tag{41.10}$$

where the effective dielectric tensor ϵ_e is given by,

$$\epsilon_e = \begin{pmatrix} 1 - \sum_r \dfrac{a_r}{1 - \Omega_r^2} & i\sum_r \dfrac{a_r \Omega_r}{1 - \Omega_r^2} & 0 \\ -i\sum_r \dfrac{a_r \Omega_r}{1 - \Omega_r^2} & 1 - \sum_r \dfrac{a_r}{1 - \Omega_r^2} & 0 \\ 0 & 0 & 1 - \sum_r a_r \end{pmatrix} \tag{41.11}$$

It will prove convenient to define the following new quantities, which are suggested by the development in Chapter II.

$$\epsilon_1 \equiv \epsilon_{e11} + i\epsilon_{e12} = 1 - \sum_r \frac{a_r}{1 - \Omega_r^2} - \sum_r \frac{a_r \Omega_r}{1 - \Omega_r^2} = 1 - \sum_r \frac{a_r(1 + \Omega_r)}{1 - \Omega_r^2} \quad , \tag{41.12a}$$

$$= 1 - \sum_r \frac{a_r}{1 - \Omega_r} \quad ,$$

$$\epsilon_2 \equiv \epsilon_{e11} - i\epsilon_{e12} = 1 - \sum_r \frac{a_r}{1 + \Omega_r} \quad , \tag{41.12b}$$

$$\epsilon_3 = \epsilon_{e33} = 1 - \sum_r a_r \quad , \tag{41.12c}$$

It should also be noted that

$$\begin{aligned} \epsilon_{e11} &= \epsilon_{e22} \quad , \\ \epsilon_{e12} &= -\epsilon_{e21} \end{aligned} \tag{41.13}$$

we shall also set $\Omega_r = \omega_{c,r}/\omega$ where $\omega_{c,r}$ is the gyrofrequency of the rth species. In terms of the plasma frequency ω_r and ω_{cr} expanding summation terms in partial fraction the new quantities become,

$$\epsilon_1 = 1 - \sum_r \frac{\omega_r^2}{\omega(\omega - \omega_{c,r})} = 1 + \sum_r \frac{\omega_r^2}{\omega_{c,r}} \left[\frac{1}{(\omega_{c,r} - \omega)} + \frac{1}{\omega} \right] \qquad (41.14a)$$

$$\epsilon_2 = 1 - \sum_r \frac{\omega_r^2}{\omega(\omega + \omega_{c,r})} = 1 + \sum_r \frac{\omega_r^2}{\omega_{c,r}} \left[\frac{1}{(\omega_{c,r} + \omega)} - \frac{1}{\omega} \right] \qquad (41.14b)$$

$$\epsilon_3 = 1 - \sum_r \frac{\omega_r^2}{\omega^2} \quad . \qquad (41.14c)$$

Since,

$$\sum_r \frac{\omega_r^2}{\omega_{c,r}} = \sum_r \frac{N_{0r} e_r}{\epsilon_0 B_0} \quad , \qquad (41.15)$$

the last sums in the expressions for ϵ_1, ϵ_2 vanish for a neutral medium.

From the expression

$$(\mathbf{k} \cdot \mathbf{k})\mathbf{E} - (\mathbf{k} \cdot \mathbf{E})\mathbf{k} = \mu_0 \epsilon_0 \omega^2 \mathbf{D}_e \qquad (41.16)$$

together with

$$\mathbf{k} = \frac{\omega}{V}\mathbf{n} \quad , \qquad \mathbf{n} \cdot \mathbf{n} = 1 \quad , \qquad (41.17)$$

and (41.10), we get

$$\left[\mathbf{I} - \left(\frac{V}{V_0} \right)^2 \epsilon_e \right] \mathbf{E} - (\mathbf{n} \cdot \mathbf{E})\mathbf{n} = 0 \qquad (41.18)$$

without any real loss of generality we can assume that $\mathbf{n}$ lies in the $x_2 x_3$ plane, so that $\mathbf{n} \equiv (0, n_2, n_3)$. The angle between $\mathbf{B}_0$ and $\mathbf{n}$ is denoted by θ. Equation (41.18) written in tensor notation becomes

$$\left(\delta_{ij} - \frac{1}{M^2}\epsilon_{eij}\right)E_j - (n_j E_j)n_i = 0, \qquad (i = 1, 2, 3), \quad (41.18)$$

where

$$\left(\frac{V}{V_0}\right)^2 = \frac{1}{M^2} \quad ,$$

or,

$$\left(\delta_{ij} - \frac{1}{M^2}\epsilon_{eij} - n_i n_j\right)E_i = 0 \quad , \qquad (i = 1, 2, 3), \quad (41.19)$$

which for non-trivial solutions must have its determinant vanish. By the choice of orientation of **n**, we have $n_2 = \sin\theta$, $n_3 = \cos\theta$, and since $\epsilon_{e13} = \epsilon_{e23} = \epsilon_{e31} = \epsilon_{e32} = 0$, we can write the determinant as follows,

$$\Delta = \begin{vmatrix} 1 - \frac{1}{M^2}\epsilon_{e11} & -\frac{1}{M^2}\epsilon_{e12} & 0 \\ -\frac{1}{M^2}\epsilon_{e21} & 1 - \sin^2\theta - \frac{1}{M^2}\epsilon_{e22} & -\sin\theta\cos\theta \\ 0 & -\sin\theta\cos\theta & 1 - \cos^2\theta - \frac{1}{M^2}\epsilon_{e33} \end{vmatrix} . \quad (41.20)$$

Since $\epsilon_{e12} = -\epsilon_{e12}$, $\epsilon_{e11} = \epsilon_{e22}$,

$$\Delta = \begin{vmatrix} 1 - \frac{1}{M^2}\epsilon_{e11} & -\frac{1}{M^2}\epsilon_{e12} & 0 \\ \frac{1}{M^2}\epsilon_{e12} & \cos^2\theta - \frac{1}{M^2}\epsilon_{e11} & -\sin\theta\cos\theta \\ 0 & -\sin\theta\cos\theta & \sin^2\theta - \frac{1}{M^2}\epsilon_{e33} \end{vmatrix}, \quad (41.21)$$

We now multiply the first row of Δ by i and add it to the second row, and utilize the definitions (41.12) to obtain,

$$\Delta = \begin{vmatrix} 1 - \dfrac{1}{M^2}\,\epsilon_{e11} & -\dfrac{1}{M^2}\,\epsilon_{e12} & 0 \\ i - i\,\dfrac{\epsilon_1}{M^2} & \cos^2\theta - \dfrac{\epsilon_1}{M^2} & -\sin\theta\cos\theta \\ 0 & -\sin\theta\cos\theta & \sin^2\theta - \dfrac{\epsilon_3}{M^2} \end{vmatrix}$$

$$= \left(1 - \frac{\epsilon_{e11}}{M^2}\right)\left[\left(\cos^2\theta - \frac{\epsilon_1}{M^2}\right)\left(\sin^2\theta - \frac{\epsilon_3}{M^2}\right) - \sin^2\theta\cos^2\theta\right]$$

$$- i\left(1 - \frac{\epsilon_1}{M^2}\right)\left(\frac{\epsilon_{e12}\epsilon_3}{M^4} - \frac{\epsilon_{e12}\sin^2\theta}{M^2}\right) . \qquad (41.22)$$

The complete expansion gives, [replacing $(\epsilon_{e11}\epsilon_3/M^4)\cos^2\theta$ by $(\epsilon_{e11}\epsilon_3/M^4)(1 - \sin^2\theta)$],

$$\Delta = -\frac{\epsilon_3}{M^2}\cos^2\theta - \frac{\epsilon_1}{M^2}\sin^2\theta + \frac{\epsilon_1\epsilon_3}{M^4} + \frac{\epsilon_{e11}\epsilon_3}{M^4} - i\,\frac{\epsilon_{e12}\epsilon_3}{M^4}$$

$$- \frac{\epsilon_{e11}\epsilon_3\sin^2\theta}{M^4} + \frac{\epsilon_1}{M^4}(\epsilon_{e11} - i\epsilon_{e12})\sin^2\theta$$

$$- \frac{\epsilon_1\epsilon_3}{M^6}(\epsilon_{e11} - i\epsilon_{e12}) + i\,\frac{\epsilon_{e12}'}{M^2}\sin^2\theta \quad . \qquad (41.23)$$

We can eliminate all of the ϵ_{e12} terms by cancellation after putting $-(\epsilon_1\sin^2\theta/M^2) = -[(\epsilon_{e11} + i\epsilon_{e12})/M^2]\sin^2\theta$, and if we replace ϵ_{e11} by $[(\epsilon_1 + \epsilon_2)/2]$, Δ can be expressed in terms of ϵ_1, ϵ_2, ϵ_3, $\sin^2\theta$, $\cos^2\theta$. It is desirable to express Δ in the form

$$\Delta = f(\epsilon_1, \epsilon_2, \epsilon_3) \cos^2 \theta + g(\epsilon_1, \epsilon_2, \epsilon_3) \sin^2 \theta \tag{41.24}$$

where f and g are two distinct algebraic functions of the parameters shown. By using the identity $\sin^2 \theta + \cos^2 \theta = 1$ we accomplish this representation, hence

$$\Delta = \left(\epsilon_3 \frac{\epsilon_1 + \epsilon_2}{M^4} - \frac{\epsilon_1\epsilon_2\epsilon_3}{M^6} - \frac{\epsilon_3}{M^2}\right) \cos^2 \theta$$

$$+ \left[\frac{\epsilon_1\epsilon_2}{M^4} + \frac{\frac{1}{2}(\epsilon_1 + \epsilon_2)\epsilon_3}{M^4} - \frac{\frac{1}{2}(\epsilon_1 + \epsilon_2)}{M^2} - \frac{\epsilon_1\epsilon_2\epsilon_3}{M^6}\right] \sin^2 \theta$$

which takes the final form,

$$\Delta = -\frac{\epsilon_1\epsilon_2\epsilon_3}{M^2} \left\{\left(\frac{1}{M^2} - \frac{1}{\epsilon_1}\right)\left(\frac{1}{M^2} - \frac{1}{\epsilon_3}\right) \cos^2 \theta \right.$$

$$\left. + \left(\frac{1}{M^2} - \frac{1}{\epsilon_3}\right)\left[\frac{1}{M^2} - \frac{1}{2}\left(\frac{1}{\epsilon_1} + \frac{1}{\epsilon_2}\right)\right] \sin^2 \theta\right\} . \tag{41.25}$$

Since $\epsilon_1\epsilon_2\epsilon_3 \neq 0$, the vanishing of Δ implies the following form of the dispersion equation,

$$\tan^2 \theta = -\frac{\left(\frac{1}{M^2} - \frac{1}{\epsilon_1}\right)\left(\frac{1}{M^2} - \frac{1}{\epsilon_2}\right)}{\left(\frac{1}{M^2} - \frac{1}{\epsilon_3}\right)\left[\frac{1}{M^2} - \frac{1}{2}\left(\frac{1}{\epsilon_1} + \frac{1}{\epsilon_2}\right)\right]} . \tag{41.26}$$

Longitudinal Propagation—As in the case of an electron plasma we shall first consider the nature of the propagation along $\mathbf{B}_0$. Propagation along the magnetic field implies $\theta = 0$, so the numerator of Eq. (41.26) must vanish. This yields the two solutions,

$$\left.\begin{aligned} \left(\frac{V}{V_0}\right)_1^2 &= \frac{1}{\epsilon_1} , \\ \left(\frac{V}{V_0}\right)^2 &= \frac{1}{\epsilon_2} , \end{aligned}\right\} \tag{41.27}$$

the field corresponding to the first solution is most easily obtained using the expression for the determinant given by (41.22). That is for $\theta = 0$, we find,

$$\left(1 - \frac{\epsilon_{e11}}{\epsilon_1}\right) E_1 - \frac{\epsilon_{e12}}{\epsilon_1} E_2 = 0$$

or,

$$(\epsilon_1 - \epsilon_{e11}) E_1 - \epsilon_{e12} E_2 = 0$$

$$(\epsilon_{e11} + i\epsilon_{e12} - \epsilon_{e11}) E_1 - \epsilon_{e12} E_2 = 0$$

hence,

$$\mathbf{E}_{(1)} \propto (1, i, 0) \quad , \tag{41.28}$$

and in a similar way, the field corresponding to the second solution is

$$\mathbf{E}_{(2)} \propto (1, -i, 0) \quad . \tag{41.29}$$

The wave associated with the first solution is therefore a left handed circularly polarized purely transverse wave; for the second solution it is a right circularly polarized purely transverse wave. One should note the close similarity to the case of the electron plasma treated in Chapter 2.

Transverse Propagation—For this situation, we find two waves of the same frequency are possible, whose phase velocities are obtained from the roots of the denominator of (41.26). Since $\theta = \pi/2$ in this case,

$$\left.\begin{aligned} \left(\frac{V}{V_0}\right)_3^2 &= \frac{1}{\epsilon_3} \quad , \\ \left(\frac{V}{V_0}\right)_4 &= \frac{1}{2}\left(\frac{1}{\epsilon_1} + \frac{1}{\epsilon_2}\right) \quad . \end{aligned}\right\} \tag{41.30}$$

The wave associated with V_3 is a plane-polarized purely transverse wave independent of the magnetic field. This can be deduced by utilizing the determinant (41.22) and the definition of ϵ_3. The electric vector is along the magnetic field. This wave is analogous to the one for an electron plasma, if we were to define the plasma frequency in this case by

$$\omega_p^2 = \sum_r \omega_r^2 \quad , \tag{41.31}$$

then the same form for the phase velocity results, (see Chapter 2, Eq. (14.12a). Clearly, if $\omega > \omega_p$, propagation is possible but for $\omega < \omega_p$, no propagation is possible. From the definition of ϵ_3 and (41.31), the phase velocity V_3 satisfies the inequality $V_3 > V_0$, *i.e.*, it is greater than the speed of light in a reference medium. The wave associated with V_4 has one component of the electric vector along the magnetic field and the other component in perpendicular to it but is linearly polarized, [see Chapter 2, Eq. (14.12b)]

If **n**(or θ) is arbitrary, Eq. (41.26) is a quadratic in $(V/V_0)^2$ and has two real roots. Special cases can always be examined to ascertain the propagation properties associated with them. Eq. (41.26) lends itself well to such an examination. For example, all possibilities can be examined graphically by considering Eq. (41.26) in a three dimensional space defined by the variables, $(V/V_0)^2$, θ and ω. In such a space there exists two uniquely defined surfaces which are continuous everywhere except at points on the lines $\theta = 0$, and $\theta = \pi/2$. We shall not pursue the detials further here.

42. MAGNETOHYDRODYNAMIC WAVES---LOW FREQUENCY PHENOMENA

In this section we shall examine some of the consequences of the formulas derived in the previous section for frequencies ω which are much smaller than the gyrofrequencies of the ionic constituents. For a neutral medium we may expand the expressions for ϵ_1 and ϵ_2 in Eq. (41.14) in a power series in ω. By retaining only terms up to the first order in ω we obtain, (convergent for $\omega/\omega_{c,r} < 1$)

$$\epsilon_1 = 1 + \sum_r \frac{N_{0r} m_r}{\epsilon_0 B^2} + \omega \sum_r \frac{N_{0r} m_r^2}{\epsilon_0 e_r B^3} + \ldots \tag{42.1a}$$

$$\epsilon_2 = 1 + \sum_r \frac{N_{0r} m_r}{\epsilon_0 B^2} - \omega \sum_r \frac{N_{0r} m_r^2}{\epsilon_0 e_r B^3} + \ldots \tag{42.1b}$$

$$\epsilon_3 = 1 - \sum_r \frac{\omega_r^2}{\omega^2} \tag{42.1c}$$

$$2\frac{\epsilon_1 \epsilon_2}{\epsilon_1 + \epsilon_2} = 1 + \sum_r \frac{N_{0r} m_r}{\epsilon_0 B^2} + \ldots \tag{42.1d}$$

Let us define

$$\sum_r N_{0r} m_r \equiv \rho, \tag{42.2}$$

the mass density of the ionic constituents, and also use (41.31). Even with the approximations for ϵ_1, ϵ_2 in (42.1) the dispersion equation (41.26) (which is valid for all ω), has as before two solutions which are still called the ordinary and extraordinary waves.

To the order of approximation used, the first solution is given by

$$\frac{V_0^2}{V_1^2} = 1 + \frac{\rho}{\epsilon_0 B^2} = 1 + \frac{\rho}{\mu_0 \epsilon_0 BH} = 1 + \frac{\rho V_0^2}{BH} \qquad (42.3a)$$

or,

$$\frac{1}{V_1^2} = \frac{1}{V_0^2} + \frac{\rho}{BH} \quad , \qquad (42.3b)$$

which implies that if $1/2\ \rho V_0^2 >> 1/2\ BH$, then we may neglect unity with respect to $\rho V_0^2/BH$ in (42.3) and we therefore obtain for the speed of propagation

$$V_1 = \sqrt{\frac{BH}{\rho}} \quad , \qquad (42.4)$$

a result first obtained by Alfvén from different considerations. The direction of this mode of propagation is along the magnetic field lines since the right side of (42.3) is approximately equal to ϵ_1. Physically, we can interpret ρV_0^2 as the relativistic rest energy density of the medium and $1/2\ BH$ as the magnetic field energy density. The second form of (42.3) can then be interpreted by saying that the term $1/V_0^2$ has its origin in the displacement current while the term ρ/BH has its origin in the conduction (or convection) current. The expression (42.4) then re-results from the neglect of the displacement current with respect to the conduction current. This approximation is the one used by Alfvén in his derivation. Because the phase velocity is independent of the wave normal, we call the wave associated with V_1 the "ordinary wave." From (41.22) we find the electric field strength corresponding to V_1 to be

$$\mathbf{E}_{(1)} = (E_1,\ 0,\ 0) \quad . \qquad (42.5)$$

This result can also be obtained from the following reasoning: at low frequencies, the rate of rotation of a linearly polarized wave is small, and we may therefore study the propagation of such a linearly polarized wave. The x_2 and x_3 components tend to zero as $\omega \to 0$, and only the x_1 component is nonvanishing.

The vector $\mathbf{E}_{(1)}$ is perpendicular to both $\mathbf{B}_0$ and $\mathbf{n}$. For the value of V_1 obtained in (42.3), Eq. (41.18) is satisfied, therefore the effective displacement vector $\mathbf{D}_e$ is given by,

$$\mathbf{D}_e = \epsilon_0\left(\frac{V_0}{V}\right)^2 [\mathbf{E} - \mathbf{n} \cdot \mathbf{E}\,\mathbf{n}] \tag{42.6}$$

Using (42.3) and (42.5), Eq. (42.6) yields

$$(\mathbf{D}_e)_1 \approx \left[\epsilon_0\left(1 + \frac{\rho}{\epsilon_0 B^2}\right)E_1,\ 0,\ 0\right] \quad . \tag{42.7}$$

Note that in this case we have an effective scalar dielectric constant, $(1 + \rho/\epsilon_0 B^2)$. The current density vector, $\mathbf{J}$, is calculated from (42.6) and gives

$$(\mathbf{J})_1 \approx \left(i\omega \frac{\rho}{B^2} E_1,\ 0,\ 0\right) \tag{42.8}$$

Which shows that the current is parallel to $(\mathbf{E})_1$, but out of phase by 90° and the effective conductivity is $i\omega\rho/B^2$.

The electric field energy according to (42.5) and (42.7) is,

$$\frac{1}{2}\mathbf{E} \cdot \mathbf{D}^* = \frac{1}{2}\epsilon_0 E^2 + \frac{1}{2}\frac{E^2}{B^2}\rho \quad , \tag{42.9}$$

the field $\mathbf{B}_{AC}$, *i.e.*, the AC-field according to Maxwell's equations is

$$\mathbf{B}_{AC} = (\mathbf{n}\mathbf{x}\mathbf{E})/V_1, \tag{42.10}$$

and the velocity field is (for any particle), $\mathbf{v} = [0,\ -(E_1/B),\ 0]$. It should be noted that the plasma as a whole, *regardless* of *particle mass* or charge has this velocity perpendicular to the **EB**-plane.

Since $\mathbf{n}$ is perpendicular to $\mathbf{E}$ we find,

$$\frac{1}{2}\mathbf{E} \cdot \mathbf{D}^* = \frac{1}{2}\epsilon_0 E^2 + \frac{1}{2}\rho v^2 = \frac{1}{2}(\mathbf{B}_{AC} \cdot \mathbf{H}_{AC}) \tag{42.11}$$

The energy is therefore shared equally between the electric field energy and magnetic energy. The electric field energy is also the sum of the field energy $1/2\ \epsilon_0 E^2$ and the kinetic energy $1/2\ \rho v^2$. If the propagation proceeds in the direction of the magnetic field lines then the right hand side of (42.11) is the total AC component of the energy, while for any other direction of propagation it gives only the average value of that energy taken over a magnetic tube of force.

For the wave discussed in the foregoing it is clear that the medium behaves as though it were isotropic with a dielectric constant ϵ_1. Moreover, one can easily show that for this wave the divergence of the velocity field is different from zero except along the magnetic field. For a finite compressible medium this causes a pressure wave and a transition between a magneto-hydrodynamic and longitudinal sound wave is obtained. In an incompressible medium the pressure at all points is such that the divergence of the velocity field vanishes. This causes the apparent isotropy of the medium for the ordinary wave to vanish.

General Low-Frequency Solutions—If we neglect terms of order $(\omega/B)^2$ and smaller in the low-frequency approximation we can derive solutions for the phase-velocity fron the dispersion relation (41.26). Let us first multiply this equation by $M^4\epsilon_1\epsilon_2\epsilon_3$ in the numerator and denominator of the right side:

$$\tan^2\theta = -\frac{\epsilon_3[\epsilon_1\epsilon_2 - M^2(\epsilon_1+\epsilon_2) + M^4]}{(\epsilon_3 - M^2)\left[\epsilon_1\epsilon_2 - \dfrac{M^2(\epsilon_1+\epsilon_2)}{2}\right]} \qquad (42.12)$$

Within our low-frequency approximation it is true that:

$$\epsilon_1 + \epsilon_2 = 2(1 + \rho/\epsilon_0 B^2) \qquad (42.13)$$

and

$$\epsilon_1\epsilon_2 = (1 + \rho/\epsilon_0 B^2)^2 \qquad (42.14)$$

Thus we can express the numerator of Eq. (42.12) as

$$\epsilon_3[1 + \rho/\epsilon_0 B^2 - M^2]^2$$

and the denominator as

$$(\epsilon_3 - M^2)(1 + \rho/\epsilon_0 B^2)(1 + \rho/\epsilon_0 B^2 - M^2)$$

thus Eq. (42.12) becomes;

$$(M^2 - \epsilon_3)(1 + \rho/\epsilon_0 B^2) \tan^2 \theta = \epsilon_3(1 + \rho/\epsilon_0 B^2 - M^2) \tag{42.15}$$

and we can solve for M^2; therefore, for the phase-velocity, V:

$$1/V^2 = \frac{\epsilon_3(1/V_0^2 + \rho/BH) \sec^2 \theta}{\epsilon_3 + (1 + \rho/\epsilon_0 B^2) \tan^2 \theta} \tag{42.16}$$

since,

$$\epsilon_3 = 1 - \frac{\omega_p^2}{\omega^2} ,$$

we multiply both numerator and denominator of (42.16) by ω^2 and in the resulting expression we drop all terms involving ω^2 and higher. This yields,

$$\frac{1}{V_2^2} = \left(\frac{1}{V_0^2} + \frac{\rho}{BH}\right)\frac{1}{\cos^2 \theta}$$

as the second solution, which defines the extraordinary wave. Consequently, if we measure the phase velocity along the magnetic field lines where $\theta = 0$, we obtain the uniform value $[(1/V_0^2) + (\rho/BH)$, which implies that the energy is propagated only along the magnetic field lines.

For those values of B for which we may neglect $1/V_0^2$ compared with ρ/BH we find

$$V_2 = \sqrt{\frac{BH}{\rho}} \cos \theta . \tag{42.17}$$

The electric field for this wave is coplanar with the wave normal and the magnetic field, and we obtain

$$(\mathbf{E})_2 = (0,\ E_2,\ 0) \tag{42.18}$$

As in the case of the ordinary wave, this wave originates as a circularly polarized wave (opposite in polarization to the ordinary wave) and degenerates into a linearly polarized wave. The effective displacement vector is,

$$(\mathbf{D}_e)_2 = \epsilon_0 \left(1 + \frac{\rho}{\epsilon_0 B_0^2}\right)[0,\ 1,\ -\tan\theta] \cdot E_2 \tag{42.19}$$

In this case $(\mathbf{D}_e)_2$ is perpendicular to $\mathbf{n}$ but not parallel to $(\mathbf{E})_2$. Further, $(\mathbf{D}_e)_2$ has a component along $\mathbf{B}_0$ while $(\mathbf{E})_2$ does not. The reason for this lies in the expression for ϵ_3 which has a pole of order two in ω at $\omega = 0$, while $(\mathbf{E})_2$ has a component along $\mathbf{B}_0$ of order ω^2, which we neglect in our low frequency approximation. The current density for this case is,

$$(\mathbf{J})_2 \doteq \left[0,\ i\omega \frac{\rho}{B_0^2},\ -i\omega \frac{\rho}{B_0^2}\left(1 + \frac{B_0^2 \epsilon_0}{\rho}\right)\tan\theta\right] \quad . \tag{42.20}$$

Therefore, $\mathbf{B}$, $\mathbf{n}$, $\mathbf{E}$, $\mathbf{D}_e$ and $\mathbf{J}$ are all coplanar. The induced magnetic field and the velocity field are perpendicular to this plane. We find,

$$\mathbf{B}_{AC} = \frac{(\mathbf{n} \mathbf{x} \mathbf{E})}{V_2} \tag{42.21}$$

and

$$\mathbf{v} = \left(\frac{E_2}{B},\ 0,\ 0\right) \quad . \tag{42.22}$$

A calculation of the electric field energy yields as before,

$$\frac{1}{2}\mathbf{E} \cdot \mathbf{D}^* = \frac{\epsilon_0 E^2}{2} + \frac{\rho v^2}{2} = \frac{1}{2}(\mathbf{B}_{AC} \cdot \mathbf{H}_{AC}) , \tag{42.23}$$

In this case the induced magnetic field is always perpendicular to $\mathbf{B}_0$ and according to (42.19) we always have equipartition between the AC magnetic field energy and the electric field energy. For this wave, div $\mathbf{v}$ = 0 and we therefore identify this wave with that in a liquid of infinite conductivity. In a finite compressible medium this same property is preserved. Summarizing, when the motion of the ions are included in the ordinary magneto-ionic theory and frequencies below the ion gyrofrequencies are considered, new types of waves are apparently introduced. These magneto-hydrodynamic waves arise in a plasma (ionized gas) with infinite compressibility. The connection between these waves and the usual ionospheric waves is demonstrated. These waves are no different in principle from the high frequency radio waves. For both vanishing and infinite compressibility these magneto hydrodynamic waves are possible below the ion gyrofrequencies. If the compressibility is finite the conditions are more complicated, for then, transition waves between electromagnetic (magneto-hydrodynamic) waves and sound waves occur as we have shown previously.

It is worth stating in passing that Alfvén discovered these magneto hydrodynamic waves by considering an incompressible infinitely-conducting liquid in the presence of a uniform magnetic field $\mathbf{B}_0$. He used Maxwell's equations

$$\text{Curl } \mathbf{E} = -\frac{\partial \mathbf{B}}{\partial t} , \tag{42.24}$$

$$\text{Curl } \mathbf{H} = \mathbf{J} + \frac{\partial \mathbf{D}}{\partial t} , \tag{42.25}$$

Combined with,

$$\mathbf{J} = \sigma (\mathbf{E} + \mathbf{v}\mathbf{x}\mathbf{B}) \tag{42.26}$$

and

$$\rho \frac{d\mathbf{v}}{dt} = \mathbf{J}\mathbf{x}\mathbf{B} - \mathbf{grad}\ p . \tag{42.27}$$

Because of the incompressibility assumption, the equation of continuity takes the form,

$$\text{div } \mathbf{v} = 0 .$$

Alfvén then showed from these equations that waves can be propagated along the magnetic lines of force and that the phase velocity, for infinite conductivity is given by

$$V = \sqrt{\frac{H_0 B_0}{\rho}} ,$$

where ρ is the mass density of the conducting liquid. In deriving this result, the displacement current is assumed to be negligible compared with the conduction current. The conduction current is capacitive which stores energy as kinetic energy and which plays the same role as the electric field energy in the vacuum wave.

43. FIELDS AND CURRENTS IN WEAKLY IONIZED MEDIA

In this section we shall examine the consequences of the theory set forth in section (40), but with some additional restrictions. We still assume that mean velocities and forces are operative as in the simple magneto-ionic theory. The forces are assumed to have their origin in the macroscopic electromagnetic effects on the charges and from the collisions between the free charges and the neutral particles which constitute the background material. We shall neglect electron-ion and ion-ion interactions, and assume a weakly ionized non-viscous medium.

The friction-like forces due to the collisions between the charged particles and the neutral background is of the action and reaction type, that is, equal in magnitude but opposite in direction. The effect of pressure gradients is neglected but unlike the treatments in the previous sections damping is taken into account. The equation of motion for the r-th species is now given by,

$$\frac{\partial \mathbf{v}_r}{\partial t} + (\mathbf{v}_r \cdot \nabla)\mathbf{v}_r = \frac{e_r}{m_r}(\mathbf{E} + \mathbf{v}_r \mathbf{x} \mathbf{B}_0) + \nu_r(\mathbf{u} - \mathbf{v}_r) , \qquad (43.1)$$

where the second term on the right side indicates that the collision force on the r-th species is proportional to the relative velocity of the uncharged background material, and ν_r is the assumed constant collision frequency of the r-th species with the neutral background. Following the perturbation procedure given previously and the assumption of true harmonic variations for the field quantities we are led to the linearized equation,

$$i\omega \mathbf{v}_r = \frac{e_r}{m_r}\mathbf{E} + \frac{e_r}{m_r}\mathbf{v}_r \mathbf{x} \mathbf{B}_0 + \nu_r(\mathbf{u} - \mathbf{v}_r) . \qquad (43.2)$$

Here, $\mathbf{B}_0$ is directed along the x_3-axes, and we give the alternative matrix form of Eq. (43.2), namely,

$$(\beta_r \mathbf{I} + i\mathbf{\Omega}_r)\mathbf{v}_r = -\frac{i}{\omega}\frac{e_r}{m_r}\mathbf{E} - \frac{i}{\omega}\nu_r \mathbf{u} , \qquad (43.3)$$

with $\beta_r = (1 - i\,\nu_r/\omega)$. We note that if $\mathbf{u} = 0$, an immobile background, then (43.3) together with Maxwell's equations would lead to the Appleton-Hartree magneto-ionic relations. The presence of the term $\mathbf{u}$ then provides the magneto-hydrodynamic aspects of the formulae.

The force which the charges exert on the neutral background, that is, the frictional reaction is given by

$$\mathbf{F} = \sum_r N_{0r} m_r \nu_r (\mathbf{v}_r - \mathbf{u}) \ . \tag{43.4}$$

Thus, it will also be necessary to introduce the equation of motion of the background fluid.

Dispersion Relation—It is not too difficult a task to derive a dispersion equation for the case treated above. Indeed, we have from (43.3) after multiplication of both sides by $N_{0r} e_r$, the result

$$(\beta_r \mathbf{I} + i\Omega_r)\,\mathbf{J}_r = - i a_r \omega \epsilon_0 \mathbf{E} - i \frac{N_{0r} e_r \nu_r}{\omega} \mathbf{u} \ . \tag{43.5}$$

Now, if ρ is the density of the background matter, the linearized equation of motion is, neglecting its own viscosity,

$$\rho \frac{\partial \mathbf{u}}{\partial t} = \mathbf{F} \ , \tag{43.6}$$

which for harmonic time variations of $\mathbf{u}$ gives,

$$i\omega\rho\mathbf{u} = \mathbf{F} \ . \tag{43.7}$$

This equation together with (43.4) permits us to find an expression for $\mathbf{u}$ as,

$$\mathbf{u} = \frac{\sum_r N_{0r} m_r \nu_r \mathbf{v}_r}{i\omega\rho + \sum_r N_{0r} m_r \nu_r} = \frac{\sum_r \left(m_r \dfrac{\nu_r}{e_r}\right)\mathbf{J}_r}{i\omega\rho + f} \tag{43.8}$$

where,

$$f \equiv \sum_r N_{0r} m_r \nu_r \ . \tag{43.9}$$

We recall from section (40), that Maxwell's equations take the form,

$$\left(k^2 - \frac{\omega^2}{V_0^2}\right)\omega\epsilon_0\mathbf{E} = -i\mu_0\epsilon_0\omega^2\mathbf{J} + i(\mathbf{J}\cdot\mathbf{k})\mathbf{k} \qquad (40.20)$$

so that by combining this equation together with Eqs. (43.5) and (43.8) we get,

$$(\beta_r\mathbf{I} + i\Omega_r)\mathbf{J}_r = \frac{a_r\omega^2}{(\omega^2 - k^2V_0^2)}\mathbf{J} - \frac{a_rV_0^2}{(\omega^2 - k^2V_0^2)}(\mathbf{J}\cdot\mathbf{k})\mathbf{k} - \frac{iN_{0r}e_r\nu_r}{\omega}\,\frac{\sum_s\left(m_s\dfrac{\nu_s}{e_s}\right)\mathbf{J}_s}{i\omega\rho + f}$$

$$= \frac{a_r\omega^2}{(\omega^2 - k^2V_0^2)}\mathbf{J} - \frac{a_rV_0^2}{(\omega^2 - k^2V_0^2)}(\mathbf{J}\cdot\mathbf{k})\mathbf{k} + \frac{N_{0r}e_r\nu_r}{\omega^2}\,\frac{\sum_s\left(\dfrac{m_s\nu_s}{e_s}\right)\mathbf{J}_s}{\left(-\rho + i\dfrac{f}{\omega}\right)}\,. \qquad (43.10)$$

Put,

$$\left.\begin{aligned} N_{0r}e_r\nu_r &= \alpha_r, \\ \frac{\left(\dfrac{m_s\nu_s}{e_s}\right)}{\left(-\rho + i\dfrac{f}{\omega}\right)} &= \gamma_s, \end{aligned}\right\} \qquad (43.11)$$

hence, (43.10) becomes,

$$\begin{aligned} \omega^2(\omega^2 - k^2V_0^2)[\beta_rI + i\Omega_r]\mathbf{J}_r &= \omega_r^2\omega^2\sum_s\mathbf{J}_s - \omega_r^2V_0^2\left(\sum_s\mathbf{J}_s\cdot\mathbf{k}\right)\mathbf{k} \\ &\quad + \alpha_r(\omega^2 - k^2V_0^2)\sum_s\gamma_s\mathbf{J}_s \\ &= \omega_r^2\omega^2\mathbf{J}_r - \omega_r^2V_0^2(\mathbf{J}_r\cdot\mathbf{k})\mathbf{k} + \alpha_r(\omega^2 - k^2V_0^2)\gamma_r\mathbf{J}_r \\ &\quad + \omega_r^2\omega^2\sum_{s\neq r}\mathbf{J}_s - \omega_r^2V_0^2\sum_{s\neq r}(\mathbf{J}_s\cdot\mathbf{k})\mathbf{k} \\ &\quad + \alpha_r(\omega^2 - k^2V_0^2)\sum_{s\neq r}\gamma_s\mathbf{J}_s\,. \end{aligned} \qquad (43.12)$$

or in component form, using summation convention on j, we have for $(i = 1,2,3)$, and for $r = 1,2, \ldots, p$; $s = 1,2, \ldots, p$, $s \neq r$

$$[\omega^2(\omega^2 - k^2V_0^2)\beta_r - \omega^2\omega_r^2 - (\omega^2 - k^2V_0^2)\alpha_r\gamma_r]\delta_{ij}J_{r,j} + \omega_r^2V_0^2k_ik_jJ_{r,j}$$

$$+ i\omega^2(\omega^2 - k^2V_0^2)\Omega_{r,ij}J_{r,j} = \omega_r^2 \sum_{s\neq r}(\omega^2\delta_{ij}J_{s,j}$$

$$- V_0^2J_{s,j}k_ik_j) + \alpha_r(\omega^2 - k^2V_0^2)\sum_{s=r}\gamma_s\delta_{ij}J_{s,j} \quad . \quad (43.13)$$

This is to be considered as a system of equations for the unknowns $(J_{1,1}, J_{1,2}; J_{1,3}, J_{2,1}, J_{2,2}, \ldots, J_{p,3})$, this system is linear and homogeneous. The matrix of this system has the following structure.

$$\mathbf{M} \equiv \begin{pmatrix} \mathbf{M}_1 & \mathbf{A}_1 & . & . & . & \mathbf{A}_p \\ \mathbf{A}_1 & \mathbf{M}_2 & \mathbf{A}_3 & . & . & \mathbf{A}_p \\ . & & & & & . \\ & & & & & \\ . & & & & & . \\ . & & & & & . \\ . & & & & & . \\ \mathbf{A}_1 & \mathbf{A}_2 & . & . & . & \mathbf{M}_p \end{pmatrix} \quad (43.14)$$

where each submatrix $\mathbf{M}_r$ and $\mathbf{A}_r$ has components defined by,

$$M_{r,ij} = \{\omega^2(\omega^2 - k^2V_0^2)\beta_r - \omega^2\omega_r^2 - (\omega^2 - k^2V_0^2)\alpha_r\gamma_r\}\delta_{ij}$$

$$+ \omega_r^2V_0^2k_ik_j + i\omega^2(\omega^2 - k^2V_0^2)\Omega_{r,ij} \quad (43.15)$$

$$A_{s,ij} = -\omega_r^2(\omega^2\delta_{ij} - V_0^2k_ik_j) - \alpha_r(\omega^2 - k^2V_0^2)\gamma_s\delta_{ij}$$

The vanishing of the determinant of $\mathbf{M}$ gives the dispersion equation associated with the system.

Current and Force Densities—We shall now calculate the current and force densities associated with the system of charges defined above. The current density due to the r-th species is, from Eq. (43.5),

$$\mathbf{J}_r = i\omega\epsilon_0[-a_r(\beta_r\mathbf{I} + i\boldsymbol{\Omega}_r)^{-1}]\mathbf{E} + i\,\frac{N_{0r}e_r\nu_r}{a_r\omega}\,[-a_r(\beta_r\mathbf{I} + i\boldsymbol{\Omega}_r)^{-1}]\mathbf{u} \tag{43.16}$$

which shows how the motion of the background matter contributes to the current density. We recall from chapter 2 that

$$\mathbf{S}_r = -\,a_r(\beta_r\mathbf{I} + i\boldsymbol{\Omega}_r)^{-1}$$

$$\mathbf{S}_r = \frac{-a_r}{\beta_r(\beta_r^2 - \Omega_r^2)}\begin{pmatrix} \beta_r^2 & -i\beta_r\Omega_r & 0 \\ i\beta_r\Omega_r & \beta_r^2 & 0 \\ 0 & 0 & \beta_r^2 - \Omega_r^2 \end{pmatrix}. \tag{43.17}$$

Put

$$\mathbf{T}_r \equiv \frac{N_{0r}e_r\nu_r}{a_r}\,\mathbf{S}_r\,, \tag{43.18}$$

then

$$\mathbf{J} = \sum_r \mathbf{J}_r = i\omega\epsilon_0\Big(\sum_r \mathbf{S}_r\Big)\mathbf{E} + \frac{i}{\omega}\mathbf{T}\,\mathbf{u} \tag{43.19}$$

where,

$$\mathbf{S} = \sum_r \mathbf{S}_r\,, \qquad \mathbf{T} = \sum_r \mathbf{T}_r\,. \tag{43.20}$$

It is useful to find expressions for the longitudinal and transverse components of $\mathbf{J}$.

Longitudinal Component J_L—The longitudinal component of $\mathbf{J}$ is the simplest to obtain at first. Let $\mathbf{b}_0 \equiv \begin{pmatrix}0\\0\\1\end{pmatrix}$ be the unit vector in the direction of $\mathbf{B}_0$. Then,

$$J_L = \mathbf{J}\cdot\mathbf{b}_0 = i\omega\epsilon_0\mathbf{b}_0'\mathbf{S}\,\mathbf{E} + \frac{i}{\omega}\,\mathbf{b}_0'\mathbf{T}\,\mathbf{u} \tag{43.21}$$

where $\mathbf{b}_0' \equiv (0,0,1)$ is the transpose of $\mathbf{b}_0$. From (43.17) we find easily that

$$\mathbf{b}_0'\mathbf{S} = -\sum_r \frac{a_r}{\beta_r} ,$$

and

$$i\omega\mathbf{b}_0'\mathbf{S}\,\mathbf{E} = -\,i\omega \sum_r\left(\frac{a_r}{\beta_r}\right)E_3 \quad ; \tag{43.22}$$

in a similar manner

$$\frac{i}{\omega}\,\mathbf{b}_0'\mathbf{T}\mathbf{u} = -\frac{i}{\omega}\sum_r \frac{N_{0r}e_r\nu_r}{\beta_r}\,u_3 \quad . \tag{43.23}$$

Therefore;

$$J_L = \sum_r \frac{N_{0r}e_r^2}{m_r(\nu_r + i\omega)}\,E_3 + \sum_r \frac{N_{0r}e_r\nu_r}{(\nu_r + i\omega)}u_3 \quad , \tag{43.24}$$

and as $\omega \to 0$,

$$J_L = \sum_r \frac{N_{0r}e_r^2}{m_r\nu_r}\,E_3 + \sum_r N_{0r}e_r u_3 \quad ,$$

since in the unperturbed state $\mathbf{E} = 0$, the net space charge vanishes, hence $\sum_r N_{0r}e_r = 0$ and consequently

$$J_L = \sum_r \frac{N_{0r}e_r^2}{m_r\nu_r}\,E_L \equiv \sigma_L E_L \tag{43.25}$$

where,

$$\sigma_L \equiv \sum_r \frac{N_{0r}e_r^2}{m_r\nu_r} \tag{43.26}$$

Transverse Component

$$\mathbf{J}_T = \mathbf{J} - J_L\mathbf{b}_0 = i\omega\varepsilon_0\begin{pmatrix} S_{1j}E_j \\ S_{2j}E_j \\ S_{3j}E_j \end{pmatrix} + \frac{i}{\omega}\begin{pmatrix} T_{1j}u_j \\ T_{2j}u_j \\ T_{3j}u_j \end{pmatrix} + i\omega\varepsilon_0\sum_r \frac{a_r}{\beta_r}\begin{pmatrix} 0 \\ 0 \\ E_3 \end{pmatrix} + \frac{i}{\omega}\sum_r \frac{N_{0r}e_r\nu_r}{\beta_r}\begin{pmatrix} 0 \\ 0 \\ u_3 \end{pmatrix}$$

sum on j. (43.27)

It is clear that the x_3 component is zero and we are left with just the x_1 and x_2 components. Thus,

$$\left.\begin{aligned}
i\omega\epsilon_0 S_{1j}E_j &= -i\omega\epsilon_0 \sum_r \frac{a_r\beta_r}{\beta_r^2-\Omega_r^2} E_1 - \omega\epsilon_0 \sum_r \frac{a_r\Omega_r}{\beta_r^2-\Omega_r^2} E_2 \\
i\omega\epsilon_0 S_{2j}E_j &= \omega\epsilon_0 \sum_r \frac{a_r\Omega_r}{\beta_r^2-\Omega_r^2} E_1 - i\omega\epsilon_0 \sum_r \frac{a_r\beta_r}{\beta_r^2-\Omega_r^2} E_2 \\
\frac{i}{\omega} T_{1j}u_j &= -\frac{i}{\omega}\sum_r \frac{N_{0r}e_r\nu_r\beta_r}{\beta_r^2-\Omega_r^2} u_1 - \frac{1}{\omega}\sum_r \frac{N_{0r}e_r\nu_r\Omega_r}{\beta_r^2-\Omega_r^2} u_2 \\
\frac{i}{\omega} T_{2j}u_j &= \frac{1}{\omega}\sum_r \frac{N_{0r}e_r\nu_r\Omega_r}{\beta_r^2-\Omega_r^2} u_1 - \frac{i}{\omega}\sum_r \frac{N_{0r}e_r\nu_r\beta_r}{\beta_r^2-\Omega_r^2} u_2
\end{aligned}\right\} \quad (43.28)$$

and if we denote by J_{T1} and J_{T2} the components of J_T in the x_1 and x_2 directions respectively, we can write,

$$J_{T1} = -i\omega\epsilon_0 \sum_r \frac{a_r\beta_r}{\beta_r^2-\Omega_r^2} E_1 - \frac{i}{\omega}\sum_r \frac{N_{0r}e_r\nu_r\beta_r}{\beta_r^2-\Omega_r^2} u_1 - \epsilon_0\omega \sum_r \frac{a_r\Omega_r}{\beta_r^2-\Omega_r^2} E_2 - \frac{1}{\omega}\sum_r \frac{N_{0r}e_r\nu_r\Omega_r}{\beta_r^2-\Omega_r^2} u_2$$

$$(43.29)$$

$$J_{T2} = \epsilon_0\omega \sum_r \frac{a_r\Omega_r}{\beta_r^2-\Omega_r^2} E_1 + \frac{1}{\omega}\sum_r \frac{N_{0r}e_r\nu_r\Omega_r}{\beta_r^2-\Omega_r^2} u_1 - i\epsilon_0\omega \sum_r \frac{a_r\beta_r}{\beta_r^2-\Omega_r^2} E_2 - \frac{i}{\omega}\sum_r \frac{N_{0r}e_r\nu_r\beta_r}{\beta_r^2-\Omega_r^2} u_2$$

For convenience of notation, put

$$\left.\begin{aligned}
\Delta_r &= \nu_r^2 + \omega_{c,r}^2 \,, \\
A_1 &= \sum \frac{\nu_r\omega_r^2}{\Delta_r} \,, \qquad A_2 = \sum \frac{N_{0r}e_r\nu_r^2}{\Delta_r} \,, \\
A_3 &= \sum \frac{\omega_r^2\omega_{c,r}}{\Delta_r} \,, \qquad A_4 = \sum \frac{N_{0r}e_r\nu_r\omega_{c,r}}{\Delta_r} \,,
\end{aligned}\right\} \quad (43.30)$$

then as $\omega \to 0$, we can write

$$\left.\begin{aligned} J_{T1} &= A_1\epsilon_0 E_1 + A_2 u_1 + A_3\epsilon_0 E_2 + A_4 u_2 \\ J_{T2} &= -A_3\epsilon_0 E_1 - A_4 u_1 + A_1\epsilon_0 E_2 + A_2 u_2 \end{aligned}\right\} \tag{43.31}$$

or in matrix form,

$$\mathbf{J}_T \equiv \begin{pmatrix} J_{T1} \\ J_{T2} \end{pmatrix} = \begin{pmatrix} A_1 & A_3 \\ -A_3 & A_1 \end{pmatrix}\begin{pmatrix} \epsilon_0 E_1 \\ \epsilon_0 E_2 \end{pmatrix} + \begin{pmatrix} A_2 & A_4 \\ -A_4 & A_2 \end{pmatrix}\begin{pmatrix} u_1 \\ u_2 \end{pmatrix} \tag{43.32}$$

By decomposing the matrices above as follows

$$\left.\begin{aligned} \begin{pmatrix} A_1 & A_3 \\ -A_3 & A_1 \end{pmatrix} &= A_1\mathbf{I} + A_3\begin{pmatrix} 0 & 1 \\ -1 & 0 \end{pmatrix} \\ \begin{pmatrix} A_2 & A_4 \\ -A_4 & A_2 \end{pmatrix} &= A_2\mathbf{I} + A_4\begin{pmatrix} 0 & 1 \\ -1 & 0 \end{pmatrix} \end{aligned}\right. \tag{43.33}$$

we can express $\mathbf{J}_T$ in the form,

$$\mathbf{J}_T = A_1\epsilon_0\mathbf{E}_T + A_4\begin{pmatrix} 0 & 1 \\ -1 & 0 \end{pmatrix}\mathbf{u}_T + A_2\mathbf{u}_T + A_3\begin{pmatrix} 0 & 1 \\ -1 & 0 \end{pmatrix}\epsilon_0\mathbf{E}_T \tag{43.34}$$

By noting that $\begin{pmatrix} 0 & 1 \\ -1 & 0 \end{pmatrix}\begin{pmatrix} 0 & 1 \\ -1 & 0 \end{pmatrix} = -\begin{pmatrix} 1 & 0 \\ 0 & 1 \end{pmatrix}$ and using $\omega_{c,r} = \epsilon_r B_0/m_r$, we obtain,

$$\mathbf{J}_T = \sum_r \frac{N_{0r}e_r^2\nu_r}{m_r\Delta_r}\left[\mathbf{E}_T + B_0\begin{pmatrix} 0 & 1 \\ -1 & 0 \end{pmatrix}\mathbf{u}_T\right] + \sum_r \frac{N_{0r}e_r^2\omega_{c,r}}{m_r\Delta_r}\begin{pmatrix} 0 & 1 \\ -1 & 0 \end{pmatrix}\mathbf{E}_T$$

$$+ \sum_r \frac{N_{0r}e_r\nu_r^2}{\Delta_r}\begin{pmatrix} 0 & 1 \\ -1 & 0 \end{pmatrix}\begin{pmatrix} 0 & 1 \\ -1 & 0 \end{pmatrix}\mathbf{u}_T$$

and a further simplification obtains by using the fact that since $\sum_r N_{0r} e_r = 0$ then also $\sum_r N_{0r} e_r^2 m_r / m_r e_r = 0$, so by forming $\sum_r N_{0r} e_r \nu_r^2 / \Delta_r - \sum_r N_{0r} e_r^2 m_r / m_r e_r = + \sum_r N_{0r} e_r \omega_{c,r}^2 / \Delta_r$ we finally obtain,

$$\mathbf{J}_T = \sigma_{TD} \left[\mathbf{E}_T + B_0 \begin{pmatrix} 0 & 1 \\ -1 & 0 \end{pmatrix} \mathbf{u}_T \right] + \sigma_{TH} \begin{pmatrix} 0 & 1 \\ -1 & 0 \end{pmatrix} \left[\mathbf{E}_T + B_0 \begin{pmatrix} 0 & 1 \\ -1 & 0 \end{pmatrix} \mathbf{u}_T \right] \tag{43.35}$$

This can also be written in the usual vector notation as

$$\mathbf{J}_T = \sigma_{TD} (\mathbf{E} + \mathbf{u} \mathbf{x} \mathbf{B}_0)_T + \sigma_{TH} (\mathbf{E} + \mathbf{u} \mathbf{x} \mathbf{B}_0)_T \mathbf{x} \mathbf{b}_0 \quad , \tag{43.36}$$

where

$$\left.\begin{aligned} \sigma_{TD} &= \sum_r \frac{N_{0r} e_r^2 \nu_r}{m_r \Delta_r} , && \text{(Transverse direct conductivity)} \\ \sigma_{TH} &= \sum_r \frac{N_{0r} e_r^2 \omega_{c,r}}{m_r \Delta_r} , && \text{(Transverse Hall conductivity),} \\ \text{and} \quad \sigma_L &= \sum_r \frac{N_{0r} e_r^2}{m_r \nu_r} , && \text{is the longitudinal conductivity} \; . \end{aligned}\right\} \tag{43.37}$$

For the calculation of the longitudinal and transverse components of the force **F** exerted by the charges on the background material we write,

$$\mathbf{F} = \sum_r N_{0r} m_r \nu_r (\mathbf{v}_r - \mathbf{u})$$

and substitute for $\mathbf{v}_r$. From Eq. (43.3) to obtain

$$\mathbf{F} = \sum_r N_{0r} m_r \nu_r \left[-\frac{i e_r}{m_r \omega} (\beta_r \mathbf{I} + i\Omega_r)^{-1} \mathbf{E} - \frac{i \nu_r}{\omega} (\beta_r \mathbf{I} + i\Omega_r)^{-1} \mathbf{u} - \mathbf{I} \mathbf{u} \right]$$

or,

$$\mathbf{F} = \frac{i}{\omega} \sum_r N_{0r} e_r \nu_r \; (\beta_r \mathbf{I} + i\Omega_r)^{-1} \, \mathbf{E} - \sum_r N_{0r} m_r \nu_r \left[\frac{i\nu_r}{\omega} \; (\beta_r \mathbf{I} + i\Omega_r)^{-1} + \mathbf{I} \right] \mathbf{u}$$

$$\mathbf{F} = \frac{i}{\omega} \sum_r \mathbf{T}_r \mathbf{E} - \sum_r \mathbf{R}_r \mathbf{u}$$

$$\mathbf{F} = \frac{i}{\omega} \mathbf{T}\mathbf{E} - \mathbf{R}\mathbf{u} \tag{43.38}$$

Longitudinal Component—The computation of F_L proceeds in the same way as for the J_L, we have,

$$F_L = \mathbf{F} \cdot \mathbf{b}_0 = \frac{i}{\omega} \mathbf{b}_0' \mathbf{T}\mathbf{E} - \mathbf{b}_0' \mathbf{R}\mathbf{u} \tag{43.39}$$

which yields,

$$F_L = -\frac{i}{\omega} \sum_r \frac{N_{0r} e_r \nu_r}{\beta_r} E_3 - \sum_r N_{0r} m_r \nu_r \left(1 + \frac{i}{\omega} \frac{\nu_r}{\beta_r}\right) u_3 ,$$

$$F_L = \sum_r \frac{N_{0r} e_r \nu_r}{\nu_r + i\omega} E_3 - i\omega \sum_r \frac{N_{0r} m_r \nu_r}{\nu_r + i\omega} u_3 \tag{43.40}$$

and as $\omega \to 0$, $F_L \to 0$, since $\sum_r N_{0r} e_r = 0$. For future use we also calculate the matrix,

$$\frac{i\nu_r}{\omega} (\beta_r \mathbf{I} + i\Omega_r)^{-1} + \mathbf{I} = \begin{pmatrix} 1 + \dfrac{i\nu_r \beta_r}{\omega(\beta_r^2 - \Omega_r^2)} & \dfrac{\nu_r \Omega_r}{\omega(\beta_r^2 - \Omega_r^2)} & 0 \\ -\dfrac{\nu_r \Omega_r}{\omega(\beta_r^2 - \Omega_r^2)} & 1 + \dfrac{i\nu_r \beta_r}{\omega(\beta_r^2 - \Omega_r^2)} & 0 \\ 0 & 0 & 1 + \dfrac{i\nu_r}{\omega\beta_r} \end{pmatrix} \tag{43.41}$$

and as $\omega \to 0$, this matrix becomes,

$$\begin{pmatrix} 1 + i\dfrac{\nu_r^2}{\Delta_r} & -\dfrac{\nu_r\omega_{c,r}}{\Delta_r} & 0 \\ \dfrac{\nu_r\omega_{c,r}}{\Delta_r} & 1 + i\dfrac{\nu_r^2}{\Delta_r} & 0 \\ 0 & 0 & 0 \end{pmatrix} \tag{43.42}$$

Transverse Component $\mathbf{F}_T$--For the transverse part of $\mathbf{F}$ we write as before,

$$\mathbf{F}_T = \mathbf{F} - F_L\mathbf{b}_0$$

$$\mathbf{F}_T = \frac{i}{\omega}\begin{pmatrix} T_{1j}E_j \\ T_{2j}E_j \end{pmatrix} - \begin{pmatrix} R_{1j}u_j \\ R_{2j}u_j \end{pmatrix} \tag{43.43}$$

We have already calculated $i/\omega\ \mathbf{T}\ (\ )$ so we must calculate

$$\left.\begin{aligned} R_{1j}u_j &= \sum_r N_{0r}m_r\nu_r\left[1 + \frac{i\nu_r\beta_r}{\omega(\beta_r^2 - \Omega_r^2)}\right]u_1 + \sum_r N_{0r}m_r\nu_r\frac{\nu_r\Omega_r}{\omega(\beta_r^2 - \Omega_r^2)}u_2 \\ R_{2j}u_j &= \sum_r N_{0r}m_r\nu_r\left[-\frac{\nu_r\Omega_r}{\omega(\beta_r^2 - \Omega_r^2)}\right]u_1 + \sum_r N_{0r}m_r\nu_r\left[1 + \frac{\nu_r\beta_r}{\omega(\beta_r^2 - \Omega_r^2)}\right]u_2 \end{aligned}\right\} \tag{43.44}$$

Using our abbreviation, $N_{0r} m_r \nu_r = f_r$, we have,

$$\left.\begin{aligned} F_{T1} &= -\frac{i}{\omega}\sum_r \frac{N_{0r} e_r \nu_r \beta_r}{\beta_r^2 - \Omega_r^2} E_1 - \frac{1}{\omega}\sum_r \frac{N_{0r} e_r \nu_r \Omega_r}{\beta_r^2 - \Omega_r^2} E_2 \\ &\quad - \sum_r f_r \left[1 + \frac{i\nu_r \beta_r}{\omega(\beta_r^2 - \Omega_r^2)}\right] u_1 - \sum_r f_r \frac{\nu_r \Omega_r}{\omega(\beta_r^2 - \Omega_r^2)} u_2 \\ F_{T2} &= \frac{1}{\omega}\sum_r \frac{N_{0r} e_r \nu_r \Omega_r}{\beta_r^2 - \Omega_r^2} E_1 - \frac{i}{\omega}\sum_r \frac{N_{0r} e_r \nu_r \beta_r}{\beta_r^2 - \Omega_r^2} E_2 \\ &\quad + \sum_r f_r \frac{\nu_r \Omega_r}{\omega(\beta_r^2 - \Omega_r^2)} u_1 - \sum_r f_r \left[1 + \frac{i\nu_r \beta_r}{\omega(\beta_r^2 - \Omega_r^2)}\right] u_2 \end{aligned}\right\} \qquad (43.45)$$

As $\omega \to 0$, these expressions become respectively,

$$\left.\begin{aligned} F_{T1} &= A_2 E_1 + A_4 E_2 - \sum_r f_r \frac{\omega_{c,r}^2}{\Delta_r} u_1 + \sum_r f_r \frac{\nu_r \omega_{c,r}}{\Delta_r} u_2 \\ F_{T2} &= -A_4 E_1 + A_2 E_2 - \sum_r f_r \frac{\nu_r \omega_{c,r}}{\Delta_r} u_1 - \sum_r f_r \frac{\omega_{c,r}^2}{\Delta_r} u_2 \end{aligned}\right\} \qquad (43.46)$$

which can also be written as

$$F_T = -\sigma_{TH} B_0 (\mathbf{E} + \mathbf{u} \mathbf{x} \mathbf{B}_0)_T + \sigma_{TD} (\mathbf{E} + \mathbf{u} \mathbf{x} \mathbf{b}_0)_T \, \mathbf{x} \mathbf{B}_0 \qquad (43.47)$$

We observe that starting from Eq. (43.2) it is possible to cast this equation in an alternative form. We define

$$\mathbf{F}' = e\mathbf{E} + e\mathbf{u}\mathbf{x}\mathbf{B}_0 - i\omega m\mathbf{u} \quad , \qquad (43.48)$$

which is the force acting on a charge which moves with velocity $\mathbf{u}$, that is, the electromagnetic plus the inertial force. Now write Eq. (43.2) in the form,

$$m\nu(\mathbf{v} - \mathbf{u}) = e\mathbf{E} + e\mathbf{v}\mathbf{x}\mathbf{B}_0 - im\omega\mathbf{v}$$

and put

$$\mathbf{w} = \mathbf{v} - \mathbf{u} \quad , \tag{43.49}$$

hence,

$$m\nu\mathbf{w} = \mathbf{F}' + e\mathbf{w}\mathbf{x}\mathbf{B}_0 - im\omega\mathbf{w}$$

or,

$$m(\nu + i\omega)\mathbf{w} = \mathbf{F}' + e\mathbf{w}\mathbf{x}\mathbf{B}_0 \quad . \tag{43.50}$$

Take the vector product of both sides of this equation with $\mathbf{B}_0$ to obtain,

$$\begin{aligned} m(\nu + i\omega)\ \mathbf{w}\mathbf{x}\mathbf{B}_0 &= \mathbf{F}'\mathbf{x}\mathbf{B}_0 + e(\mathbf{w}\mathbf{x}\mathbf{B}_0)\ \mathbf{x}\mathbf{B}_0 \\ &= \mathbf{F}'\mathbf{x}\mathbf{B}_0 + e(\mathbf{B}_0 \cdot \mathbf{w})\ \mathbf{B}_0 - eB_0^2\mathbf{w} \end{aligned} \tag{43.51}$$

We substitute from (43.50) the expression for $\mathbf{w}\mathbf{x}\mathbf{B}_0$ into (43.51) and find,

$$[m^2(\nu + i\omega)^2 + e^2B_0^2]\ \mathbf{w} = m(\nu + i\omega)\ \mathbf{F}' + e\mathbf{F}'\mathbf{x}\mathbf{B}_0 + e^2(\mathbf{B}_0 \cdot \mathbf{w})\ \mathbf{B}_0 \quad . \tag{43.52}$$

The vector product of this equation with $\mathbf{B}_0$ and the same substitution for $\mathbf{w}\mathbf{x}\mathbf{B}_0$ from (43.50) finally yields,

$$\begin{aligned} \mathbf{w} = \mathbf{v} - \mathbf{u} &= \frac{1}{m(\nu + i\omega)}\ \mathbf{F}' + \frac{e}{m^2[(\nu + i\omega)^2 + \omega_c^2]}\ \mathbf{F}'\mathbf{x}\mathbf{B}_0 \\ &+ \frac{e^2}{m^3(\nu + i\omega)[(\nu + i\omega)^2 + \omega_c^2]}\ (\mathbf{F}'\mathbf{x}\mathbf{B}_0)\ \mathbf{x}\mathbf{B}_0 \end{aligned} \tag{43.53}$$

This expression can be substituted into Eq. (43.4) for **F** to obtain equations equivalent to (43.40) for F_L and (43.47) for $\mathbf{F}_T$.

(44) APPROXIMATIONS--(HIGH COLLISION FREQUENCIES)

Certain simplifications in the previous formulae result when we limit the collision frequencies of the species. Following Hines it is easy to verify that if

$$|\omega| \ll \nu_r, \quad |\omega_{c,r}| \ll \nu_r \quad \text{for all } r, \tag{44.1}$$

the expressions for J_L, $\mathbf{J}_T$, F_L and $\mathbf{F}_T$ all reduce to the simpler form

$$\mathbf{J} = \left(\sum_r \frac{N_{0,r}e_r^2}{m_r\nu_r}\right)(\mathbf{E} + \mathbf{u}\mathrm{x}\mathbf{B}_0) - i\omega\left(\sum_r \frac{N_{0,r}e_r}{\nu_r}\right)\mathbf{u} \tag{44.2}$$

$$\mathbf{F} = \left(\sum_r \frac{N_{0,r}e_r^2}{m_r\nu_r}\right)(\mathbf{E} + \mathbf{u}\mathrm{x}\mathbf{B}_0)\mathrm{x}\mathbf{B}_0 - i\omega\left(\sum_r \frac{N_{0,r}e_r}{\nu_r}\right)\mathbf{E} - i\omega(\sum_r N_{0,r}m_r)\mathbf{u} \quad . \tag{44.3}$$

If, further, the following relations hold,

$$\left|\frac{\omega}{\omega_{c,r}}\right| \ll \left|\frac{\omega_{c,r}}{\nu_r}\right| \quad , \tag{44.4}$$

we obtain the still simpler formulae

$$\mathbf{J} = \left(\sum_r \frac{N_{0,r}e_r^2}{m_r\nu_r}\right)(\mathbf{E} + \mathbf{u}\mathrm{x}\mathbf{B}_0) \quad , \tag{44.5}$$

$$\mathbf{F} = \mathbf{J}\mathrm{x}\mathbf{B}_0 \quad . \tag{44.6}$$

Now assume that

$$|\omega| \gg |\omega_{c,r}| \tag{44.7}$$

then eqs. (44.2) and (44.3) above reduce to

$$\mathbf{J} = \left(\sum_r \frac{N_{0,r} e_r^2}{m_r \nu_r}\right)\mathbf{E} - i\omega\left(\sum_r \frac{N_{0,r} e_r}{\nu_r}\right)\mathbf{u} \quad , \tag{44.8}$$

$$\mathbf{F} = -i\omega\left(\sum_r \frac{N_{0,r} e_r}{\nu_r}\right) - i\omega(\sum_r N_{0,r} m_r)\mathbf{u} \quad . \tag{44.9}$$

Low Collision Frequencies--We now restrict the collision frequencies such that

$$\nu_r << |\omega \pm \omega_{c,r}| \ , \text{ for all } r, \tag{44.10}$$

and since the frequencies ν_r can be of the same order of magnitude as ω, only the tranverse components of **J** and **F** simplify,

$$\mathbf{J}_T = \sum_r \frac{N_{0,r} e_r^2 (\nu_r + i\omega)}{m_r(\omega_{c,r}^2 - \omega^2)} \mathbf{E}_T + \sum_r \frac{N_{0,r} e_r^3}{m_r^2(\omega_{c,r}^2 - \omega^2)} \mathbf{E}_T \mathbf{x} \mathbf{B}_0$$
$$+ \sum_r \frac{i\omega N_{0,r} e_r \nu_r}{\omega_{c,r}^2 - \omega^2} \mathbf{u}_T + \sum_r \frac{N_{0,r} e_r^2 \nu_r}{m_r(\omega_{c,r}^2 - \omega^2)} \mathbf{u}_T \mathbf{x} \mathbf{B}_0 \quad , \tag{44.11}$$

$$\mathbf{F}_T = \sum_r \frac{i\omega N_{0,r} e_r \nu_r}{\omega_{c,r}^2 - \omega^2} \mathbf{E}_T + \sum_r \frac{N_{0,r} e_r^2 \nu_r}{m_r(\omega_{c,r}^2 - \omega^2)} \mathbf{E}_T \mathbf{x} \mathbf{B}_0 - (\sum_r N_{0,r} m_r \nu_r)\mathbf{u}_T \quad . \tag{44.12}$$

If,

$$|\omega| << \text{Min.}|\omega_{c,r}| \quad \text{for all } r \quad , \tag{44.13}$$

a further simplification results, namely,

$$\mathbf{J}_T = \left(\sum_r \frac{N_{0,r} m_r \nu_r}{B_0^2}\right)(\mathbf{E} + \mathbf{u}\mathbf{x}\mathbf{B}_0)_T + i\omega\left(\sum_r \frac{N_{0,r} m_r}{B_0^2}\right)\mathbf{E}_T \quad , \tag{44.14}$$

$$\mathbf{F}_T = \left(\sum_r \frac{N_{0,r} m_r \nu_r}{B_0^2}\right)(\mathbf{E} + \mathbf{u}\mathbf{x}\mathbf{B}_0)_T \mathbf{x} \mathbf{B}_0 \quad , \tag{44.15}$$

and if,

$$|\omega| \ll \text{Min. } \nu_r \quad \text{for all } r \quad , \tag{44.16}$$

we obtain

$$\mathbf{J}_T = \left(\sum_r \frac{N_{0,r} m_r \nu_r}{B_0^2}\right)(\mathbf{E} + \mathbf{u}\mathrm{x}\mathbf{B}_0)_T \quad , \tag{44.17}$$

$$\mathbf{F}_T = \mathbf{J}\mathrm{x}\mathbf{B}_0 \quad . \tag{44.18}$$

On the other hand, if

$$|\omega| \gg \text{Max.} |\omega_{c,r}| \quad \text{for all } r, \tag{44.19}$$

we can write for the resultant **J** and **F**, approximately,

$$\mathbf{J} = -i \sum_r \frac{N_{0,r} e_r^2}{\omega m_r} \mathbf{E} - i \sum_r \frac{N_{0,r} e_r \nu_r}{\omega} \mathbf{u} \quad , \tag{44.20}$$

$$\mathbf{F} = -i \left(\sum_r \frac{N_{0,r} e_r \nu_r}{\omega}\right)\mathbf{E} - \left(\sum_r N_{0,r} m_r \nu_r\right)\mathbf{u} \quad . \tag{44.21}$$

45. RELATED INVESTIGATIONS

In this section we shall sketch the important and comprehensive investigations of Baños and co-workers. This work is a systematic theoretical investigation of the soluble unbounded media and boundary value problems of magneto-hydrodynamic, magneto-acoustic and magneto-elastic phenomena. These phenomena are bound to each other by the common fact that they are concerned with the mutual interaction between the electromagnetic field and a moving conducting medium. The medium can be an elastic solid, liquid or an ionized gas. In all of these situations, the fundamental problem consists of the simultaneous solution of the field equations of electrodynamics and the equations of motion for the medium in the presence of forces of electromagnetic origin, *i.e.*, the so-called ponderomotive forces.

These studies are restricted to a purely macroscopic medium defined by the constant parameters μ, ϵ such that $\mu\epsilon = V_0^{-2}$ (vacuum-like medium), and an ohmic conductivity σ. The vacuum like medium restriction however is easily removed. The entire medium is pervaded by a constant and uniform magnetic field and only the linearized class of problems is considered. Such a systematic study provides a guide to the solution of the non linear problems which are presently under investigation by others but will not be discussed here. These non linear problems arise in plasma dynamics and are important from both the theoretical and technological point of view.

In the discussion to follow we adhere closely to the notation of Baños; detailed derivations are not given since they can be supplied by the reader or can be obtained by reference to the basic papers.

The fundamental equations are Maxwell's eqs.,

$$\text{curl } \mathbf{e} + \frac{\mu \partial \mathbf{h}}{\partial t} = 0 \quad , \tag{45.1}$$

$$\text{curl } \mathbf{h} = \mathbf{J} + \epsilon \frac{\partial \mathbf{e}}{\partial t} \quad , \tag{45.2}$$

$$\text{div } \mathbf{h} = 0 \quad , \tag{45.3}$$

$$\text{div } \mathbf{e} = \frac{\eta}{\epsilon} \quad , \tag{45.4}$$

$$\mathbf{J} = \eta \mathbf{v} + \sigma(\mathbf{e} + \mathbf{v x B}) \quad , \tag{45.5}$$

$$\frac{\partial \eta}{\partial t} + \text{div } \mathbf{J} \quad , \tag{45.6}$$

here, **e** and **h** are the electric and magnetic intensities of the induced field, **J** is the current density, **v** is the local macroscopic velocity of the medium, $\mathbf{B} = \mathbf{B}_0 + \mu\mathbf{h}$. The charge density is denoted by η. The interpretation of eqs. (45.1)-(45.6) is clear.

For any type of medium, liquid, solid or gas, in the absence of gravitational forces we denote by

$$\mathbf{F} = \mathbf{f}$$

the ponderomotive force, where

$$\mathbf{f} = \eta\mathbf{e} + \mathbf{J}\mathbf{x}\mathbf{B} \tag{45.8}$$

and

$$\mathbf{F} = \rho\frac{d\mathbf{v}}{dt} - \mathrm{div}\,\tau \quad , \tag{45.9}$$

where $\mathbf{f}$ is of electromagnetic origin and $\mathbf{F}$ is of mechanical origin, ρ is the mass density, τ is the mechanical stress tensor. The relation between the Lorentz force density $\mathbf{f}$ and τ is given by

$$\mathbf{f} = \mathrm{div}\,\tau - \frac{\partial}{\partial t}\,\mu\epsilon(\mathbf{e}\mathbf{x}\mathbf{H}) \tag{45.10}$$

where $\mu\epsilon(\mathbf{e}\mathbf{x}\mathbf{H})$ represents the electromagnetic momentum density, and

$$\tau \equiv (\tau_{ij}) = \epsilon\left(e_i e_j - \frac{1}{2}e^2\delta_{ij}\right. + \mu\left(H_i H_j - \frac{1}{2}H^2\delta_{ij}\right) \quad . \tag{45.11}$$

The rate of work done by $\mathbf{f}$ per unit volume of the conducting medium is given by

$$\mathbf{f}\cdot\mathbf{v} = \frac{(\mathbf{J} - \eta\mathbf{v})^2}{\sigma} - \frac{\partial}{\partial t}\left(\frac{1}{2}\epsilon e^2 + \frac{1}{2}\mu H^2\right) - \mathrm{div}\,(\mathbf{e}\mathbf{x}\mathbf{H}) \quad . \tag{45.12}$$

In the case of an ideal conducting fluid with no viscosity or expansive friction we can write

$$\mathbf{f} = \rho\frac{d\mathbf{v}}{dt} + \nabla p \quad , \tag{45.13}$$

where p is the hydrodynamic pressure. This equation is supplemented by an equation of continuity

$$\frac{\partial\rho}{\partial t} + \mathrm{div}\,(\rho\mathbf{v}) = 0 \quad . \tag{45.14}$$

It is possible to obtain a single vector equation which is an exact magnetohydrodynamic equation in the fluid velocity. This equation takes the form

$$\left(\sigma + \epsilon \frac{\partial}{\partial t}\right)\left(\nabla^2 - \mu\epsilon \frac{\partial^2}{\partial t^2}\right)\left\{\sigma^{-1}\left[\mathbf{F} - \nabla \cdot \tau + \mu\epsilon \frac{\partial}{\partial t} (\mathbf{exh})\right]\right.$$

$$\left. - \frac{\eta}{\sigma} (\mathbf{vxB}_0) - (\mathbf{vxB})\mathbf{xB}_0\right\} + \sigma[\nabla\nabla \cdot (\mathbf{vxB})]\mathbf{xB}_0$$

$$= \mu \frac{\partial}{\partial t}\left(\sigma + \epsilon \frac{\partial}{\partial t}\right)\left[\mathbf{F} - \nabla \cdot \tau + \mu\epsilon \frac{\partial}{\partial t} (\mathbf{exh})\right] - [\nabla\nabla \cdot (\eta\mathbf{v})]\mathbf{xB}_0 \ ,$$

(45.15)

which is highly non-linear. If the particle velocity is much smaller than the Alfvén phase velocity, that is $v << V_a = B_0 (\mu\rho)^{-1/2}$, this serves as a criterion for the applicability of the small amplitude linear theory. Consequently when all second-order terms are neglected there results the linearized form of the hydromagnetic or magneto-elastic wave equation,

$$\left(\sigma + \epsilon \frac{\partial}{\partial t}\right)\left(\nabla^2 - \mu\epsilon \frac{\partial^2}{\partial t^2}\right)\left[\frac{\mathbf{F}}{\sigma} - (\mathbf{vxB}_0)\mathbf{xB}_0\right]$$

$$= \mu\left(\sigma + \epsilon \frac{\partial}{\partial t}\right)\left(\frac{\partial \mathbf{F}}{\partial t}\right) - \sigma[\nabla\nabla \cdot (\mathbf{vxB}_0)]\mathbf{xB}_0 \quad . \qquad (45.16)$$

Put $\mathbf{B}_0 = B_0\mathbf{e}_3$, with $\mathbf{e}_3$ a unit vector, and if all field variables have a plane wave structure $\exp[i(\omega t - \mathbf{K} \cdot \mathbf{r})]$, they satisfy the wave equation

$$(\nabla^2 + K^2)\psi = 0 \ . \qquad (45.17)$$

The propagation vector $\mathbf{K}$ can be written as

$$\mathbf{K} = K\mathbf{n} = \mathbf{e}_1 K_1 + \mathbf{e}_3 K_3 \ , \qquad (45.18)$$

with the unit vector $\mathbf{n}$ given by

$$\mathbf{n} = \mathbf{e}_1 \sin\theta + \mathbf{e}_3 \cos\theta \ , \quad \left(0 \leqq \theta \leqq \frac{\pi}{2}\right), \qquad (45.19)$$

where θ is the angle between $\mathbf{n}$ and $\mathbf{B}_0$. If v_0 is an arbitrary velocity amplitude such that $v_0 \ll V_a$, the elementary solutions of eq. (45.17) are linear combinations of the fundamental wave functions,

$$\mathbf{v}_1 = v_0\psi\mathbf{e}_2 \, , \quad \mathbf{v}_2 = \mathbf{n}\mathrm{x}\mathbf{v}_1 = (\mathbf{n}\mathrm{x}\mathbf{e}_2)v_0\psi \, , \quad \mathbf{v}_3 = v_0\mathbf{n}\psi \, . \tag{45.20}$$

For real $\mathbf{K}$ it is obvious that

$$\mathrm{div}\;\mathbf{v}_1 = \mathrm{div}\;\mathbf{v}_2 = 0 \, , \tag{45.21}$$

while

$$\mathrm{curl}\;\mathbf{v}_3 = 0 \, . \tag{45.22}$$

For an incompressible fluid, *i.e.*, div $\mathbf{v} = 0$, $\mathbf{v}_1$ and $\mathbf{v}_2$ are the only permissible solutions and for a compressible fluid $\mathbf{v}_3$ must also appear in the linear combination. In an analogous way, for an elastic solid, pure shear waves, div $\mathbf{v} = 0$, can occur and if there exist also shear-compression modes, $\mathbf{v}_3$, the irrotational part must appear in the linear combination.

For ideal incompressible conducting fluids, (no viscosity) we have for harmonic oscillations,

$$\mathbf{F} = i\omega\rho\mathbf{v} + \nabla p \, . \tag{45.23}$$

By substituting this form into the linearized equation (45.16) taking respectively the x_3-component, the divergence and the x_3-component of the curl of every vector we obtain the three scalar equations,

$$\frac{\partial p}{\partial x_3} = -\, i\omega\rho v_3 \, , \tag{45.24}$$

$$\left[(\nabla^2 + K_c^2)\left(\frac{\partial^2}{\partial x_3^2} + ia\nabla^2\right) + K_a^2\nabla^2\right] v_3 = 0 \, , \tag{45.25}$$

$$[(1 + ia)(\nabla^2 + K_c^2) + K_a^2 - (1 + ib)^{-1}\nabla_t^2](\mathbf{e}_3 \cdot \nabla\mathrm{x}\mathbf{v}) = 0 \, , \tag{45.26}$$

where ∇_t^2 is the transverse part of the operator ∇^2, that is

$$\nabla^2 \equiv \nabla_t^2 + \frac{\partial^2}{\partial x_3^2} \, , \tag{45.27}$$

$$K_a = \frac{\omega}{V_a} , \quad (45.28)$$

$$K_c = \omega(\mu\epsilon)^{1/2} , \quad (45.29)$$

$$a = \frac{\omega\rho}{\sigma B_0^2} , \quad (45.30)$$

$$b = \frac{\omega\epsilon}{\sigma} . \quad (45.31)$$

Baños shows for plane waves, that the solution of eq. (45.16) after using eq. (45.23) is automatically satisfied for any solenoidal $\mathbf{v}$ which satisfies both eqs. (45.25) and (45.26), the pressure being given by eq. (45.23). Consequently, the fundamental solutions are selected from $\mathbf{v}_1$ and $\mathbf{v}_2$ of eqs. (45.20) with irrotational $\mathbf{v}_3$ excluded for the incompressible case. The solutions resulting from $\mathbf{v}_1$ and $\mathbf{v}_2$ then yield separately to two distinct modes of propagation which Baños calls velocity modes and pressure modes.

Velocity Modes--This mode arises when the fluid velocity is perpendicular to the plane defined by the wave normal and the direction of the applied magnetic field, according to eq. (45.20) when $\mathbf{v} = \mathbf{v}_1$. There is no x_3-component of the velocity vector, hence eq. (45.25) is satisfied, and eq. (45.24) implies that the pressure vanishes identically. In order to satisfy eq. (45.26) for $\theta \neq 0$, replace ∇ by $(-i\mathbf{K})$ and set the expression in brackets equal to zero. This leads to the result

$$K^2 = \frac{(1 + ib)[K_a^2 + K_c^2(1 + ia)]}{(1 + ia)(1 + ib) - \sin^2 \theta} , \quad (45.32)$$

for the propagation vector.

Pressure Modes--This mode arises in an incompressible fluid when the fluid velocity vector is in the plane defined by the wave normal and the direction of the applied magnetic field and is perpendicular to the direction of propagation. Here, eq. (45.26) is satisfied and in order to satisfy eq. (45.25), for $\theta > 0$, again we replace ∇ by $-i\mathbf{K}$ and set the expression in in brackets of eq. (45.25) equal to zero. We obtain now for the propagation constant,

$$K^2 = K_a^2(\cos^2\theta + ia)^{-1} + K_c^2 \quad . \tag{45.33}$$

The pressure is given by eq. (45.24). If $\theta = 0$, the p-modes degenerate into v-modes, and it is not possible to distinguish between two distinct directions of polarization for the solenoidal velocity vector.

Ideal Compressible Fluid (Zero Viscosity, No Expansive Friction, Zero Heat Conductivity)--A fluid of this type can sustain shear hydromagnetic waves which are isothermal. If besides, the fluid obeys the perfect gas laws then in shear compression the fluid behaves adiabatically, and satisfies the relation

$$\frac{p}{p_0} = \left(\frac{\rho}{\rho_0}\right)^{\gamma} , \tag{45.34}$$

where γ is the ratio of specific heats, p_0 and ρ_0 are equilibrium values of pressure and density respectively. Consequently we can write

$$-ia\mathbf{F} = \omega^2\rho_0\mathbf{v} - \rho_0 V_s^2\nabla\nabla \cdot \mathbf{v} \quad , \tag{45.35}$$

where

$$V_s = \left(\frac{dp}{d\rho}\right)_0^{1/2} = \gamma\left(\frac{p_0}{\rho_0}\right)^{1/2} \tag{45.36}$$

is the adiabatic velocity of sound in the medium. If we put eq. (45.35) into eq (45.16) we find now the three scalar equations

$$K_s^2 v_3 = -\left(\frac{\partial}{\partial x_3}\right)(\nabla \cdot \mathbf{v}) \quad , \tag{45.37}$$

$$\left\{(\nabla^2 + K_r^2)\left[\frac{\partial^2}{\partial x_3^2} + K_s^2 + ia(\nabla^2 + K_s^2)\right] + K_a^2(\nabla^2 + K_s^2)\right\}(\nabla \cdot \mathbf{v}) = 0 \, , \tag{45.38}$$

$$\{(1 + ia)(\nabla^2 + K_c^2) + K_a^2 - (1 + ib)^{-1}\,\nabla_t^2\}(\mathbf{e}_3 \,.\, \nabla\mathbf{x}\mathbf{v}) = 0,, \tag{45.39}$$

where,

$$K_s = \frac{\omega}{V_s} \quad . \tag{45.40}$$

Since eq. (45.39) is the same as eq. (45.26) a compressible fluid also sustains the same kind of plane velocity modes as an incompressible fluid.

Ideal Magneto-Acoustic Modes—For a compressible fluid undergoing an adiabatic process we can examine the p-modes as follows. In order to satisfy eq. (45.39) the velocity vector must be in the plane defined by the wave normal and the applied field. From eq. (45.38) we now obtain a quadratic in K^2 which has two distinct roots which yield two magneto-acoustic p-modes. From eq. (45.20) we form

$$\mathbf{v} = \mathbf{v}_3 \cos \varphi - \mathbf{v}_2 \sin \varphi = [\mathbf{n} \cos \varphi + (\mathbf{e}_2 \mathbf{x} \mathbf{n}) \sin \varphi] v_0 \psi \ , \tag{45.41}$$

where φ is chosen so that we obtain the right linear combination of solenoidal $\mathbf{v}_2$ and irrotational $\mathbf{v}_3$. The two eqs. (45.37) and (45.41) lead to the relation,

$$K_s^2 (1 - \tan \theta \tan \varphi) = K^2 \quad , \tag{45.42}$$

from which we can find φ if K is known for a given mode. In eq. (45.38) we replace ∇ by $-i\mathbf{K}$, set the expression in brackets equal to zero and obtain a quadratic in K^2 which gives two distinct modes. As $\sigma \to \infty$, $a = 0$, the quadratic becomes

$$(K^2 - K_s^2)(K^2 - K_a^2 - K_c^2) = K^2 (K^2 - K_c^2) \sin^2 \theta \quad . \tag{45.43}$$

For $\theta = 0$, we obtain $K^2 = K_s^2$, and $K^2 = K_a^2 + K_c^2$, hence in the former case we have a pure sound wave and in the latter an ordinary Alfvén p-mode. For $\theta \approx 0$, we obtain a modified sound wave and a modified Alfvén wave.

Normal Modes—In an ideal compressible fluid with zero heat conductivity there exists shear modes in which the temperature is constant and shear compressible modes which are adiabatic. One of these normal modes is a pure shear velocity mode, the remaining normal modes are the shear-compression p-modes which are defined by an equation of the form (45.41).

These latter two modes are mutually orthogonal and also orthogonal to the first normal v-mode. Summarizing these normal modes, we have,

$$\mathbf{V}_1 = \mathbf{v}_1 , \quad K = K_1 , \quad \text{defined by eq. (45.32)} , \tag{45.44}$$

$$\mathbf{V}_2 = \mathbf{v}_2 \cos \varphi + \mathbf{v}_3 \sin \varphi , \quad K = K_2 , \quad K_s \leqq K_2 < \infty , \tag{45.45}$$

$$\mathbf{V}_3 = - \mathbf{v}_2 \sin \varphi + \mathbf{v}_3 \cos \varphi , \quad K = K_3 , \quad 0 \leqq K_3 \leqq K_s , \tag{45.46}$$

where φ is defined by eq. (45.42), and is restricted by $0 \leqq \varphi \lesseqgtr \pi/2$, after setting $K = K_2$,

$$\tan \theta \tan \varphi = \frac{(K_s^2 - K_3^2)}{K_s^2} , \tag{45.47}$$

or by setting $K = K_2$ and replacing φ by $\varphi - \pi/2$,

$$\tan \theta \cot \varphi = \frac{(K_2^2 - K_s^2)}{K_s^2} . \tag{45.48}$$

It follows that as $\varphi \to 0$, $\mathbf{V}_2$ is a modified hydromagnetic wave (Alfvén wave) while $\mathbf{V}_3$ is a modified acoustic wave.*

Ideal Elastic Solids—In the following we consider in a summary fashion the waves which an ideal unbounded elastic solid can support. Here too we assume plane homogeneous waves, a conducting medium, and a pervading magnetic field. There are five distinct modes of propagation. These are respectively, a weakly attenuated shear mode whose phase velocity is modified anisotropically by magneto-elastic interaction; a highly attenuated shear mode whose propagation constant is the same as that of an electromagnetic wave of the same frequency; a shear compression mode whose phase velocity lies between the phase velocity of shear and compression waves; a shear-compression mode whose phase velocity exceeds that of compression waves and a shear-compression mode which is highly attenuated but exhibits propagation characteristics of an electromagnetic wave. As the conductivity of the medium becomes infinitely large, the

* For a detailed discussion see A. Baños, Jr., "Magneto-Hydrodynamic Waves in Incompressible and Compressible Fluids," Proc. Royal Soc. A, Vol. 233, No. 1194, pp. 350-356, December 1955.

two highly attenuated normal modes vanish and there remains three normal modes which are mutually orthogonal to each other.

For a homogeneous and isotropic conducting solid we find the expression for **F** in the case of time harmonic magneto-elastic waves to be

$$-ia\mathbf{F} = \omega^2\rho\mathbf{v} + \rho(V_p^2 - V_s^2)\nabla\nabla\cdot\mathbf{v} + \rho V_s^2\nabla^2\mathbf{v} \quad , \tag{45.49}$$

where $\mathbf{v}$ is the particle velocity, ρ is the density of the medium, and

$$V_p^2 = \frac{(\lambda + 2\mu)}{\rho} \quad , \quad V_s^2 = \frac{\mu}{\rho} \quad . \tag{45.50}$$

In these expressions λ and μ denote the elastic constants of the iostropic medium; V_p is the phase velocity of compressional waves and V_s is the phase velocity of shear waves.* Now put eq. (45.49) into eq. (45.16) to obtain as before, three scalar equations the first of which is the x_3-component, the divergence, and the x_3-component of the curl of every vector term in eq. (45.16)

$$K_p^2(\nabla^2 + K_s^2)v_3 = -(K_s^2 - K_p^2)\frac{\partial}{\partial x_3}(\nabla\cdot\mathbf{v}) \quad , \tag{45.51}$$

$$\begin{aligned}\Bigg((\nabla^2 + K_c^2)\left\{(K_s^2 - K_p^2)\frac{\partial^2}{\partial x_3^2} + (\nabla^2 + K_s^2)[K_p^2 + ia(\nabla^2 + K_p^2)]\right\} \\ + K_a^2(\nabla^2 + K_p^2)(\nabla^2 + K_s^2)\Bigg)(\nabla\cdot\mathbf{v}) = 0 \quad ,\end{aligned} \tag{45.52}$$

$$\begin{aligned}\{(\nabla^2 + K_c^2)[K_s^2 + ia(\nabla^2 + K_s^2)] + K_a^2(\nabla^2 + K_s^2) \\ - K_s^2(1 + ib)^{-1}\nabla_t^2\}[\mathbf{e}_3\cdot(\nabla\mathbf{x}\mathbf{v})] = 0 \quad ,\end{aligned} \tag{45.53}$$

where

$$K_p = \frac{\omega}{V_p} \quad , \quad K_s = \frac{\omega}{V_s} \quad , \tag{45.54}$$

* λ and μ are the Lamé constants, their physical significance is given in I. S. Sokolnikoff, "Mathematical Theory of Elasticity," Chapter III, McGraw-Hill Co., Second Ed. (1956). See also Chapter VI pp. 370-371, for the interpretation of V_p and V_s.

here, K_s and V_s denote shear or transverse oscillations, If we set $V_s = 0$, and identify the velocity of compressional waves V_p with the velocity of sound, eqs. (45.51)-(45.53) reduce to eqs. (45.37)-(45.39) for a compressible fluid undergoing adiabatic processes. Hence the magneto-acoustic modes discussed in the foregoing section are special cases of the magneto-elastic modes in the limit as the velocity of shear modes tend to zero.

Shear Modes—This set of modes which contains no compressional vibrations is included in the class of velocity modes which are generated from eqs. (45.20) by selecting from this set the velocity vector $\mathbf{v} = \mathbf{v}_1$ which satisfies eqs. (45.51) and (45.52), is solenoidal and has no x_3-component. In order to satisfy eq. (45.53), for $\theta > 0$; as before we replace ∇ by $-i\mathbf{K}$ for plane waves and set the bracket equal to zero. This yields a quadratic in K^2 which has two roots hence two shear modes.* For infinity conductivity, only one mode obtains, the first normal mode and is a pure shear wave defined by

$$\mathbf{v}_1 = \mathbf{V}_1 = \mathbf{e}_2 v_0 \psi , \quad K = K_1 , \quad (0 \leqq K_1 \leqq K_s) , \qquad (45.55)$$

where, for infinite conductivity and zero displacement current,

$$K = \frac{(K_a K_s)^2}{(K_a^2 + K_s^2 \cos^2 \theta)} . \qquad (45.56)$$

This corresponds to a pure shear mode with a phase velocity modified anisotropically by magneto-elastic interaction. As $V_s \to 0$, this mode behaves like an Alfvén wave in magneto-hydrodynamics.

For finite conductivity there are two shear modes. If $a << 1$, the first normal mode is defined by eq. (45.55) and K_1 is slightly attenuated, the second mode is highly attenuated with propagation constant approximately equal to $-i\omega\mu\sigma$, this pure shear mode is a highly attenuated "skin" wave. If $a >> 1$, that is a weak magneto-elastic coupling, the first mode becomes a shear wave with $K_1^2 \approx K_s^2$, and the second mode remains a "skin" wave.

---

* For details see, A. Baños, Jr., "Normal Modes Characterizing Magneto-Elastic Plane Waves," Physical Rev. Vol. 102, No. 2, pp. 300-305, October 15, 1956.

Shear Compression Modes--The next set of magneto-elastic modes is characterized by the simultaneous presence of shear and compressional vibrations and are contained in the class of pressure modes for a compressible fluid undergoing adiabatic processes. This set is therefore defined by eq. (45.41) and which automatically satisfies eq. (45.53) and eq. (45.51) gives an equation which defines φ as a function of K,

$$\tan\theta \tan\varphi = \frac{K_s^2 (K^2 - K_p^2)}{K_p^2 (K^2 - K_s^2)} . \tag{45.57}$$

In order to satisfy eq. (45.52), replace ∇ by $-i\mathbf{K}$ and set the bracket equal to zero. This yields a cubic in K^2, which gives three distinct shear compression modes. For infinite conductivity, the cubic degenerates into a quadratic in K^2 having two distinct roots and hence corresponds to the two additional normal modes. One of these modes has a phase velocity between that of a shear and compressional wave, the other has its phase velocity exceeding that of compressional waves in the medium. For finite conductivity, the third shear mode is a strongly attenuated "skin" wave whose propagation constant is approximately equal to $-i\omega\mu\sigma$.

The two remaining normal modes are defined by the velocity vectors

$$\mathbf{V}_2 = \mathbf{v}_2 \cos\varphi + \mathbf{v}_3 \sin\varphi , \quad K = K_2 , \quad (K_p \leqq K_2 \leqq K_s) , \tag{45.58}$$

$$\mathbf{V}_3 = -\mathbf{v}_2 \sin\varphi + \mathbf{v}_3 \cos\varphi , \quad K = K_3 , \quad (0 \leqq K_3 \leqq K_p) , \tag{45.59}$$

where φ, $(0 \leqq \varphi \leqq \pi/2)$ is found from eq. (45.57) by setting $K = K_3$ or by replacing φ with $\varphi - \pi/2$.

It can be shown that for finite conductivity, the two normal shear-compression modes become weakly attenuated, the third mode is always a strongly attenuated "skin" wave with propagation characteristics the same as those of an electromagnetic wave in the medium.

Further, because the Alfvén phase velocity for an elastic conducting solid is much smaller than the shear and compressional phase velocities in the medium, the magneto-elastic interactions are insignificant.*

---

* A. Baños, Jr., *loc.cit.*

Torsional Magneto-Hydrodynamic Waves—We now consider briefly the theory of torsional magneto-hydrodynamic waves in an incompressible fluid with finite viscosity. This problem has been treated by E. Blue in a thesis and constitutes an example of cylindrical waves.* For this case we have

$$\mathbf{F} = i\omega\rho\mathbf{v} + \nabla p - \omega\rho q\nabla^2\mathbf{v} , \tag{45.60}$$

where ρ is a constant density, p is the hydrodynamic pressure and $q = \nu/\omega$ with ν denoting the kinematic viscosity. Equation (45.16) now yields the three scalar equations valid for the case of zero displacement current,

$$\frac{\partial p}{\partial x_3} = - i\omega\rho(1 + iq\nabla^2)v_3 . \tag{45.61}$$

$$\left[\frac{\partial^2}{\partial x_3^2} + (K_a^2 + ia\nabla^2)(1 + iq\nabla^2)\right]\nabla^2 v_3 = 0 , \tag{45.62}$$

$$\left[(K_a^2 + ia\nabla^2)(1 + iq\nabla^2) + \frac{\partial^2}{\partial x_3^2}\right][\mathbf{e}_3 \cdot \nabla\mathbf{x}\mathbf{v}] = 0 . \tag{45.63}$$

For $\nu = 0$, this system reduces to eqs. (45.24)-(45.26). When $K_c = 0$. In the present case we find two additional modes due to the presence of the finite viscosity, hence a total of five cylindrical modes. From eq. (45.63) we obtain two velocity modes and Eqs. (45.61), (45.62) give three pressure modes. One of the two velocity modes is a weakly attenuated Alfvén wave resulting from the finite conductivity and viscosity. The other velocity mode is a strongly attenuated viscous "skin" wave. One of the three pressure modes is a weakly attenuated Alfvén wave, the other two modes are strongly attenuated.

Cylindrical Velocity Modes—If the applied magnetic field is chosen so that $\mathbf{B}_0 = B_0\mathbf{e}_3$ and all field vectors are assumed to be derivable from a scalar function

$$\left.\begin{aligned} \psi(\mathbf{r},t) &= A\Phi(\rho)\,\exp[i(\omega t - Kx_3)] \\ (\nabla^2 + \kappa^2)\psi &= 0 , \\ \kappa^2 &= \gamma^2 + K^2 , \end{aligned}\right\} \tag{45.64}$$

* E. Blue, "Torsional Magneto-Hydrodynamic Waves in the Presence of Finite Viscosity," PH.D. Thesis, University of California at Los Angeles, January 1957.

A is a constant, K is the longitudinal propagation constant, γ is the transverse wave number, *i.e.*, $(\nabla_t^2 + \gamma^2)\Phi = 0$. We need to calculate K for a given value of γ, where K corresponds to the two velocity modes in an incompressible fluid.

Therefore, we assume that $\mathbf{v}$ can be represented by

$$\mathbf{v} = \nabla\mathbf{x}(\mathbf{e}_3\psi) = \nabla\psi\mathbf{x}\mathbf{e}_3 , \tag{45.65}$$

with ψ given by eqs. (45.64) and satisfying the conditions

$$\nabla \cdot \mathbf{v} = 0 , \quad v_3 = 0 , \quad \mathbf{e}_3 \cdot \nabla\mathbf{x}\mathbf{v} = \gamma^2\psi . \tag{45.66}$$

Now, $v_3 = 0$, and eq. (45.61) implies that the excess pressure vanishes identically for this mode, but eq. (45.62) is automatically satisfied. In order to satisfy eq. (45.63), for $\gamma^2 \neq 0$, we replace $-\nabla^2$ by $\kappa^2 = \gamma^2 + K^2$ and $-\partial^2/\partial x_3^2$ by K^2 and set the bracket equal to zero to obtain

$$aq\kappa^4 + [1 + i(a + qK_a^2)]\kappa^2 - (\gamma^2 + K_a^2) = 0. \tag{45.67}$$

This is a quadratic in κ^2 and has two roots, therefore two distinct modes. Thus, for each mode, the above equation defines a relation between the longitudinal and transverse wave numbers which must always be satisfied. When the transverse and longitudinal wave numbers are known for each mode, the corresponding velocity vector is given by eq. (45.65).

The solution of eq. (45.67) is

$$2a\kappa^2 = -(1 + ia + iqK_a^2) \pm [(1 + ia^2 + iqK_a^2)^2 + 4aq(\gamma^2 + K_a^2)]^{1/2} , \tag{45.68}$$

it follows that if $qK_a^2 \ll 1$, one root is in the first quadrant of the complex plane, the other is in the second quadrant. The first root is of the form $\kappa^2 = \gamma^2 + K^2$ and defines K (complex) which corresponds to a propagating Alfvén cylindrical mode. The second root can be written in the $\kappa'^2 = \gamma^2 - K'^2$, defining the complex attenuating K' which corresponds to a strongly attenuated viscous mode. Therefore, in this case we find two cylindrical velocity modes; a weakly attenuated Alfvén wave and a strongly attenuated "skin" wave resulting from the viscosity of the fluid.

For a compressible fluid with finite viscosity and heat conductivity it can be shown that there exists six modes, two of which are pure shear modes, the remaining four modes are shear-compression waves which are accompanied by density, pressure and temperature fluctuations. The two shear modes are isothermal, and one is a weakly attenuated Alfvén wave, the other is a strongly attenuated viscous mode called a "vorticity" mode. The four shear-compression modes are not easily discussed in general; in the low frequency, small heat conductivity limit they are a modified adiabatic. Weakly attenuated sound wave; a weakly attenuated modified Alfvên p-wave; a strongly attenuated viscous wave; a strongly attenuated thermal wave.*

We want to mention here also the comprehensive work of Auer, Hurwitz and Miller.† These authors give a rather complete treatment of the waves that can be excited in a plasma. By considering the dielectric constant as a second order tensor which depends also on the frequency, they allow for the effects of the particle motions. They consider a range of frequencies which extends above the ion cyclotron frequency. These authors call extraordinary Alfvén waves what Baños calls a v-mode and their ordinary Alfvén waves are the p-modes in Baños' nomenclature.

46. THE REFLECTION AND REFRACTION OF MAGNETO-HYDRODYNAMIC WAVES

In this section we shall treat the problem of reflection and refraction of magneto-hydrodynamic waves at a plane boundary between two semi-infinite compressible gaseous media. The two media are assumed to be compressible and have infinite conductivity. We further assume that a uniform magnetic field $\mathbf{B}_0$ pervades all space.

We denote the first medium by M_1 the other by M_2, by γ_1 the ratio of specific heats in M_2, by γ_2 for M_2. The linearized equation of motion governing the displacement ξ of a particle for the case of infinite conductivity and zero displacement current is given by

$$\text{curl curl } (\xi \mathbf{x} \mathbf{B}_0) \mathbf{x} \mathbf{B}_0 = \mu_0 \rho_0 \frac{\partial^2 \xi}{\partial t^2} + \mu_0 \, \mathbf{grad} \, p \quad , \qquad (46.1)$$

* For details see A Baños, Jr., "Magneto-Hydrodynamic Waves in Compressible Fluids with Finite Viscosity and Heat Conductivity." Report No. AFOSR-TN-56-320, AD No. 94856.

† Auer, P. L., Hurwitz, H. Jr., and Miller, R. D. "Collective Oscillations in a Cold Plasma," Physics of Fluids, Vol. 1, p. 501 (1958).

where,

$$\frac{\partial \xi}{\partial t} = \mathbf{v} \ . \tag{46.2}$$

If we assume an adiabatic process for the gas, such that the pressure is related to the density by

$$\frac{p}{p_0} = \left(\frac{\rho}{\rho_0}\right)^{\gamma} \ , \tag{46.3}$$

we can write

$$\nabla p = V_s^2 \nabla \rho \tag{46.4}$$

where ρ_0 and p_0 correspond to the equilibrium state of the gas, p and ρ are the perturbations from this state, and

$$V_s = \left(\frac{\gamma p_0}{\rho_0}\right)^{1/2} \tag{46.5}$$

is the velocity of sound in the medium. The linearized equation of continuity in terms of ξ is

$$\rho + \nabla \cdot (\rho_0 \xi) = 0 \ . \tag{46.6}$$

Substituting eqs. (46.4) and (46.6) into (46.1) and setting $\mathbf{B}_0 = B_0\mathbf{n}$ gives

$$\ddot{\xi} = V_s^2 \text{ grad div } \xi + V_a^2 \text{ curl curl } (\xi \mathbf{x} \mathbf{n}) \mathbf{x} \mathbf{n} \tag{46.7}$$

where

$$V_a^2 = \frac{B_0 H_0}{\rho_0} \ , \tag{46.8}$$

is the square of the Alfvén velocity. To examine plane wave solutions of eq. (46.7) we put

$$\xi = \mathbf{A} \exp[i(\omega t - \mathbf{K} \cdot \mathbf{r})] \tag{46.9}$$

where $\mathbf{A},\mathbf{K}$ and ω can be complex. By definition, ξ as given by eq. (46.9) is real or complex according as $\mathbf{K}$ is real or complex. The result of substituting eq. (46.9) into eq. (46.7) leads to the dispersion equation

$$f(\omega,\mathbf{K}) = [\omega^2 - V_a^2(\mathbf{K}\cdot\mathbf{n})^2][\omega^4 - (V_a^2 + V_s^2)|\mathbf{K}|^2\omega^2 + V_a^2 V_s^2|\mathbf{K}|^2(\mathbf{K}\cdot\mathbf{n})^2] = 0\ , \tag{46.10}$$

which is the necessary and sufficient condition for non-trivial solutions $\mathbf{A}$ of eq. (46.7). Thus, for each $\mathbf{K}$ there exists three possible values for ω^2. If the first factor on the left side of eq. (46.10) is set equal to zero, we obtain the Alfvén wave. The second fact set equal to zero yields the modified Alfvén wave and the modified sound wave.

Now let M_1 and M_2 be separated by a plane interface π, let ρ_1 and ρ_2 be the gas densities of each medium respectively, but let p be the gas pressure in both. The field $\mathbf{B}_0$ is also assumed to be the same in both media, but is not parallel to π. For an incident plane wave in M_1 we seek the reflected and refracted waves such that the boundary conditions and the equation of motion is satisfied in M_1 and M_2.

If $\mathbf{b}$ is the perturbation from $\mathbf{B}_0$ and $\mathbf{e}_2$ is the unit normal directed from M_1 to M_2, it is clear that ξ, p and $\mathbf{b}\mathbf{x}\mathbf{e}_2$ must be continuous across π. In Fig. 9 x_1 is out of the plane of the paper.

If we assume that more than one reflected and refracted wave can occur, it is possible to solve the problem of reflection and refraction in terms of an incident wave of the form of eq. (46.9), the boundary conditions and the equation of motion. We denote by subscripts r and t respectively the reflected and refracted waves. Thus from the boundary conditions and the assumption of a plane wave structure $\mathbf{A}_r \exp[i(\omega_r t - \mathbf{K}_r \cdot \mathbf{r})]$ in M_1 and $\mathbf{A}_t \exp[i(\omega_t t - \mathbf{K}_t \cdot \mathbf{r})]$ in M_2 we find that for all t and $\mathbf{r}$,

$$\omega = \omega_r = \omega_t\ , \tag{46.11}$$

and

$$K_1 = K_{r,1} = K_{t,1}\ ;\quad K_3 = K_{r,3}\ K_{t,3}\ . \tag{46.12}$$

These results show that the frequency of the incident, reflected and refracted waves are equal and that the projection of the wave vectors onto

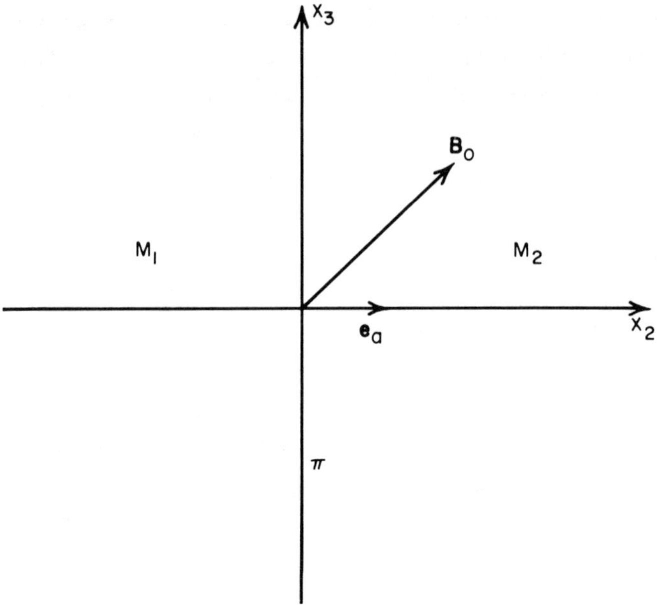

FIG. 9

the interface are also equal and these vectors therefore lie in a plane which is perpendicular to π and is determined by **K**. Thus we obtain the first law of reflection and refraction namely, the planes of reflection, refraction and incidence all coincide.

Now, the dispersion equation (46.10) which results from the equation of motion must be satisfied by all three waves, *i.e.*, the incident, reflected and refracted waves, hence, using eq. (46.11),

$$f(\omega_r, \mathbf{K}_r) = f(\omega, \mathbf{K}_r) = 0 \quad , \tag{46.13}$$

$$f(\omega_t, \mathbf{K}_t) = f(\omega, \mathbf{K}_t) = 0 \quad . \tag{46.14}$$

From these equations we can find $K_{r,2}$ and $K_{t,2}$ which together with eqs. (46.12) yield all the components of $\mathbf{K}_r$ and $\mathbf{K}_t$. Further, by hypothesis $\mathbf{n} \cdot \mathbf{e}_2 \neq 0$ so that eqs. (46.13) and (46.14) yield six values of $K_{r,2}$ and $K_{t,2}$, but since the real and imaginary parts of $K_{r,2}$ and $K_{t,2}$ can not be negative or positive, there exists only three permissible values for $K_{r,2}$ and three permissible values for $K_{t,2}$. Consequently, if we can specify the amplitudes of the reflected and refracted waves, these waves are completely determined. By using the boundary conditions on ξ, p and $\mathbf{bxe}_2$ and the equations of motion we obtain a non-homogeneous system of six equations for the determination of the amplitudes of the three reflected and three refracted waves. The details in this general case are left for the reader

$\mathbf{B}_0$ NORMAL TO π—This case is readily treated. Since $\mathbf{n}$ is normal to π, we may choose the coordinate system such that $\mathbf{n} = (0,1,0)$, then the dispersion eqs. (46.10), (46.13) and (46.14) read

$$[\omega^2 - V_a^2K_2^2][\omega^4 - (V_a^2 + V_s^2)(K_1^2 + K_2^2 + K_3^2)\omega^2 + V_a^2V_s^2(K_1^2 + K_2^2 + K_3^2)K_2^2] = 0 , \tag{46.15}$$

and two more equations of exactly the same form but replacing K_2 by $K_{r,2}$ and $K_{t,2}$. From these equations we find $\mathbf{K}_r$ and $\mathbf{K}_t$ for the three reflected and three refracted waves.

We suppose now that the incident wave is real, hence $\mathbf{K}$ is real and $\omega^2 > 0$, and let $\omega^2 \neq V_a^2K_2^2$, then from eq. (46.15) we have

$$\omega^4 - (V_a^2 + V_s^2)|\mathbf{K}|^2\omega^2 + (V_aV_s)^2|\mathbf{K}|^2K_2^2 = 0 , \tag{46.16}$$

where $\omega^2 \neq 0$, $\omega^2 \neq V_a^2|\mathbf{K}|^2$. Now with K_2 replaced by $K_{r,2}$ the first reflected wave is defined by

$$\omega^2 = V_a^2K_{r,2}^2 , \quad r = 1 , \tag{46.17}$$

and the two remaining reflected waves are defined by

$$\omega^4 -(V_a^2 + V_s^2)(K_1^2 + K_{r,2}^2 + K_3^2)\omega^2 + (V_aV_s)^2(K_1^2 + K_{r,2}^2 + K_3^2)K_{r,2}^2 = 0 . \tag{46.18}$$

Now by equating eq. (46.16) with (46.18) we obtain

$$K_{r,2}^2 = K_2^2 , \quad r = 2 ,$$

$$K_{r,2}^2 = \frac{V_a^2 + V_s^2}{(V_aV_s)^2}\omega^2 - |\mathbf{K}|^2 , \quad r = 3 . \tag{46.19}$$

Denoting by φ, φ_r and φ_t the angles of incidence, reflection and refraction respectively, we have

$$\tan^2 \varphi = \frac{K_1^2 + K_3^2}{K_2^2} ,$$

$$\tan^2 \varphi_r = \frac{K_1^2 + K_3^2}{K_{r,2}^2} , \qquad (46.20)$$

$$\tan^2 \varphi_t = \frac{K_1^2 + K_3^2}{K_{t,2}^2} .$$

From eq. (46.17) for the first reflected wave,

$$K_{r,2} = -\frac{\omega}{V_a} , \quad r = 1 ,$$

$$\tan^2 \varphi_r = (K_1^2 + K_3^2)\frac{V_a^2}{\omega^2} , \quad \omega > 0 , \quad r = 1 , \qquad (46.21)$$

which shows that the reflected wave is a real Alfvén wave, with $\varphi \neq \varphi_r$, $r = 1$, which follows from the assumption $\omega^2 \neq V_a^2 K_2^2$. The second reflected wave follows from eqs. (46.19), namely

$$K_{r,2} = -K_2 , \quad r = 2 ,$$

$$\varphi_r = \varphi , \quad r = 2 , \qquad (46.22)$$

which like the first reflected wave is also a real plane wave. The third reflected wave is obtained from the second of eqs. (46.19) and yields a modified plane wave which is real if

$$|\mathbf{K}|^2 (V_a V_s)^2 \leqq \omega^2 (V_a^2 + V_s^2) , \qquad (46.23)$$

and hence

$$\tan^2 \varphi_r = \frac{K_1^2 + K_3^2}{\left[\dfrac{\omega^2 (V_a^2 + V_s^2)}{(V_a V_s)^2 - |K|^2}\right]} \tag{46.24}$$

The first refracted wave is an Alfvén wave and is defined by eq. (46.15) with K_2 replaced by $K_{t,2}$, thus

$$K_{t,2} = \frac{\omega}{V_a}, \quad t = 1,$$

$$\tan^2 \varphi_t = (K_1^2 + K_3^2) \frac{V_{t,a}^2}{\omega^2}, \quad t = 1. \tag{46.25}$$

The second and third reflected waves are modified waves defined by

$$K_{t,2}^2 = \frac{1}{2V_{t,a}^2 V_{t,s}^2}\Big(\omega^2 (V_{t,a}^2 + V_{t,a}^2) - V_{t,a}^2 V_{t,s}^2 (K_1^2 + K_2^2)$$

$$\pm \{[\omega^2 (V_{t,a}^2 + V_{t,s}^2) + V_{t,a}^2 V_{t,s}^2 (K_1^2 + K_2^2)]^2 - 4V_{t,a}^2 V_{t,s}^2 \omega^4\}^{1/2}\Big)$$

$$t = 1,2 \tag{46.26}$$

This expression is real, but the waves will be real or imaginary depending on the sign of the expression, and we must also take into account that the real and imaginary parts of $K_{t,2}$ are not negative. Since the first refracted wave is a real Alfvén wave it is clear that total reflection can not occur under the present hypothesis.

BIBLIOGRAPHIES

1. Alfvén, H., On the existence of electromagnetic-hydrodynamical waves. Ask. Mat. Astro. Fys. Vol. 293, No. 2 (1943).

2. Astrom, E., On waves in an ionized gas. Arkiv for Fysik, Vol. 2, No. 42, pp. 443-457 (1950).

3. Bailey, V. A. and Roberts, J. A., Graphical study of the dispersion of Electro-Magneto-Ionic Waves, Austral. J. of Sci. Res., Ser. A, Vol. 1-2, pp. 307-21 (1948-49).

4. Bailey, V. A., Plane Waves in an Ionized Gas with Static Electric and Magnetic Field Present. Austral. J. of Sci. Res., Ser. A, Vol. 1-2, pp. 351-59 (1948-1949).

5. Bullard, Sir Edward, A discussion on magneto-hydrodynamics. Proc. Roy. Soc. A, Vol. 233 (1955-56).

6. Cavailles, P., Jancel, R., and Kahan, T., Magnetohydrodynamics of a Ternary Plasma and Types of Associated Waves. Comptes Rendus, Vol. 250, No. 23, pp. 3789-91 (8 June 1960).

7. Cavailles, P. Jancel, R., and Kahan, T., Statistical Mechanics of Plasmas with Several Components. Comptes Rendus, Vol. 250, No. 20, pp. 3282-84 (16 May 1960).

8. Chang, Howard H. C., Plasma Oscillations in a Static Magnetic Field. Paper presented at 1959 Summer Meeting of the American Physical Society, Honolulu, Hawaii.

9. Chopra, K. P., Tunnel Effect in Hydro-Magnetics. Pub. of the Astron. Soc. of Japan, Vol. 8, No. 2, pp. 55-62 (1956).

10. Clavier, P. A., Man Made Heating and Ionization of the Upper Atmosphere. J. App. Phys. Vol. 32, No. 4, pp. 570-77 (April 1961).

11. Clavier, P. A., Propagation in a Plasma, ibid, pp. 578-82.

12. Ferraro, V. C. A., On the Reflection and Refraction of Alfven Waves, Astrophys. J., Vol. 119, p. 393 (1954).

13. Germain, P., Introduction to the Study of Aeromagneto-dynamics, Cahiers De Physique, 13, (13) (March 1959).

14. Gershman, B. N. and Ugarov, V. A., Propagation and Generation of Low-Frequency Electromagnetic Waves in the Upper Atmosphere, Soviet Physics Uspekhi, Vol. 3, No. 5, pp. 743-764 (March-April 1961).

15. Ginsburg, V. L. and Gurevich, A. V., Non Linear Phenomena in a Plasma Located in an Alternating Electromagnetic Field, Usp. Fiz. Nauk. 70, pp. 201-246 (Feb. 1960).

16. Green, H. S., Ionic Theory of Plasma and Magnetohydradynamics, The Physics of Fluids, Vol. 2, No. 4, pp. 341-49 (July-August 1959).

17. Herlofson, N., Magnetohydrodynamic Waves in a Compressible Fluid Conductor, Nature, Vol. 165, p. 1020 (1950).

18. Hines, C. O., Generalized Magneto-Hydrodynamic Formulae. **Proc. Camb. Phil. Soc., 49,** pp. 299-307 (1953).

19. Hines, C. O., Heavy-Ion Effects in Audio-Frequency Radio Propagation. Jour. Atmos. and Terrestial Physics, Vol. 11, pp. 36-42 (1957).

20. Kadomtsev, B. B., Hydromagnetic Description of Plasma Oscillations. Zh. Eksper. Teor. Fiz. SSSR, Vol. 31, p. 1083 (1956).

21. Kahalas, S. L., Magnetohydrodynamic Wave Propagation in the Ionosphere. The Physics of Fluids, Vol. 3, No. 3, pp. 372-378 (May-June 1960).

22. Kritz, A. H., and Mintzer, D., Propagation of plasma waves across a density discontinuity. Phys. Rev. Vol. 117, No. 2; pp. 382-386 (Jan. 15, 1960).

23. Lehnert, B., Magneto-Hydrodynamic Waves in the Ionosphere and Their Application to Giant Pulsations. Tellus. Vol. 8, No. 2, pp. 241-251 (May 1956).

24. Lehnert, B., Magnetohydrodynamic Waves Under the Action of The Coriolis Force. Part I. Astrophys. J., Vol. 119, p. 647 (1954. Part II, ibid, Vol. 121, p. 481 (1955).

25. Loughhead, R. E., Eigen Oscillations of Compressible, Ionized Fluids, Austral. J. Phys. Vol. 8, p. 416 (1955).

26. Ludford, G.S.S., The Propagation of Small Disturbances in Hydro-Magnetics, J. Fluid Mech. Vol. 5, No. 3, pp. 387-400 (April 1959).

27. Lundquist, S., Experimental Demonstration of Magnetohydrodynamic Waves, Nautre, Vol. 164, p. 145 (1949).

28. Lundquist, S., Experimental Investigations of Magnetohydrodynamic Waves, Phys. Rev., Vol. 76, p. 1805 (1949).

29. Lundquist, S., Studies in Magneto-Hydrodynamics, Arkiv for Fysik., Vol. 5, No. 15, pp. 297-347 (1952).

30. Musgrave, M. J. P., The Propagation of Elastic Waves in Crystals and Other Anisotropic Media. Reports on Progress in Physics, Vol. 22, pp. 74-96 (1959).

31. Oster, L., Linearized Theory of Plasma Oscillations, Rev. of Modern Phys., Vol. 32, No. 1, pp. 141-68 (Jan. 1960).

32. Piddington, J. H., Electromagnetic Field Equations for a Moving Medium with Hall Conductivity, Royal Astr. Soc., Vol. 114, pp. 638-63 (1954).

33. Piddington, J. H., Growing Electromagnetic Waves, Phys. Rev. Vol. 101, No. 1, pp. 9-14 (Jan. 1, 1956).

34. Piddington, J. H., Hydromagnetic Waves in Ionized Gas, Nature, Vol. 176, p. 508 (1955).

35. Piddington, J. H., The Four Possible Waves in an Ionized Gas in a Magnetic Field, Nature, Vol. 176, p. 875 (1955).

36. Piddington, J. H., The Four Possible Waves in a Magneto-Ionic Medium. Phil. Mag., Vol. 46, pp. 1037-50 (1955).

37. Piddington, J. H., The Motion of Ionized Gas in Combined Magnetic, Electric and Mechanical Fields of Force, Royal Astr. Soc., Vol. 114, pp. 651-63 (1954).

38. Poeverlein, H., Propagation of Electromagnetic Waves in a Plasma with Strong Magnetic Field. The Physics of Fluids, Vol. 4, No. 4, pp. 397-405 (April 1961).

39. Rand, S., Plasma as a microwave amplifier. The Physics of Fluids, Vol. 4, No. 7, pp. 860-865 (July, 1961).

40. Scott, J. C. W., The Gyro-Frequency in the Arctic E-Layer. J. Geophys. Res., Vol. 56, No. 1, pp. 1-16 (March 1961).

41. Sen, H. K., and Wyller, A. A., On the Generalization of the Appleton-Hartree Magneto-Ionic Formulas. J. Geophys. Res. Vol. 65, No. 12, pp. 3931-50 (Dec. 1960).

42. Simon, R., On the reflection and refraction of hydro-magnetic waves at the boundary of two compressible gaseous media, Atrophysical Journal, Vol. 128, pp. 392-397 (1958).

43. Stepanov, K. N., Kinetic Theory of Magnetohydrodynamic Waves, Zh. Eksper. teor. Fiz. Vol. 34, p. 1292 (1958).

44. Stepanov, K. N., Low-Frequency Plasma Oscillations in a Magnetic Field, Zh. Eksp. i teor Fiz. Vol. 35, No. 5 (11), pp. 1155-1160 (1958) (In Russian).

45. Storey, L. R. O., Whistler Theory, XIIIth General Assembly of U.R.S.I., London (1960).

GENERAL BIBLIOGRAPHIES

1. Alfvén, H., Cosmical Electrodynamics (Oxford, Clarendon Press, 1950).
2. Bershader, D. (Editor). The Magneto Dynamics of Conducting Fluids, Stanford Univ. Press (1959).
3. Clauser, F. H. (Editor). Plasma Dynamics, Addison-Wesley Pub. Co., Reading, Mass. (1960).
4. Cole, G. H. A., Some Aspects of Magnetohydrodynamics, Advance Phys. 5, p. 452 (1956).
5. Cowling, T. G., Magnetohydrodynamics, Interscience Publishers Inc., N.Y. (1957).
6. Drummond, J. E. (Editor). Plasma Physics, McGraw-Hill Book Co., N.Y. (1961).
7. Dungey, J. W., Cosmic Electrodynamics, Cambridge Univ. Press (1958).
8. Elsasser, W. M., The Hydromagnetic Equations, Phys. Rev. Vol. 79, p. 183 (1950).
9. Elsasser, W. M., Hydromagnetism I, A Review, Amer. J. Phys. Vol. 23, p. 590 (1955). Hydromagnetism II, ibid, Vol. 24, p. 85 (1956).
10. Ferraro, V. C. A., Magnetohydrodynamics, Nature, Vol. 176, p. 234 (1953).
11. Ginzburg, V. L., Magneto-Hydrodynamic Waves in Gases, Zhur. Ekspt. i Teoret. Fiz. 21:7, pp. 788-94 (1951). (In Russian). Transl. AEC tr-2593 SLAR-227.
12. Golytsin, G. S., and Stanyukovich, K. P., Some Problems of Magnetohydrodynamics allowing for finite conductivity, Zh. Eksper Teor Fiz. Vol. 33, p. 417 (1957).
13. Golytsin, G. S., Plane Problems of Magnetohydrodynamics, Zh. eksper. teor Fiz., Vol. 34, p. 688 (1958).
14. Landau and Lifshitz, Theory of Elasticity, Addison-Wesley Pub. Co. (1959).
15. Landshoff, R. K. M. (Editor). Magnetohydrodynamics, Stanford Univ. Press (1957).
16. Landshoff, R. K. M. (Editor). The Plasma in a Magnetic Field, Stanford Univ. Press (1958).
17. Rose, D. J. and Clark, M. Jr., Plasmas and Controlled Fusion, The M.I.T. Press, and John Wiley & Sons, N.Y. (1961).
18. Rydbeck, O.E.H. and Thomasson, Proc. of the Fourth International Conference on Ionization Phenomena in Gases, Upsala, 1959 (North-Holland Pub. Co., Amsterdam 1960).
19. Sokolnikoff, I. S., The Mathematical Theory of Elasticity, McGraw-Hill Book Co., N.Y. (1956).
20. Spitzer, L., The Physics of Fully Ionized Gases, Interscience Pub. Co., N.Y. (1956).
21. Stratton, J. A.
22. Van de Hulst, H. C., and Burgers, J. M. (Editors). Gas Dynamics of Cosmic Clouds, Interscience Pub. Co. (1955).

CHAPTER V

ENERGY CONSIDERATIONS AND ELECTRODYNAMICS

In this chapter we treat the basic concepts of electrodynamics and energy as it relates to a plasma. The treatment is on the macroscopic level and we develop the various forms that the energy equations assume. As preparation for the latter we discuss first the energy concepts of the electromagnetic field for stationary bodies and then proceed to the treatment for moving bodies. The appropriate approach to the study of the electrodynamics of moving bodies is through the ideas and tools of relativity theory. Here, it becomes urgent to set down the basic mathematical concepts at the outset. This accomplished, we then develop the notions of force, and stress. In particular we construct the stress tensor and discuss its structure. From this we give a generalization of Poynting's theorem. The meaning of the effective field which forms the basis of the studies in magnetohydrodynamics results from this generalization in a natural way. With this ground work we are then able to derive the energy balance equations for a conducting fluid and thus provide a basis for studying the thermodynamics of such a fluid, following the approach of B. T. Chu.*

The energy equation for an ionized gas in the presence of a magnetic field is derived from the above considerations. For this situation, however, it is necessary to introduce the concepts of the diffusion flux vector and the total heat flux vector in a somewhat formal manner. These two vectors are more satisfactorily introduced through a microscopic analysis involving the Boltzmann equation whose introduction is deferred to a later chapter. On the other hand, it is pointed out how these two vectors are linked through the study of irreversible thermodynamics.

Following this an energy equation for magnetohydrodynamics is derived under the assumption that the total heat flux vector is given by Fourier's classical law. Some comments of a qualitative nature are brought to bear on the thermodynamics of a fully ionized gas in a strong magnetic field.

---

*Boa-Teh Chu, Thermodynamics of Electrically Conducting Fluids, pp. 473-484, The Physics of Fluids, Vol. 2, No. 5, Sept.-Oct., 1959.

By utilizing the balance equations for both energy and momentum, the latter in a simplified form, we demonstrate how it is possible to construct circuit dynamics involving a plasma. Such an approach must not be considered as rigorous, but rather should provide a beginning toward constructing circuit analogies. Here it is demonstrated how the role of Ohm's law and its generalizations for a plasma enter into the considerations. The coupling of thermal and electrodynamic variables are also put into evidence. Circuit equations for a plasma should have some real technological value if properly used.

As a further application of the developments in this and previous chapters we give a brief discussion of magnetohydrodynamic shocks and derive the shock conditions.

This is followed by a brief discourse on scaling and dimensional considerations in magnetohydrodynamics and the role of the magnetic Reynolds number.

Finally we take up the question of the possibility of obtaining a first order theory of the electrodynamics of moving matter without recourse to relativity theory. This topic is of interest because of its role in plasma physics and related problems on the interaction of rapidly moving bodies in conducting medium. In particular, the problem of determining the electrodynamic forces and torques due to the interaction of an externally applied magnetic field with a rotating magnetic conducting body calls for at least a first order theory. The first order theory is then applied to two examples for which a comparison with the results from relativity theory can be made. These examples are wave propagation in moving non-conducting isotropic matter and electromagnetic energy transport

47. ELECTROMAGNETIC FORCE—POYNTING'S THEOREM

In Chapters II and IV the Lorentz force acting on an electrical charge q in conjunction with Maxwell's equations yield the basic relations leading to dispersion equations for plane wave fields. In order to establish the connections between forces, stresses and energy in a plasma, the Lorentz force is also the point of departure for such an investigation.

For a single charge q, we recall that this force is given by

$$\mathbf{F} = q(\mathbf{E} + \mathbf{v}\mathbf{x}\mu_0\mathbf{H}) = q(\mathbf{E} + \mathbf{v}\mathbf{x}\mathbf{B}) \quad , \tag{47.1}$$

where **v** is the velocity of the charge. For a distributed charge with density $\eta_{(e)}$ and velocity **v** the Lorentz force is defined by

$$\mathbf{f} = \eta_{(e)}\mathbf{E} + \mathbf{J} \times \mathbf{B} \qquad (47.2)$$

with,

$$\mathbf{J} = \eta_{(e)}\mathbf{v} \quad , \qquad (47.3)$$

which is the current density due to the motion of the charge.

In order to hold a system of charges in dynamical equilibrium there must exist an exchange of energy between the electromagnetic field and the external forces which maintain these charges in equilibrium. Let us consider the power imparted by the electromagnetic field; it is defined by

$$\mathbf{F} \cdot \mathbf{v} = q(\mathbf{E} + \mathbf{v}\mathbf{x}\mathbf{B}) \cdot \mathbf{v} = q\mathbf{v} \cdot \mathbf{E} \qquad (47.4)$$

for a single charge q, and by

$$\mathbf{f} \cdot \mathbf{v} = \mathbf{J} \cdot \mathbf{E} \qquad (47.5)$$

for a distributed charge. For convenience we repeat Maxwell's equations here,

$$\left.\begin{aligned} \text{curl } \mathbf{E} &= -\frac{\partial \mathbf{B}}{\partial t} \\ \text{curl } \mathbf{H} &= \mathbf{J} + \epsilon_0 \frac{\partial \mathbf{E}}{\partial t} \\ \text{div } \mathbf{B} &= 0 \\ \text{div } \mathbf{D} &= \eta_{(e)} , \\ &\text{and the redundant equation (of continuity)} \\ \text{div } \mathbf{J} + \frac{\partial \eta_{(e)}}{\partial t} &= 0 \quad . \end{aligned}\right\} \qquad (47.6)$$

It follows from these equations and eq. (47.5) that

$$\mathbf{J} \cdot \mathbf{E} = \mathbf{E} \cdot \text{curl } \mathbf{H} - \epsilon_0 \mathbf{E} \cdot \frac{\partial \mathbf{E}}{\partial t} - \mathbf{H} \cdot \text{curl } \mathbf{E} - \mu_0 \mathbf{H} \cdot \frac{\partial \mathbf{H}}{\partial t}, \quad (47.7)$$

which becomes after using the identity,

$$\mathbf{H} \cdot \text{curl } \mathbf{E} - \mathbf{E} \cdot \text{curl } \mathbf{H} = \text{div } (\mathbf{E} \times \mathbf{H}) \quad , \quad (47.8)$$

$$-\mathbf{J} \cdot \mathbf{E} = \text{div } (\mathbf{E} \times \mathbf{H}) + \epsilon_0 \mathbf{E} + \mu_0 \mathbf{H} \cdot \frac{\partial \mathbf{H}}{\partial t} \quad : \quad (47.9)$$

This equation is Poynting's theorem. The left side represents the power absorbed per unit volume by the field. Following the standard procedure in electrodynamics, the Poynting vector $\mathbf{s}$ is defined by

$$\mathbf{s} = \mathbf{E} \times \mathbf{H} \quad (47.10)$$

and as we have seen in Chapter I, the quantities $\frac{1}{2}(\epsilon_0 \mathbf{E} \cdot \mathbf{E})$ and $\frac{1}{2}(\mu_0 \mathbf{H} \cdot \mathbf{H})$ represent the energy densities of the electric and magnetic fields respectively. Consequently, Poynting's theorem is cast into the form

$$\text{div } \mathbf{s} + \frac{1}{2} \frac{\partial}{\partial t} [\epsilon_0 \mathbf{E} \cdot \mathbf{E} + \mu_0 \mathbf{H} \cdot \mathbf{H}] = -\mathbf{J} \cdot \mathbf{E} \quad (47.11)$$

or by the divergence theorem applied to a stationary volume V,

$$\int_\Sigma \mathbf{s} \cdot \mathbf{n} d\Sigma + \frac{d}{dt} \int_V \frac{1}{2} [\epsilon_0 \mathbf{E} \cdot \mathbf{E} + \mu_0 \mathbf{H} \cdot \mathbf{H}] dV = -\int_V \mathbf{J} \cdot \mathbf{E} dV \ . (47.12)$$

We recall that the electric current density is composed of two parts, a polarization component $\partial \mathbf{P}/\partial t$, where $\mathbf{P}$ is the polarization vector, and a so-called free current density denoted by $\mathbf{J}_f$. Thus, in the expression $\mathbf{J} \cdot \mathbf{E}$ we have $\mathbf{E} \cdot \partial \mathbf{P}/\partial t$ representing the power imparted by the electromagnetic field to the medium when $\mathbf{P}$ varies with time. The part $\mathbf{J}_f \cdot \mathbf{E}$ is the electromagnetic power transformed into another form of energy (heat, etc.).

48. COMPLEX POYNTING THEOREM

If the constitutive relations for a medium are linear, *i.e.*,

$$\left.\begin{aligned} \mathbf{D} &= \epsilon\mathbf{E} , \\ \mathbf{B} &= \mu\mathbf{H} , \\ \mathbf{J} &= \sigma\mathbf{E} , \end{aligned}\right\} \tag{48.1}$$

where ϵ, μ, σ are functions of position only, a time harmonic steady state field can exist and the relation between the field and the free sources are given by Maxwell's equations. But now, we merely replace ϵ_0, μ_0 by ϵ, μ respectively and $\mathbf{J}$ by $\mathbf{J}_f$, also $\eta_{(e)}$ is now taken to mean the free source charge density, say η_f. Since the field vectors are complex quantities, we have

$$\mathbf{s} = \frac{1}{2}\,\mathrm{Re}\,(\mathbf{E}\times\mathbf{H}^*) + \frac{1}{2}\,\mathrm{Re}\,(\mathbf{E}\times\mathbf{H}e^{2i\omega t}) \quad . \tag{48.2}$$

This form shows that the first term on the right side is time independent and therefore represents the average value of the Poynting vector over one cycle, the second term varies with a frequency 2ω. The field energy densities are

$$\left.\begin{aligned} U_e &= \frac{1}{4}\epsilon\,(\mathbf{E}\cdot\mathbf{E}^*) + \frac{1}{4}\epsilon\,\mathrm{Re}\,(\mathbf{E}\cdot\mathbf{E}e^{2i\omega t}) , \\ U_m &= \frac{1}{4}\mu\,(\mathbf{H}\cdot\mathbf{H}^*) + \frac{1}{4}\mu\,\mathrm{Re}\,(\mathbf{H}\cdot\mathbf{H}e^{2i\omega t}) , \end{aligned}\right\} \tag{48.3}$$

and the dissipated power density is

$$\mathbf{J}_f\cdot\mathbf{E} = \frac{1}{2}\sigma\,(\mathbf{E}\cdot\mathbf{E}^*) + \frac{1}{2}\sigma\,\mathrm{Re}\,(\mathbf{E}\cdot\mathbf{E}e^{2i\omega t}) \quad . \tag{48.4}$$

Here too, the first terms standing on the right side of these equations are real, time independent quantities and so represent the average value of their respective densities. The second term on the right side of these equations simply represents the double frequency variation of their respective energy densities. We define the complex Poynting vector as

$$\frac{1}{2}(\mathbf{E}\times\mathbf{H}^*) \equiv \bar{\mathbf{s}} \quad . \tag{48.5}$$

We can develop a theorem for this vector corresponding to what was done for the non-time harmonic case. We have in fact

$$\text{div}\,\bar{\mathbf{s}} = \text{div}\frac{1}{2}(\mathbf{E}\times\mathbf{H}^*) = \frac{1}{2}(\mathbf{H}^*\cdot\text{curl}\,\mathbf{E} - \mathbf{E}\cdot\text{curl}\,\mathbf{H}^*) \tag{48.6}$$

and since for harmonic time fields, Maxwell's equations are,

$$\text{curl}\,\mathbf{E} = -i\mu\omega\mathbf{H} \quad , \qquad \text{curl}\,\mathbf{H} = \mathbf{J}_f + i\epsilon\omega\mathbf{E} \ , \tag{48.7}$$

there results,

$$\text{div}\,\bar{\mathbf{s}} = -\frac{1}{2}(\mathbf{E}\cdot\mathbf{J}_f^*) - 2i\omega\left(\frac{1}{4}\mu\,\mathbf{H}\cdot\mathbf{H}^* - \frac{1}{4}\epsilon\,\mathbf{E}\cdot\mathbf{E}^*\right) \quad . \tag{48.8}$$

Separating out the real and imaginary parts, gives

$$\left.\begin{aligned} \text{Re}\,(\text{div}\,\bar{\mathbf{s}}) &= -\frac{1}{2}\text{Re}\,(\mathbf{J}_f^*\cdot\mathbf{E}) \ , && (48.9) \\ \text{Im}\,(\text{div}\,\bar{\mathbf{s}}) &= -\frac{1}{2}\text{Im}\,(\mathbf{J}_f^*\cdot\mathbf{E}) + \left(\frac{1}{4}\epsilon\,\mathbf{E}\cdot\mathbf{E}^* - \frac{1}{4}\mu\,\mathbf{H}\cdot\mathbf{H}^*\right)2\omega \ . && (48.10) \end{aligned}\right\}$$

By integrating both of these expressions over a fixed volume V, as before and applying the divergence theorem we find,

$$-\text{Re}\int_\Sigma \bar{\mathbf{s}}\cdot\mathbf{n}\,d\Sigma = \text{Re}\int_V \frac{1}{2}(\mathbf{J}_f^*\cdot\mathbf{E})\,dV \quad , \tag{48.11}$$

$$-\text{Im}\int_\Sigma \mathbf{s}\cdot\mathbf{n}\,d\Sigma = \text{Im}\int_V \frac{1}{2}(\mathbf{J}_f^*\cdot\mathbf{E})\,dV$$

$$+ \ 2\omega\int_V\left[\frac{1}{4}\mu\,\mathbf{H}\cdot\mathbf{H}^* - \frac{1}{4}\epsilon\,\mathbf{E}\cdot\mathbf{E}^*\right]dV \quad .$$

In order to interpret these expressions physically, it is convenient to decompose the free current density $\mathbf{J}_f$ into the sum of a conduction current $\mathbf{J}_c = \sigma\mathbf{E}$ and another component $\mathbf{J}_s$ which represents a current source density. More specifically, we write

$$\frac{1}{2}\,\mathrm{Re}\,(\mathbf{J}_f^* \cdot \mathbf{E}) = \frac{1}{2}\,\sigma\mathbf{E} \cdot \mathbf{E}^* + \frac{1}{2}\,\mathrm{Re}\,[(\mathbf{J}_f^* - \mathbf{J}_c^*) \cdot \mathbf{E}] \qquad (48.13)$$

and when this is inserted into the expressions (48.11) and (48.12), we interpret the latter as follows. Equation (48.11) asserts that the sum of the average power which flows into the volume through its boundary surface Σ and the average power arising from the sources in the volume equals the average power dissipated in the volume. To interpret eq. (48.12) we consider the imaginary part as a reactive power and hence this equation says that the sum of the reactive power which flows into the volume through Σ and the reactive power arising from sources inside the volume equals the product of 2ω by the difference of the average magnetic and electric energy stored in the volume.

The relations presented above hold only for stationary media. If we want to develop a generalization of Poynting's theorem for a material medium which is also moving an approach via relativity theory provides a modus operandi. In the following section we shall set down the essentials for a consistent treatment of the electrodynamics of a material medium in motion. Although Minkowski* developed a theory for just such a purpose, his treatment is beset with some conceptual difficulties. Many other apparently valid theories have since been developed.†

MOVING BODIES--RELATIVISTIC CONSIDERATIONS

It is not our intention here to give a complete exposition on the theory of relativity, special or otherwise. We presume the reader has a nodding acquaintance with the subject at least with the special theory or can easily acquire it by reference to the many clear expositions. Consequently, we shall list certain expressions, and interpret them for our future use.

---

* H. Minkowski, Göttingen Nachrichten, Math.-Phys. Klasse I (1908) pp. 53-111; and Math. Annalen 68 (1910) pp. 472-525.

† J. Slepian, Elect. Eng. 69 (1950) pp. 456, 550, 636; Proc. Nat. Acad. Sci. (Washington) 36 (1950) pp. 485-497.

We consider two inertial rectilinear reference frames denoted by S and S'. The velocity of S' relative to S is uniform and equal to $\mathbf{V}$, that of S relative to S' is obviously $-\mathbf{V}$. The reference frame S' will be called the rest frame and all quantities referred to the coordinates of S' are denoted by primed quantities, while those for S are unprimed. We shall use a four-vector description and Minkowski coordinates (x_1, x_2, x_3, x_4) where the first three coordinates are spatial, and $x_4 = iV_0 t$; t is the time, V_0 a reference speed (many authors use C for V_0). The reference frames S and S' are related by a proper Lorentz transformation, in matrix language,

$$\mathbf{x}' = \mathbf{A}\mathbf{x} \tag{48.14}$$

and A is such that it preserves the form,

$$\mathbf{x}' \cdot \mathbf{x}' = \mathbf{x} \cdot \mathbf{x} \quad . \tag{48.15}$$

If the relative motion of S and S' is parallel to their respective x_1' and x_1 axis, the transformation $\mathbf{A}$ has the form,

$$\mathbf{A} = \begin{pmatrix} \beta & 0 & 0 & i\beta \dfrac{V}{V_0} \\ 0 & 1 & 0 & 0 \\ 0 & 0 & 1 & 0 \\ -i\beta \dfrac{V}{V_0} & 0 & 0 & \beta \end{pmatrix} , \tag{48.16}$$

where

$$\beta = \left[1 - \left(\frac{V}{V_0} \right)^2 \right]^{-\frac{1}{2}} \quad . \tag{48.17}$$

Four-vectors transform according to the rule given by eq. (48.14), that is, if $\mathbf{b}$ and $\mathbf{b}'$ represent the same four-vector in S and S' respectively, they are related by

$$\mathbf{b}' = \mathbf{A}\mathbf{b} \quad . \tag{48.18}$$

Besides the transformation of vectors we must also consider entities which depend on two indices, these are second rank tensors (*e.g.*, strain tensor, etc.). To qualify as a second rank tensor they must satisfy the following rule of transformation,

$$\epsilon'_{ij} = a_{im} a_{jn} \epsilon_{mn} \quad , \quad \text{(summation convention)} \quad , \tag{48.19}$$

where a_{im} is the element in the *i*th row and *m*th column of **A**, all indices range over (1, 2, 3, 4). If **r** denotes the displacement vector in four-space, $d\mathbf{r}$ is defined by

$$d\mathbf{r} \equiv (dx_1,\ dx_2,\ dx_3,\ iV_0 dt) \quad , \tag{48.20}$$

and the four velocity of a particle by

$$\hat{\mathbf{v}} \equiv \frac{d\mathbf{r}}{d\tau} = \frac{(dx_1,\ dx_2,\ dx_3,\ iV_0 dt)}{d\tau} = \gamma(\mathbf{v},\ iV_0) \quad , \tag{48.21}$$

with

$$\gamma = \left[1 - \left(\frac{v}{V_0}\right)^2\right]^{-\frac{1}{2}} \quad , \tag{48.21'}$$

where $d\tau$ is the proper time defined by $d\tau = dt/\gamma$, and **v** is the ordinary three space velocity. The length of **v** is given through

$$\hat{\mathbf{v}} \cdot \hat{\mathbf{v}} = (iV_0)^2 \quad . \tag{48.22}$$

The divergence of a vector in the Minkowski space is,

$$\text{div}\ \mathbf{W} \equiv \left(\frac{\partial}{\partial x_1},\ \frac{\partial}{\partial x_2},\ \frac{\partial}{\partial x_3},\ \frac{\partial}{\partial iV_0 t}\right) \mathbf{W} = \frac{\partial w_i}{\partial x_i} \quad . \tag{48.23}$$

The equation of continuity of charge in three space is

$$\nabla \cdot \mathbf{J} = -\frac{\partial \eta}{\partial t} \quad , \tag{48.24}$$

and can be written in four-space as

$$\frac{\partial}{\partial x_1} J_1 + \frac{\partial}{\partial x_2} J_2 + \frac{\partial}{\partial x_3} J_3 + \frac{\partial}{\partial(iV_0 t)} iV_0\eta = 0$$

or if we denote by $\hat{\mathbf{J}}$ the four-current, we can write

$$\hat{\mathbf{J}} = (\mathbf{J},\ iV_0\eta)$$

and eq. (48.24) becomes,

$$\operatorname{div} \hat{\mathbf{J}} = 0 \quad . \tag{48.25}$$

Now suppose that we have a material medium which contains polarizable matter. Then the current density in three space is the sum of two parts, a free current density and a contribution from the polarized matter, the polarization current density. Denoting these respectively by $\mathbf{J}_f$ and $\mathbf{J}_P$, we have the four-current density,

$$\hat{\mathbf{J}} = \hat{\mathbf{J}}_f + \hat{\mathbf{J}}_P = (\mathbf{J}_f,\ iV_0\eta_f) + (\mathbf{J}_P,\ iV_0\eta_P) \tag{48.26}$$

where η_f and η_P denote free and bound charge distributions of electric charge. The polarization current is defined in terms of the polarization vector $\mathbf{P}$ by (see Chapter II, section 8),

$$\mathbf{J}_P = \frac{\partial \mathbf{P}}{\partial t} \quad , \tag{48.27}$$

and we want to find the polarization four-vector $\mathbf{P}$ in order to establish the connection between $\mathbf{J}_P$ and $\mathbf{P}$. For this we first assert without proof that if $\mathbf{P}$ is the three space polarization vector, the four-polarization vector $\hat{\mathbf{P}}$ is given by

$$\hat{\mathbf{P}} = \left(\gamma \frac{\mathbf{P} \cdot \mathbf{v}}{V_0^2} + \frac{\mathbf{P}}{\gamma},\ i\gamma \frac{\mathbf{P} \cdot \mathbf{v}}{V_0} \right) \tag{48.28}$$

with

$$\gamma = \left[1 - \left(\frac{v}{V_0} \right)^2 \right]^{-1/2} \tag{48.29}$$

where $\mathbf{v}$ is the three-space velocity with which a dipole moves in the reference frame S. In the rest system S', γ reduces to β, $\mathbf{v} = \mathbf{V}$ and if the relative motion is along the x_1 axis,

$$\hat{\mathbf{P}} = \left(\beta P_1, \frac{P_2}{\beta}, \frac{P_3}{\beta}, i\beta P_1 \frac{V}{V_0} \right) , \qquad (48.30)$$

i.e., the polarized medium is at rest in S'. To establish the connection between $\hat{\mathbf{J}}$ and $\hat{\mathbf{P}}$ we must first introduce the outer or vector product of two four-vectors. This is achieved by analogy with the concept of the vector product in three-space. Strictly speaking, in three space, the vector product does not produce a vector but rather a second rank skew-symmetric tensor. Let **a** and **b** be two three-space vectors, the vector product yields the components,

$$c_{ij} = a_i b_j - a_j b_i , \quad (i, j = 1, 2, 3) , \qquad (48.31)$$

which is skew-symmetric in i and j. The components c_{ij} can be considered as the elements of a 3×3 matrix, but because there are only three independent elements it is also treated as a vector in three space. For the four-vector treatment we define the vector product in the same way and write for any two four-vectors **a** and **b**,

$$(\mathbf{a} \times \mathbf{b})_{ij} \equiv a_i b_j - a_j b_i , \quad (i, j = 1, 2, 3, 4) . \qquad (48.32)$$

Here too, because of the skew-symmetry, there are only six independent components and we can consider the result as a six dimensional vector. By direct calculation we first have,

$$\hat{\mathbf{P}} \times \hat{\mathbf{v}} = (\mathbf{P} \times \mathbf{v} \; ; \; iV_0 \mathbf{P}) \qquad (48.33)$$

or in matrix form,

$$\hat{\mathbf{P}} \times \hat{\mathbf{v}} \equiv \begin{bmatrix} 0 & P_1 v_2 - P_2 v_1 & P_1 v_3 - P_3 v_1 & iV_0 P_1 \\ P_2 v_1 - P_1 v_2 & 0 & P_2 v_3 - P_3 v_2 & iV_0 P_2 \\ P_3 v_1 - P_1 v_3 & P_3 v_2 - P_2 v_3 & 0 & iV_0 P_3 \\ -iV_0 P_1 & -iV_0 P_2 & -iV_0 P_3 & 0 \end{bmatrix} \qquad (48.34)$$

which reveals the structure more clearly than in eq. (48.33). Next, a straightforward calculation shows that,

$$\hat{\mathbf{J}}_P = \operatorname{div}\,(\hat{\mathbf{P}}\,\mathbf{x}\,\hat{\mathbf{v}}) = \left[\frac{\partial \mathbf{P}}{\partial t} + \operatorname{curl}\,(\mathbf{P}\,\mathbf{x}\,\mathbf{v})\;,\quad -iV_0\nabla\cdot\mathbf{P}\right]$$

$$= (\mathbf{J}_P,\; iV_0\eta_P)\;,, \tag{48.35}$$

the basic result we have sought. It is now possible to express the four-current vector $\hat{\mathbf{J}}$ as the divergence of a certain tensor of rank two, which is an electromagnetic field tensor. Another field tensor is constructed along with it and is formally similar to the first tensor. This is best seen if we rewrite Maxwell's equations in a symmetric way. The symmetry is introduced by assuming a magnetic current density and charge, fictitious of course, but nevertheless very suggestive. Instead of writing as above $\acute{\mathbf{J}}$ and η, we now write $\hat{\mathbf{J}}_{(e)}$ and $\eta_{(e)}$ and introduce the magnetic four-current vector $\hat{\mathbf{J}}_{(m)}$ and charge $\eta_{(m)}$. Maxwell's equations are rewritten in the form of two pairs of equations,

$$\left.\begin{aligned} \nabla\,\mathbf{x}\,\mathbf{H} - \frac{\partial}{\partial t}\,\epsilon_0\mathbf{E} &= \mathbf{J}_{(e)}\;, \\ \nabla\cdot\epsilon_0\mathbf{E} &= \eta_{(e)}\;. \end{aligned}\right\} \tag{48.36}$$

$$\left.\begin{aligned} -\nabla\,\mathbf{x}\,\mathbf{E} - \frac{\partial}{\partial t}\,\mu_0\mathbf{H} &= \mathbf{J}_{(m)}\;, \\ \nabla\cdot\mu_0\mathbf{H} &= \eta_{(m)}\;. \end{aligned}\right\} \tag{48.37}$$

In terms of the Minkowski coordinates, we find that these two pairs can be put in the following compact form,

$$\hat{\mathbf{J}}_{(e)} = \operatorname{div}\,\hat{\mathbf{G}}_{(e)}\;, \tag{48.38}$$

$$\hat{\mathbf{J}}_{(m)} = \operatorname{div}\,\hat{\mathbf{G}}_{(m)}\;, \tag{48.39}$$

where $\hat{\mathbf{G}}_{(e)}$ is the skew-symmetric tensor defined by

$$\hat{\mathbf{G}}_{(e)} = \begin{bmatrix} 0 & H_3 & -H_2 & -iV_0\epsilon_0E_1 \\ -H_3 & 0 & H_1 & -iV_0\epsilon_0E_2 \\ H_2 & -H_1 & 0 & -iV_0\epsilon_0E_3 \\ iV_0\epsilon_0E_1 & iV_0\epsilon_0E_2 & iV_0\epsilon_0E_3 & 0 \end{bmatrix} , \quad (48.40)$$

and $\hat{\mathbf{G}}_{(m)}$ is the skew-symmetric tensor defined by

$$\hat{\mathbf{G}}_{(m)} = \begin{bmatrix} 0 & -E_3 & E_2 & -iV_0\mu_0H_1 \\ E_3 & 0 & -E_1 & -iV_0\mu_0H_2 \\ -E_2 & E_1 & 0 & -iV_0\mu_0H_3 \\ iV_0\mu_0H_1 & iV_0\mu_0H_2 & iV_0\mu_0H_3 & 0 \end{bmatrix} . \quad (48.41)$$

These two tensors can also be written as

$$\hat{\mathbf{G}}_{(e)} = (\mathbf{H} \; ; \quad -iV_0\epsilon_0\mathbf{E}) , \quad (48.42)$$

$$\hat{\mathbf{G}}_{(m)} = (-\mathbf{E} \; ; \quad -iV_0\mu_0\mathbf{H}) , \quad \textit{i.e.}, \text{ as six-vectors.} \quad (48.43)$$

That these two tensors are not independent, but are rather related is left as an exercise. A further notational compactness can be achieved by considering both $\hat{\mathbf{J}}_{(e)}$ and $\hat{\mathbf{J}}_{(m)}$ as components of a new vector and $\hat{\mathbf{G}}_{(e)}$, $\hat{\mathbf{G}}_{(m)}$ as subtensors of a new tensor, but nothing new is obtained physically. These two tensors are called the electromagnetic field tensors.

49. FORCES AND THE ELECTROMAGNETIC STRESS-TENSOR

The relation between the ponderomotive force and an electromagnetic stress tensor is brought into focus by first examining the idea of the momentum four-vector; this is substantially the approach utilized by Einstein. If m_0 is the rest mass of a particle, the force four-vector $\hat{\mathbf{F}}$ is defined as the time (proper time) derivative of the momentum four-vector. The momentum four-vector is $m\hat{\mathbf{v}}$ and hence,

$$\hat{\mathbf{F}} = \frac{d}{d\tau} \gamma m_0 (\mathbf{v} \, , \; iV_0) , \quad (49.1)$$

where γ has been defined by Eq. (48.29). We can also write,

$$\hat{\mathbf{F}} = \frac{dt}{d\tau}\frac{d}{dt}\gamma m_0(\mathbf{v}\ ,\ iV_0)$$

or

$$\hat{\mathbf{F}} = \gamma\left(\frac{d}{dt}\gamma m_0\mathbf{v} \quad \frac{i}{V_0}\frac{d}{dt}\gamma^2 m_0 V_0^2\right) \quad . \tag{49.2}$$

Accordingly, $\gamma m_0\mathbf{v}$ is the three-space momentum and mV_0^2 or $\gamma m_0 V_0^2$ is the three-space energy, and we recognize respectively that the time rate of change of $\gamma m_0\mathbf{v}$ is the force $\mathbf{F}$ and the time rate of change of $\gamma m_0 V_0^2$ is the work done per unit time by $\mathbf{F}$. Here $\mathbf{F}$ is the ordinary three-space force, t is the ordinary time. Since $\mathbf{F}\cdot\mathbf{v}$ is the work, $\mathbf{F}\cdot\mathbf{v} = d/dt\ \gamma m_0\mathbf{v}$ and therefore the four-force can be written as

$$\hat{\mathbf{F}} = \gamma\left(\mathbf{F}\ ,\ \frac{i}{V_0}\mathbf{F}\cdot\mathbf{v}\right) \quad . \tag{49.3}$$

The generalization of the three-space Lorentz force is therefore

$$\hat{\mathbf{F}} = \gamma q\left(\mathbf{E} + \mathbf{v}\mathbf{x}\mu_0\mathbf{H}\ ,\ \frac{i}{V_0}\mathbf{E}\cdot\mathbf{v}\right) \quad , \tag{49.4}$$

where q is the charge, a relativistic invariant. It follows that this Lorentz four-force is related to the field tensor $\hat{\mathbf{G}}_{(e)}$ by the rule,

$$\hat{\mathbf{F}} = \mu_0\hat{\mathbf{G}}q\mathbf{v} \equiv \left(\mu_0\mathbf{H}\ ;\ -\frac{i}{V_0}\mathbf{E}\right)\cdot\ \gamma(q\mathbf{v}\ ,\ iqV_0) \quad . \tag{49.5}$$

The components of $\hat{\mathbf{F}}$ are obtained by carrying out the matrix operation, thus, the kth component of $\hat{\mathbf{F}}$ is,

$$\hat{F}_k = q\mu_0\hat{G}_{(e)kj}v_j \quad , \qquad \text{(recall the summation convention)}\ . \tag{49.6}$$

The generalization to a distributed charge density leads us to define the electric force density $\hat{\mathbf{f}}$ as

$$\hat{\mathbf{f}} = \left(\eta_{(e)}\mathbf{E} + \mathbf{J}\mathbf{x}\mu_0\mathbf{H} \, , \, \frac{i}{V_0}\mathbf{E}\cdot\mathbf{J} \right) = \left(\mathbf{f} \, , \, \frac{i}{V_0}\mathbf{E}\cdot\mathbf{J} \right) , \tag{49.7}$$

where $\mathbf{f}$ is the ordinary three-space Lorentz force density. By utilizing eqs. (48.38) and (48.40), we can express $\hat{\mathbf{f}}$ above in terms of the field tensor $\hat{\mathbf{G}}_{(e)}$,

$$\hat{\mathbf{f}} = \mu_0\hat{\mathbf{G}}_{(e)} \operatorname{div} \hat{\mathbf{G}}_e \quad , \tag{49.8}$$

with the understanding, naturally, that we are forming the product of a matrix $\hat{\mathbf{G}}_{(e)}$ with a vector div $\hat{\mathbf{G}}_{(e)}$. The form of eq. (49.8) suggests that we define a magnetic four-force density by

$$\hat{\mathbf{f}}_{(m)} = \epsilon_0\hat{\mathbf{G}}_{(m)} \operatorname{div} \hat{\mathbf{G}}_{(m)} \tag{49.9}$$

and therefore now write as a generalization,

$$\hat{\mathbf{f}}_{(e)} + \hat{\mathbf{f}}_{(m)} = \mu_0\hat{\mathbf{G}}_{(e)} \operatorname{div} \hat{\mathbf{G}}_{(e)} + \epsilon_0\hat{\mathbf{G}}_{(m)} \operatorname{div} \hat{\mathbf{G}}_{(m)} \quad . \tag{49.10}$$

It is desirable to seek an analogy with the nomenclature of Chapter III, and attempt to write these force densities as the divergence of a suitable stress tensor. This formal analogy can in fact be accomplished by introducing the symmetrical tensor

$$\hat{\tau} = \begin{bmatrix} \epsilon_0E_1^2 + \mu_0H_1^2 - W & \epsilon_0E_1E_2 + \mu_0H_1H_2 & \epsilon_0E_1E_3 + \mu_0H_1H_3 & -\frac{i}{V_0}S_1 \\ \epsilon_0E_1E_2 + \mu_0H_1H_2 & \epsilon_0E_2^2 + \mu_0H_2^2 - W & \epsilon_0E_2E_3 + \mu_0H_2H_3 & -\frac{i}{V_0}S_2 \\ \epsilon_0E_1E_3 + \mu_0H_1H_3 & \epsilon_0E_2E_3 + \mu_0H_2H_3 & \epsilon_0E_3^2 + \mu_0H_3^2 - W & -\frac{i}{V_0}S_3 \\ -\frac{i}{V_0}S_1 & -\frac{i}{V_0}S_2 & -\frac{i}{V_0}S_3 & W \end{bmatrix} , \tag{49.11}$$

where the S_k are the components of the Poynting vector $\mathbf{s}$ defined by eq. (47.10), and

$$W = \frac{1}{2}\epsilon_0\mathbf{E}\cdot\mathbf{E} + \frac{1}{2}\mu_0\mathbf{H}\cdot\mathbf{H} \quad , \tag{49.12}$$

it can then be verified directly that

$$\hat{\mathbf{f}}_{(e)} + \hat{\mathbf{f}}_{(m)} = \operatorname{div} \hat{\tau} \quad . \tag{49.13}$$

The symmetrical tensor $\hat{\tau}$ is called the electromagnetic stress-tensor. If we denote by τ the 3×3 matrix of the upper left part of $\hat{\tau}$, it follows that in terms of the three-space force densities,*

$$\mathbf{f}_{(e)} + \mathbf{f}_{(m)} = \nabla \cdot \tau - \frac{\partial}{\partial t} \frac{\mathbf{s}}{V_0^2} \quad . \tag{49.14}$$

This equation asserts that $\mathbf{s}/V_0^2$ is interpreted as the electromagnetic-momentum-density, or

$$\mathbf{g} = \frac{\mathbf{s}}{V_0^2} = \mu_0 \epsilon_0 (\mathbf{E} \times \mathbf{H}) \quad . \tag{49.15}$$

The fourth component of eq. (49.13) is,

$$\mathbf{E} \cdot \mathbf{J}_{(e)} + \mathbf{H} \cdot \mathbf{J}_{(m)} = -\nabla \cdot \left(\mathbf{E} \times \mathbf{H}\right) - \frac{\partial}{\partial t} \frac{1}{2} (\epsilon_0 |\mathbf{E}|^2 + \mu_0 |\mathbf{H}|^2) \quad . \tag{49.16}$$

Before we proceed to make further interpretations we want to complete the description of the electromagnetic field by postulating the relations between the field quantities for a macroscopic material medium.† For the linear case, we assume that if σ, ϵ and μ are tensors, and if η_f, $\mathbf{v}$, $\mathbf{J}_f$, $\mathbf{P}$ and $\mathbf{M}$ (the intensity of magnetization) are known, these quantities are related according to the constitutive equations, as follows,

$$(\mathbf{J}_f - \eta_f \mathbf{v}) = \sigma(\mathbf{E} + \mathbf{v} \times \mu_0 \mathbf{H}) \quad , \tag{49.17}$$

$$\mathbf{P} = (\epsilon - \epsilon_0 \mathbf{I})(\mathbf{E} + \mathbf{v} \times \mu_0 \mathbf{H}) \quad , \tag{49.18}$$

$$\mathbf{M} = (\mu - \mu_0 \mathbf{I})(\mathbf{H} - \mathbf{v} \times \epsilon_0 \mathbf{E}) \quad . \tag{49.19}$$

---

* It is often argued that the stress tensor by itself is not a legitimate physical quantity in the relativistic case, however an interesting approach toward a theory of elasticity in general relativity has recently been given by J. L. Synge, A Theory of Elasticity in General Relativity, Math. Zeitschr. 72, 82-87 (1959).

† Relativistic electromagnetic equations in material medium have been treated at great length in the literature. To cite a few lucid papers in recent years, see N. W. Taylor, A Simplified Form of the Relativistic Electromagnetic Equations, Austral. J. Sci. Res. (series A), 5, pp. 423-429 (1952); see also same author, The Relativistic Equations in a Material Medium, Austral. J. Phys. V. 6, pp. 1-9 (1953); G. Marx, Das Electromagnetische Feld in Bewegten Anisotropen Medien, Acta Physica Hungaricae, V. 3, pp. 75-94 (1953); Teodor Schlomka, Das Ohmische Gesetz bei bewegten Korpern, Annalen Der Physik, Ser. 6, Vol. 8, pp. 246-252 (1951); Ernest Schmutzer, Zur Relativistischen Elektrodynamik in Beliebigen Medien, Annalen Der Physik, Ser. 6, Vol. 18, pp. 171-180 (1956); M. Tischer und S. Hess, Die Materialgleichungen in Beliebigen Medien, Annalen Der Physik, 7. Folge, Band 3, Heft 3-4, pp. 113-121 (1959).

In the rest frame S', $\mathbf{v} = 0$, and the relations reduce to the usual ones for an anisotropic medium.

It is now possible to construct a generalized Poynting's equation by utilizing the preceding developments. First let us interpret eq. (49.14); in terms of the three-space vectors we can write,

$$\mathbf{f}_{(e)} + \mathbf{f}_{(m)} + \epsilon_0\mu_0 \frac{\partial \mathbf{s}}{\partial t} = \epsilon_0 [\mathbf{E}\nabla \cdot \mathbf{E} - \mathbf{E}\mathrm{x}(\nabla \mathrm{x}\mathbf{E})] + \mu_0 [\mathbf{H}\nabla \cdot \mathbf{H} - \mathbf{H}\mathrm{x}(\nabla \mathrm{x}\mathbf{H})] , \quad (49.20)$$

or since,

$$\mathbf{E}\mathrm{x}(\nabla \mathrm{x}\mathbf{E}) + (\mathbf{E} \cdot \nabla)\mathbf{E} = \frac{1}{2} \,\mathbf{grad}\, (\mathbf{E} \cdot \mathbf{E}) \quad (49.21)$$

and similarly for $\mathbf{H}$, we obtain,

$$\mathbf{f}_{(e)} + \mathbf{f}_{(m)} + \frac{\partial}{\partial t}\frac{\mathbf{s}}{V_0^2} = \epsilon_0 [\mathbf{E}\nabla \cdot \mathbf{E} + (\mathbf{E} \cdot \nabla)\mathbf{E}] + \mu_0 [\mathbf{H}\nabla \cdot \mathbf{H} + (\mathbf{H} \cdot \nabla)\mathbf{H}] - \mathbf{grad}\, W \,. \quad (49.22)$$

Now integrate both sides over a volume V bounded by Σ,

$$\int_V \left(\mathbf{f}_{(e)} + \mathbf{f}_{(m)} + \mu_0\epsilon_0 \frac{\partial \mathbf{s}}{\partial t}\right) dV = \int_V \{\epsilon_0 [\mathbf{E}\nabla \cdot \mathbf{E} + (\mathbf{E} \cdot \nabla)\mathbf{E}] + \mu_0 [\mathbf{H}\nabla \cdot \mathbf{H} + (\mathbf{H} \cdot \nabla)\mathbf{H}] - \mathbf{grad}\, W\} dV \,,$$

the right hand volume integral can be transformed into a surface integral to give,

$$\int_V \left(\mathbf{f}_{(e)} + \mathbf{f}_{(m)} + \mu_0\epsilon_0 \frac{\partial \mathbf{s}}{\partial t}\right) dV = \int_\Sigma [\epsilon_0 (\mathbf{n} \cdot \mathbf{E})\mathbf{E} + \mu_0 (\mathbf{n} \cdot \mathbf{H})\mathbf{H} - \mathbf{n}W] d\Sigma \,, \quad (49.23)$$

where $\mathbf{n}$ is the unit outward drawn normal to Σ. When there are no free charges or material within V, the force density terms vanish and we are left with the equation,,

$$\frac{d}{dt}\int_V \mu_0\epsilon_0 \mathbf{s}\, dV = \int_\Sigma [\epsilon_0 (\mathbf{n} \cdot \mathbf{E})\mathbf{E} + \mu_0 (\mathbf{n} \cdot \mathbf{H})\mathbf{H} - \mathbf{n}W] d\Sigma \,. \quad (49.24)$$

On the other hand, if there is matter and charges within V, then we can define a mechanical momentum $\mathbf{h}$ by

$$\mathbf{f}_{(e)} + \mathbf{f}_{(m)} = \frac{\partial \mathbf{h}}{\partial t} \qquad (49.25)$$

and hence write eq. (49.23) as

$$\frac{d}{dt}\int_V (\mathbf{g} + \mathbf{h})dV = \int_\Sigma [\qquad]d\Sigma \quad , \qquad (49.26)$$

the brackets containing the integrand of eq. (49.23). Now our statement reads; the time rate of change of electromagnetic plus mechanical momentum attributed to V is equal to the total electromagnetic stress on Σ which bounds V.

Eq. (49.16) provides us with the basis of the generalized Poynting's theorem. Indeed we have,

$$\mathbf{E}\cdot\mathbf{J}_{(e)} + \mathbf{H}\cdot\mathbf{J}_{(m)} = -\left(\nabla\cdot\mathbf{s} + \frac{\partial W}{\partial t}\right) \quad , \qquad (49.16)$$

which upon integration over V, and by use of the divergence theorem, we obtain,

$$\int_V (\mathbf{E}\cdot\mathbf{J}_{(e)} + \mathbf{H}\cdot\mathbf{J}_{(m)})dV = -\int_\Sigma \mathbf{s} : \mathbf{n}d\Sigma - \int_V \frac{\partial W}{\partial t}\,dV \quad . \qquad (49.27)$$

The left side is interpreted as the total electromagnetic power transformed in the volume to other forms of energy by means of the motion of the electrical charges and magnetic currents in the presence of the field. The surface integral gives the electromagnetic power fluxing into the volume through Σ, while the last term on the right side is the rate of change of the field energy within the volume. It must be noted that this field energy does not include the energy absorbed by magnetized or polarized material. By analogy with eq. (48.35) for $\hat{\mathbf{J}}_p$, we shall put

$$\hat{\mathbf{J}}_{(m)} = (\mathbf{J}_{(m)}, iV_0\eta_{(m)}) \qquad (49.28)$$

and define,

$$\mathbf{J}_{(m)} = \frac{\partial}{\partial t}\mu_0\mathbf{M} + \nabla\mathbf{x}(\mu_0\mathbf{M}\mathbf{x}\mathbf{v}) \quad , \tag{49.29}$$

the magnetic charge density is taken as,

$$\eta_{(m)} = -\nabla\cdot(\mu_0\mathbf{M}) \tag{49.30}$$

so that $\mathbf{P}$ stands in analogy with $\mu_0\mathbf{M}$ rather than $\mathbf{M}$. Following the analogy further, we define the force density of magnetic charge due to the action of the field by

$$\mathbf{f}_{(m)} = \eta_{(m)}\mathbf{H} - \mathbf{J}_{(m)}\mathbf{x}\epsilon_0\mathbf{E} \quad . \tag{49.31}$$

This is the magnetic counterpart of the Lorentz force on the electrical charge distribution. This force holds for charges and currents of a material medium either at rest or in motion. The sum of the force densities now takes the more explicit form,

$$\begin{aligned}\mathbf{f}_{(e)}+\mathbf{f}_{(m)} &= \eta_{(e)}\mathbf{E} + \mathbf{J}_{(e)}\mathbf{x}\mu_0\mathbf{H} + \eta_{(m)}\mathbf{H} - \mathbf{J}_{(m)}\mathbf{x}\epsilon_0\mathbf{E} \\ &= (\eta_f - \nabla\cdot\mathbf{P})\mathbf{E} + \left[\mathbf{J}_f + \frac{\partial\mathbf{P}}{\partial t} + \nabla\mathbf{x}(\mathbf{P}\mathbf{x}\mathbf{v})\right]\mathbf{x}\mu_0\mathbf{H} \\ &\quad - (\nabla\cdot\mu_0\mathbf{M})\mathbf{H} - \left[\frac{\partial}{\partial t}(\mu_0\mathbf{M}) + \nabla\mathbf{x}(\mu_0\mathbf{M}\mathbf{x}\mathbf{v})\right]\mathbf{x}\epsilon_0\mathbf{E} \quad .\end{aligned} \tag{49.32}$$

We see that the analogy is rather complete except for the correspondence of a free magnetic charge and current. This results from the non-existence (as yet) of free magnetic poles. Let us form the scalar product of this expression with $\mathbf{v}$ and obtain

$$\mathbf{v}\cdot(\mathbf{f}_{(e)}+\mathbf{f}_{(m)}) = \mathbf{v}\cdot\eta_{(e)}\mathbf{E} + \mathbf{v}\cdot(\mathbf{J}_{(e)}\mathbf{x}\mu_0\mathbf{H}) + \mathbf{v}\cdot\eta_{(m)}\mathbf{H} - \mathbf{v}\cdot(\mathbf{J}_{(m)}\mathbf{x}\epsilon_0\mathbf{E})$$

or,

$$\mathbf{v}\cdot(\mathbf{f}_{(e)}+\mathbf{f}_{(m)}) + (\mathbf{v}\mathbf{x}\mu_0\mathbf{H})\cdot\mathbf{J}_{(e)} - \mathbf{E}\cdot\eta_{(e)}\mathbf{v} - (\mathbf{v}\mathbf{x}\epsilon_0\mathbf{E})\cdot\mathbf{J}_{(m)} - \mathbf{H}\cdot\eta_{(m)}\mathbf{v} = 0 \quad . \tag{49.33}$$

This can be transformed into

$$\mathbf{v} \cdot (\mathbf{f}_{(e)} + \mathbf{f}_{(m)}) + (\mathbf{E} + \mathbf{v}\mathbf{x}\mu_0\mathbf{H}) \cdot (\mathbf{J}_{(e)} - \eta_{(e)}\mathbf{v})$$

$$+ (\mathbf{H} - \mathbf{v}\mathbf{x}\epsilon_0\mathbf{E}) \cdot (\mathbf{J}_{(m)} - \eta_{(m)}\mathbf{v}) = \mathbf{E} \cdot \mathbf{J}_{(e)} + \mathbf{H} \cdot \mathbf{J}_{(m)} \quad , \quad (49.34)$$

and putting this expression into eq. (49.16) we obtain the generalized Poynting's theorem,

$$\mathbf{v} \cdot (\mathbf{f}_{(e)} + \mathbf{f}_{(m)}) + (\mathbf{E} + \mathbf{v}\mathbf{x}\mu_0\mathbf{H}) \cdot (\mathbf{J}_{(e)} - \eta_{(e)}\mathbf{v})$$

$$+ (\mathbf{H} - \mathbf{v}\mathbf{x}\epsilon_0\mathbf{E}) \cdot (\mathbf{J}_{(m)} - \eta_{(m)}\mathbf{v}) = -\left(\nabla \cdot \mathbf{s} + \frac{\partial W}{\partial t}\right) . \quad (49.35)$$

It is clear that $\mathbf{J}_{(e)} - \eta_{(e)}\mathbf{v}$ is the current density due to the motion of the charges relative to the material, or in other words, the total current density minus the convection density arising from the motion of the net charge in the material. The term $\mathbf{E} + \mathbf{v}\mathbf{x}\mu_0\mathbf{H}$ is the force per unit charge acting on an element of the material moving with velocity $\mathbf{v}$. Consequently these quantities are the ones seen by an observer in the system S, and are different from the quantities viewed by an observer in S'. A similar interpretation holds for the quantities, $\mathbf{J}_{(m)} - \eta_{(m)}\mathbf{v}$, and $\mathbf{H} - \mathbf{v}\mathbf{x}\epsilon_0\mathbf{E}$. We can now interpret the terms in eq. (49.35). The term $\mathbf{v} \cdot (\mathbf{f}_{(e)} + \mathbf{f}_{(m)})$ is the density of the work per unit time done by the electromagnetic forces, and this work is transformed essentially into mechanical energy. The scalar product terms $(\mathbf{E} + \mathbf{v}\mathbf{x}\mu_0\mathbf{H}) \cdot (\mathbf{J}_{(e)} - \eta_{(e)}\mathbf{v})$ and $(\mathbf{H} - \mathbf{v}\mathbf{x}\epsilon_0\mathbf{E}) \cdot (\mathbf{J}_{(m)} - \eta_{(m)}\mathbf{v})$ is the power imparted by the field to the moving material, the right hand side has already been interpreted. Summarizing, we see that part of the electromagnetic power converted results from the work done per unit time by the macroscopic electromagnetic forces acting on an element of the material and the remainder is energy stored or dissipated in the material. Thus, the left side of eq. (49.35) is the total density of electromagnetic power transformed into other forms of energy.

The identification of the various forms of energy resulting from the electromagnetic terms is an interesting, useful and often times difficult task. This is particularly true in the case of non-linear media. But even the study of the energy density in continuous electromagnetic media for the linear, time-invariant case is highly rewarding. The inclusion of dispersion* in the constitutive relations, *i.e.*, ϵ is a function of frequency, and Tellegen-type media are of considerable interest.† Some of these matters will be dealt with in a later chapter.

50. CONDUCTING FLUIDS

With the brief relativistic background just presented together with the aid of the developments of Chapter III we can now deal with the thermodynamics of conducting fluids.

As in Chapter III, we consider a volume of the fluid bounded by a surface Σ and recall that the conservation of mass and momentum are given respectively by (see secs. 21-23)

$$-\frac{\partial}{\partial t}\int_V \rho dV = \int_\Sigma \rho v_i n_i d\Sigma \tag{50.1}$$

or alternatively by

$$\frac{\partial \rho}{\partial t} + \frac{\partial}{\partial x_j}(\rho v_j) \quad , \tag{50.2}$$

and

$$\frac{\partial}{\partial t}\int_V (g_i + \rho v_i) dV + \int_\Sigma \rho v_i v_j n_j d\Sigma = \int_\Sigma \tau_{ij} n_j d\Sigma + \int_V \rho F_i dV \quad . \tag{50.3}$$

In these equations, $\mathbf{v}$ is the velocity of a fluid element, in the last equation we have added the electromagnetic momentum density $\mathbf{g}$ to the mechanical momentum density $\rho\mathbf{v}$. Here, and in what follows we shall use the mixed vector and tensor notations as in previous sections. A free index takes on successively the values, say, $i = 1, 2, 3$. F_i is the external force per unit mass acting on the fluid, ρ is the mass density. Thus on the left side of eq. (50.3) we have the time rate of change of

* A. Tonning, "Energy Density in Continuous Electromagnetic Media," IRE Trans. on Antennas and Prop. Vol. AP-8, No. 4, pp 428-434, July 1960; H. Pelzer, "Energy Density of Monochromatic Radiation in a Dispersive Medium," Proc. Roy. Soc. (London) A, Vol. 208, pp 365-366, September 1951.

† B. D. H. Tellagen, "The Gyrator, a New Network Element," Phillips Res. Repts., Vol. 3, April 1948.

electromagnetic plus mechanical momentum in V plus the mechanical momentum convected away from Σ. This time rate of change of momentum must be equal to the total force acting on the medium bounded by Σ; the right side of eq. (50.3) is exactly this force. It consists of body or volume forces and the surface forces by virtue of the stresses on Σ. The ponderomotive forces which are the forces exerted by the electromagnetic field on the material do not appear in eq. (50.3) because they are internal forces. This is really due to the fact that we are considering the mechanical and electromagnetic systems as a single gross entity. The stresses τ_{ij} which act on Σ are due to the joint action of the mechanical and electromagnetic effects.

Applying the divergence theorem to eq. (50.3) yields by the standard arguments the following

$$\frac{\partial}{\partial t}(g_i + \rho v_i) + \frac{\partial}{\partial x_j}(\rho v_i v_j) = \frac{\partial \tau_{ij}}{\partial x_j} + \rho F_i \quad . \tag{50.4}$$

From eq. (49.15) it follows that we can write

$$\mathbf{g} = \mathbf{D} \times \mathbf{B} \tag{50.5}$$

and if we denote by $\tau_{ij}^{(e)}$ the electromagnetic stress tensor and by $\mathbf{f}$ the ponderomotive force, these three entities are bound by the relation,

$$\frac{\partial g_i}{\partial t} = \frac{\partial \tau_{ij}^{(e)}}{\partial x_j} - f_i \quad . \tag{50.6}$$

We postulate that the stress tensor appearing in eq. (50.3) can be decomposed into two parts, one of which is due to a mechanical origin and the remaining part of electromagnetic origin. Thus we can write,*

$$\tau_{ij} = \tau_{ij}^{(m)} + \tau_{ij}^{(e)} \quad , \tag{50.7}$$

and therefore eq. (50.4) takes the form,

$$\frac{\partial}{\partial t}(\rho v_i) + \frac{\partial}{\partial x_j}(\rho v_i v_j) = \frac{\partial \tau_{ij}^{(m)}}{\partial x_j} + f_i + \rho F_i \quad . \tag{50.8}$$

*The use of the symbols (e) and (m) should not be confused to mean electrical and magnetic as they were used in previous sections.

51. ENERGY AND WORK RELATIONS

The energy and work relations are easily established following the ideas set forth in Chapter III, section 30. Consider a portion of the fluid isolated from the remainder. As a free body the mass of this volume will move and its volume will be deformed. The rate of work done by the forces producing the motion and deformation is

$$\frac{dW}{dt} = \int_{\Sigma} \tau_{ij} v_i n_j d\Sigma + \int_V \rho F_i v_i dV$$

$$= \int_V \left[\frac{\partial}{\partial x_j} (\tau_{ij} v_i) + \rho F_i v_i \right] dV \quad , \qquad (51.1)$$

where the integrations are carried out over the entire mass. For future use it is convenient to rewrite eqs. (50.2), (50.4), (50.8) in the alternative forms respectively,

$$\frac{\partial v_j}{\partial x_j} = \rho \frac{d}{dt}\left(\frac{1}{\rho}\right) \quad , \qquad (51.2)$$

$$\frac{\partial g_i}{\partial t} + \rho \frac{dv_i}{dt} = \frac{\partial \tau_{ij}}{\partial x_j} + \rho F_i \quad , \qquad (51.3)$$

$$\rho \frac{dv_i}{dt} = \frac{\partial \tau_{ij}^{(m)}}{\partial x_j} + f_i + \rho F_i \quad . \qquad (51.4)$$

By utilizing these forms, the integrand of eq. (51.1) becomes

$$\frac{\partial \tau_{ij} v_i}{\partial x_j} + \rho F_i v_i = v_i \left(\frac{\partial \tau_{ij}}{\partial x_j} + \rho F_i \right) + \tau_{ij} \frac{\partial v_i}{\partial x_j}$$

$$= v_i \left(\frac{\partial g_i}{\partial t} + \rho \frac{dv_i}{dt} \right) + \tau_{ij} \frac{\partial v_i}{\partial x_j} \qquad (51.5)$$

At this point it is desirable to express the stress tensor τ_{ij} in explicit terms, as a function of the field quantities. For a medium with a dielect constant and permeability which are independent of the density ρ, temperature T, and field strength, the electromagnetic tensor* $\tau^{(e)}_{ij}$ is obtained according to eq. (49.11) as,

$$\tau^{(e)}_{ij} = -\frac{1}{2}(D_k E_k + B_k E_k)\delta_{ij} + D_i E_j + B_i H_j \quad . \tag{51.6}$$

For a dissipative fluid, the dissipation is accounted for by means of the viscosity stress tensor σ_{ij}, already introduced in section 26. Moreover, we shall also establish the thermodynamic arguments which lead to the representation of τ_{ij} in the form,

$$\tau_{ij} = -p\delta_{ij} + D_i E_j + B_i H_j + \sigma_{ij} \quad , \tag{51.7}$$

where p is here the sum of a mechanical and electromagnetic pressure. For the moment however let us tentatively accept this representation and util it in eq. (51.5) which becomes

$$\frac{\partial}{\partial x_j}(\tau_{ij}v_i) + \rho F_i v_i = v_i\left(\frac{\partial g_i}{\partial t} + \rho\frac{dv_i}{dt}\right) - p\frac{\partial v_i}{\partial x_i} + \left(D_i E_j + B_i H_j\right)\frac{\partial v_i}{\partial x_j} + \sigma_{ij}\frac{\partial v_i}{\partial x_j}$$

$$= \mathbf{v}\cdot\frac{\partial}{\partial t}(\mathbf{D}\mathrm{x}\mathbf{B}) + \mathbf{E}\cdot(\mathbf{D}\cdot\nabla)\mathbf{v} + \mathbf{H}\cdot(\mathbf{B}\cdot\nabla)\mathbf{v}$$

$$+ \rho\left[\frac{d}{dt}\left(\frac{v^2}{2}\right) - p\frac{d}{dt}\left(\frac{1}{\rho}\right)\right] + \psi \tag{51.8}$$

where,

$$\psi \equiv \sigma_{ij}\frac{\partial v_i}{\partial x_j} \quad , \tag{51.9}$$

this function ψ, a scalar quantity, represents the rate of dissipation pe unit volume taking place in the fluid. To complete the description of th

* See also C. Moller, The Theory of Relativity (Oxford Univ. Press, New York, 1952).

work equation we must of course use Maxwell's equations but for a moving medium . This has been done in the previous sections. But, in order to make more clear the necessary relations we shall define the coordinate systems which are used here.

One reference frame is fixed in space and all quantities **B**, **D**, **H**, **E**, **J** and η the charge density (we consider here only the electrical charge density) are referred to this system. The other system is attached locally to a fluid element and relative to an observer in this system, the medium in the neighborhood of the origin is quasi-stationary. All quantities relative to this reference frame are denoted by primes. The velocity of the fluid element satisfies the relation $|\mathbf{v}| << V_0$ and hence terms of order $(v/V_0)^2$ are to be neglected compared to unity. Consequently, we have the relations,

$$\mathbf{E}' = \mathbf{E} + \mathbf{v} \times \mathbf{B} \quad , \qquad (51.10)$$

$$\mathbf{D}' = \mathbf{D} + \frac{\mathbf{v} \times \mathbf{H}}{V_0^2} \quad , \qquad (51.11)$$

$$\mathbf{B}' = \mathbf{B} - \frac{\mathbf{v} \times \mathbf{E}}{V_0^2} \quad , \qquad (51.12)$$

$$\mathbf{H}' = \mathbf{H} - \mathbf{v} \times \mathbf{D} \quad , \qquad (51.13)$$

$$\mathbf{J}' = \mathbf{J} - \eta \mathbf{v} \quad , \qquad (51.14)$$

while the constitutive relations are,

$$\left.\begin{aligned} \mathbf{B}' &= \mu \mathbf{H}' \ , \\ \mathbf{D}' &= \epsilon \mathbf{E}' \ , \\ \mathbf{J}' &= \sigma \mathbf{E}' \ , \end{aligned}\right\} . \qquad (51.15)$$

After substituting eqs. (51.10 - 51.14) into eq. (51.15), and neglecting terms of order $(v/V_0)^2$, we obtain,

$$\mathbf{D} = \epsilon \mathbf{E} + \left(\frac{\epsilon \mu}{\epsilon_0 \mu_0} - 1 \right) \frac{\mathbf{v} \times \mathbf{H}}{V_0^2} \quad , \qquad (51.16)$$

$$\mathbf{B} = \mu \mathbf{H} - \left(\frac{\epsilon \mu}{\epsilon_0 \mu_0} - 1 \right) \frac{\mathbf{v} \times \mathbf{E}}{V_0^2} \quad . \qquad (51.17)$$

We must recognize that although the medium is non-relativistic we have used a relativistic approach to obtain a first order description, *i.e.*, order v/V_0, of the basic field relations. The legitimacy of using what is substantially a Lorentz transformation of the field quantities, for accelerated media is an assumption whose validity must ultimately rest on experimental verification.*

By utilizing these relations, Maxwell's equations together with some standard vector identities, we find,

$$\mathbf{H}\cdot\frac{\partial \mathbf{B}}{\partial t} + \mathbf{E}\cdot\frac{\partial \mathbf{D}}{\partial t} + \nabla\cdot\left(\mathbf{E}\mathbf{x}\mathbf{H}\right) + \mathbf{J}'\cdot\mathbf{E}' + \mathbf{v}\cdot[\eta\mathbf{E} + \mathbf{J}\mathbf{x}\mathbf{B}] = 0 \quad , \qquad (51.18)$$

where we have used the relation,

$$\mathbf{J}\cdot\mathbf{E} = \mathbf{J}'\cdot\mathbf{E}' + \mathbf{v}\cdot[\eta\mathbf{E} + \mathbf{J}\mathbf{x}\mathbf{B}] \quad . \qquad (51.19)$$

Here, we take note that it is $\mathbf{J}'\cdot\mathbf{E}'$ and not $\mathbf{J}\cdot\mathbf{E}$ which is the Joule heat, for a moving medium, whereas for a medium at rest it is $\mathbf{J}\cdot\mathbf{E}$. The reason for this difference will be made clear after the thermodynamics has been introduced. To continue, the following useful relation obtains from using eqs. (51.10) and (51.13),

$$\mathbf{E}'\cdot\mathbf{H}' = \mathbf{E}\mathbf{x}\mathbf{H} - \mathbf{H}\mathbf{x}(\mathbf{v}\mathbf{x}\mathbf{B}) - \mathbf{E}\mathbf{x}(\mathbf{v}\mathbf{x}\mathbf{D}) = \mathbf{E}\mathbf{x}\mathbf{H} + (\mathbf{v}\cdot\mathbf{H})\mathbf{B} + (\mathbf{v}\cdot\mathbf{E})\mathbf{D} - (\mathbf{B}\cdot\mathbf{H} + \mathbf{D}\cdot\mathbf{E})\mathbf{v} \quad , \qquad (51.20)$$

here too we have neglected the term $(\mathbf{v}\mathbf{x}\mathbf{B})\,\mathbf{x}\,(\mathbf{v}\mathbf{x}\mathbf{D})$ which is of order $(v/V_0)^2|\mathbf{E}\mathbf{x}\mathbf{H}|$. Finally from eqs. (51.18) and (51.20) and a rather lengthy vector calculation, there results,

$$\mathbf{v}\cdot\frac{\partial}{\partial t}(\mathbf{D}\mathbf{x}\mathbf{B}) + \mathbf{E}\cdot(\mathbf{D}\cdot\nabla)\mathbf{v} + \mathbf{H}\cdot(\mathbf{B}\cdot\nabla)\mathbf{v} = \nabla\cdot(\mathbf{E}'\mathbf{x}\mathbf{H}') + \mathbf{J}'\cdot\mathbf{E}' + \rho\left[\mathbf{E}\cdot\frac{d}{dt}\left(\frac{\mathbf{D}}{\rho}\right) + \mathbf{H}\cdot\frac{d}{dt}\left(\frac{\mathbf{B}}{\rho}\right)\right] \quad . \qquad (51.21)$$

---

* In this connection we cite an interesting and important paper by Schlomka and Schenkel, "Relativity and Unipolar Induction," Ann. Physik, Bd. 5, 1950, p 51-62, wherein the problem of rotating media is carefully treated. See also, H. Arzelies, La Dynamique Relativiste et Ses Applications, Chapter XIII, Fascicule I (1957), Gauthier-Villars, Paris. Podolsky, Boris and Denman, Harry, "A Derivation of Generalized Macroscopic Electro-dynamic Eqs." I. Non-Relativistic, Journal of Math and Physics, Vol. 34, No. 1, pp 198-207, 1955.

Substituting this result into eq. (51.8) gives

$$\frac{\partial}{\partial x_j}(\tau_{ij}v_i) + \rho F_i v_i = \rho\left[\frac{d}{dt}\left(\frac{v^2}{2}\right) - p\frac{d}{dt}\left(\frac{1}{\rho}\right) + \mathbf{E}\cdot\frac{d}{dt}\left(\frac{\mathbf{D}}{\rho}\right) + \mathbf{H}\cdot\frac{d}{dt}\left(\frac{\mathbf{B}}{\rho}\right)\right]$$

$$+ \psi + \mathbf{J}'\cdot\mathbf{E}' + \nabla\cdot(\mathbf{E}'\mathbf{x}\mathbf{H}') \quad , \qquad (51.22)$$

and after integrating this expression over the volume V as indicated by eq. (51.1) we obtain the rate of work done by both surface and body forces, namely

$$\frac{dW}{dt} = \frac{d}{dt}\int_V \frac{1}{2}\rho v^2 dV + \int_\Sigma (\mathbf{E}'\mathbf{x}\mathbf{H}')\cdot\mathbf{n}\,\Sigma + \int_V \psi dV + \int_V \mathbf{J}'\cdot\mathbf{E}'dV$$

$$+ \int_V\left[-p\frac{d}{dt}\left(\frac{1}{\rho}\right) + \mathbf{H}\cdot\frac{d}{dt}\left(\frac{\mathbf{B}}{\rho}\right) + \mathbf{E}\cdot\frac{d}{dt}\left(\frac{\mathbf{D}}{\rho}\right)\right]dV.^* \qquad (51.23)$$

The terms occurring on the right side are interpreted respectively as follows. The first is the rate of increase of the kinetic energy of the mass; the rate of energy radiated away from the mass; the irreversible work done against internal friction, *i.e.*, the viscous dissipation; the irreversible work against electric resistance, *i.e.*, the Joule loss; and the last term is the rate of reversible work done in creating the magnetohydrodynamical field. That is, the integrand is the reversible work done per unit mass of the medium in a time increment dt.

52. THE THERMODYNAMICS OF A CONDUCTING FLUID

The foregoing considerations permit us to develop in a systematic manner the fundamentals of the thermodynamics of a conducting fluid. We consider a differential element of the fluid and an observer who is fixed with respect to the center of mass of this fluid element. For such an observer eqs. (51.22) and (51.23) are still valid but the kinetic energy term now vanishes since for an observer riding along with the fluid element $\mathbf{v} = 0$. As before we denote by dW the work done, by the surface and body forces acting on the element, per unit mass during a time in which a

---

* In obtaining this equation we have also used the relation $(d/dt)(\rho dV) = 0$, which expresses the conservation of mass.

differential change of state occurs for the element. Also, let $dQ_R = -(1/\rho)\nabla \cdot (\mathbf{E}'\mathrm{x}\mathbf{H}')dt$ denote the energy radiated into the element in time dt per unit mass of the element; by $dW^{(n)} = (1/\rho)(\psi + \mathbf{J}' \cdot \mathbf{E}')dt$ we mean the energy dissipated into heat by internal friction and electrical resistance per unit mass in time dt. Finally, let

$$dW^{(r)} = -pd\left(\frac{1}{\rho}\right) + \mathbf{E} \cdot d\left(\frac{\mathbf{D}}{\rho}\right) + \mathbf{H} \cdot d\left(\frac{\mathbf{B}}{\rho}\right)$$

denote the reversible work done per unit mass of the medium in time dt. With these designations we can write eq. (51.22) in the form

$$dW + dQ_R = dW^{(n)} + dW^{(r)} \quad . \tag{52.1}$$

Now for an observer fixed with respect to a differential element of the fluid we can invoke the first law of thermodynamics,* namely,

$$dU = dQ + dQ_R + dW \tag{52.2}$$

which states that the increase in the internal energy dU of the fluid element is equal to the amount of heat added to the element plus the energy radiated into the element plus the work done on the element. In eq. (52.2), dU is the increase in the internal energy per unit mass. If we use eq. (52.1) we can write eq. (52.2) in the form

$$dU = dQ + dW^{(n)} + dW^{(r)} \quad . \tag{52.3}$$

Since, $dQ + dW^{(n)}$ is the total heat entering the element from the external source and internal dissipation, we have from the second law of thermodynamics†

$$dQ + dW^{(n)} = TdS \tag{52.4}$$

where T is the temperature of the medium and S is its entropy. Eq. (52.3) therefore becomes,

$$TdS + dW^{(r)} = dU \quad , \tag{52.5}$$

---

* Epstein, Paul S. Textbook of Thermodynamics, John Wiley and Sons, New York, 1937.

† Epstein, Paul S., loc. cit.

hence,

$$TdS = dU + pd\left(\frac{1}{\rho}\right) - \mathbf{E}\cdot d\left(\frac{\mathbf{D}}{\rho}\right) - \mathbf{H}\cdot d\left(\frac{\mathbf{B}}{\rho}\right) \quad . \tag{52.6}$$

We introduce at this point the free energy of the system which is by definition the difference between the internal energy and the product TS, it follows from eq. (52.6) that

$$d(U - TS) = -SdT - pd\left(\frac{1}{\rho}\right) + \mathbf{E}\cdot d\left(\frac{\mathbf{D}}{\rho}\right) + \mathbf{H}\cdot d\left(\frac{\mathbf{B}}{\rho}\right) \quad . \tag{52.7}$$

Eqs. (52.6) and (52.7) hold therefore for the irreversible change accompanying the deformation and change of state of an electrically conducting viscous compressible fluid. Thermodynamics teaches us that in the absence of an electromagnetic field the thermodynamic state of a system is completely specified when two of its independent state variables are given. If, in the case of a fluid, we specify the density ρ and temperature T as the independent variables, the entire thermodynamic behavior of the fluid is obtained from the state function

$$A(\rho,T) = U - TS \quad , \tag{52.8}$$

which is the free energy per unit mass. Accordingly, the variables ρ,T are considered as the mechanical state variables. If now we assume the presence of an electromagnetic field the complete thermodynamic behavior of the fluid is governed by the single state function

$$A = A(\rho,T,\mathbf{B},\mathbf{D}) \quad . \tag{52.9}$$

The introduction of this characteristic function together with eq. (52.7) allows us to deduce the important relations,

$$S = -\frac{\partial A}{\partial T} \quad , \tag{52.10}$$

$$E_i = \rho\frac{\partial A}{\partial D_i} \quad , \tag{52.11}$$

$$H_i = \rho\frac{\partial A}{\partial B_i} \quad , \tag{52.12}$$

and

$$p = \mathbf{D} \cdot \mathbf{E} + \mathbf{B} \cdot \mathbf{H} + \rho^2 \frac{\partial A}{\partial \rho} \quad . \tag{52.13}$$

Since A is a state function, dA is an exact differential in the eight variables (ρ, T, B_i, D_i), $(i = 1,2,3)$; further relations can be readily derived. The relation (52.13) clearly shows the separation of p into an electromagnetic and mechanical part. We remind ourselves further that the derivations above did not in any way assume any constitutive relations for the electromagnetic field variables. It is obvious that if constitutive relations are introduced the results can be specialized.

53, AN ALTERNATIVE FORMULATION OF THE ENERGY RELATION

In the derivation of basic relations it is oftentimes instructive to derive such relations from alternative points of view. This is the situation for the energy relation just derived.

By starting from the momentum balance equation in the form of eq. (51.3) we can obtain an alternative representation of eq. (51.22) or (51.23). From Maxwell's equations together with eq. (51.3) we form the expressions,

$$v_i \left(\frac{\partial g_i}{\partial t} + \rho \frac{dv_i}{dt} \right) = v_i \left(\frac{\partial \tau_{ij}}{\partial x_j} + \rho F_i \right) \quad , \tag{53.1}$$

$$\mathbf{H} \cdot \nabla \mathbf{x} \mathbf{E} = - \mathbf{H} \cdot \frac{\partial \mathbf{B}}{\partial t} \tag{53.2}$$

$$\mathbf{E} \cdot \nabla \mathbf{x} \mathbf{H} = \mathbf{E} \cdot \left(\frac{\partial \mathbf{D}}{\partial t} + \mathbf{J} \right) \tag{53.3}$$

$$v_i \left(\frac{\partial g_i}{\partial t} \right) = v_i \frac{\partial \tau_{ij}^{(e)}}{\partial x_j} - v_i f_i \quad , \tag{53.4}$$

and,

$$\rho \frac{dv_i}{dt} = \frac{\partial \tau_{ij}^{(m)}}{\partial x_j} + f_i + \rho F_i \quad . \tag{53.5}$$

The addition of eqs. (53.2), (53.3) and (53.4) gives

$$\frac{\partial(\tau_{ij}^{(e)} v_i)}{\partial x_j} = \rho\left[- p^{(e)} \frac{d}{dt}\left(\frac{1}{\rho}\right) + \mathbf{H} \cdot \frac{d}{dt}\left(\frac{\mathbf{B}}{\rho}\right) + \mathbf{E} \cdot \frac{d}{dt}\left(\frac{\mathbf{D}}{\rho}\right)\right]$$

$$+ \nabla \cdot (\mathbf{E}'\mathbf{x}\mathbf{H}') + \mathbf{J}' \cdot \mathbf{E}' + \mathbf{f} \cdot \mathbf{v} \quad , \qquad (53.6)$$

where $\mathbf{f}$ is the ponderomotive force. We emphasize that this result follows from the assumption of the separability of the system into a purely mechanical and purely electromagnetic part.

An energy relation for the mechanical part is obtained by simply forming the scalar product of $\mathbf{v}$ with eq. (53.5), that is,

$$\frac{\partial(\tau_{ij}^{(m)} v_i)}{\partial x_j} + \rho F_i v_i + f_i v_i = \rho\left[\frac{d}{dt}\left(\frac{v^2}{2}\right) - p^{(m)} \frac{d}{dt}\left(\frac{1}{\rho}\right)\right] + \psi \quad . \qquad (53.7)$$

Equation (53.6) asserts that part of the work done on the fluid by the electromagnetic stress goes into creating the electromagnetic field in the mass, partly radiated away from the mass, and partly dissipated into heat, with the remaining work used in driving the fluid. The relation (53.7) says that the work done on the fluid by the mechanical stress, external body force and ponderomotive force on a mass of the fluid, treated as an isolated body is partly expended in increasing the kinetic energy of the mass, and partly expended in changing the volume of the element, with the remainder dissipated in heat.

54. THE ENERGY EQUATION FOR AN IONIZED GAS IN THE PRESENCE OF A MAGNETIC FIELD

The thermodynamic quantities which we have introduced, naturally are applicable for establishing an energy equation for an ionized gas. But it is also necessary to introduce other quantities which have hitherto not appeared.

We assume as in Chapters II and IV that the absolute dielectric constant and absolute magnetic permeability of the ionized gas is the same as free space. For sufficiently dilute plasmas this is a tenable assumption and we shall comment on this in a later chapter where these and other related questions regarding equations of state arise in a natural way. The thermodynamic quantities which enter into the discussion here for an ionized gas are the specific (per unit mass) entropy S, internal energy U, enthalpy I, and the pressure p. All of these quantities are total ones, that is, they refer to the sum of the mechanical and electromagnetic actions. Since the electromagnetic energy density for the ionized gas is $\frac{1}{2}(\epsilon_0 E^2 + \mu_0 H^2)$ we can write immediately the following expressions,

$$p = p^{(m)} + \frac{1}{2}(\epsilon_0 E^2 + \mu_0 H^2) \quad , \tag{54.1}$$

$$U = U^{(m)} + \frac{1}{\rho}\frac{1}{2}(\epsilon_0 E^2 + \mu_0 H^2) \quad , \tag{54.2}$$

$$I = I^{(m)} + \frac{1}{\rho}(\epsilon_0 E^2 + \mu_0 H^2) \quad . \tag{54.3}$$

Consequently eq. (53.6) simplifies to

$$TdS = dU^{(m)} + pd\left(\frac{1}{\rho}\right) \quad , \tag{54.4}$$

or in terms of the enthalpy,

$$TdS = dI^{(m)} - \frac{1}{\rho}dp \quad . \tag{54.5}$$

For an ionized gas containing r distinct species each of which has an average velocity $\mathbf{v}_i$ and mass density ρ_i we define the mass averaged velocity of the average velocities by the formula

$$\langle\mathbf{v}\rangle = \sum_{i=1}^{r} \frac{\rho_i \mathbf{v}_i}{\rho} \tag{54.6}$$

where ρ is the density of the over-all constituents, *i.e.*, the mixture. It follows readily that for the mixture we have the equations of continuity and momentum, respectively,

$$\frac{\partial \rho}{\partial t} + \frac{\partial}{\partial x_j} \langle \mathbf{v} \rangle_j = 0 \quad , \tag{54.7}$$

$$\rho \frac{d\langle \mathbf{v} \rangle_i}{dt} + \frac{\partial p}{\partial x_i} - \frac{\partial \sigma_{ij}}{\partial x_j} - \rho_e E_i - \rho_e (\langle \mathbf{v} \rangle \times \mathbf{B})_i - (\mathbf{J} \times \mathbf{B})_i = 0 \, , \tag{54.8}$$

where ρ_e is the net charge density defined by

$$\rho_e = \sum_{i=1}^{r} N_i e_i \quad , \tag{54.9}$$

and,

$$\mathbf{J} = \sum_{i=1}^{r} N_i e_i \mathbf{V}_i \quad . \tag{54.10}$$

Here N_i is the number density of each species, and in this definition of $\mathbf{J}$ we use the mean diffusion velocity $\mathbf{V}_i$ of the i-th species. This velocity is defined by

$$\mathbf{V}_i = \mathbf{v}_i - \langle \mathbf{v} \rangle \quad . \tag{54.11}$$

For the case of an ionized gas the quantities $p^{(m)}$, σ_{ij} and $\mathbf{V}_i$ are bound by a relation of the form

$$p\delta_{ij} - \sigma_{ij} = \sum_{k=1}^{r} \rho_k Q_{ijk} \quad , \tag{54.12}$$

where the quantity Q_{ijk} is a tensor of the type indicated.* Let us also define the relative concentration of the i-th species by

$$C_i = \frac{\rho_i}{\rho} \quad , \tag{54.13}$$

---

* At this point it is not necessary to give the explicit form of Q_{ijk} and we can take eq. (54.12) as the defining equation of this tensor. Its fundamental meaning and structure is put into evidence from a microscopic description involving the Boltzmann equation and a distribution function. Q_{ijk} then results from a moment description which will be given in Chapter VIII. The interested reader will refer to Chapman and Cowling, The Mathematical Theory of Non-Uniform Gases, p 18, Cambridge Univ. Press, 1958. See also, Kolodner, I. I., "Moment Description of Gas Mixtures," AEC Research and Development Report NYO-7980, Inst. of Math. Sciences, NYU, Sept. 1957; and Burgers, J. M. (Editor), "Statistical Plasma Mechanics," Plasma Dynamics (ed. by F. H. Clauser), pp 119-186, Addison-Wesley Publ. Co., Inc., Reading, Massachusetts, 1960.

where C_i satisfies the equation,

$$\rho \frac{dC_i}{dt} + \text{div } (\rho \mathbf{V}_i) = 0 \quad , \tag{54.14}$$

or if we put

$$\mathbf{f}_i = \rho_i \mathbf{V}_i \tag{54.15}$$

which is called the "diffusion flux" vector of the i-th species, we can write,

$$\rho \frac{dC_i}{dt} + \text{div } \mathbf{f}_i = 0 \quad . \tag{54.16}$$

It follows at once that,

$$\sum_{i=1}^{r} C_i = 1 \quad , \tag{54.17}$$

and,

$$\sum_{i=1}^{r} \mathbf{f}_i = 0 \quad . \tag{54.18}$$

In terms of the definitions of $\mathbf{V}_i$ and $\langle \mathbf{v} \rangle$, the total specific energy of the i-th species is given by

$$\epsilon_i = U_i + \mathbf{V}_i \cdot \langle \mathbf{v} \rangle + \frac{v^2}{2} \tag{54.19}$$

where

$$v = |\langle \mathbf{v} \rangle| \quad ,$$

and the enthalpy is

$$I_i = U_i + \frac{p_i}{\rho_i} \quad , \tag{54.20}$$

hence the total specific energy, enthalpy and entropy can be written for the mixture. They are,

$$\epsilon = \sum_{i=1}^{r} \frac{\rho_i}{\rho} \epsilon_i \quad , \tag{54.21}$$

$$I = \sum_{i=1}^{r} \frac{\rho_i}{\rho} I_i \quad , \tag{54.22}$$

$$S = \sum_{i=1}^{r} \frac{\rho_i}{\rho} S_i \quad . \tag{54.23}$$

The energy balance equation for the mixture is therefore,

$$\rho \frac{d}{dt}\left(\epsilon + \frac{v^2}{2}\right) + \operatorname{div} \sum_{i=1}^{r} \rho_i \epsilon_i \mathbf{V}_i = \sum_{i=1}^{r} N_i e_i (\mathbf{E} + \mathbf{v}_i \mathbf{x} \mathbf{B}) \cdot \mathbf{v}_i \quad , \tag{54.24}$$

but,

$$\sum_{i=1}^{r} N_i e_i (\mathbf{E} + \mathbf{v}_i \mathbf{x} \mathbf{B}) \cdot \mathbf{v}_i = \langle \mathbf{v} \rangle \cdot \sum_{i=1}^{r} N_i e_i (\mathbf{E} + \mathbf{v}_i \mathbf{x} \mathbf{B}) + \sum_{i=1}^{r} N_i e_i \mathbf{V}_i \cdot (\mathbf{E} + \mathbf{v}_i \mathbf{x} \mathbf{B})$$

$$= \langle \mathbf{v} \rangle \cdot (\rho_e \mathbf{E} + \rho_e \mathbf{v} \mathbf{x} \mathbf{B} + \mathbf{J} \mathbf{x} \mathbf{B}) + \sum_{i=1}^{r} \mathbf{f}_i \cdot \frac{e_i}{m_i} (\mathbf{E} + \mathbf{v}_i \mathbf{x} \mathbf{B}) \, , \tag{54.25}$$

where m_i is the mass of each species and the diffusion flux vector from eq. (54.15) has been introduced. We also have

$$\sum_{i=1}^{r} \rho_i \epsilon_i \mathbf{V}_i = \langle \mathbf{v} \rangle \cdot \sum_{i=1}^{r} \rho_i Q_{ijk} + \sum_{i=1}^{r} \rho_i U_i \mathbf{V}_i = \langle \mathbf{v} \rangle \cdot (p\mathbf{I} - \sigma) + \mathbf{Q} \quad , \tag{54.26}$$

where $p\mathbf{I} - \sigma \equiv (p\delta_{ij} - \sigma_{ij})$ so that the dot notation implies that if $\langle \mathbf{v} \rangle_j$ is the j-th component of $\langle \mathbf{v} \rangle$, $\langle \mathbf{v} \rangle \cdot (p\mathbf{I} - \sigma) \equiv \langle \mathbf{v} \rangle_j (p\delta_{ij} - \sigma_{ij})$, (summation convention on j) is a vector, and

$$\mathbf{Q} = \sum_{i=1}^{r} \rho_i U_i \mathbf{V}_i \quad , \tag{54.27}$$

is called the "total heat flux" vector. The energy equation therefore takes the form,

$$\rho \frac{d}{dt}\left(\epsilon + \frac{v^2}{2}\right) + \mathrm{div}\ [\langle\mathbf{v}\rangle \cdot (p\mathbf{I} - \sigma) + \mathbf{Q}] = \langle\mathbf{v}\rangle \cdot [\rho_e\mathbf{E} + \rho_e\langle\mathbf{v}\rangle \mathbf{x} \mathbf{B} + \mathbf{J} \mathbf{x} \mathbf{B}]$$

$$+ \sum_{i=1}^{r} \mathbf{f}_i \cdot \frac{e}{m_i} (\mathbf{E} + \mathbf{v}_i \mathbf{x} \mathbf{B}) \quad . \tag{54.28}$$

With the use of the identity

$$\mathrm{div}\ p\langle\mathbf{v}\rangle = \langle\mathbf{v}\rangle \cdot \mathbf{grad}\ p + \rho p \frac{d}{dt}\left(\frac{1}{\rho}\right) \quad ,$$

we can transform eq. (54.28) into

$$\rho\left[\frac{d\epsilon}{dt} + p\ \frac{d}{dt}\left(\frac{1}{\rho}\right)\right] = -\ \mathrm{div}\ \mathbf{Q} + (\sigma \cdot \mathbf{grad})\langle\mathbf{v}\rangle$$

$$+ \sum_{i=1}^{r} \mathbf{f}_i \cdot \frac{e_i}{m_i} (\mathbf{E} + \mathbf{v}_i \mathbf{x}\mathbf{B}) \quad , \tag{54.29}$$

or in terms of the enthalpy

$$\rho\left(\frac{dI}{dt} - \frac{1}{\rho}\frac{d\rho}{dt}\right) = -\ \mathrm{div}\ \mathbf{Q} + (\sigma \cdot \mathbf{grad})\langle\mathbf{v}\rangle + \sum_{i=1}^{r} \mathbf{f}_i \cdot \frac{e_i}{m_i} (\mathbf{E} + \mathbf{v}_i \mathbf{x}\mathbf{B}) \ ; \tag{54.30}$$

The second term on the right hand side of eq. (54.30) is defined by

$$\sigma_{jk} \frac{\partial\langle\mathbf{v}\rangle_j}{\partial x_k} = (\sigma \cdot \mathbf{grad})\langle\mathbf{v}\rangle \quad , \qquad \text{sum over } j,k \quad ,$$

where we recall that σ is the viscous stress tensor. The last term in both eqs. (54.29) or (54.30) is the Joule heat, for

$$\sum_{i=1}^{r} \mathbf{f}_i \cdot \frac{e_i}{m_i} (\mathbf{E} + \mathbf{v}_i \mathbf{x}\mathbf{B}) = \sum_{i=1}^{r} N_i e_i (\mathbf{E} + \mathbf{v}_i\ \mathbf{x}\mathbf{B}) \cdot \mathbf{V}_i = \mathbf{J} \cdot (\mathbf{E} + \langle\mathbf{v}\rangle \mathbf{x}\mathbf{B}) \quad , \tag{54.31}$$

therefore if $\mathbf{J}$ is simply proportional to $(\mathbf{E} + \langle\mathbf{v}\rangle\, \mathbf{x}\, \mathbf{B})$, this last term takes the form (J^2/σ), (here σ denotes the usual isotropic conductivity).

By using eq. (54.31) the energy balance equation can be put in the alternative forms,

$$\rho\left[\frac{d\epsilon}{dt} + p\,\frac{d}{dt}\left(\frac{1}{\rho}\right)\right] + \mathrm{div}\,\mathbf{Q} = \mathbf{J}\cdot(\mathbf{E} + \langle\mathbf{v}\rangle\times\mathbf{B}) + (\sigma\cdot\mathbf{grad})\langle\mathbf{v}\rangle \quad , \tag{54.32}$$

or,

$$\rho\left(\frac{dI}{dt} - \frac{1}{\rho}\frac{d\rho}{dt}\right) + \mathrm{div}\,\mathbf{Q} = \mathbf{J}\cdot(\mathbf{E} + \langle\mathbf{v}\rangle\times\mathbf{B}) + (\sigma\cdot\mathbf{grad})\langle\mathbf{v}\rangle \quad , \tag{54.33}$$

in which the last term on the right side is clearly dissipative and can be identified with the viscous dissipation function ψ.

55. SOME COMMENTS ON IRREVERSIBLE THERMODYNAMICS

All of the derivations given thus far are macroscopic in form, and they are quite useful in that they yield the principal features for the energy relations. However, they lack completeness, particularly in the last derivation above. This lack, as is obvious, results from the introduction of the diffusion flux vector **f** and the total heat flux vector **Q**. They entered into the description of the energy balance equation only by definition and thus seem to be of a purely formal nature. These quantities, even though introduced in a consistent way, are not formal entities at all. They have a very definite physical meaning when defined through a microscopic approach. In a later chapter we shall carry out such a program. But at this stage we can still shed some light on their meaning from a macroscopic point of view. To effect this we utilize the notions of irreversible thermodynamics. Here too, we can not give a thorough account of this topic because it is a subject to be studied on its own.* We can however sketch its role as regards our initial queries about **f** and **Q**.

For irreversible processes an entropy balance equation can be written in terms of an entropy flux vector $\boldsymbol{\psi}$.

$$\rho\,\frac{dS}{dt} + \mathrm{div}\,(\boldsymbol{\psi}) = \psi_S \tag{55.1}$$

---

* deGroot, S. R., "Thermodynamics of Irreversible Processes," North-Holland Publishing Company, 1951. See also, Landau and Lifshitz, "Statistical Physics," p 31 Addison-Wesley, 1958; M. A. Biot, "Variational Principles in Irreversible Thermodynamics," Phy. Rev. Vol. 97, No. 6, pp 1463-1469 (1955); T. Kihara and Y. Midzuno, "Irreversible Processes in Plasmas in a Strong Magnetic Field," Rev. Mod. Phys. Vol. 32, No. 4, pp 722-730, Oct. 1960.

where ψ_S is the entropy source or production. The production term is always positive, while the divergence term can be either positive or negative. Denoting by $\mathbf{F}$ the forces acting in the system, the function ψ_S is expressible in the form

$$T\psi_S = \sum_i \boldsymbol{\psi}_i \cdot \mathbf{F}_i \quad . \tag{55.2}$$

To interpret the statements more physically, these forces can be temperature gradients, concentration gradients, etc., and are the sources of the irreversible phenomena. The significant feature of the irreversible theory is the ability to write the entropy source term in the summand form of eq. (55.2). The irreversible flux quantities can be viscous stresses, heat flux, diffusion flux and many other entities.

Following Onsager, the fluxes are related to the forces by the phenomenological relations,

$$\boldsymbol{\psi}_i = \sum_K L_{iK}\mathbf{F}_K \tag{55.3}$$

with the matrix $L_{iK} = L_{Ki}$, *i.e.*, symmetric, which expresses a reciprocity relation. According to this relation, any force is the source of any flux, provided the system deviates slightly from the equilibrium state. We state without proof that if reciprocity holds as defined above, for a given multi-component system, there exists a determinate relation between $\mathbf{f}$ and $\mathbf{Q}$, via the temperature T and the field quantities. To exhibit this relation here is beyond the express purpose of this chapter.

56. THE ENERGY EQUATION FOR MAGNETOHYDRODYNAMICS

Once the thermodynamics is understood, the energy equation for magnetohydrodynamics can be written straightforwardly. The arguments proceed as before. We consider a mass of fluid as a free body and take the mechanical and electromagnetic systems as a single system.

The amount of work done by the surface stresses and external body forces plus the amount of heat conducted and energy radiated into the mass of fluid must be equal to the rate of increase of the internal energy and kinetic energy of the mass.

We relate the "total heat flux" vector $\mathbf{Q}$ to the temperature T by Fourier's law,

$$\mathbf{Q} = -k \ \mathbf{grad} \ T \quad , \tag{56.1}$$

where k is here, the coefficient of thermal conductivity. The balance equation in this case takes the following form,

$$\int_{\Sigma} \tau_{ij} v_i n_j d\Sigma + \int_V \rho F_i v_i dV + \int_{\Sigma} k \frac{\partial T}{\partial x_j} n_j d\Sigma - \int_{\Sigma} (\mathbf{E}' \mathbf{x} \mathbf{H}')_j n_j d\Sigma = \frac{d}{dt} \int_V \left(U + \frac{1}{2} v^2\right) \rho dV \quad . \tag{56.2}$$

By utilizing the equation of conservation of mass and the divergence theorem we deduce,

$$\rho \frac{d}{dt} \left(U + \frac{1}{2} v^2\right) = \frac{\partial(\tau_{ij} v_i)}{\partial x_j} + \rho F_j v_j + \frac{\partial}{\partial x_j} \left(k \frac{\partial T}{\partial x_j}\right) - \frac{\partial}{\partial x_j} (\mathbf{E}' \mathbf{x} \mathbf{H}')_j \tag{56.3}$$

as the differential form of the energy equation. Using eq. (51.22) we transform eq. (56.3) into

$$\rho \left[\frac{dU}{dt} + p \frac{d}{dt}\left(\frac{1}{\rho}\right) - \mathbf{H} \cdot \frac{d}{dt}\left(\frac{\mathbf{B}}{\rho}\right) - \mathbf{E} \cdot \frac{d}{dt}\left(\frac{\mathbf{D}}{\rho}\right)\right] = \mathrm{div} \ (k \ \mathbf{grad} \ T) + \mathbf{J}' \cdot \mathbf{E}' + \psi \quad ; \tag{56.4}$$

if σ denotes the conductivity of the conducting fluid and assume that Ohm's Law is valid in the form,

$$\mathbf{J}' = \sigma \mathbf{E}' \quad , \tag{56.5}$$

the second term on the right side of eq. (56.4) is $(J')^2/\sigma$. The entire right hand side of eq. (56.4) can be written in terms of the entropy by using eq. (52.6) and this gives,

$$\rho T \frac{dS}{dt} = \mathrm{div} \left(\frac{k \ \mathbf{grad} \ T}{T}\right) \frac{(J')^2}{\sigma} + \psi \quad , \tag{56.6}$$

or as an entropy balance equation it becomes

$$\rho T \frac{dS}{dt} - \mathrm{div} \left(\frac{k \ \mathbf{grad} \ T}{T}\right) = k \left(\frac{\mathbf{grad} \ T}{T}\right)^2 + \frac{(J')^2}{\sigma} + \psi \quad . \tag{56.7}$$

57. FULLY IONIZED GAS IN A STRONG MAGNETIC FIELD

In this section we want to make a few comments on the subject of the thermodynamics of a fully ionized gas in a strong magnetic field. First, there have been two approaches to the study of the static and dynamic behavior of fully ionized gases in a strong magnetic field. These are the statistical approach of which the papers of Chew, Goldberger, Low, Watson, Brueckner, Chandrasekhar and Kaufman are cited.* In this approach one commences with the Boltzmann transport equation describing the change of the distribution function of the particles in phase space. Then by the method of perturbations an attempt is made to solve the equation about a stationary state. Because of the mathematical difficulties encountered no results which are truly satisfactory have been obtained. In the other approach, exemplified by the papers of Rosenbluth, Longmire, and Parker,† an orbital concept is used. Here, the detailed motions of the individual particles are considered and the average properties of the whole plasma are derived. If the particle collisions can be ignored, the method is useful and provides an insight into the mechanics of a problem. It suffers in providing the general relations between the macroscopic parameters.

Whether one uses a statistical or orbital approach the end description of the properties of the plasma are in terms of the dynamical behavior of the macroscopic parameters of the system. These are, as already noted, the hydrodynamic, and electromagnetic variables and the electric current. The hydrodynamic variables may be defined from the moments of the distribution function, and if this function is known in explicit terms this is all the more advantageous. But since this is still a central problem, a compromise is obtained at least in applications, by using the macroscopic variables, which are after all the physically observed quantities.

We should mention yet another method, which is an energy method. This method in principle is not new and has been used in mechanics, *i.e.*, theory of elasticity, hydrodynamics. etc. Its principal utility however has been in stability problems.§

---

* Chew, Goldberger and Low, Proc. Roy Soc. (London) *236*, 112 (1956); K. M. Watson, Phys. Rev. *102*, 12 (1956); K. A. Brueckner and K. M. Watson, Phys. Rev. *102*, 19 (1956); Chandrasekhar, Kaufman and Watson, Annals of Physics, 2, 435 (1957).

† M. N. Rosenbluth and C. L. Longmire, Annals of Physics, *1*, 120 (1957); E. N. Parker, Phys. Rev. *107*, 924 (1957).

§ Bernstein, Frieman, Kruskal and Kulsrud, Proc. Royal Soc. (London) *244*, 17 (1958); Frieman and Kulsrud, "Problems in Hydromagnetics," pp 195-231, Advances in Applied Mechanics, V, Academic Press, 1956.

It should by now be apparent to the reader that when the fluid dynamics of a plasma are developed according to the continuum theory that the thermodynamics should enter into the development to obtain a better understanding of the nature of the processes. Moreover, the study of the temperature and entropy functions of a magneto-plasma which causes the thermodynamic non-equilibrium state sheds considerable light on the whole subject, since it is only these functions or variables which are not directly involved in the basic hydromagnetic equations. This statement will be further clarified in Chapter VIII where it will be shown that these quantities are not simple moments of the distribution function in velocity space. It is possible however to make some intuitive inferences regarding the behavior of a fully ionized plasma in a strong magnetic field. First we recall from thermodynamics that not all adiabatic processes are reversible and quasi-static.* Thus if we ignore a process like heating due to shock waves and cooling by radiation (*i.e.* Bremsstrahlung, which arises from the scattering of electrons in the coulomb field of the nuclei) the behavior should be quasi-static and reversible. The strong magnetic field produces the mechanism for the quasi-static behavior, this mechanism is rapid gyromotion of the charged particles about the magnetic field lines. The reversibility is due to the lack of randomization processes, for example, collisions. Both of these hypotheses then, strong magnetic field and no collisions, are tantamount to an adiabatic approximation. It is possible to verify these intuitively plausible statements by formal mathematical and physical reasonings.

---

* As an example we know that a free expansion process is neither quasi-static nor reversible.

58. CIRCUIT CONSIDERATIONS FOR A PLASMA

The balance equations developed in the preceding sections are quite useful in establishing circuit concepts of a plasma. By starting from the fact that the total energy is constant the circuit equations applicable to a plasma can be derived in terms of a Lagrangian function. The Lagrangian approach has proved very fruitful in circuit dynamics when the elements comprising the circuit are rigid.* When the circuit contains a plasma element, *e.g.*, gas discharge, the usual formulations of circuit dynamics may not necessarily hold. In the usual formulations Maxwell's equations together with Ohm's law in the form $\mathbf{J} = \sigma\mathbf{E}$ form the basis of the circuital equations. In the plasma case, the simple relation can not necessarily be retained. Moreover, the conductivity is dependent on the electron and ion temperatures, the fields and associated equations must be solved simultaneously with a thermal energy equation.

The total energy equation is written in the form

$$\frac{\partial}{\partial t}\left(\frac{1}{2}\rho v^2 + \sum_j \frac{1}{2}\alpha_j N_j k T_j\right) + \operatorname{div}\left(\mathbf{Q}_1 + \mathbf{R}_1\right) = \mathbf{E}\cdot\mathbf{J} \;, \qquad (58.1$$

where α_j is the number of degrees of freedom per particle, N_j the number density of the jth species, T_j its kinetic temperature referred to the center of mass, k is Boltzmann's constant. Here, $\mathbf{Q}_1$ is the heat flux vector referred to a rest frame, and $\mathbf{R}_1$ is the radiation flux vector associated with Bremsstrahlung, cyclotron radiation and excitation. In this equation we have allowed for radiation losses in addition to heat losses.

THERMAL ENERGY EQUATION

The thermal energy balance per unit volume is defined by

$$\frac{\partial}{\partial t}\left(\sum_j \frac{1}{2}\alpha_j N_j k T_j\right) + \operatorname{div}\left[\sum_j\left(\mathbf{Q}_{2,j} + \frac{1}{2}\alpha_j N_j k T_j\langle\mathbf{v}\rangle\right) + \mathbf{R}_2\right]$$

$$+\sum (\mathbf{p}\cdot\mathbf{grad})\langle\mathbf{v}\rangle = (\mathbf{J} - \rho_e\langle\mathbf{v}\rangle)\cdot(\mathbf{E} + \langle\mathbf{v}\rangle\mathbf{x}\mathbf{B}) \;, \qquad (58.2)$$

* See for example H. Goldstein, Classical Mechanics, p. 45, Addison Wesley Press, Inc., 1950.

here, $\mathbf{Q}_2$ is the heat flux vector referred to the center of mass, $\mathbf{R}_2$ is the radiation flux vector associated with thermal energy losses, $\mathbf{p}$ is the pressure tensor referred to the center of mass. The right side results from eqs. (54.9), (54.10) and (58.1). In eqs. (58.1) and (58.2) we have neglected ionization processes.

MOMENTUM EQUATION

We take the momentum equation in the following form

$$\rho \frac{d\langle\mathbf{v}\rangle}{dt} = \rho_e\mathbf{E} + \mathbf{J}\mathrm{x}\mathbf{B} - \mathrm{div}\ \mathbf{p} \quad , \tag{58.3}$$

which is just the magneto-hydrodynamical equation. To complete our description of these balance equations, we should like to know the relation between $\mathbf{J}$ and $\mathbf{E}$, which leads us to discuss some aspects of a generalized Ohm's law.

Generalizations of Ohm's Law—As stated above, see also Chapter IV it is not obvious that Ohm's law in its classical form can be retained as applicable to a plasma. In fact it has been recognized for some time that it holds only under restricted conditions. This law in its classical guise asserts that the current is proportional and parallel to the electrical field. In considering generalizations of this law there have been two distinct lines of approach. We can either extend the definition of $\mathbf{E}$ or generalize the classical law so as to include the Hall effect. In the former, $\mathbf{E}$ is taken as the effective electrical field and may include the field generated by the diffusion phenomena due to pressure and concentration gradients. Chapman and Cowling have derived a rather general expression of the electrical current from kinetic theory considerations.* They consider in detail the cases in which $\mathbf{B}$ is parallel to $\mathbf{E}$ and $\mathbf{B}$ perpendicular to $\mathbf{E}$.

Another important feature of the generalizations should be pointed up. The law may be expressed in either explicit or implicit form. Thus, Cowling in his monograph gives a generalization in implicit form, but using a simpler theory.† Finkelnburg and Maecker, and Spitzer to cite a few others, also develop generalizations.§ In Chapter IV, the Hall effect

* Chapman and Cowling, *loc. cit.*

† Cowling, Magnetohydrodynamics, Interscience Publishers, Inc., New York, 1957.

§ Finkelnburg, W., and Maecker, H., "Elektrische Bögen und Thermisches Plasma," Handbuch der Physik, Berlin, Springer-Verlag, 1956. Spitzer, L. "Physics of Fully Ionized Gas," Interscience Pub., Inc., 1956.

was put into evidence by essentially taking $\mathbf{J}$ in the form $\mathbf{J} = J_i \mathbf{e}_i$ where the $\mathbf{e}_i$ form an orthonormal set of vectors. In particular if the directions of these $\mathbf{e}_i$ are respectively $\mathbf{E}$, $(\mathbf{B}\mathbf{x}\mathbf{E})$ and $\mathbf{E}\mathbf{x}\,(\mathbf{B}\mathbf{x}\mathbf{E})$, one obtains the generalized Hall current as the J_2 component. It is interesting to mention that in proceeding along both distinct lines of generalization, the end results are remarkably similar. That this is so, results from the fact that the underlying assumptions are equivalent but somewhat disguised. Following Finkelnburg and Maecker, we shall adopt their basic form of the law. By neglecting viscosity and electron inertial effects, Ohm's law takes the following form,

$$\frac{1}{N_e e}\,\mathbf{grad}\,p_e + (\mathbf{E} + \langle\mathbf{v}\rangle\mathbf{x}\mathbf{B}) - \frac{1}{N_e e}(\mathbf{J} - \rho_e\langle\mathbf{v}\rangle)\mathbf{x}\mathbf{B} = C_1(\mathbf{J} - \rho_e\langle\mathbf{v}\rangle) + C_2\mathbf{Q}_{3,e}\,, \tag{58.4}$$

in adopting this form we have modified Finkelnburg by adding the term involving $\mathbf{Q}_{3,e}$ which is by definition,

$$\mathbf{Q}_{3,e} = \mathbf{Q}_{2,e} + \frac{5}{2}\frac{kT_e}{e}(\mathbf{J} - \rho_e\langle\mathbf{v}\rangle)\,, \tag{58.5}$$

where p_e is the electron hydrostatic pressure, C_1 is a parameter whose dimensions are that of resistivity, similarly for C_2, and N_e is the free electron density. Actually, if, the following restrictions are satisfied

$$\left.\begin{aligned} |grad\,\langle\mathbf{v}\rangle| &\leqq C_3 \\ \left|\frac{1}{T_e}\frac{dT_e}{dt}\right| &\leqq C_3 \end{aligned}\right\} \tag{58.6}$$

where C_3 is some constant, the vector $\mathbf{Q}_{3,e}$ satisfies the electron heat-flux equation

$$\frac{5}{2}p_e\frac{k}{m_e}\,gradT_e + \frac{e}{m_e}\mathbf{Q}_{3,e}\mathbf{x}\mathbf{B} = -C_3\mathbf{Q}_{3,e} - C_4(\mathbf{J} - \rho_e\langle\mathbf{v}\rangle)\,. \tag{58.7}$$

The parameters C_3 and C_4 are similar to C_1, C_2; this last equation can be derived from the moments of a distribution function using Boltzmann's equation. In all fairness to the reader, we have adopted the above form only to demonstrate the factors which enter into the construction of a generalization of Ohm's law. At the same time the salient features are brought out regarding the couplings of the terms. The detailed derivations using a distribution function is deferred to a later chapter.

The first term on the left side of eq. (58.4) gives rise to the Thomson effect, the second is the effective electrical field, the third gives use to Hall currents (see Chapter IV). The first term on the right side accounts for collisions between particles, while $\mathbf{Q}_{3,e}$ involves thermal-diffusion effects. We see from this equation the coupling between the electrical and thermal properties of a plasma. An additional equation holds for the ionic heat-flux vector.

Let us suppose that our medium of interest is characterized by constitutive parameters μ and ϵ, and take Poynting's theorem in the form

$$-\frac{\epsilon}{2}\frac{\partial E^2}{\partial t} - \frac{1}{2\mu}\frac{\partial B^2}{\partial t} - \operatorname{div}\left(\mathbf{E} \times \frac{\mathbf{B}}{\mu}\right) = \mathbf{E} \cdot \mathbf{J} \quad , \tag{58.8}$$

where E and B are the magnitudes of $\mathbf{E}$ and $\mathbf{B}$ respectively. We can now eliminate $(\mathbf{E} \cdot \mathbf{J})$ between eqs. (58.1) and (58.8) to obtain, after integration over the volume of interest, the first integral

$$\frac{d}{dt}\left[\int_V \frac{1}{2}\rho v^2 dV + \int_V \left(\sum_j \frac{\alpha_j}{2} N_j k T_j\right) dV + \int_V \frac{B^2}{2\mu}\, dV + \int_V \frac{\epsilon E^2}{2}\, dV\right] = 0 \quad . \tag{58.9}$$

We denote these integrals by T_0, T_R, U_m, U_e which are respectively the kinetic energy of directed motion, kinetic energy of random motion, magnetic energy and electric energy. In eq. (58.9), the volume is taken sufficiently large so that the boundary terms arising from the div ( ) are neglected.

To obtain a second integral we first assume that $|\rho_e \langle \mathbf{v} \rangle| \ll |\mathbf{J}|$, then we can solve for $\mathbf{Q}_{3,e}$ in eq. (58.7)

$$\mathbf{Q}_{3,e} = -\frac{C_4 \tau_e}{1 + (\omega_c \tau_e)^2}\left[\mathbf{J} + \left(\frac{\omega_c \tau_e}{B}\right)^2 \mathbf{B} \cdot \mathbf{J}\,\mathbf{B} + \left(\frac{\omega_c \tau_e}{B}\right)\mathbf{B} \times \mathbf{J}\right]$$

$$- \frac{\lambda}{1 + (\omega_c \tau_e)^2}\left[\mathbf{grad}\, T_e + \left(\frac{\omega_c \tau_e}{B}\right)^2 \mathbf{B} \cdot grad T_e B + \left(\frac{\omega_c \tau_e}{B}\right)\mathbf{B} \times \mathbf{grad}\, T_e\right], \tag{58.10}$$

where ω_c is the electron gyro frequency, τ_e is the electron collison time, *i.e.*, $1/C_3$, and $\lambda = (5/2)p_e(k/m_e)\tau_e$. With this result in eq. (58.4) and using eq. (58.2), we find after integrating the thermal equation, the result,

$$\frac{dT_R}{dt} = \int_V \langle\mathbf{v}\rangle \cdot \text{div}\,\mathbf{p}\,dV + \int_V C\mathbf{J} \cdot (\mathbf{J} + \mathbf{K})\,dV \quad , \tag{58.11}$$

where $C = C_1[1 - (\tau_e C_2/C_1 C_4)]$. The form of the vector $\mathbf{K}$ is rather complex and for the future discussion need not be known explicitly.

Lumped Parameters—We follow the conventional approach and language of circuit analysis in attempting to express the behavior of a plasma. This is accomplished by utilizing lumped parameters. In general, these parameters are categorized as geometrical, electrical, and thermal. In the first category we have the over-all dimensions or characteristic length of a body, in the second category we have the total charges on different bodies, such as a condenser, etc, and in the last category we utilize the mean temperatures of the conductors in the system.

We should like to express eqs. (58.9) and (58.11) by appropriate lumped parameters. The magnetic energy, we recall from elementary circuit theory is expressible in terms of inductance coefficients and total currents i_j, for example,

$$U_m = \int \frac{B^2}{2\mu}\,dV = \sum_{j,k} L_{jk}\, i_j\, i_k \quad , \tag{58.12}$$

where L_{jk} is the coefficient of inductance, i_j the total current in the jth circuit. If $\mathbf{B}_j$ is induction vector associated with i_j and $\mathbf{B}_k$ the vector associated with i_k, we have (neglecting displacement currents),

$$L_{jk} = \int_V \frac{\mathbf{B}_j \cdot \mathbf{B}_k}{\mu}\,dV = L_{kj} \quad . \tag{58.13}$$

For the electrical energy we separate $\mathbf{E}$ into the sum of two parts, $\mathbf{E}_q$ and $\mathbf{E}_i$, the first due to charge accumulation, the second is the induced field arising from flux changes. We can therefore write,

$$\frac{1}{2}\epsilon E^2 = \frac{1}{2}\epsilon E_q^2 + \epsilon \mathbf{E}_q \cdot \mathbf{E}_i + \frac{1}{2}\epsilon E_i^2 \quad , \tag{58.14}$$

as the electrical energy per unit volume. The induced field $\mathbf{E}_i$ is derived from Maxwell's equation

$$\text{curl } \mathbf{E}_i + \frac{\partial \mathbf{B}}{\partial t} = 0 \quad , \tag{58.15}$$

and if ω is some characteristic frequency of the over-all system, $\mathbf{E}_i$ is of order $\omega \mathbf{B} d$ where d is the characteristic length of the system. It follows that $1/2\ \epsilon E_i^2$ is of order $\epsilon\mu\omega^2 d^2\ (B^2/2\mu)$; moreover, if $\epsilon\mu\omega^2 d^2$ is very much less than unity, we can neglect the induced electrical energy compared with the magnetic energy. Generally, the terms $\epsilon \mathbf{E}_i \cdot \mathbf{E}_q$ are negligible with respect to the electrostatic energy $1/2\ \epsilon E_q^2$. Consequently, the electrical energy is approximately equal to $\int_V 1/2\ \epsilon E_q^2 dV \doteq U_e$ from which we define the capacitance, *i.e.*,

$$U_e = \sum_{j,k} \frac{q_j q_k}{2C_{jk}} \quad , \tag{58.16}$$

in which,

$$\frac{1}{C_{jk}} = \frac{1}{q_j q_k} \int_V \epsilon \mathbf{E}_j \cdot \mathbf{E}_k dV = \frac{1}{C_{kj}} \quad . \tag{58.17}$$

The kinetic energy T_R is used to define the mean temperature according to the definition,

$$T_R = \int_V \sum_j \left(\frac{\alpha_j}{2} N_j k T_j\right) dV \equiv \sum_r \frac{\overline{\alpha}_r}{2} n_r k \overline{T}_r \quad , \tag{58.18}$$

where $\overline{\alpha}_r$ is the average number of degrees of freedom of a particle in a conductor, n_r is the total number of particles of all species in the conductor, $\overline{T}_r$ is the mean temperature of the conductor.

Let us introduce generalized coordinates of the system by the notation η_k and its time derivative $\dot{\eta}_k$. The directed energy is given by*

* It should be remembered that M_{jk} does not necessarily have the dimensions of a mass when using generalized coordinates. See H. Goldstein, *loc. cit.*

$$T_D = \int_V \frac{1}{2} \rho v^2 dV = \sum_{j,k} \frac{1}{2} M_{jk} \dot{\eta}_j \dot{\eta}_k \quad . \tag{58.19}$$

The total energy of the system is then expressed by the sum,

$$U = \text{Total Energy} = \sum_{j,k} \frac{1}{2}\left(L_{jk} i_j i_k + M_{jk} \dot{\eta}_j \dot{\eta}_k + \frac{1}{2} \frac{q_j q_k}{C_{jk}}\right) + \sum_r \frac{\overline{\alpha}_r}{2} n_r k \overline{T}_r$$

$$= T + U_e + T_R \tag{58.20}$$

We comment that the coefficients L_{jk}, M_{jk}, C_{jk} can be functions of $\dot{\boldsymbol{\eta}}$, $\mathbf{i}$, $\mathbf{i}$ and $\overline{T}$ as well as $\boldsymbol{\eta}$. For simplicity of exposition we shall suppress the dependence of the L_{jk}, M_{jk} and C_{jk} on all variables except $\boldsymbol{\eta}$. Now introduce the generalized forces F_i (these forces do not have the dimensions of a force, necessarily), then we can write

$$\frac{dT_R}{dt} = - \sum_i F_i \dot{\xi}_i \tag{58.21}$$

where we have subsumed the $\dot{\eta}_j$ and i_j into $\dot{\xi}_j$, where the generalized force associated with the η_j is defined by

$$F_{\eta_j} \equiv - \frac{1}{\dot{\eta}_j} \int_V \langle \mathbf{v}(\dot{\eta}_j) \rangle \cdot \operatorname{div} \mathbf{p} \, dV \quad , \tag{58.22}$$

[see eq. (58.11)], in which $\langle v(\dot{\eta}_j) \rangle$ is the component of the mass velocity in the η_k direction. Similarly,

$$F_{i_j} \equiv - \frac{1}{i_j} \int C\mathbf{J}(i_j) \cdot (\mathbf{J} + \mathbf{K}) dV \quad , \tag{58.23}$$

where $J(i_j)$ is that component of current density $\mathbf{J}$ which contributes to the total current $\mathbf{i}_j$. Let us decompose F_{i_j} as follows,

$$F_{ij} = - \sum_k (R_{jk} i_k + e_{kT} + e_{kD}) \quad , \tag{58.24}$$

where the R_{jk} denote the resistance, that is, R_{jj} is the resistance in the jth circuit, R_{jk} the mutual resistance between the jth and kth circuit, the e_{kT} and e_{kD} are called generalized electromotive forces. These quantities are defined by

$$R_{jk} = R_{kj} = \frac{1}{i_j i_k} \int_V C\mathbf{J}(i_j) \cdot \mathbf{J}(i_k)\,dV \quad , \tag{58.25}$$

$$e_{jD} \equiv -\frac{1}{i_j} \int_V C\mathbf{J}(i_j) \cdot \mathbf{K}_D dV \quad , \tag{58.26}$$

$$e_{jT} \equiv -\frac{1}{i_j} \int_V C\mathbf{J}(i_j) \cdot \mathbf{K}_T dV \quad , \tag{58.27}$$

where we have split $\mathbf{K}$ into two components along and transverse to the magnetic field. If there is no externally applied field we can decompose $\mathbf{K}$ along and transverse to any other direction of interest. In this sense, the definitions (58.26), (58.27) are somewhat arbitrary. With these designations eq. (58.21) takes the form

$$\frac{d}{dt}\left(\sum_r \frac{\alpha_r}{2} n_r k T_r\right) = -\sum_{\dot{\eta}_i} F_{\eta_r}\dot{\eta}_r + \sum_{ir}\left[\sum_K (R_{rk} i_k) - e_{rD} - e_{rT}\right] i_r \quad . \tag{58.28}$$

59. CIRCUIT DYNAMICS

With the assumptions made in the preceding section, namely that the coefficients are functions of η alone we write the Lagrangian in the form

$$L(\xi,\dot{\xi}) = T(\xi,\dot{\xi}) - V(\xi) \quad , \tag{59.1}$$

where $V(\xi) = U_e$. Since T is quadratic in $\dot{\xi}$, we have

$$2T = \sum_j \dot{\xi}_j \frac{\partial T}{\partial \dot{\xi}_j} \tag{59.2}$$

(by Euler's theorem on homogeneous functions), and because U is a function of ξ, $\dot{\xi}$ and $\bar{T}$, we also have

$$\frac{d}{dt} = \sum_j \dot{\xi}_j \frac{\partial}{\partial \xi_j} + \ddot{\xi}_j \frac{\partial}{\partial \dot{\xi}_j} + {}_k \dot{\bar{T}}_k \frac{\partial}{\partial \bar{T}_k} \quad . \tag{59.3}$$

From eqs. (59.1), (59.2) and (59.3) we find,

$$\frac{d}{dt}(T + U) = \sum_j \dot{\xi}_j \left[\frac{d}{dt}\left(\frac{\partial L}{\partial \dot{\xi}_j}\right) - \frac{\partial L}{\partial \xi_j}\right] \quad . \tag{59.4}$$

The function L is the over-all or lumped Lagrangian of the plasma dynamical system. From eq. (58.9) we find,

$$\frac{dU}{dt} = \frac{d(T + V)}{dt} + \frac{dT_R}{dt} = 0 \quad , \tag{59.5}$$

and from eq. (58.21),

$$\frac{dU}{dt} = \sum_j f_j \dot{\xi}_j = 0 \quad , \tag{59.6}$$

with

$$f_j \equiv \frac{d}{dt}\left(\frac{\partial L}{\partial \dot{\xi}_j}\right) - \frac{\partial L}{\partial \xi_j} - F_j \quad , \tag{59.7}$$

the range of j is determined by the number of generalized coordinates ξ_j. We shall postulate that $f_j = 0$ for all j, and this may be considered as a generalization postulate since it holds for the case in which the conductors are rigid for $F_j = 0$.* The ξ_j are obtained as functions of time from Lagrange's equations with appropriate initial conditions, *i.e.*,

$$\frac{d}{dt}\frac{\partial L}{\partial \dot{\xi}_j} - \frac{\partial L}{\partial \xi_j} = F_j \quad . \tag{59.8}$$

By choosing as a generalized coordinate $\xi_j = q_k$ and denoting by ϕ the flux of induction, we obtain with the use of eqs. (58.20) for T, eq. (58.16) for $V(\xi)$ and Eq. (58.24) for F_{ij}, the flux equations for the circuit,

---

* Page, L. and N. I. Adams, "Electrodynamics," (Van Nostrand, 1940).

$$\frac{d\phi_k}{dt} + \sum_j \frac{q_{kj}}{C_{kj}} + \sum_j R_{kj} i_j = e_{kT} + e_{kD} \tag{59.9}$$

where $\phi_k = \sum_j L_{kj} i_j$ is the flux linking the kth circuit. Now by setting $\xi = \eta$ we obtain the force equations,

$$\frac{d}{dt}\left(\sum_j M_{kj}\dot{\eta}_j\right) = \sum_{j,k} \frac{1}{2} \dot{\eta}_j\dot{\eta}_k \frac{\partial M_{jk}}{\partial \eta_j} + \sum_{r,h} \frac{1}{2} i_r i_h \frac{\partial L_{rh}}{\partial \eta_k}$$

$$- \sum_{r,h} \frac{1}{2} q_r q_h \frac{\partial}{\partial \eta_k}\left(\frac{1}{C_{rh}}\right) + F_{\eta_k} \quad . \tag{59.10}$$

In order to understand better the physical significance of the circuit dynamical equations, we shall restrict ourselves to one geometrical and one electrical coordinate, hence we can drop the subscripts k and write the flux equation as

$$-\frac{q}{C} = Ri - e_T - e_D + \frac{d}{dt}(Li) \quad , \tag{59.11}$$

or,

$$-\frac{d\left(\dfrac{q^2}{2C}\right)}{dt} = (Ri - e_T - e_D)i + \frac{d\left(\dfrac{1}{2}Li^2\right)}{dt}$$

$$+ \frac{1}{2} i^2 \frac{dL}{dt} - \frac{1}{2} q^2 \frac{d}{dt}\left(\frac{1}{C}\right) \quad ; \tag{59.12}$$

and the momentum equation becomes,

$$\frac{d}{dt}(M\dot{\eta}) = \frac{1}{2}\dot{\eta}^2 \frac{\partial M}{\partial \eta} + \frac{1}{2} i^2 \frac{\partial L}{\partial \eta} - \frac{1}{2} q^2 \frac{\partial}{\partial \eta}\left(\frac{1}{C}\right) + F_\eta \quad , \tag{59.13}$$

now multiply by $\dot{\eta}$ on both sides of this equation to obtain, (since M, L, C are explicit functions of t),

$$\frac{d}{dt}\left(\frac{1}{2} M\dot{\eta}^2\right) = \frac{1}{2} i^2 \frac{dL}{dt} - \frac{1}{2} q^2 \frac{d}{dt}\left(\frac{1}{C}\right) + F_\eta \dot{\eta} \quad . \tag{59.14}$$

In eq. (59.12) we see that the rate of decrease of stored electrical energy is equal to the rate at which energy is dissipated as heat plus the rate of increase of stored magnetic energy. The last two terms on the right side are just the rate at which mechanical work is done on the system. As for eq. (59..14), the last term on the right side is rate at which thermal energy is converted into mechanical energy, *i.e.*, energy of directed motion.

We can proceed further with a network analysis but this is best done by treating special cases. This however is outside of our intentions. We wish to emphasize that although the above treatment appears to be straight forward and rigorous, it is not. The transition from the plasma equations to the equations of circuit dynamics for it should be viewed as heuristic in nature. We have been guided by analogy with rigid conductors and this is the only validity that we can at present attribute to the circuit equations for the plasma.* There remains much work to be done on this topic particularly in its engineering applications.

60. MAGNETOHYDRODYNAMIC SHOCKS

In Chapter III we established the concepts and formalism for the discussion of shocks for ideal gases and it is natural to inquire about the nature of shocks in magnetohydrodynamics. We shall exhibit the shock conditions analogous to those derived in Chapter III. We must however restrict ourselves to a system of equations less general than the full set of magnetohydrodynamics equations. Consequently we shall make the following physical hypothesis.

- H_1) The medium can be considered as a single component fluid.
- H_2) The flow is adiabatic
- H_3) The viscosity is negligible.
- H_4) The stress tensor can be replaced by an isotropic pressure which is a function only of density and entropy.
- H_5) The flow is non-relativistic, *i.e.*, small compared with V_0, but not necessarily small compared with the speed of sound in the medium. The latter

* Liley, B. S., "The Bulk Dynamics of Plasma," A.E.I. Research Report No. A. 852, 1958. R. Herdan and B. S. Liley, Rev. Modern Phys. Vol. 32, No. 4, October 1960.

assumption asserts the medium is compressible. However the Alfvén speed $\sqrt{B^2/2\mu}$ is comparable with the sound speed, since otherwise the compressibility effects can be separated from the hydromagnetic ones.

H_6) The conductivity of the medium is infinite which implies that Ohm's law takes the form $\mathbf{E} = -\mathbf{v}\mathbf{x}\mathbf{B}$, where $\mathbf{v}$ is the velocity of a fluid element.

H_7) The medium is over-all neutral and displacement currents are negligible.

With these hypotheses the governing equations become

$$\left.\begin{aligned} \nabla \mathbf{x} \mathbf{B} &= \mu \mathbf{J} , \\ \nabla \mathbf{x} (\mathbf{B} \mathbf{x} \mathbf{v}) &= -\frac{\partial \mathbf{B}}{\partial t} , \\ \text{div } \mathbf{B} &= 0 , \end{aligned}\right\} , \qquad \begin{aligned} &(60.1a) \\ &(60.1b) \\ &(60.1c) \end{aligned}$$

with the momentum equation,

$$\rho \dot{\mathbf{v}} + \rho(\mathbf{v} \cdot \nabla)\mathbf{v} + \nabla p + \frac{1}{\mu} \mathbf{B} \mathbf{x} (\nabla \mathbf{x} \mathbf{B}) = 0 , \qquad (60.2)$$

the last term is the Lorentz force and we have used (60.1a) for $\mathbf{J}$. To this system we add the two conservation laws

$$\frac{\partial \rho}{\partial t} + \text{div } (\rho \mathbf{v}) = 0 , \qquad (60.3)$$

and

$$S + (\mathbf{v} \cdot \nabla) S = 0 , \qquad (60.4)$$

which states that the entropy per unit mass is transported unchanged by the fluid particles, (see Section 32, Chapter III).

Eqs. (60.1) to (60.4) formed the basis for investigations in magnetohydrodynamics by Lundquist.* As shown by Friedrichs and Kranzer,†

* Lundquist, S., Studies in magnetohydrodynamics, ArKiv für Fysik, Band 5, nr. 15 (1952)

† Friedrichs, K. O. and H. Kranzer, Notes on Magnetohydrodynamics VIII, "Non-Linear Wave Motion," NYO-6486, July 1958, AEC Comput. and App. Math. Center, Inst. of Math. Sciences, N.Y.U.

this set of equations constitute a set of eight non-linear partial differential equations for the components of **B** and **v**, ρ and S. In mathematical description they are symmetrical hyperbolic equations. For such a system, closed form solutions are obtained for the propagation of disturbances in an arbitrary magnetic field and flow field. These disturbances are propagated with finite speed and there are three modes of propagation in each direction. These three modes are called the "slow wave," the "fast wave" and the "transverse wave," (see Chapter IV).

In contrast to this situation of perfect conductivity, the system of equations describing the magnetogasdynamic propagation field of disturbances in a medium of finite conductivity is also non-linear but parabolically degenerate.* Consequently the resulting dispersion equation is not simple and closed form solutions of the system of partial differential equations obtains only for special orientations of the direction of magnetic field and direction of propagation.

Following the ideas of Chapter III and Friedrichs,† we introduce the term "characteristic manifold," that is, a three dimensional manifold in a four-space $(\mathbf{r}, t)$ associated with a differential equation. By this we mean that solutions of differential equations may have discontinuities only on certain surfaces and these surfaces are termed "characteristic." These manifolds are generated or swept out by surfaces $\Sigma'(t)$ in $\mathbf{r}$-space and the motion of these surfaces are also called "characteristic." More precisely, suppose we are given a differential equation which describes some physical phenomena and that there exists a small discontinuity or "disturbance" on a surface $\Sigma'(t_0)$ at $t = t_0$ which may be present only on surfaces $\Sigma'(t)$ at later times which move characteristically. This moving discontinuity is called a "disturbance wave" or just simply a "wave."

The surface $\Sigma'(t)$ is the singular surface introduced in Chapter III. Historically speaking, it was Hadamard who used this concept in his studies on wave propagation.§ It is important to distinguish the types of

---

* Golitsyn, G. S., and K. P. Stanyukovich, Soviet Physics JETP **6**, 1090 (1958).

† Friedrichs, K. O., *loc. cit.*

§ Hadamard, J., Lecons sur la Propagation des Ondes et les Equations de l'Hydrodynamique, Paris, 1903. See also the following papers which bear on these concepts in an impressively clear manner. T. Y. Thomas, Extended compatability conditions for the study of surfaces of discontinuity in continuum mechanics, Jour. Math and Mechanics; 6 (1957) pp. 311-322, On the characteristic surfaces of the von Mises plasticity eqs., J. Rat. Mech. and Anal. 1 (1952) pp. 343-357; Singular surfaces and flow lines in the theory of plasticity, ibid. 2, (1953) pp. 339-381; characteristic surfaces in the Prandtl-Reuss plasticity theory, ibid. 5 (1956) pp. 251-262; Kinematically preferred coordinate systems, Proc. N.A.S. 41 (1955) pp 762-770; on

discontinuities associated with such singular or wave surfaces. We call a discontinuity "weak" if the solution functions of our problem have discontinuities only in the derivatives across the surface. Surfaces over which the actual functions are discontinuous are called "strong" discontinuities or "shocks." The appearance of these shocks means that the physical process with which we are concerned can no longer be described by the system of differential equations which govern the process. These shocks in ordinary continuous gas dynamics arise because of compression. At the time of appearance of the shock, the differential equations are no longer valid. As we have seen in Chapter III for gas dynamics, shock conservation laws result from laws of conservation for the quantities of interest on both sides of the shock front. For the magnetohydrodynamic case, the same considerations apply but the conservation laws are more general.

61. THE CONSERVATION LAWS

The conservation laws for the magnetohydrodynamic case are listed as follows.

$$\operatorname{div} \mathbf{B} = 0 \quad , \tag{61.1}$$

$$\frac{\partial \mathbf{B}}{\partial t} + \frac{\partial}{\partial x_i} (v_i B_j - B_i v_j) \mathbf{e}_j = 0 \quad , \tag{61.2}$$

$$\frac{\partial}{\partial t} (\rho \mathbf{v}) + \frac{\partial}{\partial x_i} v_i (\rho v_j) \mathbf{e}_j + \mathbf{grad}\, p + \mathbf{grad} \left(\frac{B^2}{2\mu} \right) - \frac{\partial}{\partial x_i} B_i \frac{B_j}{\mu} \mathbf{e}_j = 0 \quad , \tag{61.3}$$

where $\mathbf{e}_j$ is an orthonormal set of vectors and we sum on i, j;

$$\frac{\partial \rho}{\partial t} + \operatorname{div} (\rho \mathbf{v}) = 0 \quad . \tag{61.4}$$

Before proceeding to list the remaining equations we want to point out that in general when we talk about conservation laws resulting from a system of partial differential equations we mean that each equation is written as the sum of derivatives of functions of the unknown quantities of interest.

---

the propagation of weak discontinuities in perfectly plastic solids, J. Math and Mech. V. 6, (1957) pp. 67-85; see also J. L. Ericksen, Singular surfaces in plasticity, J. Math. and Physics 34 (1955) pp. 74-79.

Following a method developed by N. Coburn, Math. Mag. 27, 245 (1954) It was shown by R. S. Ong, The Physics of Fluids, Vol. 2, No. 3, May-June, 1959, pp. 247-251, that the general theory of discontinuities is readily adaptable to the study of discontinuity manifolds in unsteady flow of magnetohydrodynamics.

Thus equations (61.1) and (61.2) are rewrites of eqs. (60.1b,c) eq. (61.3) is the law of conservation of momentum, eq. (61.4) is the law of mass conservation. Now eq. (60.4) represents the entropy transport and should be replaced by an energy conservation law, which is expressed as

$$\frac{\partial}{\partial t}\left(\frac{1}{2}\rho v^2 + \rho U + \frac{B^2}{2\mu}\right) + \text{div } \mathbf{v}\left(\frac{1}{2}\rho v^2 + \rho U + p + \frac{B^2}{\mu}\right)$$

$$- \text{div } \mathbf{B}\frac{(\mathbf{v} \cdot \mathbf{B})}{\mu} = 0 , \qquad (61.5)$$

where U is the specific internal energy of the fluid and is a function of the density and entropy. It satisfies eq. (54.4). Let us note that if the last term in eq. (61.3) vanishes then this conservation law reduces to that of ordinary gas dynamics except that **grad** p is replaced by **grad** $[p + (B^2/2\mu)]$, the additional term here, $B^2/2\mu$ is called the "magnetic pressure." This term in eq. (61.5) however is interpreted as the magnetic energy per unit volume, but B^2/μ in this same equation is interpreted as the magnetic enthalpy per unit volume. Finally, the two terms in this equation, $\mathbf{v}\,(B^2/\mu) - \mathbf{B}\,(\mathbf{v} \cdot \mathbf{B})/\mu$ is nothing more than $(\mathbf{E} \times \mathbf{B})/\mu$ or $\mathbf{E} \times \mathbf{H}$ which is Poynting's vector.

The change or jump across the shock front is still denoted by (ΔA) for any quantity A, that is, $(\Delta A) = A_2 - A_1$, with A_2 denoting the value on the side toward which the normal $\mathbf{n}$ points and A_1 the value on the other side. The velocity of the shock front will be denoted by $\mathbf{u}$, then by following the procedure in Section 36, Chapter III, applied to eqs. (61.1)-(61.5), we obtain the following shock conditions.

$$(\Delta B_n) = 0 , \qquad (61.6)$$

$$\{\Delta[(v_n - u_n)\mathbf{B} - B_n\mathbf{v}]\} = 0 , \qquad (61.7)$$

$$\left\{\Delta\left[(v_n - u_n)\rho\mathbf{v} + \left(p + \frac{B^2}{2\mu}\right)\mathbf{n} - \frac{B_n}{\mu}\mathbf{B}\right]\right\} = 0 , \qquad (61.8)$$

$$\{\Delta[(v_n - u_n)\rho]\} = 0 \qquad (61.9)$$

$$\left\{\Delta\left[(v_n - u_n)\left(\frac{1}{2}\rho v^2 + \rho u + \frac{B^2}{2\mu}\right) + v_n\left(p + \frac{B^2}{2\mu}\right) - B_n\frac{(\mathbf{B} \cdot \mathbf{u})}{\mu}\right]\right\} = 0 . \qquad (61.10)$$

Thus far we have not considered eq. (60.1a), hence to complete the physical description of the shock conditions we assume that there exists a current sheet flowing in the singular surface and that the density of this current $\bar{\mathbf{J}}$ is determined by the jump in $\mathbf{B}$ according to the formula

$$\mu\bar{\mathbf{J}} = \mathbf{n}\times(\Delta\mathbf{B}) . \qquad (61.11)$$

We see at once that when $\mathbf{B} \to 0$, we recover the usual shock relations of gas dynamics. Besides the definitions we have given for "weak" and "strong" discontinuities, the shock conditions lead to another kind of discontinuity. This is the "contact" discontinuity defined by the condition that no fluid crosses the shock front, or mathematically, $v_n - u_n = 0$. Accordingly we say that a shock exists if fluid crosses the front, *i.e.*, $v_n - u_n \neq 0$, and we choose the normal vector $\mathbf{n}$ in such a way that $v_n - u_n > 0$.

62. THE ENTROPY CHANGE ACROSS A SHOCK FRONT

In Section 39 it was shown that when a particle traverses a shock front the density and the entropy per unit mass associated with the particle are increased. In magnetohydrodynamics there exist shocks such that there are no changes in entropy, density and pressure.* Because of this possibility we state the relations between these quantities in the form of a theorem.

"If the entropy increases across a shock front then the pressure and density increase."

The proof of this theorem is given by Friedrichs and we refer the reader to the cited report. There exists, just as in the case of propagation of weak discontinuities, slow, fast and intermediate shock velocities.

It is possible to give a relativistic extension of magnetohydrodynamics, the basic notions of which have already been treated by Reichel.† This treatment contains the results of Teller and de Hoffmann,§ and others.

---

* Friedrichs, K. O., *loc. cit.*

† Reichel, P., Basic notions of relativistic hydromagnetics, Report NYO-7697, Inst. of Math. Sciences, New York Univ., 1958.

§ de Hoffmann, F. and E. Teller, Magnetohydrodynamic shocks, Phys. Rev., 80, 692 (1952). See also, B. Zumino, Some questions in relativistic hydromagnetics, Phys. Rev. 108, 1116 (1957).

63. DIMENSIONAL CONSIDERATIONS-SCALING IN MAGNETOHYDRODYNAMICS

It is of interest here to touch briefly on the question of scaling and dimensional aspects of magnetohydrodynamic phenomena. These matters in terms of the coupling between the electromagnetic and fluid dynamic quantities have been treated in the literature and we discuss here the meaning of certain dimensionless quantities which arise when viscosity is considered. In hydrodynamics (fluid mechanics) there exists a fundamental dimensionless parameter called the Reynolds number, denoted by R. This parameter is by definition a measure of the order of the ratio of the inertial forces to the viscous forces,

$$R = \frac{\rho v^2}{\rho \nu \dfrac{v}{L}} = \frac{vL}{\nu} \quad , \tag{63.1}$$

where v, L and ν are respectively the average speed of flow, a characteristic length (dimension of the system) and the kinematic viscosity. In the usual case, $R \gg 1$, and so the viscous effects are substantially negligible throughout the flow field. The viscous forces are then of the order of the inertial forces only in the boundary layer, *i.e.*, the thin layer close to the boundary of the system.

The magnetohydrodynamic analogy of the ordinary Reynolds number starts with the ratio of the magnetic force to the dynamic force, $JBL/\rho v^2$. Now the induced current J is of the order $\sigma v B$, where σ is the conductivity, and the ratio $\sigma B^2 L/\rho v$ is a magnetic interaction number. This parameter occurs when free stream conditions are altered by the magnetic interaction. A measure of the order of magnetic force compared to the viscous force is the square of the Hartmann number M_H^2 defined by

$$M_H^2 = B^2 L^2 \frac{\sigma}{\rho \nu} \quad . \tag{63.2}$$

This parameter occurs in viscous flow problems in magnetohydrodynamics. If M_H is very much greater than unity, the magnetic forces overide the viscous forces. Finally, the magnetic Reynolds number R_m is defined by

$$R_m = \mu \sigma v L \quad , \tag{63.3}$$

and has been interpreted in a variety of ways. For example, as a measure of the order of distortion of the applied magnetic field by the field of the induced currents, or as a measure of the rate of decay of a magnetic field compared to the rate of macroscopic motion, etc. It should be pointed out however that the analogy between the ordinary Reynolds number and the magnetic one is a purely formal one and this is as far as one should pursue it. The physics of the situation is different in both cases.*

64. REMARKS ON THE ELECTRODYNAMICS OF MOVING MATTER

In all of the treatments of magnetohydrodynamic phenomena we have seen that the fundamental quantity which enters is the effective field, $\mathbf{E} + \mathbf{v} \times \mathbf{B}$. This expression for the electrical field has its origin, rigorously speaking, in the special theory of relativity. This of course implies that the only physically legitimate quantities are Lorentz invariant. However it is instructive to see how far one can proceed within the framework of Galilean transformations which are the limiting cases of Lorentz transformation. A program of this sort is in essence an attempt to construct a first order theory of electrodynamics retaining the concept of absolute time. We are not suggesting that one should reject relativity theory but rather we shall sketch a compatable first order theory which will yield results consistent with those deduced from a relativistic treatment, at least to a first order approximation.

To pursue a first order theory we make the following assumptions regarding the constitutive relations.

In Vacuum

$$\mathbf{B} = \mu_0 \mathbf{H} \quad , \quad \mathbf{D} = \epsilon_0 \mathbf{E} \tag{64.1}$$

are invariant with respect to rotations, proper and improper, and translations.

---

* W. H. Elsasser, Phys. Rev. **95**, 1 (1954), Am. J. Phys. 23, 590 (1955), ibid. 24, 85 (1956) T. J. Cowling, Magnetohydrodynamics, Interscience Pub., N.Y. (1957) E. L. Resler and W. R. Sears, J. Aero. Sci., (April 1958). F. D. Hains, Y. A. Yoler, and E. Ehlers, Proc. of Am. Rocket Soc. Gas Dynamics Symposium at Northwestern Univ., August 1959. Rev. Mod. Phys. Vol. 32, No. 4, October (1960)—contains topics of direct interest here. See also, for other analogies, G. K. Batchelor, Proc. Roy. Soc. London A-201, 405, (1950) V. D. Shafranov, Soviet Physics JETP, pp. 545-554 (March 1958). F. H. Clauser, Plasma Dynamics, *loc. cit.* Chapter 6. K. P. Chopra, Some Problems in Hydromagnetics, Univ. of S. Cal. Eng. Cent. Report 56-205, Jan. 1959. (In this report there is a wealth of interesting problems discussed including the subject of wave drag phenomena, the latter arising in problems concerning the rapid motions of conducting bodies through conducting media.)

In Isotropic Matter

$$\mathbf{B} = \mu\mu_0\mathbf{H} \quad , \quad \mathbf{D} = \epsilon\epsilon_0\mathbf{E} \tag{64.2}$$

are defined with respect to a coordinate system fixed in the material body, and are invariant only with respect to rotations (proper and improper).

In Anisotropic Matter

$$\mathbf{B} = \boldsymbol{\mu}\mu_0\mathbf{H} \quad , \quad \mathbf{D} = \boldsymbol{\epsilon}\epsilon_0\mathbf{E} \tag{64.3}$$

are defined with respect to a coordinate system fixed in the material body. The quantities $\boldsymbol{\mu}$ and $\boldsymbol{\epsilon}$ are second order tensors. The equations of state (64.3) are invariant with respect to the group of symmetry operations of the medium.*

FIELD QUANTITIES

Let us now turn to the field quantities and recall that in electrodynamics, experiments are performed on bodies of finite dimensions and not on fields. More specifically, the integral form of Maxwell's equations represent the result of observations on macroscopic bodies. In particular the circuital laws involve the time derivative of an integral. Consider the flux of a vector field **E** which is a function of both position and time,

$$\phi = \int_\Sigma \mathbf{F} \cdot d\boldsymbol{\Sigma} \quad . \tag{64.4}$$

The total time derivative involves the change of the field **F** with time and the change in position and shape of Σ with time. Thus we have

$$\frac{d}{dt}\int_\Sigma \mathbf{F} \cdot d\boldsymbol{\Sigma} = \int_\Sigma \frac{\partial \mathbf{F}}{\partial t} \cdot d\boldsymbol{\Sigma} + \lim_{\Delta t \to 0} \frac{\int \mathbf{F} \cdot d\boldsymbol{\Sigma}' - \int \mathbf{F} \cdot d\boldsymbol{\Sigma}}{\Delta t} \quad ; \tag{64.5}$$

the last expression is evaluated by referring to Fig. 10,
Here $\mathbf{v}\Delta t$ measures the height of the cylinder swept out by Σ, and Σ' is the

---

* For a particularly clear treatment on symmetry group transformations see, Landau and Lifshitz, Quantum Mechanics--Non-relativistic theory, Chapter XII, Addison-Wesley, 1958.

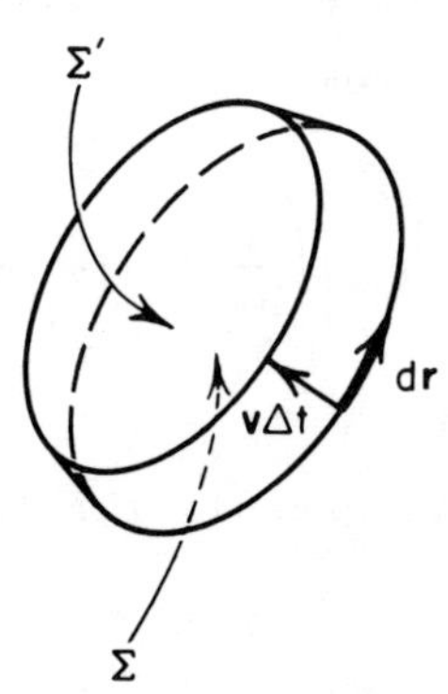

FIG. 10

surface Σ after a time Δt. The vector $d\mathbf{r}$ is tangent to the contour bounding Σ, hence $d\mathbf{r} \times \mathbf{v}\,\Delta t$ is normal to the lateral surface of the cylinder. Also, $d\mathbf{\Sigma}'$ points approximately in the same direction as $d\mathbf{\Sigma}$ since the surface is assumed to move continuously with time. Now we apply the divergence theorem to the whole cylinder.

$$\int_V (\text{div } \mathbf{F})\mathbf{v}\,\Delta t \cdot d\mathbf{\Sigma} = \int \mathbf{F} \cdot d\mathbf{\Sigma}' - \int \mathbf{F} \cdot d\mathbf{\Sigma} + \int \mathbf{F} \cdot d\mathbf{r} \times \mathbf{v}\,\Delta t \tag{64.6}$$

where $\mathbf{v}\Delta t \cdot d\mathbf{\Sigma} = dV$ is the element of volume of the cylinder and $d\mathbf{r} \times \mathbf{v}\,\Delta t$ is the vector element of the lateral surface. From the vector identity $\mathbf{F} \cdot d\mathbf{r} \times \mathbf{v} = -\mathbf{F} \times \mathbf{v} \cdot d\mathbf{r}$, and Stokes theorem we can write

$$\int \mathbf{F} \cdot d\mathbf{r} \times \mathbf{v}\,\Delta t = -\int \mathbf{F} \times \mathbf{v}\,\Delta t \cdot d\mathbf{r} = \Delta t \int \text{curl } (\mathbf{F} \times \mathbf{v}) \cdot d\mathbf{\Sigma}\,, \tag{64.7}$$

hence eq. (64.6) becomes

$$\Delta t \int [\mathbf{v} \text{ div } \mathbf{F} + \text{curl } (\mathbf{F} \times \mathbf{v})] \cdot d\mathbf{\Sigma} = \int \mathbf{F} \cdot d\mathbf{\Sigma}' - \int \mathbf{F} \cdot d\mathbf{\Sigma}\quad . \tag{64.8}$$

Substituting this expression into eq. (64.5) and passing to the limit as $\Delta t \to 0$, we obtain the expression,

$$\frac{d}{dt} \int_\Sigma \mathbf{F} \cdot d\mathbf{\Sigma} = \int_\Sigma \left[\frac{\partial \mathbf{F}}{\partial t} + \text{curl } (\mathbf{F} \times \mathbf{v}) + \mathbf{v} \text{ div } \mathbf{F} \right] \cdot d\mathbf{\Sigma}\quad . \tag{64.9}$$

If in particular we take ρ = div $\mathbf{F}$ and recall that div curl $\equiv$ 0, we find, using the divergence theorem,

$$\frac{d}{dt}\int_V \rho dV = \int_V \left(\frac{\partial \rho}{\partial t} + \mathrm{div}\ \rho\mathbf{v}\right) dV \quad . \tag{64.10}$$

Analogous reasonings lead to the result for line integrals,*

$$\frac{d}{dt}\int_C \mathbf{F}\cdot d\mathbf{r} = \int_C \left[\frac{\partial \mathbf{F}}{\partial t} - \mathbf{v}\times \mathrm{curl}\ \mathbf{F} + \mathbf{grad}\ (\mathbf{v}\cdot\mathbf{F})\right]\cdot d\mathbf{r} \quad . \tag{64.11}$$

Therefore, when the surface moves with velocity $\mathbf{v}$, the flux changes according to eq. (64.9). It is clear that only if $\mathbf{v}$ is uniform then the order of integration and differentiation can be changed. Let us examine Maxwell's equations in integral form,

$$\int_C \mathbf{E}'\cdot d\mathbf{r} = -\frac{d}{dt}\int_\Sigma \mathbf{B}\cdot d\boldsymbol{\Sigma} \tag{64.12}$$

$$\int_C \mathbf{H}'\cdot d\mathbf{r} = \int_\Sigma \mathbf{J}'\cdot d\boldsymbol{\Sigma} + \int_\Sigma \mathbf{D}\cdot d\boldsymbol{\Sigma} \quad . \tag{64.13}$$

In these expressions, the line integrals are assumed to be the results of experimental observations, and the contours themselves can be moving with respect to the chosen coordinate system. Consequently it is plausible to assume that the measurements are performed in a coordinate system moving with some velocity relative to the original system. The field quantities denoted by primes indicate this possibility. This is also true for the current density which is the amount of charged matter passing through the contour per unit time. Regarding the quantities $\mathbf{B}$ and $\mathbf{D}$, it is clear from the derivations of eqs. (64.9)-(64.11), that these quantities are defined in the original coordinate system.

---

* It is interesting to note that the formulas (64.9)-(64.11) are special cases of a formula involving the Lie derivative. If $\mathbf{F}$ is any vector field, and u some parameter, and if the integral $\int \mathbf{F}\, du$ has an invariant meaning, then $(d/dt)\int \mathbf{F}\, du = \int \left[(\partial \mathbf{F}/\partial t) + L_v \mathbf{F}\right]\cdot du$, where L_v is the simultaneous differential invariant of $\mathbf{F}$ and v and is called the Lie derivative. See in this connection, J. A. Schouten, Ricci Calculus, Chapter II and p. 111, prob. II, 10, 11, also Tensor Analyses for Physicists, p. 74, Oxford, 1954.

By applying Stokes theorem to eqs. (64.12) and (64.13), recalling that div $\mathbf{B} = 0$, but div $\mathbf{D} = \rho$, (both of these laws hold for translations of axis), and utilizing eqs. (64.9), (64.10), we find

$$\int_{\Sigma} \text{curl } (\mathbf{E}' - \mathbf{v} \times \mathbf{B}) \cdot d\boldsymbol{\Sigma} = -\int_{\Sigma} \frac{\partial \mathbf{B}}{\partial t} \cdot d\boldsymbol{\Sigma} \quad , \tag{64.14}$$

$$\int_{\Sigma} \text{curl } (\mathbf{H}' + \mathbf{v} \times \mathbf{D}) \cdot d\boldsymbol{\Sigma} = \int_{\Sigma} \left(\frac{\partial \mathbf{D}}{\partial t} + \mathbf{J}' + \rho \mathbf{v} \right) \cdot d\boldsymbol{\Sigma} \quad . \tag{64.15}$$

For a fixed contour, the motional terms $\mathbf{v} \times \mathbf{B}$, $\mathbf{v} \times \mathbf{D}$, $\rho \mathbf{v}$, all vanish and we are left with the conventional expressions,

$$\int_{\Sigma} \text{curl } \mathbf{E} \cdot d\boldsymbol{\Sigma} = -\int_{\Sigma} \frac{\partial \mathbf{B}}{\partial t} \cdot d\boldsymbol{\Sigma} \quad , \tag{64.16}$$

$$\int_{\Sigma} \text{curl } \mathbf{H} \cdot d\boldsymbol{\Sigma} = \int_{\Sigma} \frac{\partial \mathbf{D}}{\partial t} \cdot d\boldsymbol{\Sigma} + \int_{\Sigma} \mathbf{J} \cdot d\boldsymbol{\Sigma} \quad , \tag{64.17}$$

and in these latter expressions, **E**, **B**, **D**, **H** and **J** are all defined with respect to the fixed original coordinate system. The system (64.14), (64.15) can be brought into consonance with the system (64.16), (64.17) by the following transformation of field quantities,

$$\mathbf{E}' = \mathbf{E} + \mathbf{v} \times \mathbf{B} \quad , \tag{64.18}$$

$$\mathbf{H}' = \mathbf{H} - \mathbf{v} \times \mathbf{D} \quad , \tag{64.19}$$

and,

$$\mathbf{J}' = \mathbf{J} - \rho \mathbf{v} \quad , \tag{64.20}$$

which we recognize as the effective fields deduced from special relativity. It is to be noted that this derivation was independent of the presence of matter, so if they hold in free space, they must hold for a space with properties defined by μ and ϵ. Because of the translational invariance of ϵ_0 and μ_0, we can write,

$$\mathbf{D}' = \mathbf{D} + \epsilon_0\mu_0 \mathbf{v} \times \mathbf{H} \quad , \tag{64.21}$$

$$\mathbf{B}' = \mathbf{B} - \epsilon_0\mu_0 \mathbf{v} \times \mathbf{E} \quad . \tag{64.22}$$

It is natural to postulate that eqs. (64.18), (64.19) also hold in the presence of matter.

Equation (64.12) can be expressed in terms of a vector and scalar potential, which permits us to transform the surface integral into a line integral. The application of eq. (64.11) yields the transformation rule for the scaler potential ϕ,

$$\phi' = \phi - \mathbf{v} \cdot \mathbf{A} \quad , \tag{64.23}$$

where $\mathbf{A}$ is the vector potential. The vector potential $\mathbf{A}$ and the charge density ρ are invariant under Galilean translations.

The Constitutive Equations In Non-Conducting Isotropic Material-- From eqs. (64.18)-(64.22) we can obtain the constitutive relations in moving matter from those for stationary matter (isotropic). Denoting by primes, quantities relative to a coordinate system fixed in the body and assuming a coordinate system having a velocity $-\mathbf{u}$ relative to the primed system we obtain starting with eqs. (64.2),

$$(\mathbf{B} - \epsilon_0\mu_0 \mathbf{u} \times \mathbf{E}) = \mu\mu_0 (\mathbf{H} - \mathbf{u} \times \mathbf{D}) \tag{64.24}$$

$$(\mathbf{D} + \epsilon_0\mu_0 \mathbf{u} \times \mathbf{H}) = \epsilon\epsilon_0 (\mathbf{E} + \mathbf{u} \times \mathbf{B}) \quad . \tag{64.25}$$

This system can also be written as,

$$\mathbf{B} = \mu\mu_0 \mathbf{H} + \epsilon_0\mu_0 \mathbf{u} \times \mathbf{E} - \mu\mu_0 \mathbf{u} \times \mathbf{D} \quad , \tag{64.26}$$

$$\mathbf{D} = \epsilon\epsilon_0 \mathbf{E} - \epsilon_0\mu_0 \mathbf{u} \times \mathbf{H} + \epsilon\epsilon_0 \mathbf{u} \times \mathbf{B} \quad . \tag{64.27}$$

If we replace $\mathbf{D}$ and $\mathbf{B}$ on the right side of eqs. (64.26), (64.27) by their zero order approximations $\mathbf{D} = \epsilon\epsilon_0\mathbf{E}$, $\mathbf{B} = \mu\mu_0\mathbf{H}$, the resulting first order system is

$$\mathbf{D} = \epsilon\epsilon_0 \mathbf{E} - \epsilon\epsilon_0\mu\mu_0 \left(1 - \frac{1}{\epsilon\mu}\right) \mathbf{u} \times \mathbf{H} \quad , \tag{64.28}$$

$$\mathbf{B} = \epsilon\epsilon_0\mu\mu_0\left(1 - \frac{1}{\epsilon\mu}\right)\mathbf{u} \times \mathbf{E} + \mu\mu_0\mathbf{H} \quad , \tag{64.29}$$

in which we note Fresnel's convection coefficient $[1 - (1/\epsilon\mu)]$. The inversion of this system yields,

$$\mathbf{E} = \frac{1}{\epsilon\epsilon_0}\mathbf{D} + \left(1 - \frac{1}{\epsilon\mu}\right)\mathbf{u} \times \mathbf{B} \quad , \tag{64.30}$$

$$\mathbf{H} = -\left(1 - \frac{1}{\epsilon\mu}\right)\mathbf{u} \times \mathbf{D} + \frac{1}{\mu\mu_0}\mathbf{B} \quad , \tag{64.31}$$

in which the terms involving the cross product are the so-called "gyroscopic" terms of moving matter.*

Wave Propagation in Moving Non-Conducting Isotropic Matter--It is possible to obtain different forms of the constitutive equations from the foregoing. A useful form for wave propagation studies in moving matter is,

$$\mathbf{D} = \epsilon\epsilon_0\mathbf{E} - \epsilon\epsilon_0\left(1 - \frac{1}{\epsilon\mu}\right)\mathbf{u} \times \mathbf{B} \quad , \tag{64.32}$$

$$\mathbf{H} = -\epsilon\epsilon_0\left(1 - \frac{1}{\epsilon\mu}\right)\mathbf{u} \times \mathbf{E} + \frac{1}{\mu\mu_0}\mathbf{B} \quad , \tag{64.33}$$

For the direction of propagation in the x_1-direction, Maxwell's equations together with eqs. (64.32), (64.33) lead to the non-symmetric wave equation in ψ,

$$\left[\frac{1}{\epsilon\epsilon_0\mu\mu_0}\frac{\partial^2}{\partial x_1^2} - \frac{\partial^2}{\partial t^2} + 2u\left(1 - \frac{1}{\epsilon\mu}\right)\frac{\partial}{\partial t}\frac{\partial}{\partial x_1}\right]\psi = 0 \tag{64.34}$$

where ψ represents any field quantity. Assuming plane wave solutions $\psi = \psi_0 \exp[i(\omega t - kx_1)]$ yields for dispersion equation,

$$\omega^2 = \frac{k^2}{\epsilon\epsilon_0\mu\mu_0} - 2u\left(1 - \frac{1}{\epsilon\mu}\right)\omega k \quad , \tag{64.35}$$

---

* See, Tellegen, B., *loc. cit.*

which gives for the phase velocity (in the first order approximation),

$$\frac{\omega}{k} = \sqrt{\frac{1}{\epsilon\epsilon_0\mu\mu_0}} - u\left(1 - \frac{1}{\epsilon\mu}\right) , \tag{64.36}$$

the well known drag formula.

Electromagnetic Energy Transport-- In a linear medium we take the electromagnetic energy density to be

$$U_{(e)} = \frac{1}{2} (\mathbf{D} \cdot \mathbf{E} + \mathbf{B} \cdot \mathbf{H}) , \tag{64.37}$$

and from eq. (51.6) we have for the electromagnetic stress tensor,

$$\tau_{ij}^{(e)} = -\frac{1}{2} (\mathbf{D} \cdot \mathbf{E} + \mathbf{B} \cdot \mathbf{H})\delta_{ij} + D_iE_j + B_iH_j . \tag{64.38}$$

This stress tensor is not necessarily symmetric since in a non-isotropic medium $(\mathbf{D},\mathbf{E})$ and $(\mathbf{B},\mathbf{H})$ are in different directions. The energy transport is $(\mathbf{E} \times \mathbf{H})$, the momentum is $(\mathbf{D} \times \mathbf{B})$, hence from the transformation equations for the fields we obtain the transformation rules,

$$U'_{(e)} = U_{(e)} - \mathbf{u} \cdot (\mathbf{D} \times \mathbf{B}) - \epsilon_0\mu_0\mathbf{u} \cdot (\mathbf{E} \times \mathbf{H}) , \tag{64.39}$$

$$(\mathbf{E} \times \mathbf{H})' = \mathbf{E} \times \mathbf{H} - \mathbf{u}U_{(e)} - \mathbf{u} \cdot \tau , \tag{64.40}$$

$$(\mathbf{D} \times \mathbf{B})' = (\mathbf{D} \times \mathbf{B}) - \epsilon_0\mu_0\mathbf{u}U_{(e)} - \epsilon_0\mu_0\tau \cdot u , \tag{64.41}$$

here, $\mathbf{u} \cdot \tau$ means a row vector by the matrix τ giving a row vector, whereas $\tau \cdot \mathbf{u}$ means the product of the matrix τ by the column vector $\mathbf{u}$ which yields a column vector. In general, $\mathbf{u} \cdot \tau \neq \tau \cdot \mathbf{u}$. The rules (64.39)-(64.41) are perfectly general and are independent of the nature of the material involved. The physical interpretation of these rules is as follows.

Let $(\mathbf{E} \times \mathbf{H})$ and $(\mathbf{E} \times \mathbf{H})'$ define the rate at which energy is absorbed per unit area and unit time on absorbing screens having a mutual velocity $\mathbf{u}$. These quantities differ by two terms; $\mathbf{u}U_{(e)}$ is the extra absorption due to translational motion of the screen, while $\mathbf{u} \cdot \tau$ is the rate of work performed by radiation forces, *i.e.*, radiation pressure. In a pure sinusoidal wavefield we can write the time averaged Poynting vector, say $\langle \mathbf{E} \times \mathbf{H} \rangle$ as,

$$\langle \mathbf{E} \times \mathbf{H} \rangle = U_{(e)} \mathbf{v}_g \tag{64.42}$$

where $\mathbf{v}_g$ is the group or energy velocity. In a moving body we should like to have the same form holding,

$$\langle \mathbf{E} \times \mathbf{H} \rangle' = U'_{(e)} \mathbf{v}'_g \quad , \tag{64.43}$$

and correlate $\mathbf{v}_g$ with $\mathbf{v}'_g$. This is indeed the case, if we use the wave expressions for $\mathbf{D} \times \mathbf{B}$ and τ which correspond to eqs. (64.42) and (64.43), that is,

$$\langle \mathbf{D} \times \mathbf{B} \rangle = \frac{U_{(e)}}{\omega} \mathbf{K} \quad , \quad \mathbf{K} \text{ is the wave vector,} \tag{64.44}$$

$$\langle \tau \rangle = \frac{U_{(e)}}{\omega} \mathbf{K} \, \mathbf{v}_g \, , \tag{64.45}$$

where $\mathbf{K}\,\mathbf{v}_g$ is the matrix resulting from a row vector $\mathbf{K}$ multiplying a column vector $\mathbf{v}_g$. Using eqs. (64.39), (64.40), (64.43), (64.44) and (64.45) we deduce

$$\mathbf{v}'_g = \frac{\langle \mathbf{E} \times \mathbf{H} \rangle'}{U'_{(e)}} = \frac{U_{(e)} \mathbf{v}_g - U_{(e)} \mathbf{u} - \mathbf{u} \cdot (\mathbf{K}\mathbf{v}_g)\, U_{(e)}/\omega}{U_{(e)} - \mathbf{u} \cdot \mathbf{K}\, U_{(e)}/\omega - \epsilon_0 \mu_0 \mathbf{u} \cdot \mathbf{v}_g U_{(e)}}$$

$$= \frac{\mathbf{v}_g - \mathbf{u} - \mathbf{u} \cdot (\mathbf{K}\mathbf{v}_g)/\omega}{1 - \mathbf{u} \cdot \mathbf{K}/\omega - \epsilon_0 \mu_0 \mathbf{u} \cdot \mathbf{v}_g} \quad , \tag{64.46}$$

which to a first order approximation yields,

$$\mathbf{v}'_g = \mathbf{v}_g - \mathbf{u} + \epsilon_0 \mu_0 \, (\mathbf{u} \cdot \mathbf{v}_g) \mathbf{v}_g \quad . \tag{64.47}$$

This shows that $\mathbf{v}'_g$ is correlated with $\mathbf{v}_g$ according to the well known Fizeau convection formula. This same first-order relation results from the relativistic theorem of addition of velocities for arbitrary directions of $\mathbf{u}$ and $\mathbf{v}_g$.*

* For other first-order theories of electrodynamics see, E. G. Cullwick, Electromagnetism and Relativity, Longmans, Green and Co., London, 1957. E. J. Post, "Electromagnetic theory of moving matter," I, II, Tijdschrift van het Nederlands Radiogenootschap 20, (1955) pp. 93-102, 307-21. We have followed the lines of development of the latter rather closely.

BIBLIOGRAPHIES

1. Balzas, N. L., On Relativistic Thermodynamics, Astrophys. J., p. 398, (July-Nov. 1958).

2. Banos, A., Jr., Magneto-Hydrodynamic Waves in Incompressible and Compressible Fluids., Proc. Roy. Soc., Series A, Vol. 233, pp. 350-67, (Dec. 1955).

3. Blank, A. A., and Grad, H., Magneto-Hydrodynamics Note No. VI, N.Y.U., AEC Computing and Appl. Math. Center, AT(30-1-1480, NYO-6486 MH-VI, July 1, 1958).

4. Biot, M. A., J. Appl. Phys. Vol. 27, No. 3, pp. 240-253 (1956).

5. Carini, G., On the Equation of the Electromagnetic Momentum in the Electrodynamics of Moving Bodies, Atti della Societa Peloutana di Scienze Fisiche Matematiche e Naturali, Univ. of Messina, Messina, Vol. 2, No. 4, pp. 283-291 (1955-56).

6. Chu, B. T., Thermodynamics of Electrically Conducting Fluids and its Application to Magneto-Hydrodynamics, Brown Univ., Div. of Eng., Providence, R. I. WADC TN57-350, (Dec. 1957) (ASTIA AD-142,039).

7. Cowling, T. G., The Dissipation of Magnetic Energy in an Ionized Gas, Monthly Nat. Roy. Astron. Soc., London, Vol. 116, No. 1, pp. 114-124 (1956).

8. Durand, M. E., General Theory of Magnetic Masses at Rest and in Motion, Revue Generale de L'Electricite, Vol. 64, No. 7, pp. 350-356 (July 1955)

9. Elsasser, Walter M., Dimensional Relations in Magneto-Hydrodynamics, Phys. Rev. Vol. 95, No. 1, pp. 1-5 (July 1950).

10. Germain, P., Shock Waves and Shock-Wave Structure in Magneto-Fluid Dynamics, Rev. Modern Physics, Vol. 32, No. 2, pp. 951-958 (Oct. 1960).

11. Gyorgyi, G., The Motion of the Center of Energy and the Energy Impulse Tensor of Electromagneto Fields in Dielectrics. Acta. Phys. Hung. 4, 121-131 (1954).

12. Harris, E. G., Relativistic Magnetohydrodynamics, Phys. Rev. Vol. 108, No. 6, pp. 1357-1360 (Dec. 15, 1957).

13. Herivel, J. W., A General Variational Principle for Dissipative Systems, Proc. Roy. Irish Acad. Vol. 56, pp. 37-44, (1954).

14. Khalatnikov, I. M., On Magnetohydrodynamic Waves and Magnetic Tangential Discountinuities in Relativistic Hydrodynamics, Zh. Eks, i teor. Fiz., Vol. 32, No. 5, pp. 1102-1107 (1957).

15. Kihara, T., Macroscopic Foundations of Plasma Dynamics, J. Phys. Soc. of Japan, Vol. 13, No. 5, pp. 473-481 (May 1958).

16. Kihara, T., Thermodynamics Foundations of the Theory of Plasma, J. Phys. Soc. Japan, pp. 128-133 (Feb. 1959).

17. Lehnert, B., Energy Balance and Confinement of a Magnetized Plasma, Rev. Mod. Phys. Vol. 32, No. 4, pp. 1012-1019 (Oct. 1960).

18. Maecker, H. and Peters, Th., The Unified Dynamics and Thermodynamics of Thermal Plasmas, Zeitschuft fur Physik Vol. 144, pp. 586-611 (1956).

19. Marshall, W., The Structure of Magneto-Hydrodynamic Shock Waves, Proc. Roy, Soc. Series A, Vol. 233, pp. 367-376 (Dec. 1955).

20. Marx, G., and Gyorgyi, G., The Energy Impulse Tensor of the Electromagnetic Field and Ponderomotive Forces in Dielectrics, ibid., 3, 213-242 (1954).

21. Marx, G., and Gyorgyi, G., The Energy Impulse Tensor of Electromagnetic Fields in Dielectrics. Annalen der Physik, 6, 241-256 (1955).

22. McCune, J. E., and Sears, W. R., Concepts of Moving Electric and Magnetic Fields in Magnetohydrodynamics, J. Aero/Space Sciences, Vol. 26, pp. 674-675 (Oct. 1959).

23. Meyers, N. H., A Poynting Theorem for Moving Bodies and the Relativistic Mechanics of Extended Objects, J. Franklin Inst., Vol. 266, No. 6, pp. 439-464 (Dec. 1958).

24. Miller, Donald G., Thermodynamic Theory of Irreversible Processes, Part I, Amer. J. Phys. Vol. 24, pp. 433-444. (1956).

25. Miller, Donald G., Chem. Revs. Vol. 60, pp. 15-37 (1960).

26. Moore, F. K. and Gibson, W. W., Propagation of Weak Disturbances in a Gas Subject to Relaxation Effects, IAS Meeting Report No. 59-64, Presented at the IAS Twenty-Seventh Annual Meeting, N.Y., Jan. 26-29 (1959).

27. Nachbar, W., Williams, F., and Penner, S. S., The Conservation Equations for Independent Coexistent Media and for Multicomponent Reacting Gas Mixtures, AFOSRTN 56-458 (1956) (ASTIA Doc. AD 97074).

28. Napolitano, L. G., Discontinuity Surfaces in Magneto-Fluid-Dynamics, Brooklyn Poly. Inst., Aeron. Eng. and Appl. Mech. Dept. Report 503 (Dec. 1958).

29. Pai, S. I., Energy Equation of Magneto-Gas Dynamics, Phys. Rev. Vol. 105, No. 5, p. 1424 (1957).

30. Resler, E. L., Characteristics and Sound Speed in Nonisentropic Gas Flows with Non-Equilibrium Thermodynamic States, Jour. of the Aeronautical Sciences, Vol. 24, No. 11, pp. 785-90 (Nov. 1957).

31. Rosen, P., On Variational Principles for Irreversible Processes, J. Chem. Phys, Vol. 21, No. 7, pp. 1220-1221, (1958).

32. Scarf, F., Wave Propagation in a Moving Plasma, Amer. J. Phys. Vol. 29, No. 2, pp. 101-107 (Feb. 1961).

33. Sen, Hari K., Structure of a Magneto-Hydrodynamic Shock Wave in a Plasma of Infinite Conductivity, Phys. Rev. Vol. 102, No. 1, pp. 5-11 (April 1956).

34. Tang, C. L., and Meixner, J., Relativistic Theory of the Propagation of Plane Electromagnetic Waves, The Physics of Fluids, Vol. 4, No. 1, pp. 148-54 (Jan. 1961).

35. Teller, E. and deHoffman, F., Rankine-Hugoniot Equations for Shock Waves in an Infinitely Conducting Fluid with Superimposed Magnetic Field, Phys. Rev. pp. 692- (1950).

36. Toupin, R. A., The Elastic Dielectric, J. Rational Mech. Analysis, 5, 849-915, (1956).

37. Toupin, R. A., Stress Tensors in Elastic Dielectrics, Archiv. Rational Mech. Anal. 5, 440-452 (1960).

38. Truesdell, C., On the Pressure and the Flux of Energy in a Gas According to Maxwell's Kinetic Theory, Jour. of Rational Mechanics and Analysis, Vol. 5, No. 1, pp. 1-126 (Jan. 1956).

39. Voyenli, K., On Plane Stationary Shock Waves in a Plasma, The Institute of Theoretical Astrophysics, Univ. of Oslo (1959) [AFOSR Report No. 3 of Contract No. AF 61(052)-49].

40. Wei, C. C., Relativistic Hydrodynamics for a Charged Nonviscous Fluid, Phys. Rev. Vol. 113, p. 1414 (March 15, 1959).

GENERAL BIBLIOGRAPHIES

1. Cambel, A li Bulent, and Fenn, J. B. (Editors). The Dynamics of Conducting Gases. Northwestern Univ. Press. Evanston (1960).

2. Cambel, A li Bulent, and Fenn, J. B. (Editors). Transport Properties in Gases, ibid. (1958).

3. Courant, R. and Friedrichs, K. O.

4. Covert, E. E., On Some Fundamentals in Magneto-Fluid Mechanics, Thesis Ph.D., Mass. Inst. Techn. (1958).

5. Fano, R. W., Chu, L. J., and Adler, R. B., Electromagnetic Fields, Energy and Forces, John Wiley & Sons, Inc., N.Y. (1960).

6. Landau & Lifshitz, Statistical Physics, Pergamon Press Co. (1958).

7. Landau & Lifshitz, Electrodynamics of Continuous Media, Pergamon Press Co. (1960).

8. Landau & Lifshitz, The Classical Theory of Fields.

9. Liepmann, H. W. and Roshko, A., Elements of Gas Dynamics, John Wiley & Sons, Inc., N.Y. (1951).

10. Pauli, W., Theory of Relativity, Pergamon Press, N.Y. (1958).

11. Sears, W. R., An Introduction to Thermodynamics, The Kinetic Theory of Gases and Statistical Mechanics, Addison-Wesley Pub. Co., Cambridge, Mass. (1953).

12. Sears, F. W., An Introduction to Thermodynamics. Addison-Wesley Pub. Co., Inc., Cambridge, Mass. (1953).

13. Sommerfeld, A., Mechanics of Deformable Bodies, Academic Press, Inc., N.Y., (1950).

14. Sommerfeld, A., Electrodynamics, ibid (1952).

15. Sommerfled, A., Statistical Mechan.

16. Stratton, J. A.

17. Synge, J. L., Relativity, The Special Theory (North-Holland, Amsterdam) (1956).

18. Tolman, R. C., Relativity, Thermodynamics and Cosmology, Clarendon Press, Oxford (1950).

19. Weber, J., General Relativity and Gravitational Waves, Interscience Pub. Co., N.Y., (1961).

CHAPTER VI

THE STRUCTURE OF WAVES IN NON-HOMOGENEOUS MEDIA

65. PROPAGATION IN NON-HOMOGENEOUS MEDIA

In this chapter we shall concern ourselves with some of the basic aspects of propagation in non-homogeneous absorbing media. From a realistic point of view, nature presents us with non-homogeneous media more often then it does with homogeneous media. Consequently it is important to develop analytical methods in order to cope with problems in non-homogeneous media. In Chapter II we discussed briefly the mechanism of propagation but treated only propagation in a homogeneous medium. If we restrict ourselves now to stratified media it is natural to inquire about the difference between propagation in a homogeneous and in a stratified medium. According to Hartree, in a homogeneous medium the wavelets scattered by the particles of the medium combine such that a single travelling wave is a solution of the equation of the medium, so that a solution corresponding to an advancing wave at one point always corresponds to an advancing wave only, whereas in a non-homogeneous medium a solution corresponding at one point to an advancing wave only gives at other points an advancing and a retreating wave.*

In order to make concrete the various facets of propagation in non-homogeneous absorbing media we consider first the geometric optics in an isotropic medium. In particular we define the notion of the decrement of attenuation or extinction, then we derive Snell's Law for a semi-infinite absorbing stratified medium separated by a plane interface from a semi-infinite vacuum medium. An expression for the attenuation of energy is also defined for such a medium. A discussion on the path of a light ray in an isotropic non-homogeneous absorbing medium is given together with a deduction of an extended Fermat's Principle. This principle is then applied to find the trajectories in a stratified medium.

* D. R. Hartree, "The Propagation of Electromagnetic Waves in a Stratified Medium," Cambridge Phil. Soc. Proc. Vol. 25, (1929), see also, "The Propagation of Electromagnetic Waves in a Refracting Medium in a Magnetic Field" *ibid.* Vol. 27, (1931).

The next section is devoted to the nature of the electromagnetic waves in an unbounded non-homogeneous anisotropic and absorbing medium which is characterized by a dielectric tensor but is not gyromagnetic, that is, the magnetic permeability is a scalar. Here the analysis is based on the vector-wave equation for such a medium. As an example we derive the reflection coefficients for a semi-infinite stratified plasma starting from the homogeneous case. Cylindrical waves are treated subsequently and here also, we derive the reflection coefficients for a cylindrically stratified plasma.

Following this section we treat in considerable detail the propagation of an electromagnetic wave in a continuously stratified anisotropic and absorbing finite layer which is bounded below and above by infinite vacuum media. To find the reflected and transmitted waves an integral equation is derived by introducing a Hertz vector potential generalized from the isotropic case. Following Lurye, the Schwinger integral equation-variational technique is used to construct variational expressions for the reflection and transmission matrices of the scattering medium. For the derivation of the variational expressions it is convenient to utilize the language and techniques of functional analysis and a brief exposition is therefore included as preparation for the derivation.

We have not incorporated any of the classic investigations on propagation of electromagnetic waves in non-homogeneous media such as Rydbeck's, Forsterling *et al.* since they are adequately treated elsewhere.* For other reasons we have not included any treatment of hydromagnetic waves in non-homogeneous media.† In the next chapter we shall develop some powerful ray-theoretic methods in a comprehensive manner to deal with problems in non-homogeneous anisotropic and absorbing media.

Rays In Isotropic Media—In Chapter I we considered the Eikonal equation or the equation of geometrical optics for an absorbing medium and we were led to the two equations (5.13a, b). These equations defined the refractive index and extinction index surfaces. Apart from a constant multiplier the Eikonal equation is of the form

---

* K. G. Budden, "Radio Waves in the Ionosphere," Cambridge Press, 1961.

† V. C. A. Ferraro and C. Plumpton, "Hydromagnetic Waves in a Horizontally Stratified Atmosphere," Astroph. Jour. Vol. 127, (1958).

$$(\nabla\psi)^2 = M^2 = p - iq, \; p, q \text{ real} \quad , \qquad (65.1)$$

in which the right side is complex, and is a function of position. Consequently we can write

$$\nabla\psi = \boldsymbol{\mu} - i\boldsymbol{\chi} \qquad (65.2)$$

where $\boldsymbol{\mu}$ is the index of refraction multiplied by a unit vector in the direction of the phase, and $\boldsymbol{\chi}$ is the index of extinction multiplied by a unit vector in the direction of extinction. Both $\boldsymbol{\mu}$ and $\boldsymbol{\chi}$ are in general in different directions, but the medium is assumed to be isotropic.

For a non-absorbing medium the following relation is valid,

$$d\psi = \nabla\psi \cdot d\mathbf{r} \quad , \qquad (65.3)$$

where ψ is real and $d\mathbf{r}$ is an element of the ray path. From this equation we obtain

$$\psi = \int_{P_1}^{P_2} \nabla\psi \cdot d\mathbf{r} \qquad (65.4)$$

and this integral is independent of the path. For the absorbing case we extend eq. (65.3) as follows,

$$d\psi = \nabla\psi_1 \cdot d\mathbf{r} - i\nabla\psi_2 \cdot d\mathbf{r} \quad , \qquad (65.5)$$

where ψ_2 is defined by

$$\psi_2 = \int_{P_1}^{P} \nabla\psi \cdot d\mathbf{r} \quad , \qquad (65.6)$$

and ψ_1 and ψ_2 are real functions of position. The introduction of ψ_2 allows us to define the decrement of attenuation (the attenuation of a wave in an inhomogeneous medium). For example, if the extinction is in the x_3-direction, the decrement is given by,

$$\delta = \int_{P_1}^{P} |\nabla\psi_2| \, dx_3 \qquad (65.7)$$

which according to eq. (65.2) is equal to

$$\delta = \int_{P_1}^{P} \chi(x_3)\,dx_3 \quad . \tag{65.8}$$

Apart from the factor ω/V_0 and provided χ is a function of x_3 alone, the above formula is true for a stratified medium as will be seen below.

Stratified Media—Consider two semi-infinite media, one of which is nonabsorbing, say, Medium 1 and the other, Medium 2 is absorbing with the planes of stratification parallel to the x_1x_2 plane as shown in Fig. 11.

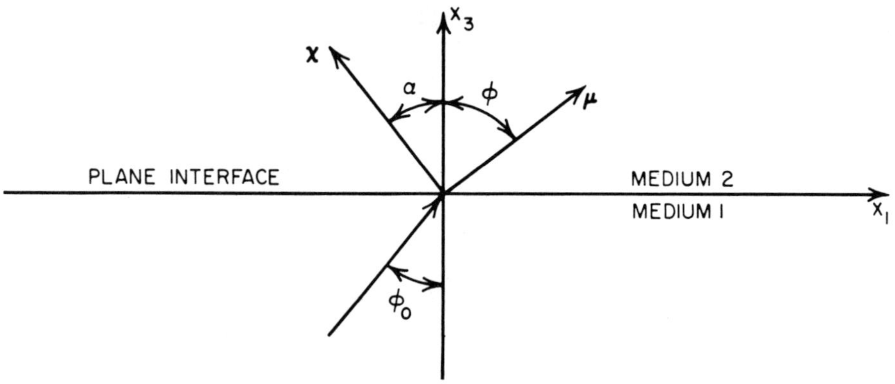

FIG. 11

Without loss of generality we can take Medium 1 to be a homogeneous reference medium with index of refraction $\mu_0 = 1$. We shall demonstrate that Snell's Law can be extended to an inhomogeneous absorbing medium as above. For this, we start with the equivalent relation of $\nabla\psi = \boldsymbol{\mu} - i\boldsymbol{\chi}$ which is

$$\text{curl } (\nabla\psi) = \nabla\mathbf{x}\nabla\psi = 0 \quad , \tag{65.9}$$

and from the figure we have the obvious relations,

$$\left.\begin{aligned} |\boldsymbol{\mu}| \sin\phi + i|\boldsymbol{\chi}| \sin\alpha &= \mu_1 + i\chi_1 \quad , \\ |\boldsymbol{\mu}| \cos\phi + i|\boldsymbol{\chi}| \cos\alpha &= \mu_3 + i\chi_3 \quad , \end{aligned}\right\} \tag{65.10}$$

where, $\boldsymbol{\mu} \equiv (\mu_1, \mu_2, \mu_3)$, $\boldsymbol{\chi} \equiv (\chi_1, \chi_2, \chi_3)$. The angle φ_0 is the angle of incidence of a plane wave incident upon the interface of both media. Since both $\boldsymbol{\mu}$ and $\boldsymbol{\chi}$ are functions of the coordinate x_3 alone, there results only one component of the curl relation, namely

$$(\nabla \mathbf{x} \nabla \psi)_2 = \left(\frac{\partial \mu_1}{\partial x_3} - \frac{\partial \mu_3}{\partial x_1}\right) + i\left(\frac{\partial \chi_1}{\partial x_3} - \frac{\partial \chi_3}{\partial x_1}\right) = 0 \quad , \qquad (65.11)$$

and therefore,

$$\frac{\partial \mu_3}{\partial x_1} = \frac{\partial \chi_3}{\partial x_1} = 0 \quad . \qquad (65.12)$$

From this it follows that both μ_1 and χ_1 are constants. By hypothesis there is no absorption at the interface of the two media which implies that $\chi_1 = 0$. By combining this result with the relations (65.10) we deduce that the angle $\alpha = 0$, hence

$$\mu \sin \varphi = \mu_0 \sin \varphi_0 \quad , \quad \text{with } \mu_0 = 1 \quad , \qquad (65.13)$$

which is Snell's Law for the non-homogeneous absorbing medium. The vector $\boldsymbol{\chi}(x_3)$ is directed along the x_3-axes or in other words the extinction of the wave is normal to the plane interface. From eqs. (65.1), (65.2) and (65.13) we obtain

$$\left.\begin{aligned} \mu^2 &= \frac{1}{2}[p + \sin^2 \varphi_0 + \sqrt{(p - \sin^2 \varphi_0)^2 + q^2}] \quad , \\ \chi^2 &= \frac{1}{2}[-(p - \sin^2 \varphi_0) + \sqrt{(p - \sin^2 \varphi_0)^2 + q^2}] \quad , \end{aligned}\right\} \qquad (65.14)$$

in which the dependence on the angle of incidence φ_0 is apparent. The differential equation of the phase trajectories is easily obtained for a stratified medium. By definition $\boldsymbol{\mu}$ is tangent to the trajectory at each point, thus

$$\frac{dx_1}{\mu_1} = \frac{dx_3}{\mu_3} \qquad (65.15)$$

or,

$$\left(\frac{dx_1}{dx_3}\right)^2 = \left(\frac{\mu_1}{\mu_3}\right)^2 = \tan^2 \varphi \tag{65.16}$$

which, after using eq. (65.13) and the first equation of (65.14), yields

$$\left(\frac{dx_1}{dx_3}\right)^2 = \frac{2 \sin^2 \varphi_0}{p - \sin^2 \varphi_0 + \sqrt{(p - \sin^2 \varphi_0)^2 + q^2}} \quad . \tag{65.17}$$

Energy Attenuation—The attenuation of energy in the stratified medium is defined (by analogy with a plane wave) by

$$\Delta = 2 \frac{\omega}{V_0} \int_0^{\bar{x}_3} \chi(x_3)\, dx_3 \quad . \tag{65.18}$$

From the second equation of (65.14) we can write

$$\Delta = \sqrt{2} \frac{\omega}{V_0} \int_0^{\bar{x}_3} \sqrt{-(p - \sin^2 \varphi_0) + \sqrt{(p - \sin^2 \varphi_0)^2 + q^2}}\, dx_3 , \tag{65.19}$$

where both p and q are functions of x_3 alone, and $\bar{x}_3$ denotes the smallest root of $p - \sin^2 \varphi_0 = 0$. If the absorption is calculated along the direction of the phase trajectory then we have,

$$\Delta' = 2 \frac{\omega}{V_0} \int_0^{\bar{x}_3} \boldsymbol{\chi} \cdot d\mathbf{r} = 2 \frac{\omega}{V_0} \int_0^{\bar{x}_3} \frac{q\, dx_3}{2\mu \cos^2 \varphi} \quad , \tag{65.20}$$

where $d\mathbf{r}$ is along the phase trajectory. If the medium is weakly absorbing, that is, one which is defined by the condition

$$(p - \sin^2 \varphi_0) >> q^2 \quad , \tag{65.21}$$

and if we define both $p(x_3)$ and $q(x_3)$ by the formulas*

$$\left.\begin{aligned} p(x_3) &= 1 - \frac{\omega_c^2(x_3)}{\omega^2 + \nu^2(x_3)} , \\ q(x_3) &= \frac{\nu(x_3)}{\omega} \frac{\omega_c^2(x_3)}{\omega^2 + \nu^2(x_3)} , \end{aligned}\right\} \tag{65.22}$$

and neglect also powers of ν/ω from the second power on, we find

$$\Delta' = \int_0^{x_3' - h} \frac{\nu}{V_0} \frac{(\omega_c/\omega)^2 \sqrt{1 - (\omega_c/\omega)^2}}{\cos^2 \varphi_0 - (\omega_c/\omega)^2} dx_3 + \int_{x_3' - h}^{x_3'} \frac{\omega}{V_0} \frac{q}{\mu \cos^2 \varphi} dx_3 . \tag{65.23}$$

The limits of integration $(0, x_3' - h)$ are relative to the region for which $(p - \sin^2 \varphi_0) >> q$ and x_3' is the smallest root of $\cos^2 \varphi_0 - (\omega_c/\omega)^2 = 0$. For normal incidence we obtain, approximately,

$$\Delta' \approx \int_0^{x_3'} \frac{\nu}{V_0} \frac{(\omega_c/\omega)^2}{\sqrt{1 - (\omega_c/\omega)^2}} dx_3 + 2 \int_{x_3' - h}^{x_3'} \frac{\omega}{V_0} \sqrt{-\frac{p}{2} + \sqrt{\left(\frac{p}{2}\right)^2 + \left(\frac{q}{2}\right)^2}} dx_3 , \tag{65.24}$$

and for very weak absorption, $\omega^2 >> \nu^2$, the second integral vanishes almost since $h \approx 0$.

The Path of a Light Ray in an Inhomogeneous Absorbing Medium—In a non-absorbing isotropic medium, the phase path and the energy path (defined through the time averaged Poynting vector) are coincident. The results of Section 7 in Chapter I show that for an absorbing, homogeneous and isotropic medium this coincidence fails. If the electromagnetic field is known at all points of an inhomogeneous medium, the energy trajectory is defined by

---

* From eq. (14.1a) of Chapter II, in the absence of a magnetic field, the index of refraction of a homogeneous electron plasma yields the above expressions for p and q. The stratification assumption for a non-homogeneous electron plasma implies that p and q become functions of x_3 through ω_c and ν, the plasma and collision frequencies respectively.

$$\frac{dx_i}{dt} = \frac{\langle \dot{\mathbf{E}}\mathbf{x}\mathbf{H}\rangle_i}{\langle U\rangle} \quad , \quad (i = 1,2,3) \quad , \tag{65.25}$$

where $\langle \mathbf{ExH}\rangle_i$ and $\langle U\rangle$ are the time averaged components of the Poynting vector and the time averaged value of the energy density of the electromagnetic field respectively. The averaging is over one period of the alternating field. For an electron or ion plasma the energy density contains contributions from the **E** and **H** field and from the motions of the charged particles themselves. There is no need to actually calculate $\langle U\rangle$ itself in order to obtain the trajectory since it is equivalently defined by the ratios

$$\frac{dx_1}{\langle \mathbf{ExH}\rangle_1} = \frac{dx_2}{\langle \mathbf{ExH}\rangle_2} = \frac{dx_3}{\langle \mathbf{ExH}\rangle_3} \quad . \tag{65.26}$$

If the field is not known but the medium is characterized by an index of refraction then the path of a light ray is by definition determined by Fermat's Principle. For an absorbing medium the refractive index is complex and hence there is a conceptual difficulty in using Fermat's Principle without further consideration. We shall demonstrate a minimum principle for an inhomogeneous, isotropic and absorbing medium which constitutes a variational principle and can be considered as an extension of the ordinary Fermat's Principle. The situation for a non-isotropic medium will be treated in the next chapter.

The starting point for the proof are the scalar and vector Eikonal equations (65.1) and (65.2) which yield the relations

$$\left.\begin{aligned} |\mu|^2 - |\chi|^2 &= p \quad , \\ 2|\mu||\chi| &= q/\cos\varphi \quad , \end{aligned}\right\} \tag{65.27}$$

where φ is the angle between $\boldsymbol{\mu}$ and $\boldsymbol{\chi}$; p and q are functions of position. From equation (65.9), setting both the real and imaginary parts equal to zero, we find

$$\nabla \mathbf{x} \mu = 0 \quad . \tag{65.28}$$

Now consider an arbitrary surface denoted by Σ, bounded by the true path C_1, and an arbitrary path C_2, with both paths starting at P_1 and terminating at P_2 as shown in Fig. 12.

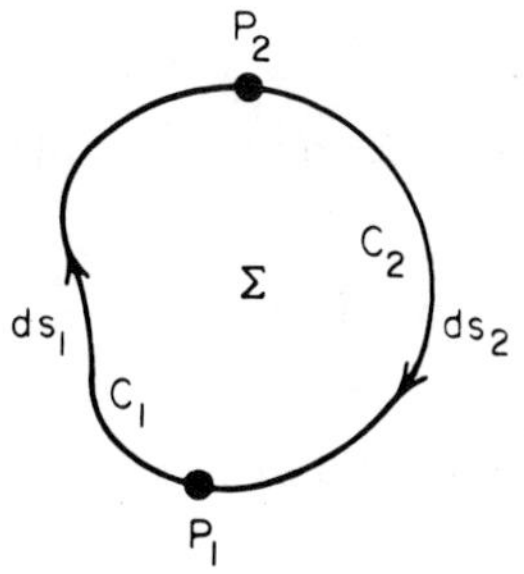

FIG. 12

Let the element of path length along C_1 be given by $|d\mathbf{r}_1| = ds_1$, and that of C_2 by $|d\mathbf{r}_2| = ds_2$. By definition of the ray path the vector $\boldsymbol{\mu}$ is tangent to $d\mathbf{r}_1$; but along C_2, $\boldsymbol{\mu}$ makes an angle with $d\mathbf{r}_2$. By (65.28) and Stokes theorem, we have,

$$\int_{\Sigma} (\nabla \times \mu) \cdot \mathbf{n} d\Sigma = \oint \mu \cdot d\mathbf{r} = \int_{C_1 P_1}^{P_2} \mu \cdot d\mathbf{r}_1 - \int_{C_2 P_1}^{P_2} \mu \cdot d\mathbf{r}_2 = 0 , \tag{65.29}$$

where $\mathbf{n}d\Sigma$ is the vector area normal to Σ. But,

$$\left.\begin{aligned} \mu \cdot d\mathbf{r}_1 &= |\mu| ds_1 \quad \text{by definition of the true path ,} \\ \text{and} \\ \mu \cdot d\mathbf{r}_2 &= |\mu| ds_2 \cos (\mu, d\mathbf{r}_2) ; \end{aligned}\right\} \tag{65.30}$$

since,

$$|\cos (\mu, d\mathbf{r}_2)| \leqq 1 , \tag{65.31}$$

then the relations (65.29) and (65.31) imply,

$$\int_{C_1 P_1}^{P_2} |\mu| ds_1 < \int_{C_2 P_1}^{P_2} |\mu| ds_2 . \tag{65.32}$$

This last inequality is equivalent to the statement that

$$\int_{C_1 P_1}^{P_2} |\mu| ds_1 \text{ is a minimum} \quad , \tag{65.33}$$

because C_2 is an arbitrary path from P_1 to P_2. Therefore, we conclude that Fermat's Principle for non-absorbing media, *i.e.*,

$$\int |\mu| ds \;=\; \text{minimum} \quad , \quad \chi \;=\; 0 \quad , \tag{65.34}$$

should be replaced by the extended Fermat's Principle for absorbing media, namely,

$$\int_{P_1}^{P_2} |\mu| ds \;=\; \text{minimum} \quad , \quad \chi \;\neq\; 0 \quad , \tag{65.35}$$

with $|\mu|$ and $|\chi|$ given by

$$\left.\begin{aligned} |\mu|^2 &= \frac{1}{2}\left[p + \sqrt{p^2 + (q/\cos\varphi)^2}\right] \quad , \\ |\chi|^2 &= \frac{1}{2}\left[-p + \sqrt{p^2 + (q/\cos\varphi)^2}\right] \quad . \end{aligned}\right\} \tag{65.36}$$

It is easily seen that in the limit of no-absorption,

$$\lim_{\chi \to 0} \int |\mu| ds \to \int \sqrt{p}\, ds \quad . \tag{65.37}$$

Consequently, the ray path in an inhomogeneous, isotropic and absorbing medium is obtained from the variational principle,

$$\delta \int_{P_1}^{P_2} |\mu| ds \;=\; 0 \quad , \tag{65.38}$$

which gives the Euler-Lagrange equations for the path

$$\frac{d}{ds}\frac{\partial |\mu|}{\partial \alpha_i} - \frac{\partial |\mu|}{\partial x_i} \;=\; 0 \quad , \quad (i \;=\; 1,2,3) \quad , \tag{65.39}$$

where,

$$\alpha_i = \frac{dx_i}{ds}, \quad (i = 1,2,3), \tag{65.40}$$

and with $|\mu|$ defined by (65.36)

Application of the Extended Fermat Principle to a Stratified Medium— Let us look at Figure 11 and consider a bundle of plane waves which make an angle φ_0 as shown at the interface between the vacuum-absorbing medium. Then,

$$\cos\varphi = \sqrt{\frac{1}{1 + (dx_1/dx_3)^2}}, \tag{65.41}$$

now put

$$ds = \sqrt{1 + \left(\frac{dx_1}{dx_3}\right)^2}\, dx_3, \tag{65.42}$$

from which we obtain,

$$\frac{\sqrt{2}}{2}\int\sqrt{p + \sqrt{p^2 + q^2\left[1 + \left(\frac{dx_1}{dx_3}\right)^2\right]}}\sqrt{1 + \left(\frac{dx_1}{dx_3}\right)^2}\, dx_3, \tag{65.43}$$

as the integral to be minimized. If we let $x_1' \equiv dx_1/dx_3$, then since p and q are functions of x_3 alone, Fermat's Principle leads to,

$$\frac{\partial}{\partial x_1'}\sqrt{p + \sqrt{p^2 + q^2[1 + (x_1')^2]}}\,\sqrt{1 + (x_1')^2} = \text{const.}, \tag{65.44}$$

which after some formal manipulations yields as the equation for the trajectories of phase,

$$\left(\frac{dx_1}{dx_3}\right)^2 = \frac{2\sin^2\varphi_0}{p - \sin^2\varphi_0 + \sqrt{(p - \sin^2\varphi_0) + q^2}} \tag{65.45}$$

This expression is identical with eq. (65.17), which expresses the situation for a stratified medium. For a homogeneous medium eq. (65.45) also gives the equation for the trajectories by setting $p = p(0)$, $q = q(0)$, the values of $p(x_3)$ and $q(x_3)$ at the plane $x_3 = 0$, and they obviously must reduce to the p, q of eqs. (65.22) with ω_c and ν both constant.

66. PROPAGATION OF ELECTROMAGNETIC WAVES IN UNBOUNDED NON-HOMOGENEOUS, ANISOTROPIC MEDIA. DERIVATION OF THE BASIC EQUATIONS

We shall consider now the nature of electromagnetic waves in an unbounded non-homogeneous medium which is also anisotropic. The anisotropy is defined through a dielectric tensor, however we assume that the medium is not gyromagnetic (*i.e.*, the permeability is not a tensor) but that μ, the permeability is a constant independent of field strength and position. For ferromagnetic media μ is a tensor but the dielectric tensor reduces to a pure scalar.

For time harmonic fields of angular frequency ω we already know the structure of the field equations from Chapter II, and which we repeat here for convenience,

$$\left.\begin{aligned} \nabla \mathbf{x} \mathbf{E} &= -i\mu\omega \mathbf{H} \;, \\ \nabla \mathbf{x} \mathbf{H} &= i\omega\epsilon_0 \boldsymbol{\epsilon} \mathbf{E} \;, \\ \nabla \cdot \mathbf{D} &= 0 \;, \\ \nabla \cdot \mathbf{B} &= 0 \;, \end{aligned}\right\} \quad (66.1)$$

the constitutive relations are

$$\left.\begin{aligned} \mathbf{D} &= \epsilon_0 \boldsymbol{\epsilon} \mathbf{E} \;, \\ \mathbf{B} &= \mu \mathbf{H} \;. \end{aligned}\right\} \quad (66.2)$$

Here, $\boldsymbol{\epsilon}$ is the dielectric tensor, μ is the uniform permeability. In the case of a plasma we identify $\boldsymbol{\epsilon}$ as the effective dielectric tensor, and $\mathbf{D}$ as the effective displacement vector. In the above equations the elements of the tensor $\boldsymbol{\epsilon}$ are functions of position but not of time. In Chapters II and IV we have already derived the structure of the dielectric tensor when the uniform magnetic field is chosen to be parallel with the x_3-axis.

Moreover, if we neglect pressure and temperature gradients in the plasma the structure of the dielectric tensor is

$$\boldsymbol{\epsilon} \equiv \begin{pmatrix} \epsilon_{11} & i\epsilon_{12} & 0 \\ -i\epsilon_{12} & \epsilon_{22} & 0 \\ 0 & 0 & \epsilon_{33} \end{pmatrix} \tag{66.3}$$

with $\epsilon_{11} = \epsilon_{22}$. The zero elements occur because we are neglecting the pressure and temperature gradients (see Chapter IV). In order to describe the propagation of the electromagnetic waves it will be more convenient to work with the $\mathbf{H}$ vector rather than $\mathbf{E}$. This is clear since $\nabla \cdot \mathbf{B} = \nabla \cdot \mu\mathbf{H} = \mu\nabla \cdot \mathbf{H} = 0$ whereas $\nabla \cdot \mathbf{E} \neq 0$ in general. Thus, we shall derive a wave equation for $\mathbf{H}$ and after having determined the $\mathbf{H}$ field we readily obtain $\mathbf{E}$ from Maxwell's equations. From the second of Maxwell's eqs.(66.1) we find, after multiplying both sides by the inverse of $\underset{\sim}{\epsilon}$, denoted by $\boldsymbol{\epsilon}^{-1}$, the following

$$\mathbf{E} = \left(\frac{-i}{\epsilon_0\omega}\right) \boldsymbol{\epsilon}^{-1}(\nabla\mathbf{x}\mathbf{H}) \quad . \tag{66.4}$$

The inverse tensor $\boldsymbol{\epsilon}^{-1}$ has the form

$$\boldsymbol{\epsilon}^{-1} \equiv \begin{pmatrix} e_{11} & ie_{12} & 0 \\ -ie_{12} & e_{11} & 0 \\ 0 & 0 & e_{33} \end{pmatrix} , \tag{66.5}$$

where,

$$\left.\begin{aligned} e_{11} &= \frac{\epsilon_{11}}{\epsilon_{11}^2 - \epsilon_{12}^2} , \\ e_{12} &= \frac{-\epsilon_{12}}{\epsilon_{11}^2 - \epsilon_{12}^2} , \\ e_{33} &= \frac{1}{\epsilon_{33}} . \end{aligned}\right\} \tag{66.6}$$

Now take the curl of both sides of eq. (66.4) and use the first equation of (66.1) to obtain

$$\nabla\mathbf{x}\mathbf{E} = \left(\frac{-i}{\epsilon_0\omega}\right)\nabla\mathbf{x}\boldsymbol{\epsilon}^{-1}(\nabla\mathbf{x}\mathbf{H}) = -i\mu\omega\mathbf{H}$$

or,

$$\nabla\mathbf{x}\boldsymbol{\epsilon}^{-1}(\nabla\mathbf{x}\mathbf{H}) = \mu\epsilon_0\omega^2\mathbf{H} = K^2\mathbf{H} \qquad (66.7)$$

where,

$$K^2 = \omega^2\mu\epsilon_0 \quad . \qquad (66.8)$$

Since div curl ≡ 0, we also have

$$\nabla\cdot\mathbf{H} = 0 \quad , \qquad (66.9)$$

and therefore both eqs. (66.7) and (66.9) are the equations which determine the nature of the waves in the inhomogeneous, anisotropic medium (plasma). If $\mathbf{e}_1$, $\mathbf{e}_2$, $\mathbf{e}_3$ are unit vectors along the x_1, x_2, x_3 axis respectively of a right handed rectangular cartesian set, the expansion of eq. (66.7) together with (66.5) and the divergence eq. (66.9) yields the vector equation

$$\Bigg\{\left[K^2 + e_{11}\left(\frac{\partial^2}{\partial x_1^2} + \frac{\partial^2}{\partial x_3^2}\right) + e_{33}\frac{\partial^2}{\partial x_2^2} + ie_{12}\frac{\partial^2}{\partial x_1\partial x_2} + \frac{\partial e_{33}}{\partial x_2}\frac{\partial}{\partial x_2} + \frac{\partial e_{11}}{\partial x_3}\frac{\partial}{\partial x_3}\right]H_1$$

$$+\left[(e_{11} - e_{33})\frac{\partial^2}{\partial x_1\partial x_2} + ie_{12}\left(\frac{\partial^2}{\partial x_2^2} + \frac{\partial^2}{\partial x_3^2}\right) - \frac{\partial e_{33}}{\partial x_2}\frac{\partial}{\partial x_1} + i\frac{\partial e_{12}}{\partial x_3}\frac{\partial}{\partial x_3}\right]H_2$$

$$-\left(\frac{\partial e_{11}}{\partial x_3}\frac{\partial}{\partial x_1} + i\frac{\partial e_{12}}{\partial x_3}\frac{\partial}{\partial x_2}\right)H_3\Bigg\}\mathbf{e}_1$$

$$+\Bigg\{\left[(e_{11} - e_{33})\frac{\partial^2}{\partial x_1\partial x_2} + ie_{12}\left(\frac{\partial^2}{\partial x_1^2} + \frac{\partial^2}{\partial x_3^2}\right) - \frac{\partial e_{33}}{\partial x_1}\frac{\partial}{\partial x_2} - i\frac{\partial e_{12}}{\partial x_3}\frac{\partial}{\partial x_3}\right]H_1 \qquad (66.10)$$

$$+\left[K^2 + e_{33}\frac{\partial^2}{\partial x_1^2} + e_{11}\left(\frac{\partial^2}{\partial x_2^2} + \frac{\partial^2}{\partial x_3^2}\right) - ie_{12}\frac{\partial^2}{\partial x_1 \partial x_2} + \frac{\partial e_{33}}{\partial x_1}\frac{\partial}{\partial x_1} + \frac{\partial e_{11}}{\partial x_3}\frac{\partial}{\partial x_3}\right] H_2$$

$$\left. - \left(\frac{\partial e_{11}}{\partial x_3}\frac{\partial}{\partial x_2} - i\frac{\partial e_{12}}{\partial x_3}\frac{\partial}{\partial x_1}\right) H_3 \right\} \mathbf{e}_2$$

$$+\left\{\left[ie_{12}\frac{\partial^2}{\partial x_2 \partial x_3} - \left(\frac{\partial e_{11}}{\partial x_1} - i\frac{\partial e_{12}}{\partial x_2}\right)\frac{\partial}{\partial x_3}\right] H_1 + \left[-ie_{12}\frac{\partial^2}{\partial x_1 \partial x_2} - \left(\frac{\partial e_{11}}{\partial x_2} + i\frac{\partial e_{12}}{\partial x_1}\right)\frac{\partial}{\partial x_3}\right] H_2\right.$$

$$\left. + \left[K^2 + e_{11}\left(\frac{\partial^2}{\partial x_1^2} + \frac{\partial^2}{\partial x_2^2} + \frac{\partial^2}{\partial x_3^2}\right) + \left(\frac{\partial e_{11}}{\partial x_2} + i\frac{\partial e_{12}}{\partial x_1}\right)\frac{\partial}{\partial x_2} + \left(\frac{\partial e_{11}}{\partial x_1} - i\frac{\partial e_{12}}{\partial x_2}\right)\frac{\partial}{\partial x_1}\right] H_3 \right\} \mathbf{e}_3$$

$$= 0 \quad . \tag{66.10}$$

This equation determines rigorously the vector $\mathbf{H}$ in the medium.

Special Case of a Homogeneous, Anisotropic Plasma—Although we have treated this case in Chapter IV it is of interest to deduce the properties of a homogeneous plasma from the more general situation above. For a homogeneous plasma

$$\frac{\partial e_{ij}}{\partial x_k} = 0 \quad , \quad k = 1, 2, 3 \quad . \tag{66.11}$$

i.e., all elements e_{ij} are independent of position. Equation (66.10) then simplifies to the following,

$$[\{K^2 + e_{33}D_2^2 + e_{11}\nabla_{13}^2 + ie_{12}D_{12}^2\}H_1 + \{(e_{11} - e_{33})D_{12}^2 + ie_{12}\nabla_{23}^2\}H_2]\ \mathbf{e}_1$$

$$+ [\{(e_{11} - e_{33})D_{12}^2 - ie_{12}\nabla_{13}^2\}H_1 + \{K^2 + e_{33}D_{11}^2 + e_{11}\nabla_{23}^2 - ie_{12}D_{12}^2\}H_2]\ \mathbf{e}_2$$

$$+ [\{ie_{12}D_{23}^2\}H_1 + \{-ie_{12}D_{12}^2\}H_2 + \{K^2 + e_{11}\nabla^2\}H_3]\ \mathbf{e}_3$$

$$= 0 \quad . \tag{66.12}$$

where,

$$D^2_{ij} \equiv \frac{\partial^2}{\partial x_i \partial x_j} \quad , \quad \nabla^2_{ij} \equiv \frac{\partial^2}{\partial x_i^2} + \frac{\partial^2}{\partial x_j^2} \quad , \quad \nabla^2 \equiv \frac{\partial^2}{\partial x_1^2} + \frac{\partial^2}{\partial x_2^2} + \frac{\partial^2}{\partial x_3^2} \quad .$$

If $\mathbf{H}$ has a plane wave structure,

$$\mathbf{H} = \mathbf{H}_0 \exp\left[i(\omega t - K\mathbf{M} \cdot \mathbf{r})\right] \tag{66.13}$$

where $M = |\mathbf{M}|$ is the refractive index of the medium, with M_i $(i = 1,2,3)$, the components of $\mathbf{M}$ in the x_i directions, by substituting (66.13) into (66.12) we obtain in the usual fashion the determinental equation for the refractive index,

$$\begin{vmatrix} 1 - e_{33}M_2^2 - e_{11}(M_1^2 + M_3^2) - ie_{12}M_1M_2 & -(e_{11} - e_{33})M_1M_2 - ie_{12}(M_2^2 + M_3^2) & 0 \\ -(e_{11} - e_{33})M_1M_2 + ie_{12}(M_1^2 + M_2^2) & 1 - e_{33}M_1^2 - e_{11}(M_2^2 + M_3^2) + ie_{12}M_1M_2 & 0 \\ -ie_{12}M_2M_3 & ie_{12}M_1M_3 & 1 - e_{11}M^2 \end{vmatrix} = 0 \; . \tag{66.14}$$

Put,

$$\left.\begin{aligned} M_1^2 + M_2^2 &= M^2 \sin^2\theta \quad , \\ M_3^2 &= M^2 \cos^2\theta \quad , \end{aligned}\right\} \tag{66.15}$$

where θ denotes the angle between the wave normal and the x_3-axis. With these designations, the determinental equation becomes,

$$\begin{aligned} &(1 - e_{11}M^2)[1 - \{(e_{11} + e_{33}) \sin^2\theta + 2e_{11}\cos^2\theta\}M^2 \\ &+ \{e_{11}e_{33} \sin^2\theta + (e_{11}^2 - e_{12}^2)\cos^2\theta\}M^4] \\ &= 0 \quad . \end{aligned} \tag{66.16}$$

This equation is of sixth degree in M but the factor $(1 - e_{11}M^2)$ is extraneous and results from using the divergence condition (66.9) to obtai eq. (66.10). Consequently we shall disregard this factor. From eq. (66.16) we obtain the relation,

$$\tan^2\theta = -\frac{[1 - 2e_{11}M^2 + (e_{11}^2 - e_{12}^2)M^4]}{[1 - (e_{11} + e_{33})M^2 + e_{11}e_{33}M^4]} . \qquad (66.17)$$

For propagation along the x_3-axis, *i.e.*, parallel to the externally applied magnetic field, $\theta = 0$, we obtain

$$M^2 = \frac{1}{e_{11} \pm e_{12}} = \epsilon_{11} \pm \epsilon_{12} . \qquad (66.18)$$

The waves corresponding to the above refractive indices imply the rotation of the electric vector in the same direction as the electrons, and positive ions respectively, rotate about the uniform magnetic field. The wave-particle coupling produces electron and ion gyro resonances at certain frequencies.

For $\theta = \pi/2$, we have transverse propagation and we find from eq.(66.17) the two values,

$$M^2 = \frac{1}{e_{33}} \quad \text{or} \quad \frac{1}{e_{11}} , \qquad (66.19)$$

equivalent to,

$$M^2 = \epsilon_{33} \quad \text{or} \quad \frac{\epsilon_{11}^2 - \epsilon_{12}^2}{\epsilon_{11}} , \qquad (66.20)$$

which yield the "ordinary" and "extraordinary" waves respectively. We shall not pursue the analysis further since it follows that already given in Chapter IV.

Isotropic, Inhomogeneous Plasma—By definition of isotropy, the tensors defined by (66.3) or (66.13) must be scalar quantities, hence we must set $e_{12} = 0$, $e_{11} = e_{33} \equiv e$ with $e = 1/\epsilon$ which is a function of position. Accordingly, eq. (66.10) is simplified and terms of the form $\partial e/\partial x_i = (\partial/\partial x_i)(1/\epsilon)$ appear in the vector wave equation. It is interesting to compare eq. (66.10) for this case with ordinary scalar wave equation which has the form,

$$\left(\nabla^2 + \frac{K^2}{e}\right)H_i = 0 \quad , \qquad (i = 1,2,3) \quad , \qquad (66.21)$$

and which contains no gradients of e. If the medium is isotropic and homogeneous eq. (66.10) reduces to eq. (66.21) but with e = constant as we already know from Chapter I.

67. PROPERTIES OF THE WAVES WHEN INHOMOGENEITIES ARE PRESENT

We shall now determine the effects of inhomogeneities on wave propagation utilizing the general equation (66.10).

Longitudinal Propagation—Consider a plane wave propagating along the x_3-direction, that is, parallel to the uniform external applied field. If the medium varies only along this direction, then we need consider only gradients $\partial/\partial x_3$. The field is a function of x_3 alone. In this case eq. (66.10) reduces to

$$\left\{\left[K^2 + \frac{\partial}{\partial x_3}\left(e_{11}\frac{\partial}{\partial x_3}\right)\right]H_1 + i\left(\frac{\partial}{\partial x_3}\,e_{12}\,\frac{\partial}{\partial x_3}\right)H_2\right\}\mathbf{e}_1$$

$$+\left[-i\left(\frac{\partial}{\partial x_3}\,e_{12}\,\frac{\partial}{\partial x_3}\right)H_1 + \left(K^2 + \frac{\partial}{\partial x_3}\,e_{11}\,\frac{\partial}{\partial x_3}\right)H_2\right]\mathbf{e}_2$$

$$= 0 \quad . \qquad (67.1)$$

We note that for a homogeneous medium, terms of the form $e_{ij}(\partial^2/\partial x_3^2)$ occur whereas in the inhomogeneous case we have $\partial/\partial_{x3}[e_{ij}(\partial/\partial_{x3})]$; also note that $H_3 = 0$ in either case. Because of this, only the transverse components of **H** are involved. From eq. (66.4) we see in this case that **E** depends only on x_3 and that $E_3 = 0$. Consequently, we have, using the language of wave guides, a transverse electric and magnetic mode. The initially given plane wave remains a plane wave. The equations for x_1 and x_2 components are in general different and this implies that the right and left handed polarized waves have different phase velocities. As a consequence of this, the Faraday rotation in the inhomogeneous plasma differs from that in a homogeneous plasma.

Transverse Propagation—Let the direction of propagation be normal to the x_3-axis, then we find,

$$\left[\left(K^2 + \frac{\partial}{\partial x_2} e_{33} \frac{\partial}{\partial x_2}\right) H_1 - \left(\frac{\partial}{\partial x_2} e_{33} \frac{\partial}{\partial x_2}\right) H_2\right] \mathbf{e}_1$$

$$+ \left[\left(- \frac{\partial}{\partial x_1} e_{33} \frac{\partial}{\partial x_2}\right) H_1 + \left(K^2 + \frac{\partial}{\partial x_1} e_{33} \frac{\partial}{\partial x_1}\right) H_2\right] \mathbf{e}_2 = 0 \qquad (67.2)$$

and,

$$\left[K^2 + \frac{\partial}{\partial x_1} e_{11} \frac{\partial}{\partial x_1} + \frac{\partial}{\partial x_2} e_{11} \frac{\partial}{\partial x_2} + i \left(\frac{\partial e_{12}}{\partial x_1} \frac{\partial}{\partial x_2} - \frac{\partial e_{12}}{\partial x_2} \frac{\partial}{\partial x_1}\right)\right] H_3 \mathbf{e}_3 = 0 \ . \qquad (67.3)$$

Equation (67.2) yields the ordinary wave (the electric vector is parallel to the uniform magnetic field) and eq. (67.3) corresponds to the extraordinary wave (the magnetic vector is parallel to the uniform external field). If the x_1 axis is chosen to coincide with the direction of propagation, and if the dielectric tensor varies only with x_1 we find $H_1 = 0$. Therefore the solution of eq. (67.2) in this case is a single component in the original direction. As in the preceding case of longitudinal propagation, here too, the initial orientation of both ordinary and extraordinary waves is unchanged but the magnitudes of the components are altered. The vector **H** is always transverse to x_1, the direction of propagation.

For the ordinary wave, eq. (66.4) implies that **E** has only an x_3-component. But for the extraordinary wave $\nabla \times \mathbf{H}$ has only a component transverse to **H** and eq. (66.4) shows that the electric vector has a component in the x_1-direction. Therefore, the ordinary waves and transverse electric-magnetic waves and the extraordinary wave is a transverse-magnetic wave. This conclusion holds also in the homogeneous plasma, even though the components of the vectors in the inhomogeneous plasma are different.

Transverse Variations (Longitudinal Propagation)—Suppose now that the dielectric tensor varies transversely to the x_3-axis and let the direction of propagation be along the x_3-axis. In this case, **H** is a function of all coordinates (x_1, x_2, x_3) but $(\partial e_{ij}/\partial x_3) = 0$. The general equation (66.1c) becomes in this case:

$$[\{K^2 + e_{11}\nabla^2_{13} + e_{33}D^2_2 + ie_{12}D^2_{12} + D_2 e_{33} D_2\}H_1 + \{(e_{11} - e_{33})D^2_{12} + ie_{12}\nabla^2_{23} - D_2 e_{33} D_1\}H_2]\mathbf{e}_1$$

$$+ [\{(e_{11} - e_{33})D^2_{12} - ie_{12}\nabla^2_{13} - D_1 e_{33} D_2\}H_1 + \{K^2 + e_{33}D^2_1 + e_{11}\nabla^2_{23} - ie_{12}D^2_{12} + D_1 e_{33} D_1\}H_2]\mathbf{e}_2$$

$$+ [\{ie_{12}D^2_{23} - (D_1 e_{12} - iD_2 e_{12})D_3\}H_1 + \{-ie_{12}D^2_{23} - (D_2 e_{11} + iD_1 e_{12})D_3\}H_2$$

$$+ \{K^2 + e_{11}\nabla^2 + (D_2 e_{11} + iD_1 e_{12})D_2 + (D_1 e_{11} - iD_2 e_{12})D_1\}H_3]\mathbf{e}_3$$

$$= 0 \quad . \tag{67.4}$$

We see from this equation that there exists an H_3 component in the direction of propagation and that the plane of polarization has been rotated. This is due of course to the inhomogeneities. The **E** vector undergoes a similar alteration. Therefore, none of the field vectors of the propagating wave are transverse to the direction of propagation.

If the medium varies in the direction of the **E** vector then the component of **H** in the x_3 direction arises from the element of the dielectric tensor e_{12}, which is a measure of the anisotropy of the medium. On the other hand, if the variations are in the direction of the magnetic vector then $\mathbf{H} \cdot \mathbf{e}_3$ is due to e_{11}, which is a measure of the medium coupling.

Ordinary and Extraordinary Waves (Transverse Propagation)—If we expand eq. (66.7) and assume that both $\partial e_{ij}/\partial x_1$ and $\partial e_{ij}/\partial x_2$ are bounded then for propagation transverse to the x_3-axis, *i.e.*, transverse to the uniform magnetic field, the **H** vector depends only on x_1 and x_2, and therefore

$$\left[\left(K^2 + \frac{\partial}{\partial x_2} e_{33} \frac{\partial}{\partial x_2}\right) H_1 - \left(\frac{\partial}{\partial x_2} e_{33} \frac{\partial}{\partial x_1}\right) H_2\right] \mathbf{e}_1$$

$$+ \left[\frac{\partial}{\partial x_1}\left(e_{33} \frac{\partial}{\partial x_2}\right) H_1 + \left(K^2 + \frac{\partial}{\partial x_1} e_{33} \frac{\partial}{\partial x_1}\right) H_2\right] \mathbf{e}_2 = 0 \, , \tag{67.5}$$

and,

$$\left\{\left[K^2 + \frac{\partial}{\partial x_1} e_{11} \frac{\partial}{\partial x_1} + \frac{\partial}{\partial x_2} e_{11} \frac{\partial}{\partial x_2} + i\left(\frac{\partial e_{12}}{\partial x_1}\frac{\partial}{\partial x_2} - \frac{\partial e_{12}}{\partial x_2}\frac{\partial}{\partial x_1}\right)\right] H_3\right\} \mathbf{e}_3 = 0 \quad . \tag{67.6}$$

For **E** parallel to x_3, eq. (67.5) corresponds to the ordinary wave when the gradients are in the direction of **H**. So, if H_2 is the only non-vanishing component (and if $\partial e_{ij}/\partial x_2 \neq 0$) then a component of **H** along the direction of propagation arises.

For **H** along x_3, eq. (67.6) corresponds to the extraordinary wave when the gradients are parallel to **E**. Thus the inhomogeneities change the H_3 component of **H**.

For the ordinary wave with gradients along **H**, even though **H** has a non-zero component in the direction of propagation, the **E** vector is transverse to the direction of propagation. For the extraordinary wave with gradients along **E**, no E_3 component exists, but a component of **E** in the direction of propagation exists.

Summarizing, the inhomogeneities produce a transverse magnetic mode for the extraordinary wave with gradient along **E** but no pure transverse fields for the ordinary wave with gradients along **H**.

If only gradients along x_3 are assumed, so that $\partial e_{ij}/\partial x_3 \neq 0$, **H** is a function of all coordinates x_1, x_2, x_3 and eq. (66.7) expands into,

$$\begin{aligned}
&\left[\left(K^2 + \frac{\partial}{\partial x_3} e_{11} \frac{\partial}{\partial x_3} + e_{33} \frac{\partial^2}{\partial x_2^2}\right) H_1 + \left(i \frac{\partial}{\partial x_3} e_{12} \frac{\partial}{\partial x_3} - e_{33} \frac{\partial^2}{\partial x_1 \partial x_2}\right) H_2 \right.\\
&\left. - \left(i \frac{\partial}{\partial x_3} e_{12} \frac{\partial}{\partial x_2} + \frac{\partial}{\partial x_3} e_{11} \frac{\partial}{\partial x_1}\right) H_3\right] \mathbf{e}_1 + \left\{ -\left(i \frac{\partial}{\partial x_3} e_{12} \frac{\partial}{\partial x_3} + e_{33} \frac{\partial^2}{\partial x_1 \partial x_2}\right) H_1 \right.\\
&\left. + \left(K^2 + e_{33} \frac{\partial^2}{\partial x_1^2} + \frac{\partial}{\partial x_3} e_{11} \frac{\partial}{\partial x_3}\right) H_2 + \left(i \frac{\partial}{\partial x_3} e_{12} \frac{\partial}{\partial x_1} - \frac{\partial}{\partial x_3} e_{11} \frac{\partial}{\partial x_2}\right) H_3 \right\} \mathbf{e}_2 \\
&+ \left\{\left(i e_{12} \frac{\partial^2}{\partial x_2 \partial x_3} - e_{11} \frac{\partial^2}{\partial x_1 \partial x_3}\right) H_1 - \left(i e_{12} \frac{\partial^2}{\partial x_1 \partial x_3} + e_{11} \frac{\partial^2}{\partial x_2 \partial x_3}\right) H_2 \right.\\
&\left. + \left[K^2 + e_{11}\left(\frac{\partial^2}{\partial x_1^2} + \frac{\partial^2}{\partial x_2^2}\right)\right] H_3 \right\} \mathbf{e}_3 = 0 \quad .
\end{aligned} \tag{67.7}$$

The foregoing relations cover both the extraordinary wave with gradients in the **H** direction and the ordinary wave with gradients along the **E** direction. We associate the x_3 component H_3 of **H** with the extraordinary wave and the H_1, H_2 components with the ordinary wave. Hence, for both the extraordinary wave with a gradient along **H**, and for the ordinary wave with a gradient along **E**, there exist components of **H** along all three axes. The same is true for the **E** vector. Consequently, no transverse electric or magnetic fields exist.

Based on the preceding analysis we conclude that for a homogeneous anisotropic medium the ordinary wave has both the electric and magnetic vectors transverse to the direction of propagation whereas the extraordinary wave has only its magnetic vector transverse. The waves which are launched along the uniform magnetic field also have both the electric and magnetic vector transverse to the direction of propagation. For an inhomogeneous anisotropic medium and for the ordinary wave we have respectively; if the dielectric tensor varies along the direction of propagation the electric and magnetic vectors are transverse to the direction of propagation, if the tensor varies along the electric field neither the electric nor magnetic vector is transverse to the propagation direction, if the tensor varies along the magnetic vector, the electric vector is transverse to the propagation direction. For the extraordinary wave and if the tensor varies along the direction of propagation only the magnetic vector is transverse, for tensor variation along the electric field also the magnetic vector is transverse and for tensor variation along the magnetic vector neither the electric nor the magnetic vector is transverse. For the waves launched in the direction of the uniform magnetic field and for tensor variation along the direction of propagation both the electric and magnetic vectors are transverse. If the tensor varies along the electric field or the magnetic field or both, neither the electric nor the magnetic vector is transverse.

In the case of an isotropic inhomogeneous medium the following conclusions can be made. For tensor variation along the direction of propagation both the electric and magnetic vectors are transverse. When the tensor varies along the electric vector, only the magnetic vector is transverse, but for tensor variation along the magnetic vector only the electric vector is transverse.

68. REFRACTIVE INDEX CONSIDERATIONS

In this section we shall reduce the equations for propagation in an anisotropic, inhomogeneous plasma to an equation for the refractive index. This approach is the same one which we followed in Chapters I and II. The principal reason for considering such a reduction is because of the limitation in the number of precise solutions of Maxwell's equations.

We shall see that the reduction to an equation for the refractive index is possible only for those waves which have field components transverse to the direction of propagation. This means that either the wave itself or one of the field vectors is always plane. Consequently, for transverse electric-magnetic waves, the refractive index equations are obtained from either the equation for **E** or **H**. For transverse electric waves the equations for the electric vector must be used and for transverse magnetic waves, equations for the magnetic vector must be used. In either case, the other field vector is then obtained from Maxwell's equation. If none of the fields are transverse, the reduction is not possible.

In the treatment of the homogeneous medium the structure of the plane wave is of the form

$$\mathbf{H} = \mathbf{H}_0 \exp\left[i(\omega t - \mathbf{K} \cdot \mathbf{r})\right] \tag{68.1}$$

from which we obtained the dispersion equation, or an equation for the refractive index. This equation is algebraic, a consequence of the homogeneous nature of the medium.

The description of the inhomogeneous plasma that we have assumed implies that the dielectric tensor is a function of position, *i.e.*, the e_{ij} are functions of position. Therefore, the refractive index is also a function of position. From the results of the previous sections regarding the form of the wave propagating in the homogeneous case, we saw that if the wave that results is transverse electric-magnetic or purely transverse magnetic then the magnetic vector remains plane. This suggests that for the inhomogeneous plasma we consider a structure for **H** or **E** which is a generalization of the simple plane wave. In Chapter I we have already done this, and we now follow the procedure set forth there. Consequently, we take the magnetic vector in the form of an Eikonal

$$\mathbf{H} = \mathbf{H}_0 \exp[i(\omega t - \int \mathbf{K} \cdot d\mathbf{r})] \tag{68.2}$$

which clearly reduces to (68.1) if **K** is uniform. Now set

$$\mathbf{K} = K\mathbf{M} \tag{68.3}$$

with K a constant and **M** a function of position. By substituting the form (68.2) into the field equations we obtain in general a non-linear differential equation for M the magnitude of **M**. Instead of writing out the general differential equation a formidable exercise in vector manipulation, we shall consider some simpler examples in order to gain some insight into the general case.

Dielectric Tensor Varying in the Direction of Propagation--In this case **M** is a function of x_3 alone and the result of substituting the form (68.2) into the general equation (66.10), gives

$$\left.\begin{aligned} \frac{\partial \mathbf{H}}{\partial x_3} &= -\,iKM(x_3)\mathbf{H} \,, \\ \frac{\partial^2 \mathbf{H}}{\partial x_3^2} &= \left[-K^2M^2(x_3) - iK\frac{\partial M(x_3)}{\partial x_3}\right]\mathbf{H} \,. \end{aligned}\right\} \tag{68.4}$$

The dispersion equation, which results from eq. (67.1) is

$$\left[1 - e_{11}M^2(x_3) - \frac{i}{K}\frac{\partial}{\partial x_3}(e_{11}M)\right]^2 - \left[e_{12}M^2(x_3) + \frac{i}{K}\frac{\partial}{\partial x_3}(e_{12}M)\right]^2 = 0 \,. \tag{68.5}$$

By neglecting all higher order terms,

$$\left(\frac{\partial M}{\partial x_3}\right)^2 , \quad \left(\frac{\partial e_{ij}}{\partial x_3}\right)^2 , \quad \left(\frac{\partial M}{\partial x_3}\frac{\partial e_{ij}}{\partial x_3}\right) ,$$

we obtain,

$$\frac{i}{K}\left[(1 - e_{11}M^2)\frac{\partial}{\partial x_3}(e_{11}M) + e_{12}M^2\frac{\partial}{\partial x_3}(e_{12}M)\right]$$

$$= \frac{1}{2}\left[(e_{11}^2 - e_{12}^2)M^4 - 2e_{11}M^2 + 1\right] , \tag{68.6}$$

which is a non-linear differential equation for M. We note that since the e_{ij} are functions of x_3, the coefficients of the derivative terms are not uniform.

Ordinary and Extraordinary Waves in the Case of the Dielectric Tensor Varying in the Direction of Propagation— In the case of an ordinary wave we take a linearly polarized wave propagating in the x_1-direction with **E** directed along the x_3-direction and **H** along the x_2-direction,

$$\mathbf{H} = \mathbf{H}_2\mathbf{e}_2 = \mathbf{H}_0 \exp\{i[\omega t - K\int M(x_1)dx_1]\} \tag{68.7}$$

and eq. (67.5) gives

$$i\frac{\partial}{\partial x_1}[e_{33}M(x_1)] = K[1 - e_{33}M^2(x_1)] \quad . \tag{68.8}$$

For the extraordinary wave, we take the wave propagating in the x_1-direction but since H_3 is not a function of x_2, and because the gradients of the dielectric tensor vary only along x_1, equation (67.6) yields,

$$i\frac{\partial}{\partial x_1}[e_{11}M(x_1)] = K[1 - e_{11}M^2(x_1)] \quad . \tag{68.9}$$

69. REFLECTION COEFFICIENTS

The simplest example of a non-homogeneous medium is where all space consists of two semi-infinite spaces each of which is homogeneous but with different dielectric properties. We shall first consider the problem of calculating the reflection coefficient for a plane boundary between free space and a uniform plasma.

Assume that the plasma occupies the region $x_2 > 0$ and the free space occupies $x_2 < 0$. The externally applied magnetic field is parallel to the x_3-axis. The coordinate system is shown in Fig. 13. The magnetic field is out of the plane of the paper.

The polarization of the incident wave is such that $\mathbf{H}_i = H_{3,i}$ where subscript i stands for incident. Thus,

$$H_{3,i} = H \exp\left(-i\frac{\omega}{V_0}x_2 \cos\varphi_0\right)\exp\left(-i\frac{\omega}{V_0}x_1 \sin\varphi_0\right) \quad , \tag{69.1}$$

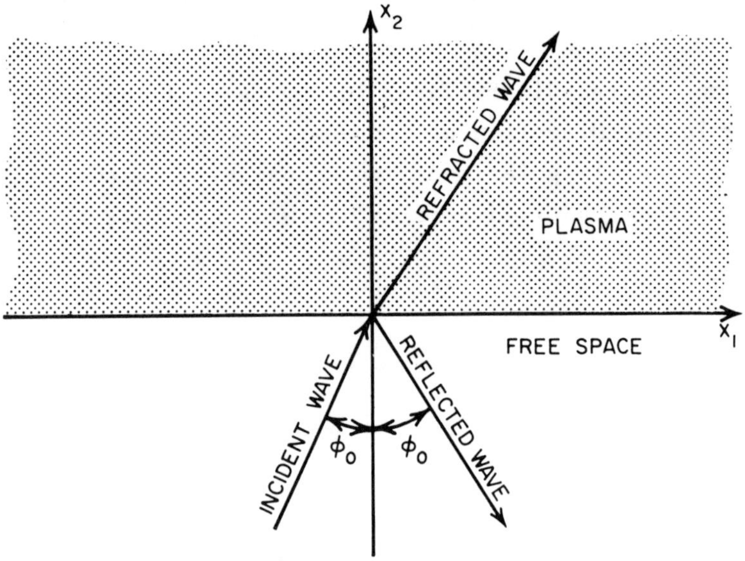

FIG. 13

where H is a constant. Denoting by subscript r the reflected wave, it is clear that it must have the form

$$H_{3,r} = HR \exp\left(i \frac{\omega}{V_0} x_2 \cos \varphi_0\right) \exp\left(-i \frac{\omega}{V_0} x_1 \sin \varphi_0\right) , \quad (69.2)$$

where R is the reflection coefficient.

Since the fields by assumption do not vary with x_3 Maxwell's equations become

$$i \epsilon_0 \omega \mathbf{E} = \epsilon^{-1} \begin{pmatrix} \dfrac{\partial H_3}{\partial x_2} \\ -\dfrac{\partial H_3}{\partial x_1} \\ \dfrac{\partial H_2}{\partial x_1} - \dfrac{\partial H_1}{\partial x_2} \end{pmatrix} \quad (69.3)$$

$$-i\mu\omega\mathbf{H} = \begin{pmatrix} \dfrac{\partial E_3}{\partial x_2} \\ \\ -\dfrac{\partial E_3}{\partial x_1} \\ \\ \dfrac{\partial E_2}{\partial x_1} - \dfrac{\partial H_1}{\partial x_2} \end{pmatrix} \tag{69.4}$$

where ϵ^{-1} is given by eqs. (66.5) and (66.6). The component H_3 satisfies

$$\left(\frac{\partial^2}{\partial x_1^2} + \frac{\partial^2}{\partial x_2^2} + \frac{K^2}{e_{11}}\right) H_3 = 0 \quad , \tag{69.5}$$

while E_3 satisfies

$$\left(\frac{\partial^2}{\partial x_1^2} + \frac{\partial^2}{\partial x_2^2} + \frac{K^2}{e_{33}}\right) E_3 = 0 \quad . \tag{69.6}$$

The refracted or plasma wave must have the form

$$H_3 = h(x_2) \exp\left(-i \frac{\omega}{V_0} x_1 \sin \varphi_0\right) \quad , \quad \text{for} \quad x_2 > 0 \quad , \tag{69.7}$$

$h(x_2)$ is a function of x_2-alone. Since H_3 satisfies eq. (69.5), the function $h(x_2)$ satisfies the equation

$$\left\{\frac{\partial^2}{\partial x_2^2} + K_0^2\left[\left(\frac{1}{\bar{\mu} e_{11}}\right)^{\frac{1}{2}} - \sin^2 \varphi_0\right]\right\} h(x_2) = 0 \quad , \tag{69.8}$$

where $K_0^2 = \mu_0 \epsilon_0 \omega^2$ and $\bar{\mu} = \mu_0/\mu$. The solutions of eq. (69.8) are

$$h(x_2) = \exp\left\{\pm i K_0\left[\left(\frac{1}{\bar{\mu} e_{11}}\right)^{\frac{1}{2}} - \sin^2 \varphi_0\right]^{\frac{1}{2}} x_2\right\} \quad , \tag{69.9}$$

but since we are concerned with the region $0 < x_2 < \infty$ we use only the negative sign solution. The plasma wave therefore is given by

$$H_3 = HT \exp\left\{-iK_0\left[\left(\frac{1}{\bar{\mu}e_{11}}\right)^{1/2} - \sin^2\varphi_0\right]^{1/2} x_2\right\} \exp\left(-iK_0 x_1 \sin\varphi_0\right) , \quad (69.10)$$

where T is a transmission coefficient. To find R and T we use the boundary conditions on the tangential components of the field quantities, *i.e.*, they must be continuous across the interface $x_2 = 0$. Thus, continuity of H_3 at $x_2 = 0$ gives

$$T = 1 + R , \quad (69.11)$$

and from eq. (69.3), for the continuity of E_1, we find at $x_2 = 0$,

$$(1 - R)\cos\varphi_2 = T\left\{\left[\left(\frac{1}{\bar{\mu}e_{11}}\right)^{1/2} - \sin^2\varphi_0\right]^{1/2} e_{11} - ie_{12}\sin\varphi_0\right\} . \quad (69.12)$$

Put,

$$\delta = \left[\left(\frac{1}{\bar{\mu}e_{11}}\right)^{1/2} - \sin^2\varphi_0\right]^{1/2} e_{11} - ie_{12}\sin\varphi_0 , \quad (69.13)$$

then eqs. (69.11) and (69.12) yield*

$$R = \frac{\cos\varphi_0 - \delta}{\cos\varphi_0 + \delta} , \quad (69.14)$$

$$T = \frac{2\cos\varphi_0}{\cos\varphi_0 + \delta} . \quad (69.15)$$

Stratified Media—The results of the preceding will now be generalize to a stratified medium. The stratification consists of layers which are parallel to the interface $x_2 = 0$ as shown in Fig. 14.

We have n parallel layers each of thickness d_j, $j = 1, 2, \ldots,$ with $d_n = \infty$. The free space region is denoted by subscript zero. Assuming

---

* For very low frequency reflection coefficients see, N. F. Barber and D. D. Crombie, "VLF Reflections from the Ionosphere in the Presence of a Transverse Magnetic Field," Jour. Atmos. Ten. Phys. 16, 37, (October 1959).

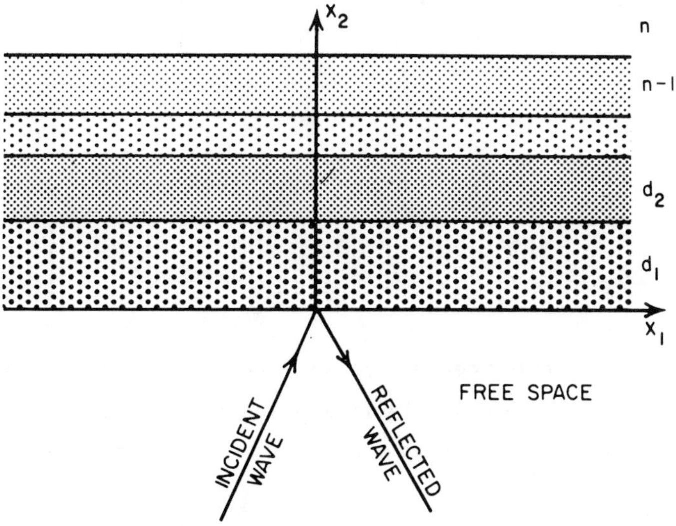

FIG. 14

as before that the incident wave is polarized with its magnetic vector in the x_3 direction,

$$H_3 = H[\exp(-iK_0 x_2 \cos\varphi_0) + R\exp(iK_0 x_2 \cos\varphi_0)]\exp(-iK_0 x_1 \sin\varphi_0),$$

for $x_2 < 0$. (69.16)

To find R as a function of the layer parameters we define the wave impedances for the jth layer by

$$K_j^+ = -\frac{E_1^+}{H_3^+}, \tag{69.17}$$

$$K_j^- = \frac{E_1^-}{H_3^-}, \tag{69.18}$$

where + means we use $\exp(-i\gamma_j x_2)$ and − means we use $\exp(i\gamma_j x_2)$,

and,

$$\gamma_j = K_0 \left[\left(\frac{1}{\bar{\mu}_j e_{11,j}}\right)^{1/2} - \sin^2 \varphi_0\right]^{1/2*} . \qquad (69.19)$$

Eqs. (69.17) and (69.18) lead to

$$\left.\begin{aligned} K_j^+ &= \eta_0 (e_{11,j}\gamma_j - i e_{12,j} \sin \varphi_0) , \\ K_j^- &= \eta_0 (e_{11,j}\gamma_j + i e_{12,j} \sin \varphi_0) , \end{aligned}\right\} \qquad (69.20)$$

where $\eta_0 = (\mu_0/\epsilon_0)^{1/2}$ is the free space impedance. Since the medium is anisotropic, $K_j^+ \neq K_j^-$ in general. Consider now the interface between the $(j - 1)$-th and jth layer; we define the reflection coefficients by

$$\left.\begin{aligned} R_{j-1} &= \frac{H_3^-}{H_3^+} , \\ S_{j-1} &= \frac{E_3^-}{E_3^+} , \end{aligned}\right\} \qquad (69.21)$$

all quantities are evaluated at the $(j - 1)$-th layer. Therefore,

$$\left.\begin{aligned} R_{j-1} &= \frac{K_{j-1}^+ - K_j^+}{K_{j-1}^- + K_j^+} , \\ S_{j-1} &= \frac{(K_{j-1}^+)^{-1} - (K_j^+)^{-1}}{(K_{j-1}^-)^{-1} + (K_j^+)^{-1}} , \end{aligned}\right\} \qquad (69.22)$$

at the interface between $(j - 2)$ and $(j - 1)$ we have

$$\left.\begin{aligned} R_{j-2} &= \frac{K_{j-2}^+ - Z_{j-1}}{K_{j-2}^- + Z_{j-1}} , \\ S_{j',-2} &= \frac{(K_{j-2}^+)^{-1} - (Z_{j-1})^{-1}}{(K_{j-2}^-)^{-1} + (Z_{j-1})^{-1}} , \end{aligned}\right\} \qquad (69.23)$$

---

* See for example, S.. A. Schelkunoff, Electromagnetic Waves, D. Van Nostrand, New York, (1943), section on Non-Uniform Transmission Lines. Also, R. W. P. King, Transmission Line Theory, Chapter V, McGraw-Hill Book Co. N.Y. (1955).

where Z_{j-1} is the impedance at the $(j - 1)$-th boundary. By definition,

$$Z_{j-1} = K_{j-1} \frac{1 + S_{j-1} \exp(-2i\gamma_{j-1} d_{j-1})}{1 + R_{j-1} \exp(-2i\gamma_{j-1} d_{j-1})} , \qquad (69.24)$$

with R_{j-1} and S_{j-1} defined by eqs. (69.21). Replacing $j - 1$ by j,

$$Z_j = K_j \frac{1 + S_j \exp(-2i\gamma_j d_j)}{1 + R_j \exp(-2i\gamma_j d_j)} , \qquad (69.25)$$

then for $j = 1$,

$$R_1 = \frac{K_1^+ - Z_2}{K_1^- + Z_2} . \qquad (69.26)$$

At the lowest interface

$$R_0 = \frac{K_0^+ - Z_1}{K_0^- + Z_1} , \qquad (69.27)$$

or,

$$R = \frac{\cos \varphi_0 - \delta}{\cos \varphi_0 + \delta} , \qquad (69.28)$$

here, $\delta = Z_1/\eta_0$ because $K_0^+ = K_0^- = \eta_0 \cos \varphi_0$. The two-layered results are easily obtained by setting $d_2 = \infty$ and for the single homogeneous case by letting $d_1 \to \infty$.

70. CYLINDRICAL WAVES

For a certain class of problems dealing with anisotropic plasmas, *e.g.*, propagation in wave guides, the axis of symmetry is along the constant and uniform magnetic field. It is therefore useful to consider the fundamental equations in cylindrical coordinates.

The cylindrical coordinates will be denoted by (r, θ, z) with the applied magnetic field direction along the z-axis. With the dielectric tensor given by eq. (66.3), its inverse by eq. (66.5), and denoting the unit orthogonal vectors along r, θ and z respectively by $\mathbf{e}_r$, $\mathbf{e}_\theta$ and $\mathbf{e}_z$, eq. (66.7) becomes,

$$
\Bigg\{\Bigg[K^2 + e_{11}\left(\frac{\partial^2}{\partial z^2} + \frac{\partial}{\partial r}\frac{1}{r}\frac{\partial}{\partial r}r\right) + e_{33}\frac{1}{r}\frac{\partial}{\partial\theta}\frac{1}{r}\frac{\partial}{\partial\theta} + ie_{12}\frac{1}{r}\frac{\partial}{\partial\theta}\left(\frac{1}{r}\frac{\partial}{\partial r}r\right)
$$

$$
+ \frac{1}{r}\frac{\partial e_{33}}{\partial\theta}\frac{1}{r}\frac{\partial}{\partial\theta} + \frac{\partial e_{11}}{\partial z}\frac{\partial}{\partial z}\Bigg]H_r + \Bigg[-e_{33}\frac{1}{r}\frac{\partial}{\partial\theta}\left(\frac{1}{r}\frac{\partial}{\partial\theta}r\right) + e_{11}\frac{\partial}{\partial r}\left(\frac{1}{r}\frac{\partial}{\partial\theta}\right)
$$

$$
+ ie_{12}\left(\frac{\partial^2}{\partial z^2} + \frac{1}{r}\frac{\partial}{\partial\theta}\frac{1}{r}\frac{\partial}{\partial\theta}\right) - \frac{1}{r}\frac{\partial e_{33}}{\partial\theta}\left(\frac{1}{r}\frac{\partial}{\partial r}r\right) + i\frac{\partial e_{12}}{\partial z}\frac{\partial}{\partial z}\Bigg]H_\theta
$$

$$
- \left[\frac{\partial e_{11}}{\partial z}\frac{\partial}{\partial r} + i\frac{\partial e_{12}}{\partial z}\left(\frac{1}{r}\frac{\partial}{\partial\theta}\right)\right]H_z\Bigg\}\mathbf{e}_r + \Bigg\{\Bigg[e_{11}\frac{1}{r}\frac{\partial}{\partial\theta}\frac{1}{r}\frac{\partial}{\partial r}r - e_{33}\frac{\partial}{\partial r}\frac{1}{r}\frac{\partial}{\partial\theta}
$$

$$
- ie_{12}\left(\frac{\partial^2}{\partial z^2} + \frac{\partial}{\partial r}\frac{1}{r}\frac{\partial}{\partial r}r\right) - \frac{\partial e_{33}}{\partial\theta}\frac{1}{r}\frac{\partial}{\partial\theta} - i\frac{\partial e_{12}}{\partial z}\frac{\partial}{\partial z}\Bigg]H_r
$$

$$
+ \Bigg[K^2 + e_{11}\left(\frac{\partial^2}{\partial z^2} + \frac{1}{r}\frac{\partial}{\partial\theta}\frac{1}{r}\frac{\partial}{\partial\theta}\right) + e_{33}\frac{\partial}{\partial r}\frac{1}{r}\frac{\partial}{\partial r}r - ie_{12}\frac{\partial}{\partial r}\frac{1}{r}\frac{\partial}{\partial\theta}
$$

$$
+ \frac{\partial e_{33}}{\partial r}\frac{1}{r}\frac{\partial}{\partial r}r + \frac{\partial e_{11}}{\partial z}\frac{\partial}{\partial z}\Bigg]H_\theta - \left(\frac{\partial e_{11}}{\partial z}\frac{1}{r}\frac{\partial}{\partial\theta} - i\frac{\partial e_{12}}{\partial z}\frac{\partial}{\partial r}\right)H_z\Bigg\}\mathbf{e}_\theta
$$

$$
+ \Bigg\{\left(ie_{12}\frac{1}{r}\frac{\partial^2}{\partial\theta\partial z} - \frac{1}{r}\frac{\partial e_{11}}{\partial r}r\frac{\partial}{\partial z} + i\frac{1}{r}\frac{\partial e_{12}}{\partial\theta}\frac{\partial}{\partial z}\right)H_r - \Bigg(ie_{12}\frac{1}{r}\frac{\partial}{\partial r}r\frac{\partial}{\partial z}
$$

$$
+ i\frac{1}{r}\frac{\partial e_{12}}{\partial r}r\frac{\partial}{\partial z} + \frac{1}{r}\frac{\partial e_{11}}{\partial\theta}\frac{\partial}{\partial z}\Bigg)H_\theta + \Bigg[K^2 + e_{11}\left(\frac{1}{r}\frac{\partial}{\partial r}r\frac{\partial}{\partial r} + \frac{1}{r}\frac{\partial}{\partial\theta}\frac{1}{r}\frac{\partial}{\partial\theta} + \frac{\partial^2}{\partial z^2}\right.
$$

$$
\left. + \frac{1}{r}\left(\left[r\frac{\partial e_{11}}{\partial r} - i\frac{\partial e_{12}}{\partial\theta}\right]\frac{\partial}{\partial r} + \left[\frac{1}{r}\frac{\partial e_{11}}{\partial\theta} + i\frac{\partial e_{12}}{\partial r}\right]\frac{\partial}{\partial\theta}\right)\right)\Bigg]H_z\Bigg\}\mathbf{e}_z = 0\,, \qquad (70.1)
$$

the field components are also related by the divergence condition

$$
\operatorname{div}\mathbf{B} = \mu\operatorname{div}\mathbf{H} = \mu\left\{\frac{1}{r}\left[\frac{\partial}{\partial r}(rH_r)\right] + \frac{1}{r}\frac{\partial H_\theta}{\partial\theta} + \frac{\partial H_z}{\partial z}\right\} = 0\,, \qquad (70.2)
$$

a result which has been used to simplify eq. (70.1) somewhat. The isotropic medium is obtained by setting $e_{11} = e_{33}$, $e_{12} = 0$.

Homogeneous Anisotropic Case—To obtain the homogeneous case we put all derivatives $\partial e_{ij}/\partial r$, etc., equal to zero in eq. (70.1). For propagation transverse to the magnetic field H_θ and H_z are functions of r alone and eq. (70.1) reduces to

$$\left.\begin{aligned}\left(K^2 + e_{33}\frac{\partial}{\partial r}\frac{1}{r}\frac{\partial}{\partial r}\, r\right) H_\theta \mathbf{e}_\theta &= 0 \,, \\ \left(K^2 + e_{11}\frac{1}{r}\frac{\partial}{\partial r}\, r\, \frac{\partial}{\partial r}\right) H_z \mathbf{e}_z &= 0 \,.\end{aligned}\right\} \qquad (70.3)$$

The first equation takes the form

$$\frac{\partial^2 H_\theta}{\partial r^2} + \frac{1}{r}\frac{\partial H_\theta}{\partial r} + \left(\frac{K^2}{e_{33}} - \frac{1}{r^2}\right) H_\theta = 0 \qquad (70.4)$$

which is recognized as Bessel's equation, whose solution is a cylindrical function of the first kind with argument $[K/(e_{33})^{1/2} r]$. The second equation is written as

$$\frac{\partial^2 H_z}{\partial r^2} + \frac{1}{r}\frac{\partial H_z}{\partial r} + \frac{K^2}{e_{11}} H_z = 0 \,, \qquad (70.5)$$

a Bessel equation whose solution is a cylindrical function of zero order with argument $[K/(e_{11})^{1/2} r]$. The vector **E** is transverse to the direction of propagation for the ordinary wave, but has a component along the direction of propagation for the extraordinary wave, which is a consequence of the anisotropy. However, the magnetic field **H** is transverse to the direction of propagation for both the ordinary and extraordinary waves.

For propagation along the magnetic field, the field is a function of r. Hence, if we also have rotational symmetry, eq. (70.1) becomes

$$\left\{\left[K^2 + e_{11}\left(\frac{\partial^2}{\partial z^2} + \frac{\partial}{\partial r}\frac{1}{r}\frac{\partial}{\partial r}\, r\right)\right] H_r + i e_{12}\frac{\partial^2 H_\theta}{\partial z^2}\right\}\mathbf{e}_r + \left[-i e_{12}\left(\frac{\partial^2}{\partial z^2} + \frac{\partial}{\partial r}\frac{1}{r}\frac{\partial}{\partial r}\, r\right) H_r \right.$$
$$\left. + \left(K^2 + e_{11}\frac{\partial^2}{\partial z^2} + e_{33}\frac{\partial}{\partial r}\frac{1}{r}\frac{\partial}{\partial r}\, r\right) H_\theta\right]\mathbf{e}_\theta + \left\{-i e_{12}\frac{1}{r}\frac{\partial}{\partial r}\, r\, \frac{\partial}{\partial z} H_\theta\right.$$
$$\left. + \left[K^2 + e_{11}\left(\frac{1}{r}\frac{\partial}{\partial r}\, r\, \frac{\partial}{\partial r}\right) + \frac{\partial^2}{\partial z^2}\right] H_z\right\}\mathbf{e}_z = 0 \,. \qquad (70.6)$$

We can conclude from this that there do not exist pure transverse wave vectors for cylindrical waves, a consequence of the anisotropy.* For an inhomogeneous anisotropic medium, it can be shown that the following results obtain. For the ordinary wave, if the dielectric tensor varies along the direction of propagation the electric and magnetic vectors are transverse to the direction of propagation; if the tensor varies along **E** neither the magnetic nor electric vector is transverse to the direction of propagation and if the tensor varies along **H**, only the electric vector is transverse. For the extraordinary wave, if the dielectric tensor varies along the direction of propagation, the resulting wave is transverse magnetic. If the tensor varies along **E** the resulting wave is also transverse magnetic, but if the tensor varies along **H** the resulting wave is neither transverse electric nor transverse magnetic. Finally, if a wave propagates along the z-direction and if the dielectric varies along this direction there is neither a transverse electric nor magnetic field. The same holds when the dielectric varies along **E** or along **H**.

Reflection from a Homogeneous Cylindrical Plasma—Following the patter for the rectangular cartesian case we consider first the scattering from a homogeneous cylindrical plasma of infinite length as shown in Fig. 15.

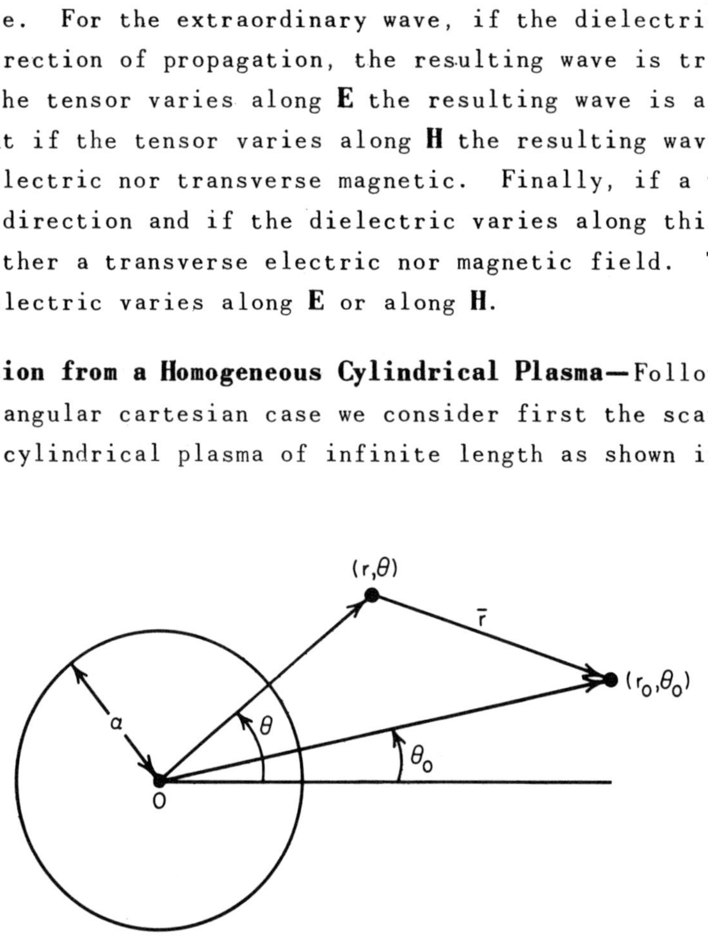

FIG. 15

We shall suppose that the line source which is parallel to the z-axis radiates a cylindrical polarized wave such that $\mathbf{H} = H_z \mathbf{e}_z$ where

* For a solution to eq. (70.6) see, Y. B. Fainberg and M. F. Gorbatenko, "Electro-Magnetic Waves in a Plasma Placed in a Magnetic Field," Jour. Tech. Phy. (USSR) 29, 549-562 (1959).

$\mathbf{e}_z$ is a unit vector along the z-axis. We take the incident field in the form

$$H_{z,i} = \frac{\epsilon_0 \omega I}{4} H_0^{(2)}(K_0 \bar{r}) \quad , \tag{70.7}$$

where I is the magnetic current or strength of the line source, and $H_0^{(2)}$ denotes the Hankel function of zero order and of the second kind.* The factor $\bar{r}$ is defined by

$$\bar{r} = [r_0^2 + r^2 - 2rr_0 \cos(\theta - \theta_0)]^{1/2} \quad , \tag{70.8}$$

and by the addition theorem for Hankel functions, in particular for $H_0^{(2)}(K_0\bar{r})$ we can write

$$H_{z,i} = \frac{\epsilon_0 \omega I}{4} \sum_{m=-\infty}^{m=\infty} H_m^{(2)}(K_0 r_0) J_m(K_0 r) \exp[-im(\theta - \theta_0)] \text{ for } r < r_0 \; ; \tag{70.9}$$

$H_m^{(2)}$ and J_m are respectively the Hankel and Bessel functions of order m. For $r > r_0$, we replace $K_0 r_0$ by $K_0 r$. The incident electric field is

$$E_{\theta,i} = \frac{iI}{4} \sum_{-\infty}^{\infty} H_m^{(2)}(K_0 r_0) K_0 J_m'(K_0 r) \exp[-im(\theta - \theta_0)] \quad , \tag{70.10}$$

where the prime denotes differentiation with respect to the argument $K_0 r$. The scattered field for $r > a$ satisfies the wave equation in free space and hence denoting it by subscript r, it can be written as

$$H_{z,r} = \frac{\epsilon_0 \omega I}{4} \sum_{-\infty}^{\infty} B_m H_m^{(2)}(K_0 r_0) H_m^{(2)}(K_0 r) \exp[-im(\theta - \theta_0)] \quad , \tag{70.11}$$

$$E_{\theta,r} = \frac{iI}{4} \sum_{-\infty}^{\infty} B_m H_m^{(2)}(K_0 r_0) K_0 [H_m^{(2)}(K_0 r)]' \exp[-im(\theta - \theta_0)] \quad , \tag{70.12}$$

---

* See for example, J. R. Wait, "Electromagnetic Radiation from Cylindrical Structures," Pergamon Press, London-New York, (1959). See also, same author, NBS Report 6715, August, 1960. Boulder Labs, Boulder, Colorado.

where the coefficients B_m are to be determined by the boundary conditions at $r = a$. Inside the plasma column, $r < a$, we see from eq. (70.1) that H_z must satisfy the wave equation

$$\left(\frac{1}{r}\frac{\partial}{\partial r} r \frac{\partial}{\partial r} + \frac{1}{r^2}\frac{\partial^2}{\partial\theta^2} + \frac{K_0^2}{e_{11}\bar{\mu}}\right) H_z = 0 , \tag{70.13}$$

whose formal solution is represented by

$$H_z = \frac{\epsilon_0\omega I}{4}\sum_{m=-\infty}^{m=\infty} A_m H_m^{(2)}(K_0 r_0) J_m(\gamma r) \exp\left[-im(\theta - \theta_0)\right] , \tag{70.14}$$

where the A_m are to be determined and $\gamma = K_0/(e_{11}\bar{\mu})^{1/2}$. Maxwell's equations in cylindrical coordinates are

$$\left.\begin{aligned} i\epsilon_0\omega\begin{pmatrix} E_r \\ E_\theta \\ E_z \end{pmatrix} &= \epsilon^{-1}\begin{pmatrix} \dfrac{\partial H_z}{r\partial\theta} - \dfrac{\partial H_\theta}{\partial z} \\ \dfrac{\partial H_r}{\partial z} - \dfrac{\partial H_z}{\partial r} \\ \dfrac{1}{r}\dfrac{\partial}{\partial r}(rH_\theta) - \dfrac{1}{r}\dfrac{\partial H_r}{\partial\theta} \end{pmatrix} , \\ -i\mu\omega\begin{pmatrix} H_r \\ H_\theta \\ H_z \end{pmatrix} &= \begin{pmatrix} \dfrac{\partial E_z}{r\partial\theta} - \dfrac{\partial E_\theta}{\partial z} \\ \dfrac{\partial E_r}{\partial z} - \dfrac{\partial E_z}{\partial r} \\ \dfrac{1}{r}\dfrac{\partial}{\partial r}(rE_\theta) - \dfrac{1}{r}\dfrac{\partial E_r}{\partial\theta} \end{pmatrix} , \end{aligned}\right\} \tag{70.15}$$

with $H_r = H_\theta = 0$, we find

$$i\epsilon_0\omega E_\theta = -\left(ie_{12}\frac{\partial H_z}{r\partial\theta} + e_{11}\frac{\partial H_z}{\partial r}\right) , \tag{70.16}$$

therefore,

$$E_\theta = \frac{iI}{4} \sum_{m=-\infty}^{m=\infty} A_m H_m^{(2)}(K_0 r_0) \left[\frac{me_{12}}{r} J_m(\gamma r) + e_{11}\gamma J_m'(\gamma r) \right] \exp\left[-im(\theta - \theta_0)\right] . \tag{70.17}$$

The boundary conditions at $r = a$, read

$$\left. \begin{aligned} H_z &= H_{z,i} + H_{z,r} , \\ E_\theta &= E_{\theta,i} + E_{\theta,r} , \end{aligned} \right\} \tag{70.18}$$

from which we obtain,

$$A_m = \frac{J_m(K_0 a) + B_m H_m^{(2)}(K_0 a)}{J_m(\gamma a)} , \tag{70.19}$$

$$B_m = - \left[\frac{ \left(\frac{e_{11}}{\bar{\mu}}\right)^{1/2} \frac{J_m'(\gamma a)}{J_m(\gamma a)} + \frac{me_{12}}{K_0 a} - \frac{J_m'(K_0 a)}{J_m(K_0 a)} }{ \left(\frac{e_{11}}{\bar{\mu}}\right)^{1/2} \frac{J_m'(\gamma a)}{J_m(\gamma a)} + \frac{me_{12}}{K_0 a} - \frac{H_m^{(2)\prime}(K_0 a)}{H_m^{(2)}(K_0 a)} } \right] \frac{J_m(K_0 a)}{H_m^{(2)}(K_0 a)} . \tag{70.20}$$

Since A_m and B_m are explicitly determined, we have the complete solution for the scattering from the homogeneous cylindrical plasma. With this result we can now extend the analysis to a medium stratified in the radial direction.

Cylindrically Stratified Media--Let us consider now a cylinder made up of n concentric layers. Here too we have a line source of cylindrical waves placed at (r_0, θ_0) and we want the field at (r, θ). Following the procedure given above we define the wave impedances by

$$K_{m,j}^{+} = - \frac{E_{\theta,m}^{+}}{H_{z,m}^{+}} , \quad K_{m,j}^{-} = \frac{E_{\theta,m}^{-}}{H_{z,m}^{-}} , \tag{70.21}$$

the positive and negative signs again refer to the two linearly independent wave solutions, $J_m(\gamma_j r)$ and $H_m^{(2)}(\gamma_j r)$ in the jth layer. (See Fig. 16)

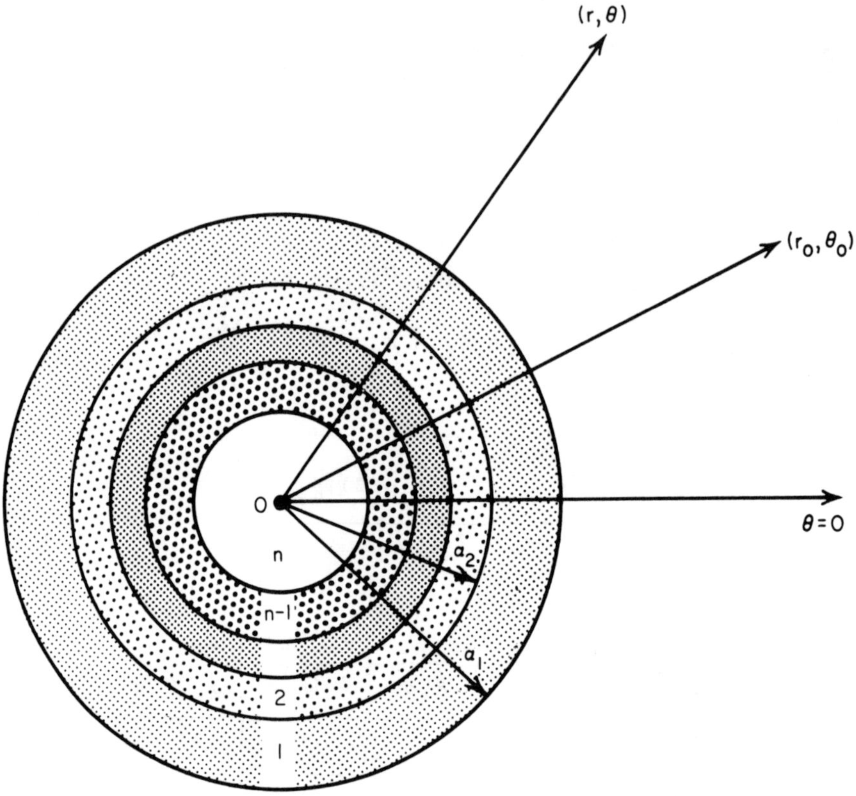

FIG. 16

For the jth layer we have

$$i\omega\epsilon_0 E_\theta = -i\left(e_{12,j}\frac{\partial H_z}{r\partial\theta} + e_{11,j}\frac{\partial H_z}{\partial r}\right) , \qquad (70.22)$$

so that

$$K^{+}_{m,j} = -i\left[\frac{me_{12,j}}{K_0 r} + \left(\frac{e_{11,j}}{\bar{\mu}_j}\right)^{\frac{1}{2}}\frac{J'_m(\gamma_j r)}{J_m(\gamma_j r)}\right], \qquad (70.23)$$

$$K^{-}_{m,j} = i\left[\frac{me_{12,j}}{K_0 r} + \left(\frac{e_{11,j}}{\bar{\mu}_j}\right)^{\frac{1}{2}}\frac{H'^{(2)}_m(\gamma_j r)}{H^{(2)}_m(\gamma_j r)}\right], \qquad (70.24)$$

where j runs from 1 to n. At the interface between the jth and $(j-1)$-th layer, the reflection coefficients are

$$R_{m,j-1} = \frac{H^-_{z,m}}{H^+_{z,m}} = \frac{K^+_{m,j-1} - Z_{m,j}}{K^-_{m,j-1} + Z_{m,j}}, \tag{70.25}$$

$$S_{m,j-1} = \frac{E^-_{\theta,m}}{E^+_{\theta,m}} = \frac{(K^+_{m,j-1})^{-1} - (Z_{m,j})^{-1}}{(K^-_{m,j-1})^{-1} + (Z_{m,j})^{-1}}; \tag{70.26}$$

$Z_{m,j}$ denotes the impedance at the interface between the jth and $(j-1)$-th layer. If we define the transmission factors $T^{\pm}_{m,E}$, $T^{\pm}_{m,H}$ which represent the fractional change of a wave in propagating from one layer to another across an interface, we can write $Z_{m,j}$ in terms of the reflection coefficients as

$$Z_{m,j} = K^+_{m,j} \frac{1 + S_{m,j} T^+_{m,E}(a_j, a_{j+1}) T^-_{m,E}(a_{j+1}, a_j)}{1 + R_{m,j} T^+_{m,H}(a_j, a_{j+1}) T^-_{m,H}(a_{j+1}, a_j)}, \tag{70.27}$$

$$T^+_{m,E}(a_j, a_{j+1}) = \frac{E^+_{\theta,m}(a_{j+1})}{E^+_{\theta,m}(a_j)} = \frac{e_{11,j}\gamma_j J'_m(\gamma_j a_{j+1}) + m e_{12,j} J_m(\gamma_j a_{j+1})/a_{j+1}}{e_{11,j}\gamma_j J'_m(\gamma_j a_j) + m e_{12,j} J_m(\gamma_j a_j)/a_j}, \tag{70.28}$$

$$T^-_{m,E}(a_{j+1}, a_j) = \frac{E^-_{\theta,m}(a_j)}{E^-_{\theta,m}(a_{j+1})} = \frac{e_{11,j}\gamma_j H^{(2)}_m(\gamma_j a_j) + m e_{12,j} H^{(2)}_m(\gamma_j a_j)/a_j}{e_{11,j}\gamma_j H^{(2)}_m(\gamma_j a_{j+1}) + m e_{12,j} H^{(2)}_m(\gamma_j a_{j+1})/a_{j+1}}, \tag{70.29}$$

$$T^+_{m,H}(a_j, a_{j+1}) = \frac{H^+_{z,m}(a_{j+1})}{H^+_{z,m}(a_j)} = \frac{J_m(\gamma_j a_{j+1})}{J_m(\gamma_j a_j)}, \tag{70.30}$$

$$T^-_{m,H}(a_{j+1}, a_j) = \frac{H^-_{z,m}(a_j)}{H^-_{z,m}(a_{j+1})} = \frac{H^{(2)}_m(\gamma_j a_j)}{H^{(2)}_m(\gamma_j a_{j+1})}, \tag{70.31}$$

Now, given $R_{m,j-1}$ and $S_{m,j-1}$ defined by

$$R_{m,j-1} = \frac{K^+_{m,j-1} - K^+_{m,j}}{K^-_{m,j-1} + K^+_{m,j}} \;, \qquad S_{m,j-1} = \frac{(K^+_{m,j-1})^{-1} - (K^+_{m,j})^{-1}}{(K^+_{m,j-1})^{-1} + (K^+_{m,j})^{-1}} \;, \tag{70.32}$$

the coefficients $R_{m,j-2}$, $S_{m,j-2}$ can be found, and hence also at the last boundary between the medium and free space,

$$R_{m,0} = \frac{K^+_{m,0} - Z_{m,1}}{K^-_{m,0} + Z_{m,1}} \;, \qquad S_{m,0} = \frac{(K^+_{m,0})^{-1} - (Z_{m,1})^{-1}}{(K^-_{m,0})^{-1} + (Z_{m,1})^{-1}} \;, \tag{70.33}$$

with,

$$K^+_{m,0} = -\,i\,\frac{J'_m(K_0 r)}{J_m(K_0 r)}\,\eta_0 \;, \tag{70.34}$$

$$K^-_{m,0} = i\,\frac{H^{(2)\prime}_m(K_0 r)}{H^{(2)}_m(K_0 r)}\,\eta_0 \;. \tag{70.35}$$

By writing

$$H_{z,r} = \frac{\epsilon_0 \omega I}{4} \sum_{m=-\infty}^{m=\infty} B_m H^{(2)}_m(K_0 r_0) H^{(2)}_m(K_0 r)\; \exp\,[-im(\theta - \theta_0)] \;, \tag{70.36}$$

we obtain

$$B_m = -\,R_{m,0}\,\frac{J_m(K_0 a)}{H^{(2)}_m(K_0 a)} \;, \tag{70.37}$$

if we put $a_2 = 0$, the result for the homogeneous plasma is recovered, *cf.* eq. (70.20)

When the line source is sufficiently far removed from the plasma column, *i.e.*, many wavelengths away, so that $K_0 r_0$ and $K_0 r$ are very much greater than unity, we can write

$$H_{z,i} \cong \frac{\epsilon_0 \omega I}{4} \left(\frac{2i}{\pi K_0 \bar{r}}\right)^{1/2} \exp(-iK_0 \bar{r}) \;, \tag{70.38}$$

which results from the asymptotic representations of the Hankel functions. In a similar manner,

$$H_{z,r} \cong \frac{\epsilon_0 \omega I}{4}\left(\frac{2i}{\pi K_0 r_0}\right)^{1/2} \exp\,(-iK_0 r_0) \sum_{-\infty}^{\infty} B_m H_m^{(2)}(K_0 r)\, \exp\left\{im\left[\frac{\pi}{2} - (\theta - \theta_0)\right]\right\} \quad ; \tag{70.39}$$

note that

$$H_{z,i}\Big|_{r_0} = \frac{\epsilon_0 \omega I}{4}\left(\frac{2i}{\pi K_0 r_0}\right)^{1/2} \exp\,(-iK_0 r_0) \tag{70.40}$$

thus,

$$H_{z,r} = H_{z,i}\Big|_{r_0} \sum_{-\infty}^{\infty} B_m H_m^{(2)}(K_0 r)\, \exp\left\{im\left[\frac{\pi}{2} - (\theta - \theta_0)\right]\right\} . \tag{70.41}$$

For a particular plasma we need to evaluate e_{11} and e_{12} in terms of the plasma parameters.

71. CONTINUOUS STRATIFIED MEDIA

The stratified media treated in the foregoing was based on the solutions obtained for a homogeneous plasma. In this section we assume at the outset a continuous stratified medium and formulate the electromagnetic problem rigorously. As in the above cases the medium is absorbing and anisotropic, the constant and uniform magnetic field is directed arbitrarily. All the information regarding the medium is subsumed in the dielectric tensor ϵ which is a continuous function of x_3 alone. This tensor is therefore complex and non-symmetric. The plasma under consideration is bounded above and below by free space as shown in Fig. 17.

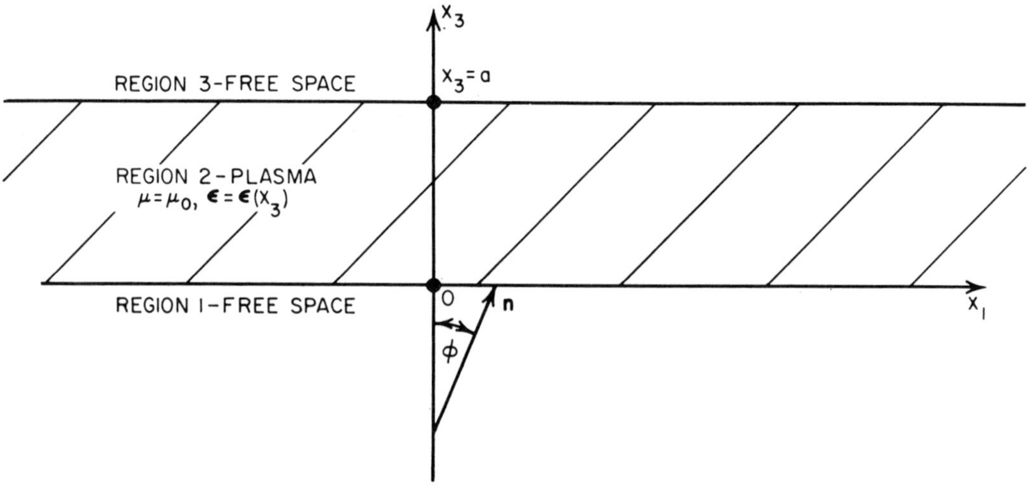

FIG. 17

The coordinate system is right handed cartesian with the x_2 axes into the plane of the paper. The incident plane wave is elliptically polarized and its plane of incidence lies in the plane $x_2 = 0$, The angle of incidence is given by φ as shown, $\mathbf{n}$ is the unit wave normal direction. The problem here is to find the reflected and transmitted waves in $x_3 < 0$ and $x_3 > a$, respectively. The problem will be solved if we can find the amplitudes and polarizations of these waves.

At the boundaries $x_3 = 0$ and $x_3 = a$, $\epsilon = \mathbf{I}$ the unit matrix. We can formulate the problem in an abstract manner quite compactly. If $\mathbf{E}$ is the total field, $\mathbf{E}_i$ the incident field and $\mathbf{E}_s$ the field in the scattering medium, we shall seek an equation of the form

$$(\mathbf{I} + \mathbf{L})\mathbf{E} = \mathbf{E}_i + \mathbf{K}\mathbf{E}_s \qquad (71.1)$$

where **L** and **K** are linear operators which will be defined later. This representation however has a physical interpretation in that it is the sum of the incident field and a field produced by the integrated effect of all the induced sources within the scattering medium.* Further, in region 1 defined by $x_3 < 0$, this equation is required to reduce to $\mathbf{E}_r$, the reflected field, and $\mathbf{L} = 0$, so that we can write

$$\mathbf{E}_r = \mathbf{K}_r\mathbf{E}_s \quad , \qquad (71.2)$$

where $\mathbf{K}_r$ is the value of the operator **K** in region 1. In region 3, defined by $x_3 > a$, again $\mathbf{L} = 0$ and the transmitted field $\mathbf{E}_t$ is given by

$$\mathbf{E}_t = \mathbf{E}_i + \mathbf{K}_t\mathbf{E}_s \qquad (71.3)$$

where $\mathbf{K}_t$ is the value of the operator **K** in region 3.

Reflection and Transmission Operators—The formulation above permits us in a simple way to define the reflection and transmission operators as follows. If **R** and **T** denote these operators respectively we define **R** by

$$\mathbf{E}_r = \mathbf{R}\mathbf{E}_s = \mathbf{K}_r\mathbf{E}_s \quad \text{in} \quad x_3 < 0 \qquad (71.4)$$

or,

$$\mathbf{R} = \mathbf{K}_r \quad ;$$

and **T** by

$$\mathbf{T} = \mathbf{I} + \mathbf{S} \qquad (71.5)$$

where **S** is a scattering operator defined by

$$\mathbf{S} = \mathbf{K}_s\mathbf{E}_s \quad , \qquad (71.6)$$

with $\mathbf{K}_s$ obtained from $\mathbf{K}_t$ by a simple rule which will be determined subsequently.

* D. R. Hartree, loc. cit. See also M. Born and E. Wolf, "Principles of Optics," Chapters II, XII, Pergamon Press, London (1959).

The Structure of the Operators L and K—Our task now is to demonstrate that the operator form given by eq. (71.1) and derived on a heuristic basis can indeed be constructed rigorously. For this we consider Maxwell's equations

$$\nabla \mathbf{x} \mathbf{E} + i\mu_0 \omega \mathbf{H} = 0 \quad , \tag{71.7}$$

$$\nabla \mathbf{x} \mathbf{H} - i\epsilon_0 \epsilon \omega \mathbf{E} = 0 \quad , \tag{71.8}$$

and note that they are satisfied in terms of a single Hertz vector potential $\Pi(x_1, x_2, x_3)$. Indeed, if we put

$$\mathbf{E} = \text{grad (div } \Pi) + K_0^2 \Pi = \nabla(\nabla \cdot \Pi) + K_0^2 \Pi \quad , \tag{71.9}$$

$$\mathbf{H} = i\omega\epsilon_0 \text{ curl } \Pi = i\omega\epsilon_0 \nabla \mathbf{x} \Pi \quad , \tag{71.10}$$

we find by direct substitution,

$$\nabla \mathbf{x} \mathbf{E} + i\omega\mu_0 \mathbf{H} = \nabla \mathbf{x} [\nabla(\nabla \cdot \Pi)] \equiv 0 \quad , \tag{71.11}$$

$$\nabla \mathbf{x} \mathbf{H} - i\omega\epsilon_0 \epsilon \mathbf{E} = -i\omega\epsilon_0 \{\nabla^2 \Pi + K_0^2 \Pi + (\epsilon - \mathbf{I})\mathbf{E}\} \ , \tag{71.12}$$

so that **both** equations are satisfied provided Π satisfies the following equation

$$\nabla^2 \Pi + K_0^2 \Pi + (\epsilon - \mathbf{I})\mathbf{E} = 0 \quad . \tag{71.13}$$

This result can be stated more precisely. Namely, if **E** and **H** are any solutions to Maxwell's equations in a region defined by μ_0, ϵ, then there exists a vector function of position Π such that eq. (71.13) holds and **E**,**H** are given by eqs. (71.9), (71.10) respectively.*

We shall find a solution for Π in integral form, *i.e.*, an integral equation from which the structure of the operators can be found explicitly. In region 1, $x_3 < 0$, we assume the field is represented by

$$\mathbf{F} = \mathbf{F}_i + \mathbf{F}_r = \mathbf{F}_0 \exp\left[-iK_0(x_1 \sin\varphi + x_3 \cos\varphi)\right] + \mathbf{F}_R \exp\left[-iK_0(x_1 \sin\varphi - x_3 \cos\varphi)\right] \tag{71.14}$$

---

* This theorem is a generalization of the isotropic case. See for example, Stratton, J. A., loc. cit.

where $\mathbf{F}$ stands for either $\mathbf{E}$ or $\mathbf{H}$, and $\mathbf{F}_0, \mathbf{F}_R$ denote complex constant vectors. In region 3, $x_3 > a$, the field is assumed to have the form,

$$\mathbf{F} = \mathbf{F}_t = \mathbf{F}_T \exp\left[-iK_0(x_1 \sin\varphi + x_3 \cos\varphi)\right] , \quad (71.15)$$

where $\mathbf{F}_T$ is a complex constant vector. It is clear that we must find $\mathbf{F}_R$ and $\mathbf{F}_T$ when $\mathbf{F}_0$ is given. Also, we note that $\mathbf{E}_0$ and $\mathbf{H}_0$ can not be given arbitrarily because both $\mathbf{E}_i$ and $\mathbf{H}_i$ must satisfy Maxwell's equations in $x_3 < 0$. The same is true for the reflected wave, *i.e.*, it must also satisfy Maxwell's equations. That both $\mathbf{F}_i$ and $\mathbf{F}_r$ separately satisfy Maxwell's equations in region 1 is clearly implied by eq. (71.14).

To find the form of Π in regions 1 and 3 we note that for $x_3 < 0$ $\epsilon(x_3) = \mathbf{I}$ so that from eqs. (71.9), (71.10), (71.14) and (71.15) we have

$$\Pi(x_1,x_3) = \Pi_0 \exp\left[-iK_0(x_1 \sin\varphi + x_3 \cos\varphi)\right]$$

$$+ \Pi_R \exp\left[-iK_0(x_1 \sin\varphi - x_3 \cos\varphi)\right] , \quad \text{for } x_3 < 0 \quad ,(71.16)$$

and

$$\Pi(x_1,x_3) = \Pi_T \exp\left[-iK_0(x_1 \sin\varphi + x_3 \cos\varphi)\right. , \quad \text{for } x_3 > a , \quad (71.17)$$

where Π_0, Π_R and Π_T are complex constant vectors. It is easy to see that Π depends on x_1 in the same way as $\mathbf{F}_i$, consequently eq. (71.13) yields for $\Pi(x_3)$, the equation

$$\frac{d^2\Pi(x_3)}{dx_3^2} + K_0^2 \cos^2\varphi\Pi(x_3) = -\left[\epsilon(x_3) - \mathbf{I}\right]\mathbf{E}(x_3) , \quad (71.18)$$

which is an inhomogeneous vector differential equation. Apart from a factor of ϵ_0 the right side of eq. (71.18) is the polarization vector $\mathbf{P}(x_3)$, hence we can write this equation in the form

$$\frac{d^2\Pi(x_3)}{dx_3^2} + K_0^2 \cos^2\varphi\Pi(x_3) = -\frac{\mathbf{P}(x_3)}{\epsilon_0} . \quad (71.19)$$

We shall transform this vector differential equation into a vector integral equation by means of a Green's tensor

$$\mathbf{G}(x_3, x_3') = \frac{e^{-iK_0|x_3 - x_3'|\cos\varphi}}{-2iK_0\cos\varphi}\mathbf{I} \equiv G(x_3, x_3')\mathbf{I} \tag{71.20}$$

which is a solution of the homogeneous equation, *i.e.*, with $\mathbf{P} = 0$. By the application of Green's second formula* for the infinite space ($-\infty < x_3 < \infty$) we find for an arbitrary but positive η,

$$-\frac{1}{\epsilon_0}\int_{-\infty}^{\infty}\mathbf{G}(x_3, x_3')\mathbf{P}(x_3')dx_3' = \left[\left\{\frac{d\mathbf{\Pi}}{dx_3'}G(x_3, x_3') - \frac{\partial G(x_3, x_3')}{\partial x_3'}\mathbf{\Pi}(x_3')\right\}\right]_{x_3'=-\infty}^{x_3'=x_3-\eta}$$

$$+\left[\left\{\frac{d\mathbf{\Pi}(x_3')}{dx_3'}G(x_3, x_3') - \frac{\partial G(x_3, x_3')}{\partial x_3'}\mathbf{\Pi}(x_3')\right\}\right]_{x_3'=x_3+\eta}^{x_3'=\infty}, \tag{71.21}$$

this formula holds in the limit as $\eta \to 0$. Now at $x_3' = -\infty$,

$$G = \frac{e^{-iK_0(x_3 - x_3')\cos\varphi}}{-2iK_0\cos\varphi}$$

while $\mathbf{\Pi}(x_3') = \mathbf{\Pi}_0\exp[-iK_0x_3'\cos\varphi] + \mathbf{\Pi}_R\exp[iK_0x_3\cos\varphi]$ which follows from eq. (71.16). By substitution of these functions into the right side of eq. (71.21) and simplification, the first term reduces to the simple form $[-\mathbf{\Pi}_0\exp(-iK_0x_3\cos\varphi)]$. At $x_3' = \infty$ we have from eq. (71.17), $\mathbf{\Pi}(x_3') = \mathbf{\Pi}_T\exp[-iK_0x_3'\cos\varphi]$ and

$$G = \frac{e^{-iK_0(x_3' - x_3)\cos\varphi}}{-2iK_0\cos\varphi}$$

* H. Sagan, Boundary and Eigenvalue Problems in Mathematical Physics, Chapter IX, John Wiley & Sons (1961).

by substitution into the second term on the right of eq. (71.21) and taking into account the continuity of $G(x_3, x_3')$ at $x_3 = x_3'$ (the derivative of G is not continuous), this term yields $\mathbf{\Pi}(x_3)$. Therefore we have

$$-\frac{1}{\epsilon_0}\int_{-\infty}^{\infty} \mathbf{G}(x_3, x_3')\mathbf{P}(x_3')dx_3' = -\mathbf{\Pi}_0 \exp(-iK_0x_3 \cos\varphi) + \mathbf{\Pi}(x_3) \quad , \tag{71.22}$$

but since $\mathbf{P} \equiv 0$ outside $(0, a)$ we can write

$$\mathbf{\Pi}(x_3) = \mathbf{\Pi}_0 \exp(-iK_0x_3 \cos\varphi) + \frac{1}{2i\epsilon_0 K_0 \cos\varphi}\int_0^a e^{-iK_0|x_3 - x_3'|\cos\varphi}\mathbf{P}(x_3')dx_3' \tag{71.23}$$

and

$$\begin{aligned}\mathbf{\Pi}(x_1, x_3) &= \mathbf{\Pi}(x_3) \exp(-iK_0x_1 \sin\varphi)\\ &= \mathbf{\Pi}_0 \exp[-iK_0(x_1 \sin\varphi + x_3 \cos\varphi)]\\ &\quad + \frac{e^{-iK_0x_1\sin\varphi}}{2i\epsilon_0 K_0 \cos\varphi}\int_0^a e^{-iK_0|x_3 - x_3'|\cos\varphi}\mathbf{P}(x_3')dx_3' \quad .\end{aligned} \tag{71.24}$$

To find the condition that must further hold for $\mathbf{\Pi}(x_1, x_3)$ we make use of eqs. (71.9), (71.14) and (71.16) to obtain

$$\begin{aligned}&[\text{grad}\,(\text{div}) + K_0^2]\,\mathbf{\Pi}_0 \exp[-iK_0(x_1 \sin\varphi + x_3 \cos\varphi)]\\ &= \mathbf{E}_0 \exp[-iK_0(x_1 \sin\varphi + x_3 \cos\varphi)] \quad ,\end{aligned} \tag{71.25}$$

which is a necessary condition on $\mathbf{\Pi}_0$ and hence a necessary condition on the structure of $\mathbf{\Pi}(x_1, x_3)$. This equation asserts that since $\mathbf{E}_0$ lies in the plane of the incident wave front there exists infinitely many $\mathbf{\Pi}_0$ such that it is satisfied.

The Integral Equation—From eqs. (71.9) and (71.25) the result of the operation (grad div + K_0^2) on eq. (71.24) yields

$$\mathbf{E}(x_1,x_3) = \mathbf{E}_0 \exp\left[-iK_0(x_1 \sin\varphi + x_3 \cos\varphi)\right] + \left[\text{grad div} + K_0^2\right] \frac{e^{-iK_0 x_1 \sin\varphi}}{2i\epsilon_0 K_0 \cos\varphi} \int_0^a e^{-iK_0 |x_3 - x_3'| \cos\varphi}\, \mathbf{P}(x_3')\,dx_3' \quad . \tag{71.26}$$

Let us define two matrices $\mathbf{A}(x_3,x_3')$ and $\mathbf{B}(x_3)$,

$$\left.\begin{aligned} \mathbf{A}(x_3,x_3') &= \begin{pmatrix} \cos^2\varphi & 0 & -\sin\varphi\cos \\ 0 & 1 & 0 \\ -\sin\varphi\cos\varphi & 0 & \sin^2\varphi \end{pmatrix} \quad \text{for } x_3 > x_3' \\ \mathbf{A}(x_3,x_3') &= \begin{pmatrix} \cos^2\varphi & 0 & \sin\varphi\cos\varphi \\ 0 & 1 & 0 \\ \sin\varphi\cos\varphi & 0 & \sin^2\varphi \end{pmatrix} \quad \text{for } x_3' > x_3 \end{aligned}\right\} \tag{71.27}$$

which is a singular matrix and

$$\mathbf{B}(x_3) = \epsilon(x_3) - \mathbf{I} \quad , \tag{71.28}$$

from which

$$\epsilon_0 \mathbf{B}(x_3)\mathbf{E}(x_3) = \mathbf{P}(x_3) \quad . \tag{71.29}$$

Now a detailed calculation of the right side of eq. (71.26) which is left for the reader leads to,

$$\mathbf{E}(x_3) + \frac{1}{\epsilon_0} P_3(x_3)\mathbf{e}_3 = \mathbf{E}_0 \exp(-iK_0 x_3 \cos\varphi) - \frac{iK_0}{2\epsilon_0 \cos\varphi} \int_0^a e^{-iK_0|x_3 - x_3'|\cos\varphi}\, \mathbf{A}(x_3,x_3')\mathbf{P}(x_3')\,dx_3' \quad , \tag{71.30}$$

where P_3 is the x_3 component of $\mathbf{P}$ and $\mathbf{e}_3$ is a unit vector in the x_3-direction. We note that $\mathbf{B}(x_3) = 0$ in regions 1 and 3. We define the matrix $\mathbf{L}(x_3)$ by

$$\mathbf{L}(x_3) = \begin{pmatrix} 0 & 0 & 0 \\ 0 & 0 & 0 \\ \epsilon_{31} & \epsilon_{32} & \epsilon_{33} - 1 \end{pmatrix} \tag{71.31}$$

then it is clear that

$$P_3(x_3)\mathbf{e}_3 = \epsilon_0 \mathbf{L}(x_3)\mathbf{E}(x_3) \tag{71.32}$$

therefore eqs. (71.29), (71.30) and (71.32) give the vector integral equation

$$(\mathbf{I} + \mathbf{L}(x_3))\mathbf{E}(x_3) = \mathbf{E}_0 \exp(-iK_0 x_3 \cos\varphi) - \frac{iK_0}{2\cos\varphi}\int_0^a e^{-iK_0|x_3 - x_3'|\cos\varphi}\,\mathbf{A}(x_3, x_3')\mathbf{B}(x_3')\mathbf{E}(x_3')\,dx_3' , \tag{71.33}$$

which holds for $\mathbf{E}(x_3)$ in the scattering medium. It is obvious however that it gives the field everywhere in space. If we multiply both sides by the x_1 dependent part of the field we have the vector integral equation for $\mathbf{E}(x_1, x_3)$ and we can then identify the resulting equation with the operator eq. (71.1). In fact $\mathbf{L}$ is already given and hence,

$$\mathbf{K} \equiv -\frac{iK_0 \exp(-iK_0 x_1 \sin\varphi)}{2\cos\varphi}\int_0^a e^{-iK_0|x_3 - x_3'|\cos\varphi}\,\mathbf{A}(x_3, x_3')\mathbf{B}(x_3')\,dx_3' . \tag{71.34}$$

From the theory of integral equations, eq. (71.33) has a unique solution.* The integral equation and the originally posed scattering problem

* E. Goursat, Cours D'Analyse Mathematique, Vol. 3, Fifth Edition, Gauthier-Villars, Paris (1956).

are completely equivalent. We note that the kernel of (71.34) is continuous except at $x_3 = x_3'$ which results from the discontinuity in $\mathbf{A}$ at this point.

It is possible now to construct the reflection and transmission matrices. From the linear character of the problem it is obvious that

$$\mathbf{E}_R = \mathbf{R}\mathbf{E}_0 \quad , \tag{71.35}$$

$$\mathbf{E}_T = \mathbf{T}\mathbf{E}_0 \quad , \tag{71.36}$$

where $\mathbf{R}$ and $\mathbf{T}$ are the reflection and transmission matrices of the medium which are in general functions of ω and φ. We consider first the region $x_3 < 0$, then $\mathbf{L}(x_3) = 0$ and $x_3' > x_3$ and $\mathbf{A} \equiv \mathbf{A}_r$ by the second equation of (71.27). Equation (71.33) yields according to eq. (71.14)

$$\mathbf{E}_R = \frac{-iK_0}{2\cos\varphi}\int_0^a e^{-iK_0 x_3'\cos\varphi}\mathbf{A}_r\mathbf{B}(x_3')\mathbf{E}(x_3')dx_3' \quad , \quad x_3 < 0 \quad , \tag{71.37}$$

while for the region $x_3 > a$; $x_3 > x_3'$, $\mathbf{L}(x_3) = 0$ and $\mathbf{A} \equiv \mathbf{A}_t$ from the first of eq. (71.27), hence eqs. (71.15) and (71.33) give

$$\mathbf{E}_T = \mathbf{E}_0 + \frac{-iK_0}{2\cos\varphi}\int_0^a e^{iK_0 x_3'\cos\varphi}\mathbf{A}_t\mathbf{B}(x_3')\mathbf{E}(x_3')dx_3' \quad , \quad x_3 > a \quad . \tag{71.38}$$

Let $(\mathbf{u}_1, \mathbf{u}_2)$ be an orthonormal set of vectors in the wavefront of the incident wave, then this set also serves for the transmitted wavefront. Similarly, let $(\mathbf{u}_1', \mathbf{u}_2')$ be an orthonormal set in the reflected wavefront. We can then write

$$\mathbf{E}_0 = E_0^{(1)}\mathbf{u}_1 + \mathbf{E}_0^{(2)}\mathbf{u}_2 \quad , \tag{71.39}$$

$$\mathbf{E}_T = E_T^{(1)}\mathbf{u}_1 + E_T^{(2)}\mathbf{u}_2 \quad , \tag{71.40}$$

$$\mathbf{E}_R = E_R^{(1)}\mathbf{u}_1' + \mathbf{E}_R^{(2)}\mathbf{u}_2' \quad ; \tag{71.41}$$

denote by $\mathbf{E}_j(x_3)$, $(j = 1,2)$, the solutions of eq. (71.33) corresponding to a choice of $\mathbf{E}_{0,j} = \mathbf{u}_j$ for the incident wave amplitude, by $\mathbf{E}_{R,j}$ and $\mathbf{E}_{T,j}$ the resulting reflection and transmission wave amplitudes. From eq. (71.37) we have

$$\mathbf{E}_{R,j} = \frac{-iK_0}{2\cos\varphi} \int_0^a e^{-iK_0 x_3' \cos\varphi} \mathbf{A}_r \mathbf{B}(x_3') \mathbf{E}_j(x_3') dx_3' \quad , \quad (j = 1,2) \quad , \tag{71.42}$$

and from eq. (71.38),

$$\mathbf{E}_{T,j} = \mathbf{u}_j + \frac{-iK_0}{2\cos\varphi} \int_0^a e^{iK_0 x_3' \cos\varphi} \mathbf{A}_t \mathbf{B}(x_3') \mathbf{E}_j(x_3') dx_3' \quad , \quad (j = 1,2) \quad . \tag{71.43}$$

Eq. (71.39) gives,

$$\mathbf{E}_{0,j} = E_{0,j}^{(1)} \mathbf{u}_1 + E_{0,j}^{(2)} \mathbf{u}_2 \quad , \tag{71.44}$$

together with the definition of $\mathbf{E}_{0,j}$, we have

$$\mathbf{E}_{0,j}^{(l)} = \delta_{lj} \quad , \quad (j, l = 1,2) \quad . \tag{71.45}$$

Equations (71.44) and (71.45) when used with eq. (71.35) leads to

$$E_{R,j}^{(i)} = R_{ik} \delta_{kj} = R_{ij} \tag{71.46}$$

where R_{ij} is the i,jth element of matrix $\mathbf{R}$. By setting $\mathbf{E}_R = \mathbf{E}_{R,j}$, eq. (71.41) gives

$$\mathbf{E}_{R,j} = E_{R,j}^{(1)} \mathbf{u}_1' + E_{R,j}^{(2)} \mathbf{u}_2' \quad , \quad (j = 1,2) \quad , \tag{71.47}$$

and therefore using eq. (71.46),

$$\mathbf{E}_{R,j} \cdot \mathbf{u}_i' = R_{ij} \tag{71.48}$$

since $\mathbf{u}_i' \cdot \mathbf{u}_j' = \delta_{ij}$. Substituting eq. (71.45) into eq. (71.36) also gives

$$E_{T,j}^{(i)} = T_{ik}\delta_{kj} = T_{ij} \quad , \qquad (i,j = 1,2) \quad , \tag{71.49}$$

but from eq. (71.40) for $\mathbf{E}_T = \mathbf{E}_{T,j}$,

$$\mathbf{E}_{T,j} = E_{T,j}^{(1)}\mathbf{u}_1 + E_{T\ j}^{(2)}\mathbf{u}_2 \tag{71.50}$$

and therefore

$$\mathbf{E}_{T,j} \cdot \mathbf{u}_i = T_{ij} \quad , \qquad (i,j = 1,2) \quad . \tag{71.51}$$

Equations (71.42) and (71.43) give respectively

$$R_{ij} = \frac{-iK_0}{2\cos\varphi}\int_0^a e^{-iK_0x_3'\cos\varphi}\mathbf{u}_i' \cdot \mathbf{A}_r\mathbf{B}(x_3')\mathbf{E}_j(x_3')dx_3' \quad , \qquad (i,j = 1,2) \quad , \tag{71.52}$$

$$T_{ij} = \delta_{ij} + \frac{-iK_0}{2\cos\varphi}\int_0^a e^{iK_0x_3'\cos\varphi}\mathbf{u}_i \cdot \mathbf{A}_t\mathbf{B}(x_3')\mathbf{E}_j(x_3')dx_3' \quad , \qquad (i,j = 1,2) \quad . \tag{71.53}$$

These formulas show that if we know $\mathbf{E}_j$, the elements of the reflection and transmission matrices can be calculated. However, we shall demonstrate below that these elements can be derived from a variational principle. Before proceeding with this problem we want to examine some properties of the matrices $\mathbf{A}_r$ and $\mathbf{A}_t$ together with some consequences of these properties.

Properties of the Matrices $\mathbf{A}_r$ and $\mathbf{A}_t$—The singular nature of these matrices has already been mentioned. We can now demonstrate the following property; if $\mathbf{u}$ is any vector lying in the plane of the incident or reflected wave front

$$\mathbf{A}_t\mathbf{u} = \mathbf{u} \quad , \tag{71.54}$$

$$\mathbf{A}_r\mathbf{u} = \mathbf{u} \quad . \tag{71.55}$$

To prove eq. (71.54) we note that in the plane of the incident wavefront we can write

$$\mathbf{u} = \begin{pmatrix} u_1 \cos\varphi \\ u_2 \\ -u_3 \sin\varphi \end{pmatrix} \tag{71.56}$$

hence

$$\mathbf{A}_t\mathbf{u} = \begin{pmatrix} u_1 \cos^3\varphi + u_1 \sin^2\varphi \cos\varphi \\ u_2 \\ -u_1 \sin\varphi \cos^2\varphi - u_1 \sin^3\varphi \end{pmatrix} = \mathbf{u} \quad , \tag{71.57}$$

in a similar way if **u** is in the reflected wave front it has the form

$$\mathbf{u} = \begin{pmatrix} u_1 \cos\varphi \\ u_2 \\ u_1 \sin\varphi \end{pmatrix} \tag{71.58}$$

and it is easily verified that eq. (71.55) holds. The properties just proved show that every vector which lies in the incident wavefront and reflected wavefront are eigenvectors of $\mathbf{A}_t$ and $\mathbf{A}_r$ respectively with eigenvalues equal to unity in both cases.

Now let **W** be any vector normal to the incident or reflected wavefront. In the former case it has the form

$$\mathbf{W} = \begin{pmatrix} W \sin\varphi \\ 0 \\ W \cos\varphi \end{pmatrix} \quad , \tag{71.59}$$

and in the latter case,

$$\mathbf{W} = \begin{pmatrix} W \sin\varphi \\ 0 \\ -W \cos\varphi \end{pmatrix} \quad , \tag{71.60}$$

from which it follows directly that

$$\mathbf{A}_t \begin{pmatrix} W \sin \varphi \\ 0 \\ W \cos \varphi \end{pmatrix} = 0 \quad , \tag{71.61}$$

and

$$\mathbf{A}_r \begin{pmatrix} W \sin \varphi \\ 0 \\ -W \cos \varphi \end{pmatrix} = 0 \quad . \tag{71.62}$$

These last two results show that every vector which is normal to the incident or reflected wavefront is respectively an eigenvector of $\mathbf{A}_t$ and $\mathbf{A}_r$ with eigenvalue zero. Thus eqs. (71.54), (71.55), (71.61) and (71.62) assert that the matrix $\mathbf{A}$ maps every vector orthogonally onto the incident and reflected wavefronts, hence it maps a three-space onto a two-space which also shows that $\mathbf{A}$ is a singular matrix.

The relations (71.54) and (71.55) can be used to simplify the expressions for R_{ij} and T_{ij}. In fact if we put $\mathbf{u} = \mathbf{u}_i$, $(i = 1,2)$ and $\mathbf{u} = \mathbf{u}'_i$, $(i = 1,2)$ we have

$$\mathbf{u}_i \cdot \mathbf{A}_t \mathbf{B} \mathbf{E}_j = \mathbf{A}_t \mathbf{u}_i \cdot \mathbf{B} \mathbf{E}_j \tag{71.63}$$

and

$$\mathbf{u}'_i \cdot \mathbf{A}_r \mathbf{B} \mathbf{E}_j = \mathbf{A}_r \mathbf{u}'_i \cdot \mathbf{B} \mathbf{E}_j \tag{71.64}$$

therefore eqs. (71.52) and (71.53) become,

$$R_{ij} = \frac{-iK_0}{2 \cos \varphi} \int_0^a e^{-iK_0 x'_3 \cos \varphi} \mathbf{u}'_i \cdot \mathbf{B}(x'_3) \mathbf{E}_j(x'_3) dx'_3 \quad , \quad (i,j = 1,2) \quad , \tag{71.65}$$

$$T_{ij} = \delta_{ij} + \frac{-iK_0}{2 \cos \varphi} \int_0^a e^{iK_0 x'_3 \cos \varphi} \mathbf{u}_i \cdot \mathbf{B}(x'_3) \mathbf{E}_j(x'_3) dx'_3 \quad , \quad (i,j = 1,2) \quad , \tag{71.66}$$

We remark that even though these formulae depend on the field **E**, which is a solution to the integral equation (71.33), the R_{ij} and T_{ij} can be approximated by knowing an approximate solution to eq. (71.33).

72. FUNCTIONAL ANALYSIS AND VARIATIONAL FORMULAE

The concepts and formulas that one uses in ordinary vector analysis can be generalized in a formal way. In what follows it will be convenient for us to think of the formal operations as vector analyses in function space. Here the points or vectors are the collection of functions $(\mathbf{f}, \mathbf{g}, \mathbf{h}, \ldots)$ defined over the domain (x_1, x_2, x_3) with sufficient differentiable properties. We first define the operation of inner or scalar product of two vectors, assuming that the ordinary rules, *i.e.*, commutative, associative, etc. hold for the elements **f**, **g**, ... The existence of an identity and null element is also presumed. Thus if **f** and **h** are any two elements the inner product is defined by the rule,

$$(\alpha\mathbf{f}, \mathbf{h}) = \alpha^*(\mathbf{f}, \mathbf{h}) \quad ,$$

where α is any complex scalar,

$$\left.\begin{aligned} (\mathbf{f} + \mathbf{h}, \mathbf{g}) &= (\mathbf{f}, \mathbf{g}) + (\mathbf{h}, \mathbf{g}) \quad , \\ (\mathbf{f}, \mathbf{h}) &= (\mathbf{h}, \mathbf{f})^* \quad , \\ (\mathbf{f}, \mathbf{f}) &> 0 \\ (\mathbf{f}, \mathbf{f}) &= 0 \text{ if and only if } \mathbf{f} \equiv 0 \quad . \end{aligned}\right\} \quad (72.1)$$

The notion of linear operator is already known but for completeness we give its defining property. The operator **K** is linear if for any two complex scalars α, β and any element **f** in the space, **Kf** belongs to the space and

$$\mathbf{K}(\alpha\mathbf{f} + \beta\mathbf{h}) = \alpha\mathbf{K}\mathbf{f} + \beta\mathbf{K}\mathbf{h} \quad (72.2)$$

so that the vector $\alpha\mathbf{f} + \beta\mathbf{h}$ is transformed into an element of the same space. In order to find variational principles we must also introduce the concept of the "adjoint" operator to **K** denoted by $\mathbf{K}'$ and defined by the property

$$(\mathbf{K}'\mathbf{f}, \mathbf{h}) = (\mathbf{f}, \mathbf{K}\mathbf{h}) \quad . \quad (72.3)$$

Now consider two linear operators $\mathbf{K}$ and $\mathbf{H}$; by definition

$$\mathbf{HKf} = \mathbf{H}(\mathbf{Kf}) \quad , \tag{72.4}$$

and its adjoint is $\mathbf{K}'\mathbf{H}'$. To make these formulas more concrete let $\mathbf{K}(x_3, x_3')$ be a matrix function of the variables shown and let $\mathbf{f}(x_3')$ be a vector function of position, then

$$\mathbf{Kf} = \int_0^a \mathbf{K}(x_3, x_3')\mathbf{f}(x_3')dx_3' \quad , \tag{72.5}$$

$$(\mathbf{f}, \mathbf{h}) = \int_0^a \mathbf{f} \cdot \mathbf{h}\, dx_3' \ , \tag{72.6}$$

and if $\mathbf{K}$ is a square matrix function of x_3' alone

$$(\mathbf{K}'\mathbf{f}, \mathbf{h}) = \int_0^a (\mathbf{K}'\mathbf{f})^* \cdot \mathbf{h} dx_3' = \int_0^a \mathbf{f}^* \cdot \mathbf{Kh} dx_3' = (\mathbf{f}, \mathbf{Kh}) \ , \tag{72.7}$$

where $\mathbf{K}'$ means that we interchange rows and columns of the square matrix and take the complex conjugate of all the elements. If $\mathbf{K}$ is a square matrix function of (x_3, x_3') the adjoint operation is defined by

$$\mathbf{K}'\mathbf{f} = \int_0^a \mathbf{K}'(x_3, x_3')\mathbf{f}(x_3)dx_3 \quad , \tag{72.8}$$

and finally,

$$(\mathbf{K}'\mathbf{f}, \mathbf{h}) = \int_0^a dx_3' \int_0^a \mathbf{K}'^*(x_3, x_3')\mathbf{f}^*(x_3) \cdot \mathbf{h}(x_3')dx_3$$

$$= \int_0^a dx_3 \mathbf{f}^*(x_3) \cdot \int_0^a \mathbf{K}(x_3, x_3')\mathbf{h}(x_3')dx_3' = (\mathbf{f}, \mathbf{Kh}) \ . \tag{72.9}$$

To find a form which is stationary with respect to small changes about some vector we consider $\mathbf{f}_0$ and $\mathbf{f}_0'$ as fixed vectors and two linear operators $\mathbf{K}$ and $\mathbf{H}$ such that

$$\mathbf{f}_0 = \mathbf{KHF} \quad , \tag{72.10}$$

$$\mathbf{f}_0' = \mathbf{K}'\mathbf{H}'\mathbf{F}' . \tag{72.11}$$

Let ϵ, ϵ' be two independent complex parameters which are not functions of the vectors $(\mathbf{f},\mathbf{h},\ldots)$, and put

$$\mathbf{f} = \mathbf{F} + \epsilon\mathbf{h} \quad , \tag{72.12}$$

$$\mathbf{f}' = \mathbf{F}' + \epsilon'\mathbf{h}' \quad , \tag{72.13}$$

where $\mathbf{h}$ and $\mathbf{h}'$ are arbitrary vectors of the space, then the functional defined by

$$I(\mathbf{f},\mathbf{f}') = \frac{(\mathbf{H}'\mathbf{f}',\mathbf{f}_0)(\mathbf{f}_0',\mathbf{H}\mathbf{f})}{(\mathbf{f}'\mathbf{H}\mathbf{K}\mathbf{H}\mathbf{f})} \tag{72.14}$$

is stationary with respect to arbitrary but small variations* in $\mathbf{f}$ and $\mathbf{f}'$. Since $I(\mathbf{f},\mathbf{f}')$ is complex the concept of stationary in the sense of maximum or minimum is meaningless. By stationary we mean the relations

$$\left.\begin{aligned} \frac{\partial}{\partial\epsilon} I(\mathbf{F} + \epsilon\mathbf{h} \,,\, \mathbf{F}' + \epsilon'\mathbf{h}')\Big|_{\epsilon'=0} &= 0 \quad , \quad \text{for all } \epsilon \quad , \\ \frac{\partial}{\partial\epsilon'} I(\mathbf{F} + \epsilon\mathbf{h} \,,\, \mathbf{F}' + \epsilon'\mathbf{h})\Big|_{\epsilon=0} &= 0 \quad , \quad \text{for all } \epsilon' \quad , \end{aligned}\right\} \tag{72.15}$$

must hold simultaneously. For the form defined by eq. (72.14) the above relations are easily verified. At the stationary point we also have after setting $\epsilon = \epsilon' = 0$,

$$I(\mathbf{F},\mathbf{F}') = \frac{(\mathbf{H}'\mathbf{F}',\mathbf{f}_0)(\mathbf{f}_0',\mathbf{H}\mathbf{F})}{(\mathbf{F}'\mathbf{H}\mathbf{K}\mathbf{H}\mathbf{F})} = (\mathbf{f}_0',\mathbf{H}\mathbf{F}) = (\mathbf{H}'\mathbf{F}',\mathbf{f}_0) \quad . \tag{72.16}$$

To derive a stationary form for R_{ij} we replace $\mathbf{f}_0$ by $\mathbf{f}_j$ $(j = 1,2)$, so that the fixed vector $\mathbf{f}_0$ is either one of the two fixed vectors $\mathbf{f}_{0j}$, and the fixed vector $\mathbf{f}_0'$ is either one of the fixed vectors $\mathbf{f}_{0i}$, $(i = 1,2)$, whereas the variable vectors $\mathbf{f}$ and $\mathbf{f}'$ are replaced by either one of the two vectors $\mathbf{f}_j$ $(j = 1,2)$ and $\mathbf{f}_i'$ $(i = 1,2)$ respectively. We then obtain four different functionals

* See for example, M. Lax, "A Variational Principle for Non-Conservative Collisions," Phys. Rev. 78, pp. 306-307 (1950).

$$I(\mathbf{f}_j,\mathbf{f}'_i) = \frac{(\mathbf{H}'\mathbf{f}'_i,\mathbf{f}_{0j})(\mathbf{f}'_{0i},\mathbf{H}\mathbf{f}_j)}{(\mathbf{f}'_i,\mathbf{HKH}\mathbf{f}_j)} , \quad (i,j = 1,2) , \tag{72.17}$$

hence, $I(\mathbf{f}_j,\mathbf{f}'_i)$ is stationary with respect to small variations in $\mathbf{f}_j$ and $\mathbf{f}'_i$ about $\mathbf{F}_j$ and $\mathbf{F}'_i$ where

$$\mathbf{f}_{0j} = \mathbf{KHF}_j , \quad (j = 1,2) , \tag{72.18}$$

$$\mathbf{f}'_{0i} = \mathbf{K}'\mathbf{H}'\mathbf{F}'_i , \quad (i = 1,2) . \tag{72.19}$$

At the stationary point we write

$$I_{ij} \equiv I(\mathbf{F}_j,\mathbf{F}'_i) = \frac{(\mathbf{H}'\mathbf{F}'_i,\mathbf{f}_{0j})(\mathbf{f}'_{0i},\mathbf{H}\mathbf{f}_j)}{(\mathbf{F}'_i,\mathbf{HKHF}_j)} = (\mathbf{f}'_{0i},\mathbf{HF}_j) = (\mathbf{H}'\mathbf{F}'_i,\mathbf{F}_j) , \quad (i,j = 1,2) . \tag{72.20}$$

In eq. (71.65) we make the following identifications (or correspondences),

$$\mathbf{f}'_{0i} \longleftrightarrow \mathbf{u}'_i e^{iK_0 x_3 \cos\varphi} , \tag{72.21}$$

$$\mathbf{H} \longleftrightarrow \frac{-iK_0}{2\cos\varphi}\mathbf{B}(x_3) , \tag{72.22}$$

$$\mathbf{F}_j \longleftrightarrow \mathbf{E}_j(x_3) , \tag{72.23}$$

hence,

$$R_{ij} = (\mathbf{f}'_{0i},\mathbf{HF}_j) . \tag{72.24}$$

But since $\mathbf{E}_j(x_3)$ satisfies the integral equation

$$\mathbf{u}_j e^{-iK_0 x_3 \cos\varphi} = (\mathbf{I} + \mathbf{L}(x_3))\mathbf{E}_j(x_3) + \frac{iK_0}{2\cos\varphi}\int_0^a e^{-iK_0|x_3-x'_3|\cos\varphi}\mathbf{A}(x_3,x'_3)\mathbf{B}(x'_3)\mathbf{E}_j(x'_3)dx'_3 , \quad (j = 1,2) , \tag{72.25}$$

then

$$\mathbf{f}_{0j} \longleftrightarrow \mathbf{u}_j e^{-iK_0 x_3\cos\varphi} \longleftrightarrow \mathbf{KHF}_j , \quad (j = 1,2) . \tag{72.26}$$

Also if

$$\mathbf{KH} \leftrightarrow (\mathbf{I} + \mathbf{L}(x_3)) + \frac{iK_0}{2\cos\varphi}\int_0^a e^{-iK_0|x_3-x_3'|\cos\varphi}\mathbf{A}(x_3,x_3')\mathbf{B}(x_3')dx_3' \quad , \qquad (72.27)$$

and from eq. (72.22), we find

$$\mathbf{K} \leftrightarrow [\mathbf{I} + \mathbf{L}(x_3)]\,\frac{2\cos\varphi}{-iK_0}\mathbf{B}^{-1}(x_3) - \int_0^a e^{-iK_0|x_3-x_3'|\cos\varphi}\mathbf{A}(x_3,x_3')dx_3 \quad .^* \qquad (72.28)$$

To complete the identification we must construct the adjoint operators $\mathbf{K}'$ and $\mathbf{H}'$. From eq. (72.22) we have

$$\mathbf{H}' \leftrightarrow \frac{iK_0}{2\cos\varphi}\mathbf{B}'(x_3) \quad , \qquad (72.29)$$

and from eq. (72 28),

$$\mathbf{K}' \leftrightarrow \frac{2\cos\varphi}{iK_0}\mathbf{B}'^{-1}[\mathbf{I} + \mathbf{L}'(x_3)] - \int_0^a e^{iK_0|x_3-x_3'|\cos\varphi}\mathbf{A}(x_3',x_3)dx_3' \quad , \qquad (72.30)$$

since $\mathbf{A}(x_3,x_3')$ is real and symmetric, $\mathbf{A}'(x_3',x_3) = \mathbf{A}(x_3',x_3)$; therefore we can write

$$\mathbf{K}'\mathbf{H}' \leftrightarrow [\mathbf{I} + \mathbf{B}'^{-1}(x_3)\mathbf{L}'(x_3)\mathbf{B}'(x_3)] - \frac{iK_0}{2\cos\varphi}\int_0^a e^{iK_0|x_3-x_3'|\cos\varphi}\mathbf{A}(x_3',x_3)\mathbf{B}'(x_3')dx_3' \quad . \qquad (72.31)$$

From eqs. (71.28) and (71.31) we get

$$\mathbf{B}'^{-1}\mathbf{L}'\mathbf{B}' = \begin{pmatrix} 0 & 0 & 0 \\ 0 & 0 & 0 \\ 0 & 0 & 1 \end{pmatrix}\mathbf{B}' = \begin{pmatrix} 0 & 0 & 0 \\ 0 & 0 & 0 \\ B_{31}' & B_{32}' & B_{33}' \end{pmatrix} \equiv \hat{\mathbf{L}}(x_3) \quad , \qquad (72.32)$$

---

* No confusion should arise here between the use of **K** in Eq. (71.34) and (72.28); the **K** used in the latter is to be identified with that used in the variational formulas.

and eq. (72.31) becomes

$$\mathbf{K'H'} \longleftrightarrow [\mathbf{I} + \hat{\mathbf{L}}(x_3)] - \frac{iK_0}{2\cos\varphi}\int_0^a e^{iK_0|x_3-x_3'|\cos\varphi}\mathbf{A}(x_3',x_3)\mathbf{B}'(x_3')dx_3' \quad . \quad (72.33)$$

Using eqs. (72.19), (72.21), (72.33) and putting

$$\mathbf{F}_i' \longleftrightarrow \mathbf{E}_i'(x_3) \quad , \quad (72\ 34)$$

we arrive at the "adjoint" equation of (72.25),

$$\mathbf{u}_i' e^{iK_0 x_3 \cos\varphi} = [\mathbf{I} + \hat{\mathbf{L}}(x_3)]\,\mathbf{E}_i'(x_3)$$

$$- \frac{iK_0}{2\cos\varphi}\int_0^a e^{iK_0|x_3-x_3'|\cos\varphi}\mathbf{A}(x_3',x_3)\mathbf{B}'(x_3')\mathbf{E}_i'(x_3')dx_3' \quad , \quad (i = 1,2) \quad .$$

(72.35)

From eqs. (72.20) and (72.24) we finally obtain

$$R_{ij} = \frac{(\mathbf{H}'\mathbf{F}_i', \mathbf{f}_{0j})(\mathbf{f}_{0i}', \mathbf{HF}_j)}{(\mathbf{F}', \mathbf{HKHF}_j)} \quad , \quad (72.36)$$

as the variational form for the reflection matrix. By direct substitution we obtain explicitly,

$$R_{ij} = \frac{-iK_0}{2\cos\varphi}\,\frac{\left(\int_0^a e^{-iK_0x_3\cos\varphi}\,\mathbf{u}_j\cdot\mathbf{B}'^*(x_3)\mathbf{E}'^*(x_3)dx_3\right)\left(\int_0^a e^{iK_0x_3\cos\varphi}\,\mathbf{u}_i'\cdot\mathbf{B}(x_3)\mathbf{E}_j(x_3)dx_3\right)}{\left\{\int_0^a \mathbf{E}_i'^*(x_3)\cdot\mathbf{B}(x_3)\,[\mathbf{I}+\mathbf{L}(x_3)]\,\mathbf{E}_j(x_3)dx_3 + \frac{iK_0}{2\cos\varphi}\int_0^a\int_0^a e^{-iK_0|x_3-x_3'|\cos\varphi}\mathbf{E}'^*_i(x_3)\mathbf{A}(x_3,x_3')\mathbf{B}(x_3')\mathbf{E}_j(x_3')dx_3'dx_3\right\}}$$

$(i,j = 1,2)$

(72.37)

In eq. (71.66) we put

$$S_{ij} = \frac{-iK_0}{2\cos\varphi}\int_0^a e^{iK_0x_3\cos\varphi}\,\mathbf{u}_i\cdot\mathbf{B}(x_3)\mathbf{E}_j(x_3)dx_3 \quad , \quad (72.38)$$

and if we also set

$$\mathbf{f}'_{0\,i} \longleftrightarrow \mathbf{u}_i e^{-iK_0 x_3 \cos\varphi} \quad , \tag{72.39}$$

$$\mathbf{F}'_i \longleftrightarrow \mathbf{E}'_i(x_3) \quad , \tag{72.40}$$

where $\mathbf{F}'_i$ satisfies eq. (72.19), we find

$$S_{ij} = (\mathbf{f}'_{0\,i}, \mathbf{HF}_j) \quad . \tag{72.41}$$

It is a consequence of eq. (72.19) together with (72.23) and (72.39) that the vector $\mathbf{E}'_i(x_3)$ satisfies

$$\mathbf{u}_i e^{-iK_0 x_3 \cos\varphi} \equiv [\mathbf{I} + \hat{\mathbf{L}}(x_3)]\mathbf{E}'_i(x_3) - \frac{iK_0}{2\cos\varphi}\int_0^a e^{iK_0 |x_3 - x'_3| \cos\varphi}\mathbf{A}(x'_3, x_3)\mathbf{B}'(x'_3)\mathbf{E}'_i(x'_3)dx'_3 \quad , \tag{72.42}$$

which is the equation adjoint to eq. (72.25) only the left side of (72.42) differs from that in eq. (72.35) for R_{ij}. From eq. (72.20) and (72.41) we obtain the variational expression for S_{ij}, namely,

$$S_{ij} = \frac{(\mathbf{H}'\mathbf{F}'_i, \mathbf{f}_{0\,j})(\mathbf{f}'_{0\,i}, \mathbf{HF}_j)}{(\mathbf{F}'_i, \mathbf{HKHF}_j)} \tag{72.43}$$

and explicitly

$$S_{ij} = \frac{-iK_0}{2\cos\varphi}\frac{\left(\int_0^a e^{-iK_0 x_3 \cos\varphi}\mathbf{u}_j \cdot \mathbf{B}'^*(x_3)\mathbf{E}'^*_i(x_3)dx_3\right)\left(\int_0^a e^{iK_0 x_3 \cos\varphi}\mathbf{u}_i \cdot \mathbf{B}(x_3)\mathbf{E}_j(x_3)dx_3\right)}{\left\{\int_0^a \mathbf{E}'^*_i(x_3) \cdot \mathbf{B}(x_3)[\mathbf{I} + \mathbf{L}(x_3)]\mathbf{E}_j(x_3)dx_3 + \frac{iK_0}{2\cos\varphi}\int_0^a\int_0^a e^{-iK_0 |x_3 - x'_3| \cos\varphi}\mathbf{E}'^*_i(x_3) \cdot \mathbf{B}(x_3)\mathbf{A}(x_3, x'_3)\mathbf{B}(x'_3)\mathbf{E}_j(x'_3)dx'_3 dx_3\right\}} \quad ,$$

$$(i,j = 1,2) . \tag{72.44}$$

The formulas (72.37) and (72.44) give the required variational expressions for the reflection and transmission matrices, the latter is given by $T_{ij} = \delta_{ij} + S_{ij}$. If we know the solutions of the integral equation (72.25) and the adjoint equations (72.35) and (72.42), eqs. (72.36) and (72.44) yield the exact values for the reflection and transmission matrices. However, if we have only a trial solution of these equations the formulas (72.36) and (72.44) are stationary with respect to small variations of these trial solutions from the exact solutions. These trial solutions yield approximate values of R_{ij} and T_{ij} which are closer to the true values than those obtained by eqs. (71.65) and (71.66). This is in essence one of the significant values of the variational formulae.

It should be clear to the reader from the foregoing sections that there is no royal road to the solution of problems involving inhomogeneities and except for specialized and trivial cases exact and closed form solutions are rare. However one should not despair since there exists approximate methods which can be brought to bear on the problems in this area and much yet remains to be done.

BIBLIOGRAPHIES

1. Argence, E., On the Absorption of Short Waves in an Isotropic Ionized Medium, Supplement, Il Nuovo Cimento, Vol. 4, Series 10, No. 4, 2nd Semester (1956).

2. Bachynski, M. P., Nature of Electromagnetic Waves in Nonhomogeneous, Anisotropic Plasmas, RCA Victor Co., Ltd., Res. Labs., Montreal, Canada, Res. Rep. No. 7-801,7 (June 1960).

3. Bailey, V. A., Reflection of Waves by an Inhomogeneous Medius Phys., Rec., Vol. 96, p. 855 (1954).

4. Bolie, V. W., Electromagnetic Propagation in an Almost Homogeneous Medium, Austral. J. of Phys., Vol. 11, pp. 118-125 (1958).

5. Cap, F. and Rover, W., loc. cit. Chapter I.

6. Davids, N., Optic Axis and Critical Coupling in the Ionosphere, J. Geophys. Res. Vol. 58, No. 3, pp. 311-321 (Sept. 1953).

7. de Francia, G. Toraldo, Variational Principles for Reflection Coefficient from Potential Barrier, Il Nuovo Cimento, Vol. 7, No. 3, p. 255 (May 1950).

8. Denisov, N. G., On the Problem of the Absorption of Electromagnetic Waves Within the Resonance Ranges of an Inhomogeneous Plasma, Zh. Eksp. i teor Fiz, Vol. 34, No. 2, pp. 528-529 (1958).

9. Denisov, N. G., On a Singularity of the Field of an Electromagnetic Wave Propagated in an Inhomogeneous Plasma, Zh. Eksper teor Fiz., Vol. 31, p. 609 (1956).

10. Epstein, P. S., Reflection of Waves in an Inhomogeneous Absorbing Medium, Proc. Nat. Acad. Sci. Am. Vol. 16, p. 627 (1930).

11. Epstein, P. S., Geometrical Optics in Absorbing Media, Proc. Nat. Acad. Sci. Amer. Vol. 16, pp. 37-45 (1930).

12. Ferraro, V. C. A. and Plumpton, C., Hydromagnetic Waves in a Horizontally Stratified Atmosphere, Astrophys. J. Vol. 127, pp. 459-76 (1958).

13. Flammer, C., Electromagnetic Wave Propagation in a Medium with Variable Dielectric Constant $1 + Kr^{-1}$. Stanford Res. Inst., Menlo Park, Cal., TR 63, AFCRC-TN-57-584, AF 19(604)-1296, Project SRI-1197 (Jan. 1958), (ASTIA AD-133,624).

14. Forsterling, K., On Reflection in a Non-homogeneous Medium, Ann. Phys. 11, p. 1 (1931), also 8 (New Series) p. 129 (1950).

15. Friedman, B. F., Propagation in a Non-Homogeneous Atmosphere, Theory of Electromagnetic Waves, Academic Press, N.Y. (1951).

16. Gunsburg, V. L., On the Influence of The Earth's Magnetic Field on the Reflection of Radio Waves from the Ionosphere, Jour. of Physics (U.S.S.R.), Vol. 7, No. 6 (1943).

17. Hartree, D. R., Optical and Equivalent Paths in a Stratified Medium Treated from a Wave Standpoint, Proc. Roy. Soc. A, 131, p. 427 (1931).

18. Herlofson, N., Plasma Resonance in Ionospheric Irregularities, Arkiv. f. Fysik, Vol. 3, No. 15, pp. 247-297 (1951).

19. Hines, C. O., Reflection of Waves from Varying Media, Quart. APPL Math. Vol. 11, p. 9 (1953).

20. Khiznyak, N. A., The Green's Function for Maxwell's Electromagnetic Equations for Inhomogeneous Media, Zh. Tekhn. Fiz., Vol. 28, No. 7, pp. 1592-1609 (1958).

21. Klein, M., et al., Interaction of Non-Uniform Plasma with Microwave Radiation, General Electric Co. (Missile and Space Vehicle Dept.) Report R59SD467 (Nov. 1959).

22. Lurye, J. R., Electromagnetic Scattering Matrices of Stratified Anisotropic Media, New York Univ. Math. Res. Group, Res. Rep. No. EM-31 (May 1951).

23. Ludford, G. S. S., The Transmission of Electromagnetic Waves in the Presence of a Conducting Layer of Gas, Univ. of Maryland, Inst. of Fluid Dynamics and Appl. Math., College Park, Md. TN BN-160 (Feb. 1959), AFOSR TN-59-159 (ASTIA AD-211,118).

24. Osterberg, H., Propagation of Plane Electromagnetic Waves in Inhomogeneous Media, J. Opt. Soc. Amer., Vol. 48, No. 8, pp. 513-521 (August 1958).

25. Penico, A. J., Propagation of Electromagnetic Waves in a Plasma with an Inhomogeneous Electron Density, Proc. of Symp. on the Plasma Sheath, AFCRC-TR-60-108(1) (1960).

26. Rydbeck, O. E. H., On the Propagation of Radio Waves, Trans. Chalmers Inst. Tech., Gothenburg, No. 34 (1950).

27. Rydbeck, O. E. H., The Reflection of Electromagnetic Waves from a Parabolic Ionized Layer, Phil. Mag. 34, p. 342 (1943).

28. Rydbeck, O. E. H., On the Propagation of Waves in an Inhomogeneous Medium, Chalmers Tek. Högsk. Handl. No. 74 (1948).

29. Schelkunoff, S. A., Remarks Concerning Wave Propagation in Stratified Media Comm. Pure APPL. Math. Vol. 4, p. 117 (1951).

30. Stix, T. H., Absorption of Plasma Waves, The Physics of Fluids, Vol. 3, No. 1, pp. 19-32 (Jan.-Feb. 1960).

31. Wait, J. R., Transmission and Reflection of Electromagnetic Waves in the Presence of Stratified Media, Commerce Dept., NBS, Boulder, Colo. Boulder Labs. R-5541 (Nov. 1957).

32. Wait, J. R., Transmission and Reflection of Electromagnetic Waves in the Presence of Stratified Media, J. of Res. N.B.S. Vol. 61, No. 3, Res. Paper 2899, pp. 205-232 (Sept. 1958).

33. Weyman, R. and Howard, R., Note on Hydromagnetic Waves Passing Through an Atmosphere with a Density Gradient, Astrophys. J., Vol. 128, p. 142 (1958).

34. Wilkes, M. V., Oblique Reflection of Very Long Wireless Waves from the Ionosphere, Proc. Roy. Soc. 187, pp. 130-147 (1947).

35. Yabroff, I. W., Reflection at a Sharply Bounded Ionosphere, Proc. IRE, N.Y., Vol. 45, p. 750 (1957).

GENERAL BIBLIOGRAPHIES

1. Bachynski, M. P., et al., Plasmas and the Electromagnetic Field, Canadian Armament Res. and Dev. Establishment, Quebec (Jan. 1959).

2. Born, M. and Wolf, E.

3. Bremmer, H.

4. Bremmer, H., Propagation of Electromagnetic Waves. Handbuch der Physik, Vol. 16 (1958).

5. Budden, K. G.

6. Clauser, F. H.

7. Kerr, D., Propagation of Short Radio Waves, Radiation Lab. Series, McGraw-Hill, N.Y.

8. Landau and Lifshitz, Electrodynamics ...,.

9. Linhart, J. G., Plasma Physics, North-Holland Pub. Co., Amsterdam (1960).

10. Sommerfeld, A., Optics.

11. Stratton, J. A.

12. Wait, J. R., A Survey and Bibliography of Recent Research in the Propagation of VLF Radio Waves, Tech. Note No. 58, NBS, Boulder Labs, Boulder, Colo. (May 1960).

CHAPTER VII

THE THEORY OF PROPAGATION OF RAYS IN AN INHOMOGENEOUS, ANISOTROPIC, DISPERSIVE AND ABSORBING MEDIUM

INTRODUCTORY REMARKS

73. **The Variational Principle—** In the preceding chapters one can see or at least anticipate the somewhat difficult nature of the problems associated with inhomogenous media. The additional properties of anisotropy and absorption can be expected, naturally, to further complicate the problems of propagation in such media. If we consider at first an unbounded medium so that we can ignore the complications resulting from boundary conditions there are several ways in which some insight may be gained regarding the problems of propagation. Clearly, the most natural way to proceed is via Maxwell's equations. This obvious approach would suffice for the propagation of electromagnetic oscillations. The anisotropy and absorption would then arise from the constitutive relations in which μ, ϵ, and σ the conductivity are second order tensors whose elements are in general, functions of position and frequency, besides being complex. Such a program however, is more easily stated than carried out. The full wave picture which would result from this treatment does not lend itself easily to a sharp and clear cut analysis. One is then tempted to consider some limiting situations in which the main features of a wave picture are preserved but which is less difficult to handle mathematically. In the first chapter we demonstrated such a limiting situation in the transition from a scalar wave equation to a ray picture. It would thus appear that the same formalism could be applied to the vector wave equation to obtain a simple ray theory. Such a formal approach is indeed possible but additional philosophical and computational considerations arise. These considerations are due to the introduction of the polarization of the field quantities which on the other hand does not enter into the treatment of the scalar wave equation.

We recall that the ray theory as developed from the scalar wave equation is characterized by a single scalar function of position. That is, the refractive index is a scalar function of position alone. Consequently, the rays which are derived from such a function are the "geodesics" for an isotropic medium. On the contrary, the ray theory which would result from the full vector wave equation can not be expected to be derivable from a single scalar function of position. The vector wave equation should yield in the transition an "Eikonal Matrix" which would then constitute the generalization of the single scalar Eikonal equation. The determination of the rays from the more general vector Eikonal equation is not a simple task and for this reason it is suggestive to seek a somewhat different approach in which the mathematical analysis is simpler, but which will retain some of the flavor of the wave picture. Fortunately, since about a century the apparatus for such an approach already exists. The original researches of Sir William Rowan Hamilton provide the basis, as they have in so many other branches of physics and mathematics, for the development of the simplified approach.

This approach was recognized by J. Haselgrove in 1955 who derived a compact formulation of the theory for the study of ray propagation in the ionosphere under the influence of an external magnetic field. The origin of the formulation and method of approach has its roots in Hamilton's classical work in optics and mechanics. Haselgrove, in her development of the theory, followed the patterns laid out by J. L. Synge. Synge's development, which is clearly the most elegant, formulated the theory of propagation of rays in anisotropic, inhomogeneous media for other purposes. Namely, for the study of De Broglie waves, and he appropriately called it a theory of geometrical mechanics, and which incorporated relativistic considerations.

We have utilized the formulation and developments of both Synge and Haselgrove to generalize the theory in an obvious way to include a frequency dependence and absorption. This generalization has since found its way in applications, one of which is in the study of whistling atmospherics. Its utility in the more recently developed theories of magnetohydrodynamics, electron optics, seismic theory, sound theory, and plasma waves in general is under serious study. Ray theoretic methods in the study of propagation of weak hydromagnetic discontinuities have proved to be quite useful already. Although the use of ray theoretic methods in gaseous flow problems and electromagnetics is not new by any means, a clear and detailed exposition of a self contained theory for absorbing, dispersiv inhomogeneous, anisotropic media is in order. It is hoped that the followi exposition will prove to be a step in that direction.

In the exposition we will attempt to disclose many interesting, important and useful relations both from a physical and mathematical point of view. In order to aid the reader in the understanding we shall whenever possible inject the wave theoretic background. It should be mentioned that a ray theoretic development of propagation should not be divorced from the wave theory concepts since they are intimately bound to each other. This intimate connection as is already so well known in quantum mechanics and which formed the basis of Schroedinger's equation will be put into evidence in the exposition. The duality of rays and waves is inherent in the theory when properly interpreted. The reader may well be familiar with the standard derivations of Hamilton's canonical equations in mechanics and hence at first sight may also wonder why we are deriving them again. The reason is that the derivation that we shall give is more closely tied to Hamilton's work in optics and provides a useful geometrical background. In the usual treatments in mechanics, this geometric background is somewhat ignored, and the derivations become purely formal. It is precisely these geometrical aspects which prove to be of great value that we want to stress. Moveover, the derivation of Hamilton's equations in our treatment does not imitate completely those of mechanics. Besides, the ultimate aim here is not just the attainment of canonical equations.

In order to extend the scope of applicability of the development we shall derive in detail the structure of Hamilton's equations for a general curvilinear coordinate system. This entails the use of the concepts and methods of the tensor calculus which appears to be the most effective and simplest manner of approach. However, in order not to strain the reader's patience, the derivation will be couched in the language of vector analysis so that the treatment will not appear to be too formal. Finally, wherever it appears to be fruitful we shall illuminate the formulas with examples or discussion.

The basis of a pure ray theory is the so-called "Fermat's Principle." This principle postulated historically that in a given medium which is characterized by an "index function," *i.e.*, an index of refraction, the time of propagation of a ray of light between two fixed points in the medium is a minimum. The principle when stated in this form is rather ambiguous. Nevertheless we shall adopt the essence of the principle but will modify it and make precise its meaning. We shall assume that the medium under consideration is characterized by an index function of position $\mathbf{r}$, and direction $\boldsymbol{a}$ which we denote by $M(\mathbf{r}, \boldsymbol{a})$. This is an invariant (scalar) function of six parameters, three of them specifying the position $\mathbf{r}$ and three of them specifying the direction $\boldsymbol{a}$. The function $M(\mathbf{r}, \boldsymbol{a})$ is called the ray refractive index. The inhomogeneity is characterized by the positional dependence of M on $\mathbf{r}$, and the anisotropy of the medium by the dependence on the direction vector $\boldsymbol{a}$. Physically, the significance of M is that it is the ratio of the speed of light propagation in some reference medium (say, vacuum) to the speed of propagation along the ray in the medium. The vector $\boldsymbol{a}$ defines the direction of the ray at the point $\mathbf{r}$. We have already seen examples of the directional dependence of an index in Chapter II, *i.e.*, the indices of ordinary and extraordinary wave propagation as obtained from the Appleton-Hartree equations. The inhomogeneous property in this example is obtained by allowing the electron density, appearing in those expressions, to be functions of position. However, the directional dependence in the aforementioned example is in terms of the wave normal direction, *i.e.*, the vector defining the normal to the surfaces of constant phase, which as we shall see does not coincide with the ray direction.

It will be convenient at first to let $\mathbf{r}$ and $\boldsymbol{a}$ be referred to a right handed rectangular cartesian coordinate system so that $\mathbf{r} \equiv (x_1, x_2, x_3)$ and the line element is defined by

$$ds^2 = d\mathbf{r} \cdot d\mathbf{r} = dx_1^2 + dx_2^2 + dx_3^2 \quad . \tag{73.1}$$

The direction vector $\boldsymbol{a}$ of a ray at the point $\mathbf{r}$ is then defined by

$$\boldsymbol{a} = \frac{d\mathbf{r}}{ds} \tag{73.2}$$

so that $\boldsymbol{a}$ is the tangent vector to the ray and is therefore normalized by the identity,

$$\boldsymbol{a} \cdot \boldsymbol{a} = 1 \quad . \tag{73.3}$$

This normalization of $\boldsymbol{a}$ will be used advantageously in the subsequent discussion. We shall assume that $M(\mathbf{r}, \boldsymbol{a})$ is a homogeneous function of degree one in $\boldsymbol{a}$. That is, if λ is an arbitrary but positive parameter,

$$M(\mathbf{r}, \lambda\boldsymbol{a}) = \lambda M(\mathbf{r}, \boldsymbol{a}) \quad . \tag{73.4}$$

If the index is not initially homogeneous of degree one in $\boldsymbol{\alpha}$ it can always be made so by using the normalization condition on $\boldsymbol{\alpha}$. More specifically, when we assert that M is a function of position and direction, it is sufficient to define the directional dependence by giving only the ratios, say α_1/α_3, α_2/α_3. Consequently, when M is defined in these terms it is a homogeneous function of degree zero in the α_i. Thus, if we define a new index $\overline{M}(\mathbf{r}, \boldsymbol{\alpha})$ by the formula

$$\overline{M}(\mathbf{r}, \boldsymbol{\alpha}) = M\left(\mathbf{r}, \frac{\alpha_1}{\alpha_3}, \frac{\alpha_2}{\alpha_3}\right)\sqrt{\boldsymbol{\alpha}\cdot\boldsymbol{\alpha}} \tag{73.5}$$

we have then an homogeneous function of degree one in the α_i. In what follows we shall assume that such a homogenization has been effected and henceforth omit the bar notation.

The reason behind the construction of this homogenization stems not so much from mathematical convenience alone but rather from a more fundamental consideration. It stems from the requirement to be able to label points on a ray independent of the mode of parameterization. This statement will be made clear subsequently.

The basis of the pure ray theory is now postulated according to the variational principle,

$$\delta\int_{P_1}^{P_2} M(\mathbf{r}, \boldsymbol{\alpha})ds = 0 , \tag{73.6}$$

where δ is the sign of variation, P_1 and P_2 are two fixed points of the medium. In words, it states that we are seeking all curves,

$$C: \quad \mathbf{r} = \mathbf{r}(s) \tag{73.7}$$

which make the first variation of the integral of (73.6) vanish. In this sense, all we require is the stationary property of the integral with integrand M. The integral is not required to be either a maximum or a minimum. Stationary principles of this sort are common in all branches of physics. But besides being a formal tool for analytical exploitation, it has an underlying fundamental philosophy. Variational principles involve no statements about reference frames, *i.e.*, coordinate systems. They are coordinate free principles and are therefore eminently suited for the description of physical laws. A physical law by its very nature must be coordinate free. This property is also easily demonstrated by proving that the Euler-Lagrange equations, which are the necessary conditions for the first variation to vanish, transform in a covariant manner (a term which will be defined in a later section). Before we carry out the consequences of (73.6) let us examine the integral itself. From physical considerations it is clear that $M(\mathbf{r}, \boldsymbol{\alpha})$ must be a non-negative function of its parameters. If M were constant we could define $d\bar{s} = M ds$ and hence the integral $\int_{\bar{s}_1}^{\bar{s}} d\bar{s}$ is a monotone positive increasing function of its upper limit and would vanish at $\bar{s} = \bar{s}_1$. Therefore the integral defined in this way has the properties of a distance function or a metric as it is called in mathematical parlance. These same properties carry over when $M(\mathbf{r}, \boldsymbol{\alpha})$ is not constant and the integral

$$F(s) = \int_{s_1}^{s} M(\mathbf{r}, \boldsymbol{\alpha}) ds$$

can be interpreted as a distance function. The abstract geometric space associated with $F(s)$ is called a "Finsler Space" in honor of the man who developed the theory. The close connection between the properties of this space and those of Hamilton's canonical equations has been given in a very clear fashion by Synge.

We use the well known result from the calculus of variations to exhibit the necessary condition for (73.6) to hold, namely

$$\frac{d}{ds}\frac{\partial M}{\partial \boldsymbol{\alpha}} - \frac{\partial M}{\partial \mathbf{r}} = 0 \qquad (73.8)$$

which are the Euler-Lagrange equations. The notation employed in writing eq. (73.8) is equivalent to writing the three equations

$$\frac{d}{ds}\frac{\partial M}{\partial \alpha_i} - \frac{\partial M}{\partial x_i} = 0 \quad , \quad (i = 1, 2, 3) \ . \qquad (73.9)$$

However, eq. (73.8) seems more compact and we shall adopt it as far as possible. The use of the mixed vector and tensor notations should offer no difficulty in the exposition.

The use of s as a parameter is not essential for the description of eq. (73.8). In fact if we use another positive monotone parameter, say u, to describe the curve, we have

$$\frac{d\mathbf{r}}{ds} = \frac{d\mathbf{r}}{du}\frac{du}{ds} , \qquad (73.10)$$

or,

$$\boldsymbol{a} = \mathbf{r}' \frac{du}{ds} , \qquad (73.11)$$

where,

$$\mathbf{r}' = \frac{d\mathbf{r}}{du} . \qquad (73.12)$$

The homogeneity of $M(\mathbf{r}, \boldsymbol{a})$ implies the following relation.

$$M(\mathbf{r}, \boldsymbol{a}) = M\left(\mathbf{r}, \mathbf{r}' \frac{du}{ds}\right) = \frac{du}{ds} M(\mathbf{r}, \mathbf{r}') , \qquad (73.13)$$

and here, du/ds plays the role of λ in the definition, eq. (73.4). Therefore,

$$M(\mathbf{r}, \boldsymbol{a})ds = M(\mathbf{r}, \mathbf{r}') \frac{du}{ds} ds = M(\mathbf{r}, \mathbf{r}')du \qquad (73.14)$$

and the Euler-Lagrange eqs. can equally well be expressed in terms of the parameter u by

$$\frac{d}{du}\frac{\partial M(\mathbf{r}, \mathbf{r}')}{\partial \mathbf{r}'} - \frac{\partial M(\mathbf{r}, \mathbf{r}')}{\partial \mathbf{r}} = 0 . \qquad (73.15)$$

The invariance of the form of the Euler-Lagrange eqs. under a transformation of parameter from s to u is seen in this case to arise from the homogeneity of M in its second set of variables.* The curves that satisfy (73.8) or (73.15) are designated as "geodesics." A ray is now formally defined as a geodesic, *i.e.*, a solution of eq. (73.8) and having fixed

* The necessary and sufficient condition that the integral $\int_{P_1}^{P_2} M(\mathbf{r}, \boldsymbol{a})ds$ be independent of the arcs is the homogeneity condition $M(\mathbf{r}, \lambda\boldsymbol{a}) = \lambda M(\mathbf{r}, \boldsymbol{a})$, with $\lambda > 0$ for all positive numbers λ. A lucid proof of this is given in C. Caratheodory, "Variationsrechnung und Partielle Differentialgleichungen Erste Ordnung," p. 212 B. G. Teubner, Berlin, 1935.

end points. In general the function $M(\mathbf{r}, \boldsymbol{a})$ can give rise to more than a single curve which satisfies the variational principle with fixed end points. However, for the sake of keeping the exposition simple, we shall assume for the present that there exists only one curve satisfying our requirements.

Eqs. (73.8) or (73.15) are second order differential equations and we should like to simplify the description of a "ray" in terms of a simpler set of equations. Such a simplification is always possible as is well known by transforming the second order system into an equivalent first order system. The first order description has both a practical and theoretical significance. The practical aspects are reflected in the computational considerations of actually calculating a ray path. This facet of the description will be dealt with separately.

There is another motivation for seeking a simplification and this lies in the fact that we do not ordinarily know the ray refractive index, but we do have information on the phase refractive index $\mu(\mathbf{r}, \mathbf{n})$ which is a function of position $\mathbf{r}$ and "wave normal" direction $\mathbf{n}$. Consequently, we want to free ourselves of a description of the rays in terms of $M(\mathbf{r}, \boldsymbol{a})$ and obtain a description in terms of the function $\mu(\mathbf{r}, \mathbf{n})$, the known quantity. By expanding eq. (73.8) it is clear that this equation expresses the rate of change of the ray direction $d\mathbf{r}/ds$ along the ray path in terms of the index M and its derivatives, which are second order; hence it involves the curvature of the path. But since we do not know $M(\mathbf{r}, \boldsymbol{a})$ we can transform Eq. (73.8) for the curvature into equations which give the rate of change of wave normal direction $\mathbf{n}$ along the ray path in terms of the function $\mu(\mathbf{r}, \mathbf{n})$ and its derivatives. In this way we eliminate the ray refractive index and ray direction and obtain a simpler description of the ray paths.

The simplification is effected by reducing the order of the differential equations for the rays from a second-order to a first-order description by introducing the variables σ_i, $(i = 1, 2, 3)$, defined by

$$\boldsymbol{\sigma} \equiv \frac{\partial}{\partial \boldsymbol{a}} M(\mathbf{r}, \boldsymbol{a}) \quad . \tag{73.16}$$

We then solve this system of equations for the α_i in terms of the σ_i and $\mu(\mathbf{r}, \mathbf{n})$. Before we discuss how this is done we want to examine some of the implications of our assumptions. The connection between the magnitude of the vector $\boldsymbol{\sigma}$ and the phase refractive index $\mu(\mathbf{r}, \mathbf{n})$ will also be shown to be related simply. From the definition (73.16), we can write the ray equation (73.8) in the form

$$\frac{d\boldsymbol{\sigma}}{ds} = \frac{\partial M(\mathbf{r}, \boldsymbol{\alpha})}{\partial \mathbf{r}} \quad . \tag{73.17}$$

The task involved in effecting the simplification alluded to in the foregoing is to ultimately find the two vector differential equations relating $\boldsymbol{\sigma}$ and $\mathbf{r}$. Let us first take the scalar product of $\boldsymbol{\sigma}$ with $\boldsymbol{\alpha}$; using (73.16) we find

$$\boldsymbol{\alpha} \cdot \boldsymbol{\sigma} = \boldsymbol{\alpha} \cdot \frac{\partial M(\mathbf{r}, \boldsymbol{\alpha})}{\partial \boldsymbol{\alpha}} \quad . \tag{73.18}$$

Since $M(\mathbf{r}, \boldsymbol{\alpha})$ is homogeneous of degree one in $\boldsymbol{\alpha}$, Euler's theorem on homogeneous functions gives

$$\boldsymbol{\alpha} \cdot \boldsymbol{\sigma} = M(\mathbf{r}, \boldsymbol{\alpha}) \quad . \tag{73.19}$$

Alternatively, we can write eq. (73.18) in the form,

$$\frac{\boldsymbol{\alpha}}{M} \cdot \boldsymbol{\sigma} = 1 = \frac{V(\mathbf{r}, \boldsymbol{\alpha})}{V_0} \boldsymbol{\alpha} \cdot \boldsymbol{\sigma} \quad , \tag{73.20}$$

where, by definition,

$$M(\mathbf{r}, \boldsymbol{\alpha}) = \frac{V_0}{V(\mathbf{r}, \boldsymbol{\alpha})} \tag{73.21}$$

and $V(\mathbf{r}, \boldsymbol{\alpha})$ is the speed of propagation along the ray in the medium. For convenience let us put $V_0 = 1$ unless stated otherwise. This amounts to choosing the units of measure appropriately and is not essential in the development of the theory. If we now define $\mathbf{V}$ by

$$\mathbf{V}(\mathbf{r}, \boldsymbol{\alpha}) = V(\mathbf{r}, \boldsymbol{\alpha})\boldsymbol{\alpha} \tag{73.22}$$

then eq. (73.20) reads

$$\mathbf{V} \cdot \boldsymbol{\sigma} = 1 \quad . \tag{73.23}$$

This important symmetric relation stemming from the assumption of the homogeneity of $M(\mathbf{r}, \boldsymbol{a})$ contains a wealth of information. Already, the idea of duality of waves and rays is inherent. For, if $\boldsymbol{\sigma}$ is considered as defining the direction of phase propagation, the relation (73.23) intimately binds the ray direction to the wave normal direction. In mechanics of course such a relation is interpreted as binding waves and particles, where $\mathbf{V}$ would then represent the velocity of the particle, *i.e.*, it would define the trajectory of the particle. In this case M would be the Lagrangian. The duality of waves and particles of course is well known by now. However, the relation as expressed in (73.23) is not exploited much, if at all, in mechanics and we shall exhibit here the geometrical significance of this simple appearing equation.

GEOMETRICAL REPRESENTATION

It is useful to be able to visualize the vector relations above and to seek their physical significance in terms of a geometrical representation. The vectors $\boldsymbol{\sigma}$ and $\mathbf{V}$ are illustrated in Fig. 18. Since the relation between the ray refractive index $M(\mathbf{r}, \boldsymbol{a})$ and $\boldsymbol{a}$ gives rise in a natural way to the relation between M and V, it is of interest to consider the relation between the wave normal direction $\mathbf{n}$, the phase refractive index $\mu(\mathbf{r}, \mathbf{n})$, the velocity of phase propagation $\mathbf{W}(\mathbf{r}, \mathbf{n})$, M, $\mathbf{V}$ and $\boldsymbol{a}$. If $\mathbf{n}$ and $\boldsymbol{a}$ are the unit vectors in the directions of $\boldsymbol{\sigma}$ and $\mathbf{V}$ respectively and if θ is the angle between them, the speed of phase propagation in the wave normal direction, called $W(\mathbf{r}, \mathbf{n})$, is the projection of $\mathbf{V}$ on $\mathbf{n}$, that is,

$$\mathbf{V} \cdot \mathbf{n} = W(\mathbf{r}, \mathbf{n}) = V \cos \theta \quad . \tag{73.24}$$

The definition of the phase refractive index, μ, gives

$$\mu(\mathbf{r}, \mathbf{n}) = \frac{1}{W(\mathbf{r}, \mathbf{n})} \quad , \tag{73.25}$$

(we are omitting the factor V_0, since we are using V_0 as a unit of measure, as discussed before). From eqs. (73.21) and (73.23) it can be seen that

$$M(\mathbf{r},\ \boldsymbol{\alpha}) = \frac{1}{V(\mathbf{r},\ \boldsymbol{\alpha})} = |\boldsymbol{\sigma}| \cos\theta = \boldsymbol{\sigma} \cdot \boldsymbol{\alpha} \tag{73.26}$$

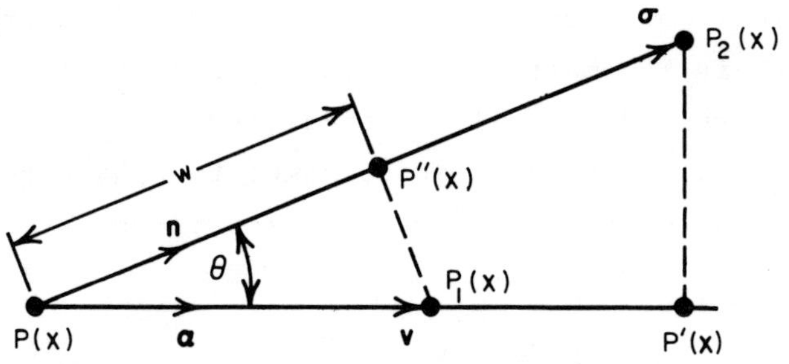

FIG. 18

Now $\mathbf{n}$ is defined by

$$\mathbf{n} = \frac{\boldsymbol{\sigma}}{|\boldsymbol{\sigma}|} \quad . \tag{73.27}$$

And, by eqs. (73.22) and (73.23),

$$\mathbf{n} \cdot \boldsymbol{\alpha} = \frac{\boldsymbol{\sigma}}{|\boldsymbol{\sigma}|} \cdot \boldsymbol{\alpha} = \frac{M}{|\boldsymbol{\sigma}|} = \frac{1}{V|\boldsymbol{\sigma}|} = \cos\theta \quad , \tag{73.28}$$

so that

$$V \cos\theta = \frac{1}{|\boldsymbol{\sigma}|} \tag{73.29}$$

and therefore from eqs. (73.24) and (73.25),

$$W = \frac{1}{|\boldsymbol{\sigma}|} = \frac{1}{\mu} \quad . \tag{73.30}$$

We conclude from this; along a ray path

$$|\sigma| = \mu \quad , \tag{73.31}$$

i.e., the magnitude of σ is equal to the phase refractive index.

RECIPROCAL SURFACES

The symmetrical equation (73.23), as stated before, reveals some interesting and useful geometrical notions. These notions will be utilized to obtain the additional vector differential equation to complete the description of the rays in terms of the phase refractive index $\mu(\mathbf{r}, \mathbf{n})$. We first note that eq. (73.23) which is repeated here for convenience,

$$\sigma \cdot \mathbf{V} = 1 \tag{73.23}$$

implies that σ and $\mathbf{V}$ are reciprocal vectors in a certain sense. Referring to the previous figure, we see that the points P'' and P_2 are reciprocal to each other. That is, if we construct a unit sphere about the point $P(\mathbf{r})$, then P'' and P_2 are inverse points with respect to this unit sphere. For, according to eq. (73.30), $\overline{PP''} \cdot \overline{PP_2} = W|\sigma| = 1$. The relationship of the points P_1, and P' is similar. A further consequence of (73.23) is obtained from the subsequent considerations.

With $P(\mathbf{r})$ fixed, let the end point of the vector $\mathbf{V}$ sweep out a surface in such a way that eq. (73.23) holds. We may consider this surface to be constructed as follows. At $P(\mathbf{r})$ we construct a local rectangular cartesian coordinate system. Then, since $P(\mathbf{r})$ is fixed, $\mathbf{V}(\mathbf{r}, \boldsymbol{a})$ is a function of the direction $\boldsymbol{a}$. Now for each direction $\boldsymbol{a}$ at $\mathbf{r}$ mark off a distance, say s, which is numerically equal to the magnitude of $\mathbf{V}(\mathbf{r}, \boldsymbol{a})$ at $\mathbf{r}$, that is, V; when this is done for all directions $\boldsymbol{a}$ at $\mathbf{r}$, we have generated a surface. Further, if we let ξ denote a point on this surface,* (that is, ξ designates the local coordinates, whose origin is at $P(\mathbf{r})$, of a point on the surface), then ξ is given by

$$\xi = V\boldsymbol{a} = s\boldsymbol{a} \quad . \tag{73.32}$$

Physically this surface represents all the points reached from $P(\mathbf{r})$ in a unit time traveling at a velocity $\mathbf{V}(\mathbf{r}, \boldsymbol{a})$. To find the equation of this surface, referring of course, to the local coordinate system we have

* The reader is advised to perform the construction in order to grasp its meaning.

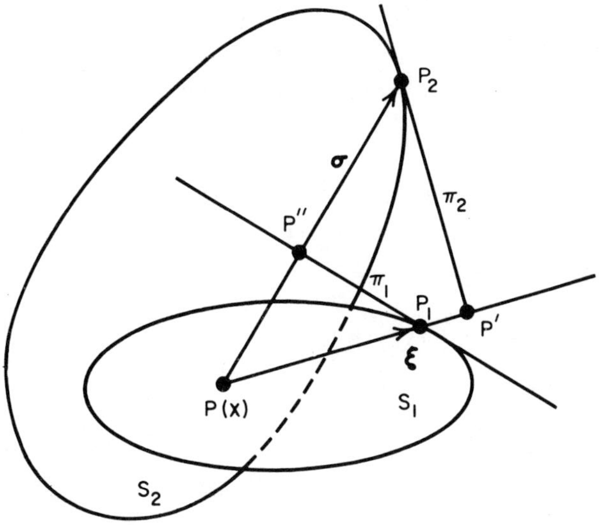

FIG. 19

$$V(\mathbf{r},\ \xi) = V(\mathbf{r},\ s\boldsymbol{a}) = [V(\mathbf{r},\ \boldsymbol{a})]/s \quad , \qquad (73.33)$$

the last term arising from the fact that $[1/V(\mathbf{r},\ \boldsymbol{a})]$ is homogeneous of degree one in the second variable.

From the construction, $s = V$, so that

$$V(\mathbf{r},\ \xi) = 1 \quad \text{or} \quad 1/[V(\mathbf{r},\ \xi)] = 1 \qquad (73.34)$$

is the equation of the surface which is also called the *ray surface*.* Now, while the end point of $\mathbf{V}(\mathbf{r},\ \boldsymbol{a})$ is tracing out the surface just described, the end point of $\boldsymbol{\sigma}$ is tracing out a surface which we will denote by $H(\mathbf{r},\ \boldsymbol{\sigma})$, with $\boldsymbol{\sigma}$ constrained by eq. (73.23). This surface $H(\mathbf{r},\ \boldsymbol{\sigma})$ is generated geometrically as follows (See Fig. 19).

Let S_1 be given by $V(\mathbf{r},\ \boldsymbol{\xi}) = 1$, and S_2 be the surface $H(\mathbf{r},\ \boldsymbol{\sigma})$, Let $\boldsymbol{\xi}$ be a point on S_1, draw the tangent plane to S_1 at P_1, and construct the perpendicular to this plane from P to cut this plane at P''. Now let P_2 be the end point of the vector $\boldsymbol{\sigma}$ along $\overline{PP''}$ such that $\boldsymbol{\sigma} \cdot \boldsymbol{\xi} = 1$. We call P_1 and P_2 reciprocal points because their respective projections satisfy the above relation. If the above construction is done for all points ξ on S_1, then the resulting surface generated by π, that is, S_2, is called the surface reciprocal to S_1, an obvious nomenclature. Moreover, if at P_2 we construct the tangent plane and draw the perpendicular from P to this plane, then by eq. (73.23), this perpendicular must cut the

* C. Caratheodory, *loc. cit.*

surface S_1 at P_1. The plane π_1 tangent to S_1 at P_1 and perpendicular to $\boldsymbol{\sigma}$ is called the polar plane of the point P_2 with respect to the unit sphere centered at P. A similar statement applies to the plane π_2, shown in the preceding figure.

We inquire now further about the origin of the surface S_2, and seek its equation with respect to the local coordinate system whose origin is at P. The relation

$$\boldsymbol{\sigma} = \frac{\partial M(\mathbf{r}, \boldsymbol{a})}{\partial \boldsymbol{a}} = \frac{\partial}{\partial \boldsymbol{a}} \frac{1}{V(\mathbf{r}, \boldsymbol{a})} \tag{73.16}$$

asserts that the right hand side is a homogeneous function of degree zero in $\boldsymbol{a}$ since $[1/V(\mathbf{r}, \boldsymbol{a})]$ is homogeneous of degree one in $\boldsymbol{a}$. This implies that the right side of (73.16) is a function of the ratio of the components of $\boldsymbol{a}$, say α_1/α_3, α_2/α_3. Equation (73.16) is equivalent to three equations; we can therefore eliminate the two ratios among the three equations and obtain a functional relation between the components of $\boldsymbol{\sigma}$. We shall denote this functional relation by

$$H(\mathbf{r}, \boldsymbol{\sigma}) = 1 \quad , \tag{73.35}$$

which must be the surface reciprocal to S_1. The surface $H(\mathbf{r}, \boldsymbol{\sigma}) = 1$ is called the *wave normal surface* associated with the ray surface defined by $[1/V(\mathbf{r}, \boldsymbol{\xi})] = 1$. It should be stressed that already the anisotropy of the medium is put in evidence. For, since $\boldsymbol{\xi}$ is in the direction of the ray and if $\boldsymbol{\sigma}$ is considered to be in the direction of the wave normal (in a wave picture) then in general $\boldsymbol{\xi}$ and $\boldsymbol{\sigma}$ are not co-directional in our local coordinate system. If the index M is a function of position only, $M(\mathbf{r})$, then $\boldsymbol{\sigma}$ coincides with $\boldsymbol{\xi}$ and the medium is isotropic, *i.e.*, $M(\mathbf{r}) \equiv \mu(\mathbf{r})$; otherwise stated, the index function M is invariant under a rotation of axis.

Another way of viewing the relation between the *wave normal surface* and the *ray surface* is to consider first the wave normal surface as given. This is, we emphasize again, the surface generated by the vectors whose directions are those of the wave normals and whose lengths are the phase refractive index in these directions. We determine the ray direction associated with a wave-normal by the following geometrical construction. Through each point of the wave normal surface we construct the plane associated with that normal. The envelope of these planes forms a new surface and the point of tangency between any one plane and the envelope lies in the direction of the ray associated with that plane. The points on this ray surface have a distance $W/\cos\theta$ from the center, where θ is the angle between ray and wave normal, [see eqs. (73.29), (73.30)].

We can find another representation of eq. (73.35). Now, just as the vector $\boldsymbol{\xi}$ was used to describe S_1, through its magnitude $|\boldsymbol{\xi}|$, the magnitude of $\boldsymbol{\sigma}$ will be used to define the reciprocal surface S_2 of S_1. With P still fixed as the origin of our local rectangular cartesian coordinate system, we can equally well describe S_2 in the polar form,

$$|\boldsymbol{\sigma}| = f\left(\mathbf{r}, \frac{\sigma_1}{\sigma_3}, \frac{\sigma_2}{\sigma_3}\right) \tag{73.36}$$

where f is writtena as a function of (σ_1/σ_3), (σ_2/σ_3), since f is a function of the vector $\boldsymbol{\sigma}$ which is defined through its direction components σ_1/σ_3, σ_2/σ_3. The form of eq. (73.36) is analogous to writing the equation of a surface in spherical polar coordinates, R, θ, ϕ, by the representation $R = f(\theta, \phi)$, so that σ_1/σ_3 and σ_2/σ_3 correspond to angles θ, ϕ, (recall that we can write the equation of a surface in many different representa tions). In the form of eq. (73.36), f is homogeneous of degree zero in the σ_i. We therefore define $H(\mathbf{r}, \boldsymbol{\sigma}) = 1$ by

$$H(\mathbf{r}, \boldsymbol{\sigma}) = \frac{|\boldsymbol{\sigma}|}{f\left(\mathbf{r}, \dfrac{\sigma_1}{\sigma_3}, \dfrac{\sigma_2}{\sigma_3}\right)} = 1 \quad . \tag{73.37}$$

The construction of the reciprocal surface S_2 given in the foregoing can be interpreted as the geometrical equivalent of analytically inverting eq. (73.16). It will prove useful to consider an alternative form for eq. (73.37) in terms of the speed of propagation $W(\mathbf{r}, \mathbf{n})$, [see eq. (73.25)]. Since the ratio of the components of $\boldsymbol{\sigma}$ is the same as for $\mathbf{n}$, we can write from eq. (73.30),

$$W(\mathbf{r}, \mathbf{n}) = W\left(\mathbf{r}, \frac{\sigma_1}{\sigma_3}, \frac{\sigma_2}{\sigma_3}\right) = \frac{1}{|\boldsymbol{\sigma}|} \quad . \tag{73.38}$$

Therefore,

$$W\left(\mathbf{r}\,,\ \frac{\sigma_1}{\sigma_3}\,,\ \frac{\sigma_2}{\sigma_3}\right)|\sigma| = 1 \tag{73.39}$$

and if we compare this with eq. (73.36), we find

$$H(\mathbf{r},\ \sigma) \equiv W(\mathbf{r},\ \sigma)\ |\sigma| = 1 \tag{73.40}$$

or by eq. (73.25),

$$H(\mathbf{r},\ \boldsymbol{\sigma}) = \frac{|\boldsymbol{\sigma}|}{\mu(\mathbf{r},\ \mathbf{n})} = 1 \quad . \tag{73.41}$$

This form which was adopted by Haselgrove as a basis for her studies in radio wave propagation is essentially a normalization of the Hamiltonian, $H(\mathbf{r},\ \sigma)$. We note that it is a homogeneous function of degree one in σ just as $[1/V(\mathbf{r},\ \boldsymbol{\alpha})]$ is homogeneous of degree one in $\boldsymbol{\alpha}$. This property of homogeneity permeates the entire structure of the ray theory. An important property of our construction is that the *ray direction* is *perpendicular* to the *phase refractive index surface, i.e.*, the surface defined by $|\sigma| = \mu(\mathbf{r},\ \mathbf{n})$.

It is perhaps instructive to illustrate in a more concrete fashion the concept of reciprocal surfaces. Such surfaces play an important role in many branches of physics and mathematics.* Let us consider two quadric surfaces whose equations when referred to a rectangular cartesian coordinate system $(x_1,\ x_2,\ x_3)$ are defined by

$$S_1:\quad a_{ij}x_ix_j = c_1 \quad , \tag{73.42}$$

$$S_2:\quad b_{ij}x_ix_j = c_2 \quad , \tag{73.43}$$

where c_1 and c_2 are parameters, and the summation convention is implied for repeated indices. We shall write these equations in matrix form,

$$S_1:\quad \mathbf{r}'\mathbf{A}\mathbf{r} = c_1 \quad , \tag{73.42'}$$

$$S_2:\quad \mathbf{r}'\mathbf{B}\mathbf{r} = c_2 \quad , \tag{73.43'}$$

* The Cauchy stress and strain quadrics in elasticity, Fresnel surfaces in crystal optics, momental ellipsoid in mechanics of rigid bodies, etc. See for example, I. S. Sokolnikoff, The Mathematical Theory of Elasticity, second edition, 1956, McGraw-Hill Co., N.Y.

where $\mathbf{r}$ is a column vector and $\mathbf{r}'$ its transpose is a row vector. We now assume that $\mathbf{A}$ and $\mathbf{B}$ are reciprocal to each other, that is, $\mathbf{B} = \mathbf{A}^{-1}$. The matrix $\mathbf{A}$ can be assumed to be symmetric.

The tangent plane π_1 to S_1 at the point P_1 whose position vector $\mathbf{r}$ relative to the origin 0, which is also the center of the surfaces, is

$$\mathbf{R}'\mathbf{A}\mathbf{r} = c_1 \tag{73.44}$$

where $\mathbf{R}$ is a running point on the tangent plane. The perpendicular distance from O to the tangent plane is given by the well known formula,

$$d_1 = \frac{c_1}{|\mathbf{A}\mathbf{r}|} . \tag{73.44'}$$

If P_2 is the point (vector) $\mathbf{s}$ on the quadric S_2 in the direction which is perpendicular to the tangent plane π_1 then since $\mathbf{A}\mathbf{r}$ defines the normal to π_1, the vector $\mathbf{s}$ is proportional to $\mathbf{A}\mathbf{r}$ and we write

$$\mathbf{s} = k\mathbf{A}\mathbf{r} \tag{73.45}$$

where k is a constant of proportionality. Eq. (73.45) can also be written as

$$\mathbf{A}^{-1}\mathbf{s} = k\mathbf{A}^{-1}\mathbf{A}\mathbf{r} = k\mathbf{r} \tag{73.46}$$

which shows that the tangent plane π_2 at P_2 to S_2 is normal to $\mathbf{r}$ since $\mathbf{A}^{-1}\mathbf{s}$ defines the normal to π_2. The line OP_1 therefore is perpendicular to this tangent plane. We conclude from this that if OP_2 is perpendicular to the tangent plane at P_1 then OP_1 is perpendicular to the tangent plane at P_2 and the relation is a reciprocal one. We can go even further analytically. The unit vector in the direction of $\mathbf{s}$ is given by

$$\mathbf{u} = \frac{\mathbf{s}}{|\mathbf{s}|} = \frac{k\mathbf{A}\mathbf{r}}{|k\mathbf{A}\mathbf{r}|} = \frac{\mathbf{A}\mathbf{r}}{|\mathbf{A}\mathbf{r}|} . \tag{73.47}$$

If l is the length of OP_2 then $l\mathbf{u}$ lies on S_2 and hence satisfies the equation of S_2 namely,

$$(l\mathbf{u})'\mathbf{A}^{-1}(l\mathbf{u}) = c_2 \tag{73.48}$$

or,

$$l^2 \mathbf{u}' \mathbf{A}^{-1} \mathbf{u} = c_2 \quad . \tag{73.49}$$

But from eq. (73.47), we obtain,

$$\frac{l^2}{|\mathbf{Ar}|^2} (\mathbf{Ar})' \mathbf{A}^{-1} (\mathbf{Ar}) = \frac{l^2}{|\mathbf{Ar}|^2} (\mathbf{Ar})' \mathbf{r} = c_2$$

which according to the rules of matrix theory and the symmetry of $\mathbf{A}$, *i.e.*, $\mathbf{A} = \mathbf{A}'$ we find

$$\frac{l^2}{|\mathbf{Ar}|^2} \mathbf{r}' \mathbf{Ar} = c_2 \quad . \tag{73.50}$$

From (73.42′) and (73.44′) there results,

$$\frac{l^2 c_1}{\left(\dfrac{c_1^2}{d_1^2}\right)} = c_2$$

or,

$$l^2 d_1^2 = c_1 c_2 \tag{73.51}$$

which links the product of c_1 and c_2. Therefore if we put

$$c_1 c_2 \equiv \epsilon^4 \tag{73.52}$$

then

$$l d_1 = \epsilon^2 \quad . \tag{73.53}$$

In an exactly similar way we can show that if d_2 is the distance from O to the tangent plane π_2 and q is the length OP_1 then also,

$$q d_2 = \epsilon^2 \quad . \tag{73.54}$$

Consequently, the points P_2 and $\mathbf{d}_2$ are inverse points to $\mathbf{d}_1$ and P_1 respectively in a sphere of radius ϵ whose center is at 0.

The point P_1 is called the pole of $\overline{P_2 d_2}$ and the point P_2 is the pole of $\overline{P_1 d_1}$, with respect to the sphere, a terminology adopted from projective geometry. The quadric surfaces S_1 and S_2 are said to be reciprocal to each other with respect to this sphere. The reciprocal aspect is seen to be tied to the fact that the matrix of one quadric is the reciprocal of the other and to the fact that the family of quadrics defined by parameter c_1 is related to the family defined by c_2 through the relation $c_1 c_2 = \epsilon^4$. This example should aid in clarifying the more general concept of reciprocal surfaces.

74. DERIVATION OF THE RAY PATH EQUATIONS

The concepts developed in the previous section permit us to derive, in a simple manner, the two first order equations describing the rays. Let us first note that the surfaces defined by the end points of ξ and σ, which are reciprocal surfaces, can be written in many alternative forms. We have already described the surface defined by the end point of σ in polar form by eq. (73.36) or in the form defined by eq. (73.37). The same situation applies to the surface defined by ξ, which can be written in the polar form

$$|\xi| = V\left(\mathbf{r}, \frac{\xi_1}{\xi_2}, \frac{\xi_2}{\xi_3}\right) = \frac{1}{M\left(\mathbf{r}, \dfrac{\xi_1}{\xi_3}, \dfrac{\xi_2}{\xi_3}\right)} \equiv \frac{1}{M(\mathbf{r}, \boldsymbol{a})} , \tag{74.1}$$

or in the form defined by

$$F(\mathbf{r}, \xi) = |\xi| M(\mathbf{r}, \boldsymbol{a}) = 1 , \tag{74.2}$$

these representations are still with respect to the local coordinate system whose origin is at $P(\mathbf{r})$; the form (74.2) is analogous to eq. (73.37). Now both surfaces, $H(\mathbf{r},\sigma) = 1$ and $F(\mathbf{r},\xi) = 1$ can be considered to be single members of a family of reciprocal surfaces. These families are defined by

$$F(\mathbf{r}, \mathbf{r}') = M(\mathbf{r}, \mathbf{r}')\,|\mathbf{r}'| = c_1 \tag{74.3}$$

$$H(\mathbf{r},\sigma) = \frac{|\sigma|}{\mu(\mathbf{r},\mathbf{n})} = c_2, \tag{74.4}$$

where,

$$\mathbf{r}' = \frac{d\mathbf{r}}{du} \quad , \tag{74.5}$$

with u a positive monotonic parameter. In writing $M(\mathbf{r},\mathbf{r}')$ we mean that M is a function of postion $\mathbf{r}$ and the ratios of the components of $\mathbf{r}'$, hence M is homogeneous of degree zero in this second set of variables. Consequently, $F(\mathbf{r},\mathbf{r}')$ is a homogeneous function of degree one in the components of $\mathbf{r}'$. Clearly the directional dependence of the index function M is represented equally well by $\mathbf{r}'$ as by $\boldsymbol{\alpha}$ since these vectors are proportional to each other, *i.e.*, colinear. However, in discussing the properties of reciprocal surfaces we are not restricted to use the parameter of arc length. These properties hold independent of the mode of parametrization of a ray. By setting $c_1 = c_2 = 1$ in eqs. (74.3) and (74.4) and also putting $u = s$ (the parameter of arc length) we obtain the surfaces of eqs. (73.37) and (74.2).

Now consider any two reciprocal surfaces S_1 and S_2 defined by eqs. (73.4) and (74.4). The normal to the tangent plane to F at a point P_1 is defined by $(\partial F/\partial \mathbf{r}')$. Since σ is also normal to this plane, σ is therefore proportional to $(\partial F/\partial \mathbf{r}')$ and we write

$$\sigma = \lambda_1 \frac{\partial F}{\partial \mathbf{r}'} \tag{74.6}$$

where λ_1 is the proportionality constant. Similarly, for the tangent plane to H at a point P_2 we can write

$$\mathbf{r}' = \lambda_2 \frac{\partial H}{\partial \sigma} \quad , \tag{74.7}$$

with λ_2 also a constant of proportionality. By the property of reciprocal surfaces,

$$\mathbf{r}' \cdot \sigma = \lambda_1 \mathbf{r}' \cdot \frac{\partial F}{\partial \mathbf{r}'} = 1 \quad , \tag{74.8}$$

and,

$$\sigma \cdot \mathbf{r}' = \lambda_2 \sigma \cdot \frac{\partial H}{\partial \mathbf{r}'} = 1 \quad . \tag{74.9}$$

But F is homogeneous of degree one in $\mathbf{r}'$ and H is homogeneous of degree one in $\boldsymbol{\sigma}$, we also have,

$$\left.\begin{aligned} \lambda_1 \mathbf{r}' \cdot \frac{\partial F}{\partial \mathbf{r}'} &= \lambda_1 F = 1 , \\ \lambda_2 \boldsymbol{\sigma} \cdot \frac{\partial H}{\partial \boldsymbol{\sigma}} &= \lambda_2 H = 1 , \end{aligned}\right\} \qquad (74.10)$$

and from eqs. (74.6), (74.7) and (74.10) we deduce the relations,

$$\boldsymbol{\sigma} = \frac{1}{F}\frac{\partial F}{\partial \mathbf{r}'} , \qquad (74.11)$$

$$\mathbf{r}' = \frac{1}{H}\frac{\partial H}{\partial \boldsymbol{\sigma}} . \qquad (74.12)$$

Again, since F is homogeneous of degree one in $\mathbf{r}'$, then $(\partial F/\partial \mathbf{r}')$ is homogeneous of degree zero in $\mathbf{r}'$ and consequently $\boldsymbol{\sigma}$ is homogeneous of degree -1 in $\mathbf{r}'$. It follows from this at once that $H(\mathbf{r},\boldsymbol{\sigma})$ when considered as a function of $\mathbf{r}'$, is homogeneous of degree -1 in $\mathbf{r}'$. Therefore, using the definition of a homogeneous function, we can write,

$$\left.\begin{aligned} F(\mathbf{r}, \mathbf{r}') &= \lambda F(\mathbf{r},\mathbf{r}') , \\ H(\mathbf{r},\lambda\mathbf{r}') &= \lambda^{-1} H(\mathbf{r},\mathbf{r}'), \end{aligned}\right\} \qquad (74.13)$$

where λ is an arbitrary positive parameter. Eliminating λ between the pair of relations in eqs. (74.13) gives,

$$F(\mathbf{r},\lambda\mathbf{r}')H(\mathbf{r},\lambda\mathbf{r}') = F(\mathbf{r},\mathbf{r}')H(\mathbf{r},\boldsymbol{\sigma}) = c_1 c_2 . \qquad (74.14)$$

Thus far we have used only the property of reciprocal surfaces and the homogeneity of the functions F and H. We now invoke the variational principle of eq. (73.6). This equation is repeated here for convenience

$$\delta \int_{P_1}^{P_2} M ds = \delta \int_{P_1}^{P_2} \frac{ds}{V} = 0 , \qquad (73.6)$$

since

$$\left|\frac{d\mathbf{r}}{ds}\right| = \left|\frac{d\mathbf{r}}{du}\frac{du}{ds}\right| = |\mathbf{r}'|\frac{du}{ds} = 1 \quad ,$$

then,

$$\delta\int_{P_1}^{P_2}\frac{ds}{V(\mathbf{r},\boldsymbol{a})} = \delta\int_{P_1}^{P_2}\frac{du}{V(\mathbf{r},\mathbf{r}')} = \delta\int_{P_1}^{P_2} M(\mathbf{r},\mathbf{r}')|\mathbf{r}'|\,du$$

$$= \delta\int_{P_1}^{P_2} F(\mathbf{r},\mathbf{r}')\,du = 0 \quad ,$$

which gives the Euler equations:

$$\frac{d}{du}\frac{\partial F(\mathbf{r},\mathbf{r}')}{\partial\mathbf{r}'} - \frac{\partial F(\mathbf{r},\mathbf{r}')}{\partial\mathbf{r}} = 0 \quad .$$

If, now, we let the parameter $u = t$, the time of phase propagation along the ray, then by definition,

$$\dot{\mathbf{r}} = \frac{d\mathbf{r}}{dt} = \mathbf{V} \quad , \tag{74.15}$$

and therefore,

$$\left.\begin{aligned} F &= \frac{|\dot{\mathbf{r}}|}{V} = 1 \quad , \\ H &= \frac{|\sigma|}{\mu} = 1 \quad , \end{aligned}\right\} \tag{74.16}$$

which, together with eq. (74.14), gives

$$F(\mathbf{r},\lambda\dot{\mathbf{r}})H(\mathbf{r},\lambda\dot{\mathbf{r}}) = c_1 c_2 = 1 \quad . \tag{74.17}$$

This relation holds for any two reciprocal surfaces of the families of eqs. (74.3) and (74.4). Since λ is an arbitrary positive parameter then also $\lambda\dot{\mathbf{r}}$ is arbitrary. The Euler equations, with parameter $u \doteq t$, now are written as,

$$\frac{d}{dt}\frac{\partial F(\mathbf{r},\dot{\mathbf{r}})}{\partial \dot{\mathbf{r}}} - \frac{\partial F(\mathbf{r},\dot{\mathbf{r}})}{\partial \mathbf{r}} = 0 \quad . \tag{74.18}$$

From eq. (73:50), we have

$$\sigma F = \frac{\partial F}{\partial \dot{\mathbf{r}}} \quad ,$$

and from eq. (74.14) with $\lambda = 1$, we find

$$\frac{d}{dt}\left(\frac{\sigma\cdot}{H}\right) - \frac{\partial}{\partial \mathbf{r}}\left(\frac{1}{H}\right) = 0 \quad . \tag{74.19}$$

The relation (74.17) shows that the family of reciprocal surfaces F and H are reciprocal with respect to a unit sphere centered at $P(\mathbf{r})$. Now, along the ray path, $H = 1$ and the total derivative is zero, that is, $dH/dt = 0$. However, the partial derivatives with respect to $\mathbf{r}, \dot{\mathbf{r}}$ and $\sigma\cdot$ are not necessarily zero, and eq. (74.19) becomes

$$\frac{d\sigma\cdot}{dt} = -\frac{\partial H(\mathbf{r},\sigma\cdot)}{\partial \mathbf{r}} \quad , \tag{74.20}$$

also eq. (74.12) becomes,

$$\frac{d\mathbf{r}}{dt} = \frac{\partial H(\mathbf{r},\sigma\cdot)}{\partial \sigma\cdot} \quad . \tag{74.21}$$

These two equations are usually written together as a system of equations in the order,

$$\left.\begin{aligned} \frac{d\mathbf{r}}{dt} &= \frac{\partial H(\mathbf{r},\sigma\cdot)}{\partial \sigma\cdot} \quad , \\ \frac{d\sigma\cdot}{dt} &= -\frac{\partial H(\mathbf{r},\sigma\cdot)}{\partial \mathbf{r}} \quad . \end{aligned}\right\} \tag{74.22}$$

These are two first order equations fully equivalent to the Euler equations for the description of the ray path. They have the form of Hamilton's canonical equations in mechanics with σ playing the role of the generalized momenta. We note that the ray refractive index M is not required for the determination of the ray path, only $\mu(\mathbf{r},\mathbf{n})$ the phase refractive index need be known. The integration of these equations, which are more convenient from a numerical integration point of view than Euler's equations, determines the ray path in the form $\mathbf{r} = \mathbf{r}(t)$.

75. AN EQUIVALENT FORMULATION

The derivation of the ray path equations in Hamiltonian form involving only a knowledge of the phase refractive index $\mu(\mathbf{r},\mathbf{n})$ suggests the possibility of deriving the canonical equations using as a starting point a knowledge of H alone. Suppose then we are given the invariant function $H(\mathbf{r},\sigma) = 1$ and the definition

$$\sigma = \frac{\partial}{\partial \mathbf{r}'} \frac{1}{V(\mathbf{r},\mathbf{r}')} \tag{75.1}$$

where,

$$\mathbf{r}' = \frac{d\mathbf{r}}{du}$$

with u some positive monotonic parameter, and $1/V$ a homogeneous function of degree one in $\mathbf{r}'$. According to eq. (73.10) and the homogeneity of $1/V$, we can write

$$\frac{ds}{V(\mathbf{r},\boldsymbol{\alpha})} = \frac{du}{V(\mathbf{r},\mathbf{r}')} \tag{75.2}$$

and

$$\sigma \cdot d\mathbf{r} = \frac{\partial}{\partial \mathbf{r}'} \frac{1}{V(\mathbf{r},\mathbf{r}')} \cdot \frac{d\mathbf{r}}{du} du = \mathbf{r}' \cdot \frac{\partial}{\partial \mathbf{r}'} \frac{1}{V(\mathbf{r},\mathbf{r}')} du \quad , \tag{75.3}$$

But since,

$$\mathbf{r}' \cdot \frac{\partial}{\partial \mathbf{r}'} \frac{1}{V(\mathbf{r},\mathbf{r}')} = \frac{1}{V(\mathbf{r},\mathbf{r}')} \quad \text{by Euler's Theorem;} \tag{75.4}$$

therefore,

$$\sigma \cdot d\mathbf{r} = \frac{du}{V(\mathbf{r},\mathbf{r}')} = \frac{ds}{V(\mathbf{r},\alpha)} \quad . \tag{75.5}$$

The variational principal, .

$$\delta \int_{P_1}^{P_2} \frac{ds}{V(\mathbf{r},\alpha)} = 0 \tag{75.6}$$

is therefore equivalent to,

$$\delta \int_{P_1}^{P_2} \sigma \cdot d\mathbf{r} = 0 \quad , \quad \text{together with the constraint} \tag{75.7}$$

$$H(\mathbf{r},\sigma) = 1 \quad . \tag{75.8}$$

Equation (75.6) expresses Fermat's Principle and eqs. (75.8) express Hamilton's Principle. The preceding discussion shows that they are fully equivalent.

If we carry out the variations on σ and $\mathbf{r}$ which are arbitrary except for the fact that the vector field σ must satisfy the second of eqs. (75.8), and $\delta\mathbf{r}$ the variation of $\mathbf{r}$ vanishes at P_1 and P_2, the end points, we obtain,

$$\int_{P_1}^{P_2} (\delta\sigma \cdot d\mathbf{r} + \sigma \cdot \delta d\mathbf{r}) = 0 \tag{75.9}$$

which upon integrating by parts, using the end conditions for $\delta\mathbf{r}$ (and the commutativity of the δ and d symbols), gives

$$\int_{P_1}^{P_2} (\delta\sigma \cdot d\mathbf{r} - \delta\mathbf{r} \cdot d\sigma) = 0 \quad , \tag{75.10}$$

for all variations, subject to

$$\frac{\partial H}{\partial \mathbf{r}} \cdot \delta \mathbf{r} + \frac{\partial H}{\partial \boldsymbol{\sigma}} \cdot \delta \boldsymbol{\sigma} = 0 \quad . \tag{75.11}$$

Eqs. (75.10) and (75.11) together imply that

$$d\mathbf{r} = du \frac{\partial H}{\partial \boldsymbol{\sigma}} , \quad d\boldsymbol{\sigma} = - du \frac{\partial H}{\partial \mathbf{r}} , \tag{75.12}$$

or,

$$\frac{dr}{du} = \frac{\partial H}{\partial \boldsymbol{\sigma}} , \quad \frac{d\boldsymbol{\sigma}}{du} = - \frac{\partial H}{\partial \mathbf{r}} , \tag{75.13}$$

must hold along the ray. If the parameter u is not the time t, the relation between u and t can be found as follows. The normal speed of propagation W, we recall is

$$W = \frac{1}{|\boldsymbol{\sigma}|}$$

with unit vector $\mathbf{n}$ along $\boldsymbol{\sigma}$ defined by $\mathbf{n} = \boldsymbol{\sigma}/|\boldsymbol{\sigma}| = W\boldsymbol{\sigma}$. The first of Hamilton's equations relates $\mathbf{r}$ with $\boldsymbol{\sigma}$ by $(75.12)_1$ Now from Fig. 20, the projection of $d\mathbf{r}$ on the unit normal $\mathbf{n}$,

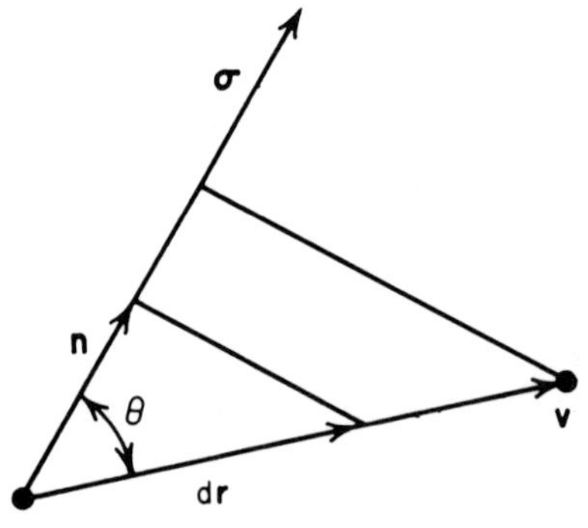

FIG. 20

is just

$$d\mathbf{r} \cdot \mathbf{n} = \frac{d\mathbf{r}}{du} du \cdot \mathbf{n} = W dt \quad , \tag{75.14}$$

since $d\mathbf{r}$ is the displacement along the ray direction in a time dt. Thus,

$$d\mathbf{r} \cdot \mathbf{n} = \frac{\partial H}{\partial \boldsymbol{\sigma}} du \cdot \mathbf{n} = W dt$$

$$= \frac{\partial H}{\partial \boldsymbol{\sigma}} du \cdot W \boldsymbol{\sigma} \quad , \tag{75.15}$$

or,

$$dt = \boldsymbol{\sigma} \cdot \frac{\partial H}{\partial \boldsymbol{\sigma}} du \tag{75.16}$$

so that,

$$t = \int \boldsymbol{\sigma} \cdot \frac{\partial H}{\partial \boldsymbol{\sigma}} du \quad , \tag{75.17}$$

which relates t as a function of u, that is, $t(u)$ can be obtained if we solve eqs. (75.13) to obtain $\mathbf{r}(u)$ and $\boldsymbol{\sigma}(u)$. If $H(\mathbf{r}, \boldsymbol{\sigma})$ is homogeneous of degree one in $\boldsymbol{\sigma}$ (and we can always make it so), then

$$\boldsymbol{\sigma} \cdot \frac{\partial H}{\partial \boldsymbol{\sigma}} = H, \tag{75.18}$$

and if we put $H = 1$, eq. (75.17) gives

$$t = u. \tag{75.19}$$

Consequently, if we are given or obtain $H = 1$, then Hamilton's equations give the rays as a function of the time.

It is not difficult to demonstrate how to obtain the function $1/V$ and prove that it is homogeneous of degree one, starting with a knowledge of H and the ray path equations. This will be left as an exercise for the reader.

76. RAY PROPAGATION

Thus far we have been using or rather carrying along the notion of wave propagation in developing the ray theory. Although we can develop the ray-theoretic concepts completely independent of any wave theory notions, it was found useful to continue with it. Moreover, we did not use any wave theory parameters except to indicate that σ was considered to be in the direction of the wave normal and that σ was bound to the ray directions through eq (73.23). In this section we shall examine the manner in which rays propagate in an inhomogeneous, anisotropic medium. The connection between wave propagation and ray propagation is also brought out more clearly by means of the characteristic function of Hamilton. This characteristic function denoted by $\psi(P_1, P_2)$ is defined by the formula

$$\psi(P_1, P_2) = \int_{P_2}^{P_2} \frac{ds}{V(\mathbf{r}, \boldsymbol{\alpha})} = \int_{P_1}^{P_2} \sigma \cdot d\mathbf{r} \quad , \qquad (76.1)$$

where the integral is taken along a ray from a point P_1 on the ray to a point P_2 also on the same ray. If $V(\mathbf{r}, \boldsymbol{\alpha})$ is a multiple valued function, there can exist more than one ray between P_1 and P_2. As before, for sake of simplicity in discussion we shall exclude this case. The function $\psi(P_1, P_2)$ clearly exists if a ray path exists, for then, σ is defined along the ray and therefore the integral has a well defined meaning. The function $\psi(P_1, P_2)$ is also proportional the the "optical distance" in a medium. We shall show later that $\psi(P_1, P_2)$ is the spatially dependent part of the phase of a wave in a nonhomogeneous medium. The reader is advised to review Chapter I briefly to establish more firmly this connection.

Consider ψ as a function of the upper and lower limits of the integra By varying the end points we obtain the pair of relations,

$$\left(\frac{\partial \psi}{\partial \mathbf{r}}\right)_{P_2} = \sigma(P_2) \; , \quad \left(\frac{\partial \psi}{\partial \mathbf{r}}\right)_{P_1} = -\sigma(P_1) \quad . \qquad (76.2)$$

From the definition of σ, (eq. 73.16),

$$\left(\frac{\partial \psi}{\partial \mathbf{r}}\right)_{P_2} = \frac{\partial}{\partial \boldsymbol{\alpha}} \frac{1}{V(P_2, \boldsymbol{\alpha})} \; , \quad \left(\frac{\partial \psi}{\partial \mathbf{r}}\right)_{P_1} = -\frac{\partial}{\partial \boldsymbol{\alpha}} \frac{1}{V(P_1, \boldsymbol{\alpha})} \qquad (76.3)$$

and by recalling that $\partial/\partial\boldsymbol{\alpha}\ 1/V(\mathbf{r},\boldsymbol{\alpha})$ is a function which is homogeneous of degree zero in $\boldsymbol{\alpha}$, we can therefore eliminate the ratios, (α_1/α_3), (α_2/α_3) from eqs. (76:2) and (76.3) to obtain,

$$\left.\begin{aligned} H\left[P_2, \left(\frac{\partial\psi}{\partial\mathbf{r}}\right)_{P_2}\right] &= 1 \quad , \\ H\left[P_1, \left(\frac{\partial\psi}{\partial\mathbf{r}}\right)_{P_1}\right] &= -1 \quad , \end{aligned}\right\} \tag{76.4}$$

or in the form

$$\left.\begin{aligned} H[P_2, \boldsymbol{\sigma}(P_2)] &= 1 \quad , \\ H[P_1, -\boldsymbol{\sigma}(P_1)] &= -1 \ . \end{aligned}\right\} \tag{76.5}$$

Equations (76.4) or (76.5) are the Hamilton-Jacobi equations. In mechanics use is made of the first equation of either set. In optical studies, particularly in the design of lenses, both equations of either set are useful. We observe from the definition of H in terms of $\boldsymbol{\sigma}$, [see eq. (73.41)], that along a ray,

$$\frac{\partial\psi}{\partial\mathbf{r}} \cdot \frac{\partial\psi}{\partial\mathbf{r}} = \boldsymbol{\sigma} \cdot \boldsymbol{\sigma} = |\boldsymbol{\sigma}|^2 = \mu^2(\mathbf{r},\mathbf{n}) \quad . \tag{76.6}$$

We see from this equation, that is, the Hamilton-Jacobi equation (76.6) is nothing more than the Eikonal equation of geometrical optics. However, we must also recall that the Eikonal equation as usually derived from a wave equation (see Chapter I) in the so-called geometrical optics approximation assumes an isotropic medium. In that case, the right side of eq. (76.6) is a function of position only. In eq. (76.6), the right side as indicated is a function of *position* and *wave normal direction* $\mathbf{n}$, and so can be considered as a generalization of the usual Eikonal equation.*

* It would be interesting to speculate about the form that the Schroedinger equation in quantum mechanics would have taken in this case, had Schroedinger taken the directional dependence into consideration. Historically, Schroedinger was guided by the analogy between the Eikonal equation of geometrical optics resulting from a scalar wave equation and the Hamilton-Jacobi equation in mechanics. See in this connection H. Goldstein-Classical Mechanics.

77. THE CHARACTERISTIC SURFACES

As we have stated above, the characteristic function $\psi(P_1, P_2)$ defin[e] only along a ray plays an important role in the understanding of the prop[-]agation of waves and rays. The characteristic surfaces derived from the characteristic function is an additional aid in this understanding. The[se] surfaces are constructed in the following way.

Suppose we are given an arbitrary function of position defined by

$$f(\mathbf{r}) = 0 \quad , \tag{77.1}$$

which is a surface. Select a point P_1 on this surface, which is arbitra[ry] except for the requirement that the normal to the surface is contained i[n] the set of directions $\sigma(P_1)$ which satisfies the equation.

$$H[P_1, \sigma(P_1)] = 1 \quad . \tag{77.2}$$

Calculate the characteristic function from P_1 along a ray to a point P_2 on the same ray. Thus the characteristic function has a fixed value. Select another point, say, Q_1 on the surface, eq. (77.1) subject to the condition of eq. (77.2), *i.e.*,

$$H[Q_1, \sigma(Q_1)] = 1 \quad . \tag{77.3}$$

Calculate ψ from Q_1 to a point Q_2 on the ray emanating from Q_1, and with Q_2 chosen as to satisfy

$$\psi(P_1, P_2) = \psi(Q_1, Q_2) \quad , \tag{77.4}$$

and continue this process for all points R_1, S_1, T_1, ... etc. on $f(\mathbf{r})$ = so that we find points R_2, S_2, T_2, ... etc such that

$$\psi(P_1, P_2) = \psi(Q_1, Q_2) = \psi(R_1, R_2) = \qquad = \text{constant.} \tag{77.5}$$

The totality of all such points O_2, Q_2, ... forms a surface,

$$\psi = \text{constant.} \tag{77.6}$$

Starting with this new surface we can continue the construction so as to generate a family of surfaces of constant ψ, as indicated in Fig. 21.

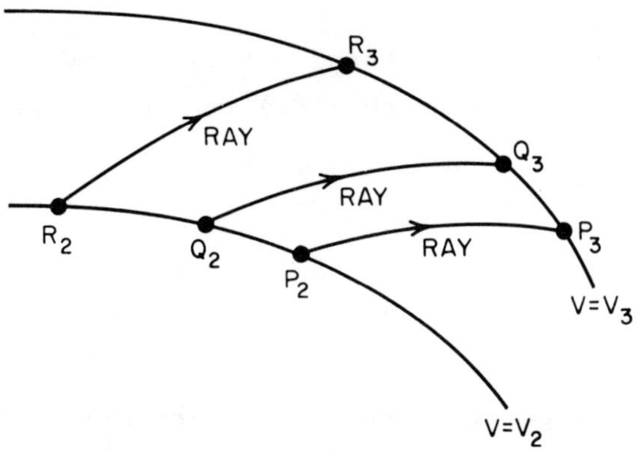

FIG. 21

78. THE GROUP PROPERTY OF THE CONSTRUCTION

The construction of the surfaces just described gives rise to an important question. Namely, if by starting with the arbitrary surface $f = 0$, by the construction we arrive at the surface say $\psi = \psi_2$ and continue to a surface $\psi = \psi_3$, how do we know that the direction of the rays on $\psi = \psi_3$ has the correct direction? More precisely posed, if we construct $\psi = \psi_3$ from the rays starting on $f = 0$, is the direction of the rays which terminate on ψ_3 the same as if we start from ψ_2 and terminate on ψ_3? To answer this question we must show that the normal to ψ_3 has the same direction as σ on ψ_3. We start with the characteristic function

$$\psi(P_1, P_2) = \int_{P_1}^{P_2} \sigma \cdot d\mathbf{r} = \text{constant}. \tag{78.1}$$

and consider ψ as a function of P_2 and P_3. The change in ψ, denoted by $\delta\psi$, which is obtained by varying the end point P_2 of the ray on $\psi = \psi_2$ gives,

$$\delta\psi = -\sigma(P_2) \cdot (\delta\mathbf{r})_{P_2} + \sigma(P_3) \cdot (\delta\mathbf{r})_{P_3} = 0 , \tag{78.2}$$

for, by the definition of a ray, the first variation of the integral of eq. (78.1) must vanish. But since $\sigma(P_2)$ is proportional to $(\partial\psi/\partial\mathbf{r})_{P_2}$ we can write,

$$\sigma(P_2) = K\left(\frac{\partial\psi}{\partial\mathbf{r}}\right)_{P_2} \tag{78.3}$$

with K a constant of proportionality. However, in the construction, the normal direction defined by $(\partial\psi/\partial\mathbf{r})_{P_2}$ is chosen to be compatible with the condition, $H[P_2,\sigma(P_2)] = 1$, and the displacement $(\delta\mathbf{r})_{P_2}$ on $\psi = \psi_2$ is in the tangent plane at P_2. Hence,

$$\sigma(P_2) \cdot (\delta\mathbf{r})_{P_2} = 0 , \tag{78.4}$$

so that this result together with eq. (78.2) implies the following relation

$$\sigma(P_3) \cdot (\delta\mathbf{r})_{P_3} = 0 . \tag{78.5}$$

Therefore, $\sigma(P_3)$ is orthogonal to the displacement $(\delta\mathbf{r})_{P_3}$ on $\psi = \psi_3$ at P_3. This proves that the ray has the correct direction at P_3. Summarizing the construction; we start with an arbitrary surface, $f = 0$, and construct surfaces of constant ψ according to the foregoing. The construction takes us from $f = 0$ to $\psi = \psi_2$ along rays then to $\psi = \psi_3$ along rays and this is equivalent to going directly from $f = 0$ along rays to $\psi = \psi_3$ (bypassing the surface $\psi = \psi_2$).

We may visualize the construction as a transformation, abstractly symbolizing it as follows. Denote by T_1 the transformation from $f = 0$ to $\psi = \psi_2$, by T_2 the transformation from $\psi = \psi_2$ to $\psi = \psi_3$, and by T_3 the transformation from $f = 0$ to $\psi = \psi_3$. Then we write symbolically,

$$T_3 = T_2 T_1 \tag{78.6}$$

and we say, mathematically speaking, the construction (*i.e.*, the transformations) has the group property and this is indeed the defining characteristic of the propagation of rays. The above will be recognized as a statement of Huygen's Principle when we think of the surfaces ψ = constant as surfaces of constant phase in a wave theory description. The condition imposed on the construction by means of eq. (77.4) is made to insure that we are actually obtaining properties of rays through eq. (78.2); this follows from the section on the equivalent formulation.

79. REFLECTION AND REFRACTION

The discussion on ray propagation thus far assumed that the medium in which the ray is propagating contained no surfaces of discontinuity; that is, surfaces, across which the index of refraction change abruptly. Consequently the only results we derived were the ray path equations in Hamiltonian form and certain of its implications. If we now admit discontinuities in the medium, the variational formulation gives rise to boundary terms which in the continuous medium case vanish. These boundary terms give rise to so-called "natural-boundary conditions," which in our case are nothing more than the laws of reflection and refraction for an anisotropic medium. The results of the analysis presented lead to an interesting practical usage of the refractive index surfaces for the different media. For simplicity we restrict ourselves to the case of just two media; the results are easily generalized.

Let M_1 and M_2 be two distinct media separated by a surface of discontinuity S, whose equation is denoted by

$$S(\mathbf{r}) = 0 \quad . \tag{79.1}$$

The variational principle now reads: for all curves starting at P_1 in M_1 and ending at P_2 in M_2 determine those curves which give a stationary value to the integral

$$\int_{P_1}^{P_2} \sigma \cdot d\mathbf{r} \quad , \qquad \text{with} \qquad H(\mathbf{r},\sigma) = 1 \quad . \tag{79.2}$$

The first variation gives

$$\delta \int_{P_1}^{P_2} \sigma \cdot d\mathbf{r} = \int_{P_1}^{P_2} (\delta\sigma \cdot d\mathbf{r} + \sigma \cdot \delta d\mathbf{r}) \quad , \tag{79.3}$$

which after integrating by parts and taking into consideration the fact that $H(\mathbf{r},\sigma)$ is discontinuous across $S(\mathbf{r}) = 0$, we obtain

$$\delta \int_{P_1}^{P_2} \sigma \cdot d\mathbf{r} = - [\sigma \cdot \delta\mathbf{r}]_{P-\epsilon}^{P+\epsilon} + \int_{P_1}^{P} (\delta\sigma \cdot d\mathbf{r} - \delta\mathbf{r} \cdot d\sigma) + \int_{P}^{P_2} (\delta\sigma \cdot d\mathbf{r} - \delta\mathbf{r} \cdot d\sigma) \tag{79.4}$$

where P is a point on $S(\mathbf{r}) = 0$. It is understood that in the first integral P is considered to lie in M_1 and in the second integral to lie in M_2. The boundary terms vanish at P_1 and P_2, so that the only part of the boundary term to survive is the first term on the right side of eq. (79,4).

Now $P - \epsilon$ is clearly in M_1; while $P + \epsilon$ lies in M_2; and ϵ is an arbitrarily small positive number. The boundary term involving ϵ is due to the surface of discontinuity. If we take the limit of the expression (79.4) as $\epsilon \to 0$, and invoke the requirement that the first variation vanish, there results, for fixed P_1 and P_2,

$$-\Delta\sigma \cdot \delta\mathbf{r} + \int_{P_1}^{P_2} (\delta\sigma \cdot d\mathbf{r} - \delta\mathbf{r} \cdot d\sigma) = 0 \quad . \tag{79.5}$$

The symbol $\Delta\sigma$ denotes the jump in σ across $S(\mathbf{r}) = 0$, that is,

$$\Delta\sigma = \lim_{\epsilon \to 0} [\sigma]_{P-\epsilon}^{P+\epsilon} \quad .$$

Equation (79.5) must hold for all variations $\delta\mathbf{r}$, $\delta\sigma$ subject to

$$\delta H = \frac{\partial H}{\partial \mathbf{r}} \cdot \delta\mathbf{r} + \frac{\partial H}{\partial \sigma} \cdot \delta\sigma = 0 \quad . \tag{79.6}$$

Therefore, we obtain Hamilton's equations

$$\frac{d\mathbf{r}}{du} = \frac{\partial H}{\partial \sigma} \quad , \quad \frac{d\sigma}{du} = -\frac{\partial H}{\partial \mathbf{r}} \quad \text{in } M_1 \text{ and } M_2 \quad , \tag{79.7}$$

and the boundary condition,

$$\Delta\sigma \cdot \delta\mathbf{r} = 0 \tag{79.8}$$

for arbitrary variations $\delta\mathbf{r}$ on $S(\mathbf{r}) = 0$. If there exists more than one surface of discontinuity, then expressions of the same form hold for each surface and medium, M_1, M_2, M_3, etc. Since $\delta\mathbf{r}$ is arbitrary but lies on $S(\mathbf{r}) = 0$, the "natural boundary" condition, eq. (79.8), shows that $\Delta\sigma$ is orthogonal to $S(\mathbf{r}) = 0$. Hence, if σ_1 lies in M_1 and σ_2 in M_2, then, since $(\partial S/\partial \mathbf{r})$ is the normal to $S(\mathbf{r}) = 0$, we can write eq. (79.8) as

$$\sigma_2 - \sigma_1 = k\mathbf{n} \tag{79.9}$$

where $\mathbf{n}$ is a unit vector normal to $S(\mathbf{r})$, and k is a constant of proportionality. This last equation expresses the laws of reflection and refraction. In accordance with the ideas set forth in Chapter III, we can consider the surface $S(\mathbf{r}) = 0$ as a singular surface relative to the vector $\boldsymbol{\sigma}$. In the spirit of Chapter III we also think of eq. (79.9) as a shock condition. It is also easy to see that by taking the dot product of both sides of eq. (79.9) with any vector tangent to the surface $S(\mathbf{r})$, that this equation implies the continuity of the tangential components of $\boldsymbol{\sigma}$ across $S(\mathbf{r}) = 0$.

Let us now examine how to determine whether a ray is reflected or refracted according to eq. (79.9). Consider first the case of refraction. Assume $\boldsymbol{\sigma}_1$ and the point P as given in M_1, where both $\boldsymbol{\sigma}_1$ and the coordinates of P must satisfy the condition $H_1(\mathbf{r},\boldsymbol{\sigma}_1) = 1$ which is given in M_1. We also assume that the vector $\boldsymbol{\sigma}_1$, which is given by $\boldsymbol{\sigma}_1 = \partial M_1/\partial \boldsymbol{a}$, and likewise $\boldsymbol{a}_1$, which determines the ray in M_1, are also known. Since the surface of discontinuity $S(\mathbf{r}) = 0$ is also known then the unit normal to it, $\mathbf{n}$ is known. Hence eq. (79.9) together with the condition $H_2(\mathbf{r},\boldsymbol{\sigma}_2) = 1$, which is defined in M_2, are four equations for the determination of the vector $\boldsymbol{\sigma}_2$ and the constant k. Having obtained $\boldsymbol{\sigma}_2$, the refracted ray defined by $\boldsymbol{a}_2$ is determined from,

$$\boldsymbol{a}_2 = c\,\frac{\partial H_2}{\partial \boldsymbol{\sigma}}, \tag{79.10}$$

where c is a proportionality constant, and the normalization condition,

$$\boldsymbol{a}_2 \cdot \boldsymbol{a}_2 = 1\ ; \tag{79.11}$$

these are four equations for determining c and $\boldsymbol{a}_2$. In order to find the reflected rays, we replace H_2 by H_1 because now the rays emerge back into M_1 instead of M_2.

More generally, it is possible that either refraction or reflection occurs, or that both occur, or that neither occurs. The reciprocal surfaces (which would correspond to the wave surfaces in a wave theory treatment) are useful in giving the information on the occurrences. Draw the surfaces $H_1 = 1$ and $H_2 = 1$ as shown in Fig. 22.

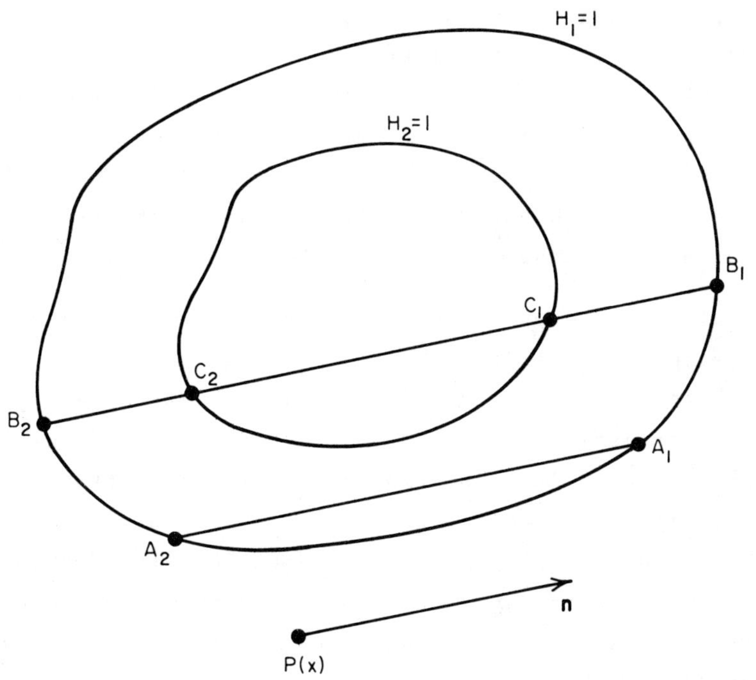

FIG. 22

Let us indicate the direction of the normal **n** to $S(\mathbf{r})$ and the point P on $S(\mathbf{r})$ schematically in the same diagram. Construct from P the vector σ_1; its end point must be on the surface $H_1 = 1$; call this end point A_1, as shown. The vector σ_2 is found by constructing a line through A_1 whose direction is parallel to **n**, and finding its intersection with the surface $H_2 = 1$ since the end point of σ_2 must satisfy $H_2(\mathbf{r},\sigma_2) = 1$. In the figure we have shown the point A_2 to lie on H_1 and, since A_1A_2 which is parallel to **n** does not intersect $H_2 = 1$, no refraction occurs. But reflection can occur and in the situation just stated, total reflection occurs since there is no refraction. In order to ensure that reflection occurs it must be shown that the reflected ray actually does emerge back into M_1 (*i.e.*, if σ_2 is not directed into M_1) then neither reflection nor refraction has occurred in this case. For the other situation shown in the figure, let σ_1 be given by PB_1, the line parallel to **n** intersects H_2 at C_1 and C_2, and also intersects $H_1 = 1$ at B_2. Hence there exists the following possible cases; two possibilities for refracted rays, and one for a reflected ray. For these possibilities we must test to see whether the refracted rays emerge into M_2 and whether the reflected ray emerges back into M_1. The situation can be summarized by stating that the laws of refraction and reflection as contained in the "shock condition," eq. (79.9), do not yield unique solutions, as illustrated by the above considerations, and each case must be treated separately.

A practical application of the technique described above; that is, the use of superimposed refractive index surfaces on the same coordinate center and with the same reference direction, to determine the direction of reflected and transmitted waves at a sharp boundary, is given in a thesis of R. L. Smith.* It is possible that different practical applications can result from the above construction or by variants of this construction. For example, the construction can be extended to determine the differential refraction in a continuous medium where the resulting refracted waves are examined only in the neighborhood of the incident wave-normal direction. In this case, **n**, the normal to the boundary, is taken to mean the direction of the space gradient of refractive index which is calculated holding the wave normal direction constant.

80. SNELL'S LAW FOR AN ANISOTROPIC MEDIUM

It is interesting to note that besides yielding the laws of reflection and refraction, the variational principle also contains Snell's law in a generalized differential form. Indeed, it is implied in eq. (74.19) which we now examine,

$$\frac{d}{dt}\left(\frac{\boldsymbol{\sigma}}{H}\right) - \frac{\partial}{\partial \mathbf{r}}\left(\frac{1}{H}\right) = 0 \quad . \tag{80.1}$$

Put $H(\mathbf{r},\boldsymbol{\sigma}) = |\boldsymbol{\sigma}|/\mu$ into this equation and obtain

$$\frac{d}{dt}\left(\frac{\mu\boldsymbol{\sigma}}{|\boldsymbol{\sigma}|}\right) - \frac{1}{|\boldsymbol{\sigma}|}\frac{\partial \mu}{\partial \mathbf{r}} = 0 \quad . \tag{80.2}$$

* R. L. Smith, The Use of Nose Whistlers in the Study of the Outer Ionosphere, Technical Report No. 6, July 1960, Stanford Electronics Labs., Stanford University.

But,

$$\sigma = |\sigma|\mathbf{n} \quad , \tag{80.3}$$

then,

$$\frac{d}{dt}(\mu\mathbf{n}) = \frac{1}{|\sigma|}\frac{\partial\mu}{\partial\mathbf{r}} \quad . \tag{80.4}$$

Before proceeding we mention an important point regarding the appearance of this equation. Although $\partial\mu/\partial\mathbf{r}$ has the appearance of a vector-*i.e.*, it resembles **grad** μ—it is not a gradient since μ is a function of both position and direction. Hence, neither the left side nor the right side of eq. (80.4) is a vector. However, the difference of the two sides is a vector (a fact that we shall prove and use later). Let us accept this statement tentatively. We define now a constant unit vector, **u**, whose components are numerically equal to the three numbers calculated from $\partial\mu/\partial\mathbf{r}$ with the wave normal direction held constant. With this understanding we form the vector product

$$\left(\frac{d}{dt}(\mu\mathbf{n}) - \frac{1}{|\sigma|}\frac{\partial\mu}{\partial\mathbf{r}}\right)\mathbf{x}\mathbf{u} = 0 \tag{80.5}$$

which gives

$$\left(\frac{d}{dt}\mu\mathbf{n}\right)\mathbf{x}\mathbf{u} = 0 \quad ,$$

or since **u** is independent of t,

$$\frac{d}{dt}(\mu\mathbf{n}\mathbf{x}\mathbf{u}) = 0 \quad , \tag{80.6}$$

from which we obtain

$$\mu\mathbf{n}\mathbf{x}\mathbf{u} = \text{constant} \quad . \tag{80.7}$$

By using the definition of a vector product, we can also write

$$\mu \sin\phi = \text{constant} \tag{80.8}$$

which is the usual form of Snell's Law. In this form, ϕ is the angle between **n** and **u**. Because the usual form of Snell's Law results from eq. (80.2) we say that eq. (80.1) or eq. (80.2) is a generalized differential form of Snell's Law. We note that the form of eq. (80.1) does not depend on the fact that $H = 1$ which holds along a ray path, but depends on the fact that $FH = 1$ which also holds on a ray path since there $F = H = 1$. As we have already remarked in the previous section, the generalized differential form of Snell's Law is a useful form in the computational considerations of ray tracing.

81. CURVATURE OF THE RAYS

The curvature of a ray at any nonsingular point is most easily formulated in terms of the Hamiltonian. Although the Euler equations are second order differential equations and therefore contain the curvature implicitly, these equations are not necessarily the most convenient means for its calculation.

By considering the Hamiltonian, we have along the ray

$$H(\mathbf{r}, \sigma) \equiv H(x_1, x_2, x_3, \sigma_1, \sigma_2, \sigma_3) = 1 . \qquad (81.1)$$

Differentiating this equation with respect to the arc length s gives,

$$\frac{\partial H}{\partial x_i}\frac{dx_i}{ds} + \frac{\partial H}{\partial \sigma_i}\frac{d\sigma_i}{ds} = \frac{\partial H}{\partial x_i}\alpha_i + \frac{\partial H}{\partial \sigma_i}\frac{d\sigma_i}{ds} = 0 . \qquad (81.2)$$

Differentiating again gives,

$$\alpha_i \frac{d}{ds}\frac{\partial H}{\partial x_i} + \frac{\partial H}{\partial x_i}\frac{d\alpha_i}{ds} + \frac{d}{ds}\left(\frac{\partial H}{\partial \sigma_i}\frac{d\sigma_i}{ds}\right) = 0 ,$$

and since $d\alpha_i/ds = d^2x_i/ds^2 = n_i/R$, where n_i denotes the normal to the ray and R is its radius of curvature; thus

$$\alpha_i \frac{d}{ds}\frac{\partial H}{\partial x_i} + \frac{1}{R}\frac{\partial H}{\partial x_i} n_i + \frac{d}{dt}\left(\frac{\partial H}{\partial \sigma_i}\frac{d\sigma_i}{ds}\right)\frac{dt}{ds} . \qquad (81.3)$$

We can now replace all of the partial derivatives but one by their equivalent from the canonical equations, which yields

$$\frac{V}{R}\frac{\partial H}{\partial x_i} n_i + \frac{d}{dt}\left(V_i \frac{d\sigma_i}{ds}\right) - V_i \frac{d}{dt}\frac{d\sigma_i}{ds} = 0 \quad . \tag{81.4}$$

Since,

$$\frac{d}{dt}\left(V_i \frac{d\sigma_i}{ds}\right) = V_i \frac{d}{dt}\frac{d\sigma_i}{ds} + \frac{dV_i}{dt}\frac{d\sigma_i}{ds}$$

we can rewrite eq. (81.4)

$$\frac{V}{R}\frac{\partial H}{\partial x_i} n_i + \frac{dV_i}{dt}\frac{d\sigma_i}{ds} = \frac{V}{R}\frac{\partial H}{\partial x_i} n_i + \frac{1}{V}\frac{dV_i}{dt}\frac{d\sigma_i}{dt} = 0$$

or, using the canonical equations again,

$$\frac{V^2}{R}\frac{\partial H}{\partial x_i} n_i = \frac{\partial H}{\partial x_i}\frac{d}{dt}\frac{\partial H}{\partial \sigma_i} \quad . \tag{81.5}$$

By definition, $(\partial H/\partial x_i)n_i = \partial H/\partial n$ which means the directional derivative of H in the direction of the normal to the ray, but with $\boldsymbol{\sigma}$ held fixed. We should not mistake $\partial H/\partial x_i$ as representing the gradient of H. Since $1/V = \mu \cos\theta$, we have for the curvature, the expression

$$\frac{1}{R} = \frac{(\mu^2 \cos^2\theta)\dfrac{\partial H}{\partial x_i}\dfrac{d}{dt}\dfrac{\partial H}{\partial \sigma_i}}{\dfrac{\partial H}{\partial n}} \quad . \tag{81.6}$$

By writing out,

$$\frac{d}{dt}\frac{\partial H}{\partial \sigma_i} = \frac{\partial^2 H}{\partial \sigma_i \partial \sigma_j}\dot{\sigma}_i + \frac{\partial^2 H}{\partial \sigma_i \partial x_j}\dot{x}_j = -\frac{\partial^2 H}{\partial \sigma_i \partial \sigma_j}\frac{\partial H}{\partial x_j} + \frac{\partial^2 H}{\partial \sigma_i \partial x_j}\frac{\partial H}{\partial \sigma_j}$$

$$= \frac{\partial H}{\partial \sigma_j}\frac{\partial}{\partial \sigma_i}\frac{\partial H}{\partial x_j} - \frac{\partial H}{\partial x_j}\frac{\partial}{\partial \sigma_i}\frac{\partial H}{\partial \sigma_j} \quad ,$$

the expression (81.6) becomes a function of the index and its derivatives and the σ_i, namely

$$\frac{1}{R} = \frac{(\mu^2 \cos^2 \theta)\left(\frac{\partial H}{\partial \sigma_j}\frac{\partial H}{\partial x_i}\frac{\partial}{\partial \sigma_i}\frac{\partial H}{\partial x_j} - \frac{\partial H}{\partial x_j}\frac{\partial H}{\partial x_i}\frac{\partial}{\partial \sigma_i}\frac{\partial H}{\partial \sigma_j}\right)}{\frac{\partial H}{\partial n}} . \tag{81.7}$$

If the medium is isotropic the expression simplifies. But for instructive purposes we shall derive the result for the isotropic case starting from the Euler equations. Since $M(\mathbf{r}, \boldsymbol{\alpha}) = \mu(x)\sqrt{\alpha_j \alpha_j}$ we write

$$\frac{d}{ds}\frac{\partial}{\partial \alpha_i}(\mu\sqrt{\alpha_j \alpha_j}) - \frac{\partial \mu}{\partial x_i} = 0 \tag{81.8}$$

or,

$$\frac{d}{ds}\mu\alpha_i - \frac{\partial \mu}{\partial x_i} = 0$$

hence,

$$\frac{d}{ds}\mu\alpha_i = \mu\frac{d^2 x_i}{ds^2} + \frac{d\mu}{ds}\frac{dx_i}{ds} = \frac{\partial \mu}{\partial x_i} ,$$

so,

$$\frac{\mu}{R} n_i = \frac{\partial \mu}{\partial x_i} - \alpha_i \frac{d\mu}{ds}$$

multiplying by n_i, summing as usual on i, and noting that $\alpha_i n_i = 0$, we find,

$$\frac{1}{R} = \frac{1}{\mu}\frac{\partial \mu}{\partial x_i} n_i = \frac{1}{\mu}\frac{\partial \mu}{\partial n} = \frac{\partial \log \mu}{\partial n} . \tag{81.9}$$

a much simpler result than for the anisotropic case. In eq. (81.9) $\partial\mu/\partial x_i$ does represent the gradient since μ is a function of position alone. The cos θ factor which appears in eq. (81.7) gives a measure of the degree of anisotropy as would be expected.

82. GROUP VELOCITY FROM RAY THEORY—An Imbedding Process*

Thus far we have made no assumptions about the index M other than its dependence on position and direction. We have developed only a pure ray theory and its geometric implications, even though we have carried along a wave picture in the background. It is of interest to seek the implications of ray theory if we somehow widen the class of admissible functions of the index M. That is, we consider the class of index functions $M(\mathbf{r}, \boldsymbol{\alpha})$ to be imbedded in the wider class of functions denoted by $M(\mathbf{r}, \boldsymbol{\alpha}, \nu)$ where ν is a parameter. We shall see that the apparatus of the ray theory already developed together with some "generalization postulates" carries with it the concept of group velocity. This concept in classical physics is usually associated with a wave theory, but we shall derive an expression which if the parameter ν is interpreted as a frequency, leads to the ordinary notion of the group velocity. In this sense, the pure ray theory is interpreted as a theory associated with a monochromatic wave.

Let us follow a moving surface, which is abritrary except for the requirement that the normal to it is included in the set of directions $\boldsymbol{\sigma}$ which now satisfy the equation

$$H(\mathbf{r}, \boldsymbol{\sigma}, \nu) = 1 \quad . \tag{82.1}$$

That is, since $\boldsymbol{\sigma}$ depends on ν, through the definition

$$\boldsymbol{\sigma} = \frac{\partial}{\partial \boldsymbol{\alpha}} M(\mathbf{r}, \boldsymbol{\alpha}, \nu) \quad , \tag{82.2}$$

hence H also depends on ν through this definition. The surface defined by eq. (82.1) is then considered to be a single member of a two parameter family of reciprocal surfaces, the additional parameter being ν. Let the moving surface be denoted by

$$\phi(\mathbf{r}, t) = 0 \quad , \tag{82.3}$$

---

* The fact that it is possible to define the concept of group velocity in a pure ray theory may at first seem surprising, since this concept is historically tied to wave-theory concepts. However, by using an imbedding process as we have done, we deduce the principal results and expressions of group velocity. Imbedding processes are not new to mathematicians but for an interesting and fascinating account together with its applications to mathematical physics we refer the reader to the paper of R. Bellman, R. Kalaba and G. M. Wing, Invariant Imbedding and Mathematical Physics I. Particle Processes, Journal of Mathematical Physics, Vol. 1, No. 4, July-August 1960.

See also, J. L. Synge, Geometrical Mechanics and deBroglie Waves, (Cambridge University Press, Cambridge, 1954).

with H now defined by

$$H(\mathbf{r},\ \boldsymbol{\sigma},\ \nu) = \frac{|\boldsymbol{\sigma}|}{\mu(\mathbf{r},\ \boldsymbol{\sigma},\ \nu)} = 1 \tag{82.4}$$

We wish to find the velocity of normal propagation, denoted by $\mathbf{W}$, for the surface propagated in a given direction, $\mathbf{n}$. This means we want $\boldsymbol{\sigma}$ to be proportional to $\mathbf{n}$, and we write

$$\boldsymbol{\sigma} = c\mathbf{n} \tag{82.5}$$

where c is a constant of proportionality. If $\phi(\mathbf{r},\ t)$ is to be a possible reciprocal surface (*i.e.* a wave surface), $\boldsymbol{\sigma}$ must satisfy the relation

$$H(\mathbf{r},\ c\mathbf{n},\ \nu) = 1 \quad , \tag{82.6}$$

which is only one equation for the two parameters c and ν. Thus if the velocity $\mathbf{W}$ is to have the same direction as $\mathbf{n}$, eq. (82.6) shows that instead of a unique velocity in a given direction, there exists, for an arbitrary choice of values of ν, a range of velocities. Because of this lack of uniqueness eq. (82.6) contains implicitly the concept of dispersion. To calculate $\mathbf{W}$, we consider in a time increment dt that the surface is displaced along the direction $\mathbf{n}$ an amount or distance $|\mathbf{dr}|$; and we therefore define $\mathbf{W}$ by the formula

$$\mathbf{W}dt = \mathbf{n} \cdot \mathbf{dr} \quad . \tag{82.7}$$

Since $\mathbf{n}$ is proportional to $\partial\phi/\partial\mathbf{r}$, we write

$$\mathbf{n} = K\frac{\partial\phi}{\partial\mathbf{r}} \quad , \tag{82.8}$$

where K is a constant of proportionality. The vector $d\mathbf{r}$ lies in the surface $\phi(\mathbf{r},\ t) = 0$, after a time dt, hence

$$\frac{\partial\phi}{\partial\mathbf{r}} \cdot \frac{d\mathbf{r}}{dt} + \frac{\partial\phi}{\partial t} = 0 \quad , \tag{82.9}$$

and from eq. (82.7) we obtain,

$$\frac{\partial\phi}{\partial \mathbf{r}} \cdot \mathbf{W} + \frac{\partial\phi}{\partial t} = 0 \quad . \tag{82.10}$$

From this expression we find K, namely,

$$\overline{K} = - \frac{\dfrac{\partial\phi}{\partial t}}{\dfrac{\partial\phi}{\partial \mathbf{r}} \cdot \dfrac{\partial\phi}{\partial \mathbf{r}}} \quad , \tag{82.11}$$

and also,

$$\mathbf{W} = - \frac{\left(\dfrac{\partial\phi}{\partial t}\right)}{\left(\dfrac{\partial\phi}{\partial \mathbf{r}} \cdot \dfrac{\partial\phi}{\partial \mathbf{r}}\right)} \frac{\partial\phi}{\partial \mathbf{r}} \quad . \tag{82.12}$$

But $\boldsymbol{\sigma}$ is also co-directional with $\partial\phi/\partial\mathbf{r}$, so that,

$$\boldsymbol{\sigma} = K \frac{\partial\phi}{\partial \mathbf{r}} \quad , \quad (K \text{ a proportionality constant}). \tag{82.13}$$

Thus far the parameter ν was arbitrary and we remove this arbitrariness by choosing it suth that

$$\nu = K \frac{\partial\phi}{\partial t} \quad , \tag{82.14}$$

where K is the same as in eq. (82.13). This choice was governed by the fact that if $\phi(\mathbf{r}, t)$ had the form $\nu t - \psi(\mathbf{r})$, then $\partial\phi/\partial t = \nu$. We note the analogy with the phase of a wave. The multiplier K is obtained from the equation,

$$H\left(\mathbf{r}, K \frac{\partial\phi}{\partial \mathbf{r}}, K \frac{\partial\phi}{\partial t}\right) = 1 \quad , \tag{82.15}$$

an equation which uniquely defines K, and which gives

$$\mathbf{W} = - \frac{\nu}{|\boldsymbol{\sigma}|^2} \boldsymbol{\sigma} \quad . \tag{82.16}$$

From eq. (82.5) we obtain

$$\mathbf{W} = -\frac{\nu}{c}\mathbf{n} \quad . \tag{82.17}$$

The constant c is easily evaluated from this equation if we take the scalar product of both sides of it with $\mathbf{n}$,

$$\mathbf{W}\cdot\mathbf{n} = -\frac{\nu}{c}\mathbf{n}\cdot\mathbf{n} = -\frac{\nu}{c} \quad . \tag{82.18}$$

But by definition,

$$\mathbf{W}\cdot\mathbf{n} = |\mathbf{W}| = W \quad , \tag{82.19}$$

consequently,

$$c = -\frac{\nu}{W} \quad . \tag{82.20}$$

Let us define,

$$\frac{\partial c}{\partial \nu} \equiv c' = -\frac{\partial}{\partial \nu}\left(\frac{\nu}{W}\right) \quad , \tag{82.21}$$

and make the "generalization postulate",

$$\mu(\mathbf{r}, \mathbf{n}, \nu)W = 1 \quad , \tag{82.22}$$

which amounts to preserving the relation of eq. (73.25), where now the functions μ and W are dependent on ν. From the relation

$$H(\mathbf{r}, \mathbf{n}, \nu) = \frac{|\boldsymbol{\sigma}|}{\mu(\mathbf{r}, \mathbf{n}, \nu)} = \frac{|c\mathbf{n}|}{\mu} = \frac{\nu}{\mu W} \tag{82.23}$$

and from the "generalization postulate", eq. (82.22),

$$H = \nu \quad , \tag{82.24}$$

therefore

$$\frac{\partial H}{\partial \nu} = 1 \quad . \tag{82.25}$$

Since $\mathbf{n}$ is given, that is, it is fixed at the outset, the relation of eq. (82.6) defines c as a function of ν,

$$c = c(\nu) \quad . \tag{82.26}$$

Differentiating eq. (82.6) with respect to ν, holding $\mathbf{n}$ fixed, gives

$$\frac{dH}{d\nu} = \frac{\partial H}{\partial \boldsymbol{\sigma}} \cdot \frac{d\boldsymbol{\sigma}}{d\nu} + \frac{\partial H}{\partial \nu} = 0 \tag{82.27}$$

with

$$\frac{d\boldsymbol{\sigma}}{d\nu} = c'(\nu)\mathbf{n} \quad , \tag{82.28}$$

and by eq. (82.25), eq. (82.27) becomes

$$\frac{\partial H}{\partial \boldsymbol{\sigma}} \cdot c'(\nu)\mathbf{n} + 1 = 0 \quad . \tag{82.29}$$

Solving for $c'(\nu)$ and using eq. (82.21) we get

$$c'(\nu) = \frac{1}{\dfrac{\partial H}{\partial \boldsymbol{\sigma}} \cdot \mathbf{n}} \tag{82.30}$$

and finally,

$$\frac{\partial}{\partial \nu}\left(\frac{\nu}{W}\right) = \frac{1}{\dfrac{\partial H}{\partial \boldsymbol{\sigma}} \cdot \mathbf{n}} \quad . \tag{82.31}$$

The left side of this equation is recognized as just the expression defining "wave group velocity", say

$$\frac{1}{W_g} \equiv \frac{\partial}{\partial \nu}\left(\frac{\nu}{W}\right) \quad . \tag{82.32}$$

The right side of eq. (82.31) now implies that

$$W_g = \frac{\partial H}{\partial \boldsymbol{\sigma}} \cdot \mathbf{n} \quad . \tag{82.33}$$

The foregoing treatment shows that ray theory, when extended to include the additional parameter ν in characterizing the medium by an index, gives the usual formula for the group velocity if we interpret this parameter as a frequency (or as proportional to frequency). Moreover, this treatment leads us to consider the appropriate ray velocity to be associated with W_g. To this end we recall that in the absence of ν, we have $\mathbf{V} = \partial H/\partial \boldsymbol{\sigma}$, defining the velocity along the ray. If we define a "ray group velocity", $\mathbf{V}_g$ by the formula

$$\mathbf{V}_g \cdot \mathbf{n} = W_g \quad , \tag{82.34}$$

we can take

$$\mathbf{V}_g = \frac{\partial H}{\partial \boldsymbol{\sigma}} (\mathbf{r}, \boldsymbol{\sigma}, \nu) \quad , \tag{82.35}$$

and therefore write,

$$\frac{\partial}{\partial \nu}\left(\frac{\nu}{W}\right) = \frac{1}{\mathbf{V}_g \cdot \mathbf{n}} = \frac{1}{W_g} \quad . \tag{82.36}$$

We must now interpret these formulas by considering instead of a single ray, a thin bundle or tube of rays. The different rays comprising the tube have associated with them a parameter value $\nu = \nu_0 + \Delta\nu$, with ν_0 some central or average frequency. The velocity $\mathbf{V}_g$ is considered as the velocity along some average ray associated with the central frequency ν_0. The vector $\mathbf{n}_0$ or $\mathbf{W}_g = W_g \mathbf{n}_0$ is in a direction which is the average of the cone of directions of $\mathbf{n}$. This situation is visualized in Fig. 23.

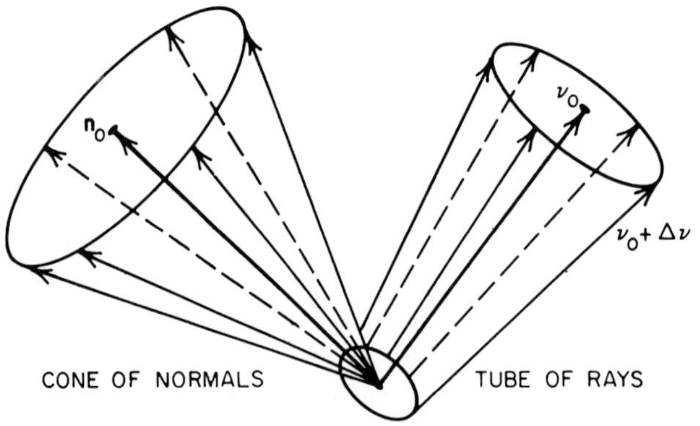

FIG. 23

With this interpretation, the equations above should now read,

$$\mathbf{V}_g \cdot \mathbf{n}_0 = W_g \quad , \tag{82.37}$$

$$\mathbf{V}_g = \left(\frac{\partial H}{\partial \sigma}\right)_{\nu=\nu_0} \quad , \tag{82.38}$$

$$\frac{1}{W_g} = \left[\frac{\partial}{\partial \nu}\left(\frac{\nu}{W}\right)\right]_{\nu=\nu_0} \quad . \tag{82.39}$$

83. THE EQUIVALENT PATH AND ABSORPTION

The developments in the preceding section can be used to define certain concepts in a dispersive medium. In what follows we shall use a scale in which V_0 is the speed of light propagating in vacuum and is not numerically equal to unity.

The time of group propagation (which can be considered as the time of flight of a pulse of energy) is defined by

$$t_g = \frac{1}{V_0}\int M_g\, ds \quad , \tag{83.1}$$

where ds is distance along the ray path and M_g is the "group ray refractive index", which is defined by

$$M_g = \mu_g \cos\theta, \tag{83.2}$$

with μ_g the "group phase refractive index". This index which is a function of frequency ν is itself given by

$$\mu_g = \frac{V_0}{W_g} = V_0 \frac{\partial}{\partial \nu}\left(\frac{\nu}{W}\right) = \frac{V_0}{W} + \nu_0 \nu \frac{\partial}{\partial \nu}\left(\frac{1}{W}\right)$$

or

$$\mu_g = \frac{V_0}{W} + \nu_0 \nu \frac{\partial}{\partial \nu}\left(\frac{1}{W}\right) = \mu + \nu \frac{\partial \mu}{\partial \nu} \quad . \tag{83.3}$$

The time of flight of a pulse is then given by

$$t_g = \frac{1}{V_0} \int \left(\mu + \nu \frac{\partial \mu}{\partial \nu} \right) \cos \theta \, ds \quad , \tag{83.4}$$

but, if t is the time of phase propagation,

$$ds = V dt \tag{83.5}$$

and

$$V \cos \theta = W \quad , \tag{83.6}$$

therefore,

$$(\cos \theta \, ds) = (V \cos \theta) dt = W dt \quad , \tag{83.7}$$

and since,

$$\frac{W}{V_0} = \frac{1}{\mu} \quad ,$$

we obtain,

$$t_g = \int \frac{\mu_g}{\mu} dt \quad , \tag{83.8}$$

which expresses the time of group propagation in terms of the time of phase propagation. Using this definition of t_g we define the equivalent path length P by the suggestive formula

$$P = V_0 t_g = V_0 \int \left(\frac{\mu_0}{\mu} \right) dt \tag{83.9}$$

and which represents the distance traversed by a pulse in free space during the time of flight. We can easily find the differential equation satisfied by the path P in terms of the time of phase propagation. Differentiating both sides of eq. (83.9) with respect to t, and using eq. (83.3) gives

$$\frac{dP}{dt} = \left(\frac{\mu + \nu \dfrac{\partial \mu}{\partial \nu}}{\mu} \right) V_0 \tag{83.10}$$

as the desired equation.

84. ABSORPTION CONSIDERATIONS

In a variety of practical applications there is sufficient absorption to warrant asking the question; how does the absorption of the medium affect the ray path. In general the ray path in an absorbing medium should be different from the ray path in a non-absorbing medium. Consequently, it is important to know how to modify the variational principle to obtain the ray path in a medium which is inhomogeneous, anisotropic and absorbing. This amounts to finding the appropriate index to use in the variational principle if we still wish to characterize the medium by an index function. The manner in which this can be accomplished is suggested by the Hamilton-Jacobi equation, that is, the Eikonal equation (76.6). However, we are also incorporating into the description the frequency dependence as discussed in the preceding sections.

We repeat here for convenience the Eikonal equation (76.6),,

$$\left(\frac{\partial\psi}{\partial\mathbf{r}}\right)^2 = |\sigma|^2 = \mu^2(\mathbf{r}, \mathbf{n}, \nu) \quad . \tag{76.6}$$

To take into account the effect of absorption we formally extend eq. (76.6) so that the right hand side is now complex. Therefore we put

$$\left(\frac{\partial\psi}{\partial\mathbf{r}}\right)^2 = p(\mathbf{r}, \mathbf{n}\ \nu) - iq(\mathbf{r}, \mathbf{n}, \nu) \quad , \tag{84.1}$$

where both p and q are real valued function of position, wave normal direction and frequency ν. The vector $\partial\psi/\partial\mathbf{r}$ is therefore complex and we can write, in general,

$$\frac{\partial\psi}{\partial\mathbf{r}} = \boldsymbol{\mu} - i\boldsymbol{\chi} \tag{84.2}$$

with $\boldsymbol{\mu}$ a vector in the direction of phase propagation and $\boldsymbol{\chi}$ a vector in a direction in which the absorption changes most rapidly. The scalar product of $\partial\psi/\partial\mathbf{r}$ with itself gives,

$$\left(\frac{\partial\psi}{\partial\mathbf{r}}\right)^2 = \boldsymbol{\mu}\cdot\boldsymbol{\mu} - \boldsymbol{\chi}\cdot\boldsymbol{\chi} - 2i\boldsymbol{\mu}\cdot\boldsymbol{\chi} \quad , \tag{84.3}$$

and by equating the real and imaginary parts of this expression with those of eq. (84.1), we obtain,

$$\left.\begin{aligned} \mu \cdot \mu - \chi \cdot \chi &= \mu^2 - \chi^2 = p \quad , \\ 2\mu \cdot \chi &= 2\mu\chi \cos\gamma = q \quad , \end{aligned}\right\} \tag{84.4}$$

where γ is the angle between $\boldsymbol{\mu}$ and $\boldsymbol{\chi}$. We note that the vector character of $\boldsymbol{\mu}$ and $\boldsymbol{\chi}$ has been taken into consideration since in general the direction in which the absorption changes most rapidly is not the same as the direction of phase propagation. This fact has been overlooked by several authors* in their attempts to generalize ray optics for an absorbing medium. This lack or oversight of the vector character leads to a certain arbitrariness in the resulting formulas.* This vector character has already been demonstrated in Chapter I, section 2, in the discussion of inhomogeneous plane waves. Indeed, we were governed by this treatment in our generalization of the Eikonal equation. Similar considerations arise in the problem of refraction in a conducting medium in which a pair of equations known as Ketteler's equations describe the phenomena.†

By solving for μ^2 and χ^2 from eq. (84.4) we find

$$\left.\begin{aligned} \mu^2 &= \frac{1}{2}\,[p + \sqrt{p \quad + (q/\cos\gamma)^2}] \quad , \\ \chi^2 &= \frac{1}{2}\,[-p + \sqrt{p^2 + (q/\cos\gamma)^2}] \quad . \end{aligned}\right\} \tag{84.5}$$

These relations are analogous to Kettleler's equations mentioned above.

If we define a function $H(\mathbf{r}, \sigma, \nu)$ by

$$H(\mathbf{r}, \sigma, \nu) = \frac{|\sigma|}{\mu(\mathbf{r}, \mathbf{n}, \nu)} \quad , \tag{84.6}$$

but with μ now given by eq. (84.5),, then we make the following "generalization postulate".

* P. S. Epstein, "Geometrical Optics in Absorbing Media," Proc. of the National Academy of Sciences, Vol. 16, 37-45 (1935).

† J. A. Stratton, Electromagnetic Theory, p. 503 (McGraw-Hill Book Co., New York City 1941).

In an inhomogeneous, anisotropic, dispersive and absorbing medium, the ray paths are obtained from the solution of the variational equation

$$\delta \int_{P_1}^{P_2} \boldsymbol{\sigma} \cdot d\mathbf{r} = 0 \quad , \tag{84.7}$$

subject to the constraint, $H(\mathbf{r}, \boldsymbol{\sigma}, \nu) = 1$, or

$$\delta H = \frac{\partial H}{\partial \mathbf{r}} \cdot \delta \mathbf{r} + \frac{\partial H}{\partial \boldsymbol{\sigma}} \cdot \delta \boldsymbol{\sigma} = 0 \quad , \tag{84.8}$$

with H given by eq. (84.6) and μ given by eq. (84.5).

This postulate shows that the problem of finding the rays in an absorbing medium is in principle the same as that for a non-absorbing medium. The index function however is more complicated and clearly contains the effects of the absorption of the medium through the inclusion of the function q. Consequently, all the apparatus developed in the previous sections for obtaining the rays and its properties carries over.

It is easily seen that as $\chi \to 0$, we recover all of the formulas of the non-absorbing case. Summarizing thus far; the Eikonal equation provided the basis for extending the theory to an absorbing medium, and the variational principle (based on the section of equivalent formulation) defines the rays through an index which depends also on the absorption of the medium.

If the medium is weakly absorbing so that q is approximately zero, then χ vanishes and we may use $\mu = \sqrt{p}$ as the index, that is, we treat the medium as though it were non-absorbing. We define the absorption of a pulse along a ray by

$$D = \exp[-\int K(\mathbf{r}, \mathbf{n}, \nu) \cos \theta \, ds] \quad , \tag{84.9}$$

where $K(\mathbf{r}, \mathbf{n}, \nu)$ denoting the absorption coefficient (see Chapter II), is assumed to be given, and is a function of position, wave normal direction, and frequency. The differential equation satisfied by D in terms of the time of phase propagation is obtained from the following

$$\frac{dD}{ds} = - KD \cos\theta \quad ,$$

and since

$$\cos\theta \, ds = Wdt = V_0 \frac{dt}{\mu}$$

therefore,

$$\frac{dD}{dt} = - \frac{K}{\mu} V_0 D \quad . \tag{84.10}$$

Equations (83.10) and (84.10) can be adjoined to the ray path equations so that all of these properties, that is, the equivalent path length and absorption, can be determined simultaneously with the ray path. For this, we must consider the integration of the simultaneous system of differential equations,

$$\left.\begin{aligned}
\frac{d\mathbf{r}}{dt} &= \frac{\partial H}{\partial \sigma} \quad , \\
\frac{d\sigma}{dt} &= - \frac{\partial H}{\partial \mathbf{r}} \quad , \\
\frac{dP}{dt} &= \left(\frac{\mu + \nu \dfrac{\partial \mu}{d\nu}}{\mu} \right) V_0 \quad , \\
\frac{dD}{dt} &= \frac{-KV_0 D}{\mu}
\end{aligned}\right\} \tag{84.11}$$

If the absorption affects the ray path, the system of equations (84.11) remain the same, but the index μ must be replaced by equation (84.5) and the absorption coefficient will depend on χ, (see Chapters I and II). The practical significance of the system of equations (84.11) or its generalization to include absorption as just described, is that they are completely general and there is no restriction on the medium, such as an assumption of stratification, etc. Although we have used a rectangular cartesian reference frame for the basic derivation, we shall show in another section that the formulation or rather the resulting equations hold for any coordinate system. But for explicit calculation in an arbitrary curvilinear system, we shall exhibit a useful representation for computational considerations.

85. THE CONNECTION BETWEEN HAMILTON'S EQUATIONS, PULSES AND A GENERAL VARIATIONAL PRINCIPLE

In Chapter I, section 5, we gave a treatment of a pulse in an absorbing, inhomogeneous and anisotropic medium. From this treatment it followed that an extension of Fermat's Principle was possible in terms of a variational principle more general than what we have given in the present chapter. The variational prescription used in Chapter I, was obtained by setting $\delta t = 0$, only, holding the other parameters $\mathbf{r}$ and $\omega = 2\pi\nu$ fixed. Now, consistent with the assumptions made in Chapter I, section 5, let us examine the consequences of varying all of the parameters, *i.e.*, let $\delta\mathbf{r} = \delta\omega = \delta t = 0$. The new variational principle thus obtained will give results which will be compared with the variational principle for obtaining the rays using the Hamiltonian method in this chapter.

For convenience we write the basic equation of Chapter I, section 5, from which we obtained the extension of Fermat's Principle. This equation has the following form

$$V_0(\omega - \omega_0) \int dt + \omega_0 \int \boldsymbol{\mu}_0 \cdot d\mathbf{r}_0 - \omega \int \boldsymbol{\mu} \cdot d\mathbf{r} = \text{const.} \tag{85.1}$$

By carrying out the variations, and setting $\delta\mathbf{r} = \delta\omega = \delta t = 0$, we obtain,

$$\omega \int \delta\boldsymbol{\mu} \cdot d\mathbf{r}_g = 0 \quad , \tag{85.2}$$

where $d\mathbf{r}_g$ is the vector element along the group path. This equation is satisfied if the integrand vanishes

$$\delta\boldsymbol{\mu} \cdot d\mathbf{r}_g = 0 \quad , \tag{85.3}$$

and conversely. But this equation asserts that the group path is orthogonal to the vector $\delta\boldsymbol{\mu}$ or in other words, the group path is orthogonal to the surface swept out by the end point of $\boldsymbol{\mu}$ for fixed values of the parameters $\mathbf{r}$, t, ω. But this surface is precisely the surface defined by

$H(\mathbf{r}, \mu) = 1$, so $d\mathbf{r}_g$ is perpendicular to the latter, a fact we already know. The variational principle defined by

$$\left.\begin{array}{l} \delta \displaystyle\int_{P_1}^{P_2} \mu \cdot d\mathbf{r} = 0 , \\ \text{subject to the constraint} \\ H(\mathbf{r}, \mu) = 1 \end{array}\right\} \tag{85.4}$$

leads to Hamiltons canonical equations in the form

$$d\mathbf{r} = \frac{\partial H}{\partial \mu} dt ,$$
$$d\mu = -\frac{\partial H}{\partial \mathbf{r}} dt , \tag{85.5}$$

where t is some positive monotonic parameter. The condition $\delta H = 0$ with $\delta\mathbf{r} = 0$ gives

$$\frac{\partial H}{\partial \mu} \cdot \delta\mu = 0 , \tag{85.6}$$

and since,

$$d\mathbf{r} = \frac{\partial H}{\partial \mu} dt ,$$

we have

$$d\mathbf{r} \cdot \delta\mu = 0 \tag{85.7}$$

so that Hamiltons equations give the group path which is also the ray path. Therefore we have demonstrated that the variational prescription $\delta\mathbf{r} = \delta\omega = \delta t = 0$ to find the group path is nothing more than finding the ray path by Hamiltons' equations. The vector μ has a magnitude which is the index of refraction, and this index is a function of position, direction, absorption and frequency. The vector index μ is identical with the vector $\boldsymbol{\sigma}$ in our "generalization postulate" for an absorbing medium.

We can derive some further interesting and useful formulae, if in μ-space, that is, for fixed $\mathbf{r}$, we represent the vector $\boldsymbol{\mu}$ in the form,

$$\boldsymbol{\mu} = \mu\mathbf{n} \tag{85.8}$$

where $\mathbf{n}$ is a unit vector, and suppose that $\mathbf{n}$ is given in terms of its rectangular cartesian components, *i.e.*, local cartesian coordinates attached to the fixed point $\mathbf{r}$ as the origin. We denote these components by (n_1, n_2, n_3). From

$$\delta\boldsymbol{\mu} = \mu\delta\mathbf{n} + \delta\mu\mathbf{n} \quad , \tag{85.9}$$

and

$$\delta\boldsymbol{\mu} \cdot d\mathbf{r}_g = \mu\delta\boldsymbol{\mu} \cdot d\mathbf{r}_g + \delta\mu\mathbf{n} \cdot d\mathbf{r}_g = 0 \tag{85.10}$$

we obtain,

$$\frac{d\mathbf{r}_g \cdot \delta\boldsymbol{\mu}}{d\mathbf{r}_g \cdot \mathbf{n}} = -\frac{\delta\mu}{\mu} \quad . \tag{85.11}$$

The denominator $d\mathbf{r}_g \cdot \mathbf{n}$ represents the longitudinal component of the group path, that is, the projection of $d\mathbf{r}_g$ in the wave normal direction and $d\mathbf{r}_g \cdot \delta\boldsymbol{\mu}$ represents the transverse component, since $\delta\mathbf{n}$ is normal to $\mathbf{n}$ because $\mathbf{n}$ is a unit vector. Also, in μ-space, we have by definition,

$$\delta\mu \equiv \mathbf{grad}_{\mu}\mu \cdot \delta\mathbf{n} \equiv \nabla_{\mu}\mu \cdot \delta\mathbf{n} \tag{85.12}$$

where $\mathbf{grad}_{\mu}$ means the gradient operator in $\boldsymbol{\mu}$-space. Therefore, we can also write eq. (85.11) as,

$$\frac{d\mathbf{r}_g \cdot \delta\boldsymbol{\mu}}{d\mathbf{r}_g \cdot \mathbf{n}} = -\frac{\nabla_{\mu}\mu \cdot \delta\mathbf{n}}{\mu} \quad . \tag{85.13}$$

Now for any function $H = H(\mu)$ we have the vector relation

$$\mathbf{grad}\, H = H'(\mu)\mathbf{grad}\, \mu \quad ,$$

where $H'(\mu)$ denotes the derivative of H with respect to μ, hence in eq. (85.13) we can replace $\nabla_{\mu}\mu$ by $\nabla_{\mu}H/(\partial H/\partial\mu)$ and finally write,

$$\frac{d\mathbf{r}_g \cdot \delta\boldsymbol{\mu}}{d\mathbf{r}_g \cdot \mathbf{n}} = -\frac{\nabla_\mu H \cdot \delta\mathbf{n}}{\mu \dfrac{\partial H}{\partial \mu}} \quad . \tag{85.14}$$

86. AN ALTERNATIVE DESCRIPTION OF THE RAY DIRECTION

We have shown previously that at a fixed point $\mathbf{r}$, it is possible to write the equation of the surface swept out by the end point of σ or μ (which we use in the following description) in polar form. This means that we can write the equation of the surface in the form,

$$|\mu| = f\left(\mathbf{r}, \frac{n_1}{n_3}, \frac{n_2}{n_3}\right) \quad , \tag{86.1}$$

in μ-space. For fixed $\mathbf{r}$, this is a function of two parameters, namely the ratio of n_1/n_3 and n_2/n_3 where the n_i refer however to a coordinate system in $\mathbf{r}$-space. The polar representation implies that we can use any two parameters for the description of the surface, in fact the description of any surface requires two independent parameters. It is therefore convenient to write the surface in a vector representation, that is,

$$\boldsymbol{\mu} = \boldsymbol{\mu}(\theta, \phi) \quad , \tag{86.2}$$

where we have dropped the $\mathbf{r}$ in writing the equation. The parameters θ and ϕ can be thought of as spherical polars in μ-space. In this space we introduce three mutually perpendicular unit vectors $\mathbf{e}_1$, $\mathbf{e}_2$, $\mathbf{e}_3$ and therefore

$$\boldsymbol{\mu} = \mu \sin\theta \cos\phi \, \mathbf{e}_1 + \mu \sin\theta \sin\phi \, \mathbf{e}_2 + \mu \cos\theta \, \mathbf{e}_3 \quad , \tag{86.3}$$

where μ is the magnitude of the index surface. The parameter θ is the angle between $\boldsymbol{\mu}$ and $\mathbf{e}_3$. The vectors $\partial\boldsymbol{\mu}/\partial\theta$ and $\partial\boldsymbol{\mu}/\partial\phi$ are vectors tangent to the θ and ϕ curves, respectively and so are tangent to the μ-surface. they are however not unit vectors. The vector formed by the vector product of these two vectors in the following sense

$$\frac{\partial\boldsymbol{\mu}}{\partial\phi} \times \frac{\partial\boldsymbol{\mu}}{\partial\theta} \quad ,$$

is perpendicular to the μ-surface at the point (θ, ϕ) and is directed outward from the surface. The ray vector is defined by

$$\boldsymbol{\alpha} = \frac{\dfrac{\partial\boldsymbol{\mu}}{\partial\phi} \times \dfrac{\partial\boldsymbol{\mu}}{\partial\theta}}{\sqrt{\left(\dfrac{\partial\boldsymbol{\mu}}{\partial\phi} \times \dfrac{\partial\boldsymbol{\mu}}{\partial\theta}\right) \cdot \left(\dfrac{\partial\boldsymbol{\mu}}{\partial\theta} \times \dfrac{\partial\boldsymbol{\mu}}{\partial\theta}\right)}} \tag{86.4}$$

and is of unit length. From the relations,

$$\left.\begin{aligned}
\frac{\partial\boldsymbol{\mu}}{\partial\phi} &= -\mu \sin\theta \sin\phi \, \mathbf{e}_1 + \mu \sin\theta \cos\phi \, \mathbf{e}_3 + \sin\theta \cos\phi \frac{\partial\mu}{\partial\phi} \mathbf{e}_1 \\
&\quad + \sin\theta \sin\phi \frac{\partial\mu}{\partial\phi} \mathbf{e}_2 + \cos\theta \frac{\partial\mu}{\partial\phi} \mathbf{e}_3 \\
&= \frac{\boldsymbol{\mu}}{\mu} \frac{\partial\mu}{\partial\phi} - \boldsymbol{\mu} \times \mathbf{e}_3 \quad , \\
\frac{\partial\boldsymbol{\mu}}{\partial\theta} &= \mu \cos\theta \cos\phi \, \mathbf{e}_1 + \mu \cos\theta \sin\phi \, \mathbf{e}_2 - \mu \sin\theta \, \mathbf{e}_3 \\
&\quad + \frac{\boldsymbol{\mu}}{\mu} \frac{\partial\mu}{\partial\theta}
\end{aligned}\right\} \tag{86.5}$$

and the identity,

$$\left(\frac{\boldsymbol{\mu}}{\sin\theta} - \frac{\mu \cos\theta}{\sin\theta} \mathbf{e}_3\right) = \mu \cos\phi \, \mathbf{e}_1 + \mu \sin\phi \, \mathbf{e}_2$$

we obtain,

$$\frac{\partial\boldsymbol{\mu}}{\partial\theta} = \frac{\boldsymbol{\mu}}{\mu}\left(\frac{\partial\mu}{\partial\theta} + \mu \operatorname{ctn}\theta\right) - \mu \csc\theta \, \mathbf{e}_3 \quad , \tag{86.6}$$

consequently,

$$\frac{\partial\boldsymbol{\mu}}{\partial\phi} \times \frac{\partial\boldsymbol{\mu}}{\partial\theta} = \left(\cos\theta \frac{\partial\mu}{\partial\theta} - \mu \sin\theta\right)\boldsymbol{\mu} - \mu \frac{\partial\mu}{\partial\theta} \mathbf{e}_3 + \csc\theta \frac{\partial\mu}{\partial\phi} \mathbf{e}_3 \times \boldsymbol{\mu} \quad ; \tag{86.7}$$

let us denote the coefficients of $\boldsymbol{\mu}$, $\mathbf{e}_3$ and $\mathbf{e}_3\mathbf{x}\boldsymbol{\mu}$ by A, μB and C, respectively and write,

$$\frac{\dfrac{\partial\boldsymbol{\mu}}{\partial\phi} \mathbf{x} \dfrac{\partial\boldsymbol{\mu}}{\partial\theta}}{A\mu} = \frac{\boldsymbol{\mu}}{\mu} - \frac{\left(B\mathbf{e}_3 - \dfrac{C}{\mu}\mathbf{e}_3\mathbf{x}\boldsymbol{\mu}\right)}{A} \tag{86.8}$$

From this it is clear that the right side is a vector which has the same direction as the ray vector $\boldsymbol{a}$. Further, if both B and C vanish then the direction of the ray coincides with that of $\boldsymbol{\mu}$ and hence the medium is isotropic. From this it follows that the coefficients B and C are measures of the degree of anisotropy of the medium.

It is instructive to apply these results to the case in which the medium is characterized by the Appleton-Hartree equation. For negligible collisions we can write from Chapter II, section 14, eq. (14.1a) putting $M_j^2 = \mu^2$,

$$\mu^2 = 1 - \frac{2a(1-a)}{2(1-a) - \Omega^2\sin^2\theta \pm \sqrt{\Omega^4\sin^4\theta + 4\Omega^2(1-a)^2\cos^2\theta}} \tag{86.9}$$

or the alternative form,

$$(1-\mu^2-a)[(\Omega^2+a-1)(1-\mu^2-a) + a\Omega^2] + a\Omega^2(1-\mu^2)\mu^2\cos^2\theta = 0 \quad . \tag{86.10}$$

We see in this case that C vanishes since $\partial\mu/\partial\phi = 0$, and the expression (86.8) simplifies. So if we define a new parameter ϵ which measures the degree of anisotropy (or isotropy) by,

$$\epsilon = 1 - \frac{\dfrac{\partial\mu}{\partial\theta}}{\dfrac{\partial\mu}{\partial\theta}\cos^2\theta - \mu\sin\theta\cos\theta} \quad , \tag{86.11}$$

(it is clear that this expression holds independent of the Appleton-Hartree equation, *i.e.*, it only requires that $\partial\mu/\partial\phi = 0$), then the ray vector can be written as,

$$\alpha = \frac{\dfrac{\mu}{\mu} - (1 - \epsilon)\cos\theta\,\mathbf{e}_3}{\sqrt{\sin^2\theta + \epsilon^2\cos^2\theta}} \quad . \tag{86.12}$$

We remind ourselves that in the Appleton-Hartree equation, the angle θ is measured between the direction of the magnetic field $\mathbf{B}_0$ and the wave normal vector μ, hence $\mathbf{e}_3$ is a unit vector in the direction of $\mathbf{B}_0$. As $\epsilon \to 1$, α tends to μ/μ, *i.e.*, the medium is isotropic. By calculation $\partial\mu/\partial\theta$ from eq. (86.10) and after some algebraic manipulations we can put ϵ in the following form

$$\epsilon = \frac{(\Omega^2 - 1)(1 - \mu^2)^2 + a^2}{\left(\dfrac{\Omega^2}{1 - a} - 1\right)(1 - \mu^2)^2 + a^2} \quad , \tag{86.13}$$

and this together with the expression for α defines the ray direction. It can be shown that if ψ is the angle between $\mathbf{e}_3$ and α then

$$\mathbf{e}_3 \cdot \alpha = \cos\psi = \frac{\epsilon\cos\theta}{\sqrt{\sin^2\theta + \epsilon^2}} \tag{86.14}$$

and,

$$\epsilon = \frac{\tan\theta}{\tan\psi} \tag{86.15}$$

which gives a geometric interpretation of the parameter ϵ. The treatment given in this section can be carried further* to determine the equivalent path length, etc.

87. THE RAY-WAVE CONNECTION IN A GENERAL REFRACTING ANISOTROPIC MEDIUM

In this section we shall establish the connection between rays and waves which hold for a medium which is more generally refracting than, for example, a doubly refracting crystal.

---

* The use of the approach in this section to determine the wave normal in a stratified low density plasma like the ionosphere, and the electron density distribution, together with numerical procedures for obtaining both on a high speed computer can be found in the paper by R. J. Marcou, W. Pfister and J. C. Ulwick, Journal of Geophysical Research, Volume 63, No. 2, June 1958.

The points of this medium will be referred to a right handed rectangular Cartesian system of axis, $0x_1\ x_2\ x_3$. If we let W_1, W_2, W_3 represent the speeds of propagation of phase of plane waves along the directions $0x_1$, $0x_2$, and $0x_3$ respectively, these three kinds of particular propagation will be represented by the wave equations,

$$W_1^2 \frac{\partial^2 \Psi}{\partial x_1^2} = \frac{\partial^2 \Psi}{\partial t^2}\ , \quad W_2^2 \frac{\partial^2 \Psi}{\partial x_2^2} = \frac{\partial^2 \Psi}{\partial x_2^2}\ , \quad W_3^2 \frac{\partial^2 \Psi}{\partial x_3^2} = \frac{\partial^2 \Psi}{\partial t^2}\ . \tag{87.1}$$

If we also assume that the speeds W_1, W_2, W_3 are slowly varying functions, it is plausible to assume that a propagation of waves in any direction can be represented approximately by the following propagation equation,

$$\frac{\partial^2}{\partial x_1^2}(W_1^2 \Psi) + \frac{\partial^2}{\partial x_2^2}(W_2^2 \Psi) + \frac{\partial}{\partial x_3^2}(W_3^2 \Psi) = \frac{\partial^2 \Psi}{\partial t^2}\ . \tag{87.2}$$

This equation in a sense is a generalization of the equation of propagation for a homogeneous isotropic medium. For, in that case, $W_1 = W_2 = W_3 = W =$ constant and the above equation takes the familiar form of eq. (1.6) of Chapter I.

Also, we further assume that the geometrical optics approximations of Chapter I is valid, and seek a monochromatic solution of eq. (87.2) of the form $A(\mathbf{r}) \exp \{2\pi i[\nu t - \psi(\mathbf{r})]\}$. There results

$$\left[\frac{\partial}{\partial x_1}(W_1 \psi)\right]^2 + \left[\frac{\partial}{\partial x_2}(W_2 \psi)\right]^2 + \left[\frac{\partial}{\partial x_3}(W_3 \psi)\right]^2 = \nu^2\ , \tag{87.3}$$

and

$$\frac{\partial}{\partial x_1}\left(A^2 W_1^2 \frac{\partial \psi}{\partial x_1}\right) + \frac{\partial}{\partial x_2}\left(A^2 W_2^2 \frac{\partial \psi}{\partial x_2}\right) + \frac{\partial}{\partial x_3}\left(A^2 W_3^2 \frac{\partial \psi}{\partial x_3}\right) = 0\ . \tag{87.4}$$

These two equations correspond to equations (3.29) and (3.30) of Chapter I. Let us consider, about the origin 0 of the axes, a sufficiently small neighborhood, so that W_1, W_2 and W_3 are sensibly constant, *i.e.*, the region is locally uniform. We can then visualize in the interior of this neighborhood a plane monochromatic wave of constant amplitude A and phase function ψ defined by

$$\psi = \nu \frac{\mathbf{n} \cdot \mathbf{r}}{W_n}, \quad \text{with } \mathbf{n} \cdot \mathbf{n} = 1 , \tag{87.5}$$

and W_n defining the normal speed of propagation of phase in the direction **n** normal to the planes of equal phase $\mathbf{n} \cdot \mathbf{r}$ = constant. By substituting this expression for ψ into eq. (87.3) we obtain the relation

$$W_n^2 = n_1^2 W_1^2 + n_2^2 W_2^2 + n_3^2 W_3^2 , \tag{87.6}$$

which defines the normal speed in each direction **n**. Analogous to the construction of the ray surface we can determine the equation of the normal speeds. Consider a local coordinate system attached to the point 0. This local rectangular Cartesian coordinate system will be denoted by $0\eta_1\eta_2\eta_3$, and is right handed. From 0 draw a line of length numerically equal to W_n in each direction. The end points of each such line forms a surface whose equation is clearly given by

$$\eta^4 = \eta_1^2 W_1^2 + \eta_2^2 W_2^2 + \eta_3^2 W_3^2 , \tag{87.7}$$

where,

$$\eta^2 = W_n^2 .$$

Eq. (87.7) is the surface of normal speeds. By setting,

$$\mu = \frac{V_0}{W_n}, \quad \mu_i = \frac{V_0}{W_i}, \quad (i = 1, 2, 3) , \tag{87.8}$$

(where V_0 is the speed of propagation in a reference homogeneous isotropic medium), we obtain

$$\frac{\eta_1^2}{\mu_1^2} + \frac{\eta_2^2}{\mu_2^2} + \frac{\eta_3^2}{\mu_3^2} = 1 , \tag{87.9}$$

which is the surface of indices, and in this case is an ellipsoid. In order to find the rays, let us recall its definition. The ray corresponding to the propagation in the direction **n** is obtained by joining the point 0 to the point where the plane of the wave touches its envelope.

According to this definition the point of contact of the plane of the wave with its envelope is the point where plane waves whose directions are arbitrarily close to each other are also in phase. Equation (87.4) which corresponds to eq. (3.30) of Chapter I is given an interpretation which carries over from the isotropic inhomogeneous medium. We recall that eq. (3.30) which resulted from eq. (3.3) led to the equation for amplitude variations and the fluid analogue. More specifically, $|A|^2 = |\Psi|^2$ is taken as a measure of the energy density. This leads us to consider the flux of energy to be in the direction of the vector whose components are respectively

$$W_1^2 \frac{\partial\psi}{\partial x_1} \quad , \quad W_2^2 \frac{\partial\psi}{\partial x_2} \quad , \quad W_3^2 \frac{\partial\psi}{\partial x_3} \qquad .$$

Therefore, we can assert that the ray is in the direction defined by these components. We must however show that this definition is consistent with the definition of the ray as defined by the envelope construction. This will now be demonstrated. It will prove more convenient to choose instead of the components $W_1^2(\partial\psi/\partial x_1)$, etc., numbers which are proportional to them, namely,

$$\alpha_i = \frac{n_i W_i^2}{W_n} \quad , \quad (i = 1,\ 2,\ 3) \quad , \quad \text{no sum on } i \quad . \tag{87.10}$$

Let us calculate the coordinates of the point where the plane of the wave

$$\frac{\mathbf{n} \cdot \mathbf{r}}{W_n} = C \tag{87.11}$$

touches its envelope. The above equation of the plane wave surface can be represented in the equivalent form, $F = 0$, *i.e.*,

$$F(\mathbf{r},\mathbf{n}) = n_1 x_1 + n_2 x_2 + (\sqrt{1 - n_1^2 - n_2^2})x_3 - C\sqrt{n_1^2W_1^2 + n_2^2W_2^2 + (1 - n_1^2 - n_2^2)W_3^2} \quad . \tag{87.12}$$

The calculation of the partial derivatives lead to

$$\frac{\partial F}{\partial n_1} = x_1 - \frac{n_1}{n_2} x_3 - \frac{Cn_1}{W_n}(W_1^2 - W_3^2) \quad , \quad \frac{\partial F}{\partial n_2} = x_2 - \frac{n_2}{n_3} x_3 - \frac{Cn_2}{W_n}(W_2^2 - W_3^2) \; . \qquad (87.13)$$

The simultaneous solution of the equations $F = 0$, as given by eqs. (87.12) and (87.13) is

$$x_1 = \frac{Cn_1}{W_n} W_1^2 \quad , \quad x_2 = \frac{Cn_2}{W_n} W_2^2 \quad , \quad x_3 = \frac{Cn_3}{W_n} W_3^2 \quad , \qquad (87.14)$$

which are the coordinates of the point of contact of the plane wave with its envelope. By comparing eq. (87.14) with eq. (87.10) we see that they are proportional and consequently we have proved our assertion.

In order to find the envelope of the planes of the wave we must eliminate the quantities n_1, n_2, n_3 between equations (87.14) by also using eq. (87.6) for W_n. The result is

$$\frac{x_1^2}{W_1^2} + \frac{x_2^2}{W_2^2} + \frac{x_3^2}{W_3^2} = C^2 \quad , \qquad (87.15)$$

which is an ellipsoid, and which is reciprocal to the surface of indices, eq. (87.9). Equation (87.7) is also called the pedal surface* of eq. (87.15).

Equation (87.11) which defines C implies that this parameter C is the time taken by the phase in its displacement from the origin. Now put $C = 1$ in eq. (87.15), then the ray vector which joins each point of the wave surface to the origin is equal to the speed of the displacement of the phase along the ray vector. This speed, which according to the interpretation given above, is the ray speed V, and (which is also the speed of energy transport along the ray if the medium is not absorbing). The surface (87.15) with $C = 1$ is also the ray surface. Figure 24 gives the relation between $\mathbf{W}_h$ and $\mathbf{V}$.

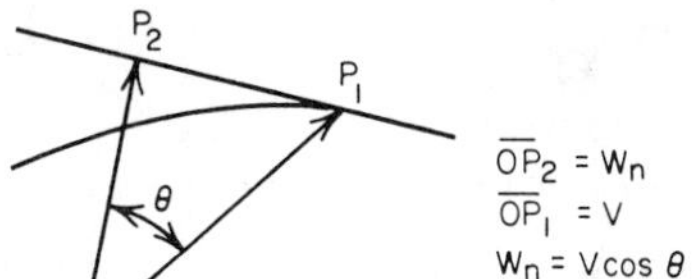

FIG. 24

*For a somewhat detailed discussion of index surfaces and other related surfaces, see A. V. Shubnikov, Principles of Optical Crystallography *loc. cit.* See also A. Sommerfeld, Optics, *loc. cit.*

88. THE RAY PATH EQUATIONS IN A GENERAL COORDINATE SYSTEM

Till now we have developed and derived the ray path equations and its implications with reference to a fixed rectangular cartesian coordinate system. Although the ray path equations arose from a variational principle which we asserted is independent of any coordinate, system, the same is true of the properties of the ray path equations. The geometry of the reciprocal surfaces likewise shares this property. However, we want to extend the utility of our treatment. For example, suppose we want to trace some rays through the ionosphere and don't want to limit ourselves to a flat earth approximation. In such a case we would be obliged to use a spherical coordinate system and consequently must know the proper representation of the ray equations in the spherical coordinate system.

We shall however treat the problem more generally and develop the appropriate apparatus so that we obtain a representation of the ray path equations in any curvilinear coordinate system. The natural tool for obtaining such a description is the tensor calculus. We shall utilize the concepts of the tensor calculus but couch it in the language of vectors in order that the reader may understand the formalism better.

In what follows we shall denote by (y^1, y^2, y^3) the coordinates of a point in a rectangular cartesian reference system and by (x^1, x^2, x^3) the coordinates of the same point when referred to an arbitrary curvilinear coordinate system. We introduce two base vector systems; the first system labeled $\mathbf{e}_1$, $\mathbf{e}_2$, $\mathbf{e}_3$ is an orthonormal system lying along the y^i axes, $\mathbf{e}_1$ along y^1, etc., the second system denoted by $\mathbf{a}^1$, $\mathbf{a}^2$, $\mathbf{a}^3$ is a local base vector system attached to the x^i system at the point P as shown in Fig. 25.

The vectors $\mathbf{a}^i$ are not unit vectors but are tangent to the coordinate lines which are not in general orthogonal. We associate with the base vectors $\mathbf{a}^i$ another set of vectors labeled by $\mathbf{a}_i$ which are biorthogonal (or reciprocal) to the set $\mathbf{a}^i$. We mean by this term that the two sets of vectors satisfy the following relations,

$$\mathbf{a}_i \cdot \mathbf{a}^j = \delta_i^j = \begin{cases} 0\ , & \text{if } i \neq j \\ 1\ , & \text{if } i = j \end{cases} \ , \qquad (i, j = 1, 2, 3) \ . \tag{88.1}$$

The vectors $\mathbf{a}_i$ are also locally attached to the x-system at P. By introducing these two sets of biorthogonal base vectors (*i.e.*, linearly independent) we are able to give a precise geometric meaning to the concepts of covariance and contravariance.

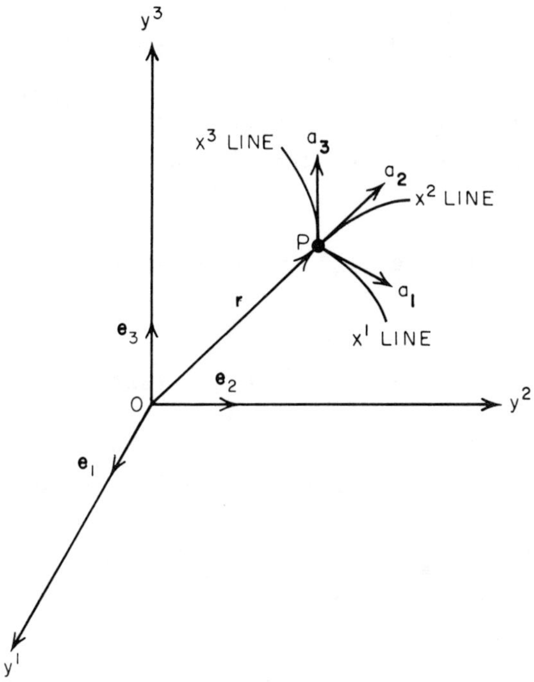

FIG. 25

That is, if **x** is any vector it has a representation, unique of course, in both systems, and we write

$$\mathbf{x} = x_1\mathbf{a}^1 + x_2\mathbf{a}^2 + x_3\mathbf{a}^3 \equiv x_i\mathbf{a}^i \quad \text{(summation convention)}$$

$$\mathbf{x} = x^1\mathbf{a}_1 + x^2\mathbf{a}_2 + x^3\mathbf{a}_3 = x^i\mathbf{a}_i \quad . \tag{88.2}$$

The first representation is called the covariant and the second is called the contravariant representation of **x**. We note from these definitions that the inner product of **x** with itself obeys the conventional rule

$$\mathbf{x}\cdot\mathbf{x} = x_i x^i \equiv |\mathbf{x}|^2 \quad . \tag{88.3}$$

If the $\mathbf{a}_i \equiv \mathbf{e}_i$, $(i = 1, 2, 3)$, then also $\mathbf{a}^i = \mathbf{a}_i = \mathbf{e}_i$ and the distinction between covariance and contravariance disappears. That is, in a rectangular cartesian reference frame the two representations are the same.

Let us denote by $y^i = y^i(x^1, x^2, x^3)$, $(i = 1, 2, 3)$, the functional transformation of the two coordinate systems, which is also assumed to have an inverse, say, $x^i = x^i(y^1, y^2, y^3)$, $(i = 1, 2, 3)$. The relation between the two base systems $\mathbf{e}_i$ and $\mathbf{a}_i$ is then given by

$$\mathbf{e}_i = \frac{\partial x^j}{\partial y^i}\,\mathbf{a}_j \quad , \quad (i = 1, 2, 3) \quad . \tag{88.4}$$

According to the definitions, the superscripts denote the contravariant and the subscripts the covariant description. Thus, the vector σ is given by either

$$\sigma = \sigma^i \mathbf{a}_i \quad , \quad \text{(contravariant)}$$

or,

$$\sigma = \sigma_i \mathbf{a}^i \quad , \quad \text{(covariant)} \quad . \tag{88.5}$$

When the base vectors transform according to the rule of eqs. (88.4), the contravariant components of σ transforms by the rule,

$$\sigma^s(x) = \sigma^m(y)\,\frac{\partial x^s}{\partial y^m} \quad , \quad (s = 1, 2, 3) \quad , \tag{88.6}$$

where the notation $\sigma^s(x) \equiv \sigma^s(x^1, x^2, x^3)$, etc. With these definitions the ray path equations when referred to a rectangular cartesian frame is written as

$$\frac{dy^i}{dt} = \frac{\partial H}{\partial \sigma_i} \quad , \quad (i = 1, 2, 3) \quad ,$$

$$\frac{d\sigma_i}{dt} + \frac{\partial H}{\partial y^i} = 0 \quad , \quad (i = 1, 2, 3) \quad , \tag{88.7}$$

and consequently we see that the first equation constitutes a contravariant vector, that is, dy^i/dt are the components of a contravariant vector and therefore so is $\partial H/\partial \sigma^i$. On the other hand, neither $d\sigma^i/dt$ nor $\partial H/\partial y^i$ are separately the components of a vector but it is easily verified that the sum $d\sigma^i/dt + \partial H/\partial y^i$ constitute the components of a covariant vector. This means that a vector, say σ, transforms according to the rule

$$\sigma_s(x) = \frac{\partial x^m}{\partial y^s}\,\sigma_m(y) \quad , \quad (s = 1, 2, 3) \quad . \tag{88.8}$$

These results, incidentally, also prove that the Euler equations transform covariantly since they are fully equivalent to the canonical equations of Hamilton. With these preliminary definitions, we consider the second set of Hamilton's equations. Since this is a null vector we shall express it first in the $\mathbf{e}_i$ base system as

$$\left(\frac{d\sigma_i}{dt} + \frac{\partial H}{\partial y^i}\right)\mathbf{e}_i = \mathbf{0} \quad , \tag{88.9}$$

and since the distinction between covariance and contravariance disappears in a cartesian frame, we can equally well write the vector σ in superscript form so that the above equation is also written as

$$\left(\frac{d\sigma^i}{dt} + \frac{\partial H}{\partial y^i}\right)\mathbf{e}_i = \mathbf{0} \quad . \tag{88.10}$$

Now we want the same vector expressed in terms of the base system $\mathbf{a}_j$. That is, we must write the components in the x-system and also change the basis from the $\mathbf{e}_i$ to the $\mathbf{a}_j$ system. In order to understand this, let us write the above equation in the following form,

$$\frac{d\sigma}{dt} + \frac{\partial H}{\partial y^i}\mathbf{e}_i = \mathbf{0} \quad , \tag{88.11}$$

with the understanding that it is still the sum of the two terms which is a vector, not each one separately. We treat the first term and seek its representation in the $\mathbf{a}_j$ system. First write,

$$\sigma = \sigma^j\mathbf{a}_j \quad , \tag{88.12}$$

and we calculate the change in σ, say $d\sigma$, when both the components σ^j change and also the base vectors $\mathbf{a}_j$ undergo a change (the $\mathbf{a}_j$ are not constant vectors). Thus, we have

$$d\sigma = d\epsilon^j\mathbf{a}_j + \sigma^j\mathbf{a}_j \quad , \tag{88.13}$$

but,

$$d\sigma^j = \frac{\partial\sigma^j}{\partial x^k}dx^k \quad , \tag{88.14}$$

and,

$$d\mathbf{a}_j = \frac{\partial \mathbf{a}_j}{\partial x^k} dx^k \quad . \tag{88.15}$$

If ds denotes the element of arc length then we have

$$ds^2 = d\mathbf{r} \cdot d\mathbf{r} = \frac{\partial y^i}{\partial x^j} \frac{\partial y^i}{\partial x^k} dx^j dx^k \equiv g_{jk} dx^j dx^k \; , \tag{88.16}$$

where,

$$g_{jk} \equiv \frac{\partial y^i}{\partial x^j} \frac{\partial y^i}{\partial x^k} \quad . \tag{88.17}$$

The metric tensor g_{jk} is also given by

$$g_{jk} = \mathbf{a}_j \cdot \mathbf{a}_k \tag{88.18}$$

and its reciprocal denoted by g^{jk} is defined by

$$g^{jk} = \mathbf{a}^j \cdot \mathbf{a}^k \quad . \tag{88.19}$$

We introduce the Christoffel symbols of the first kind,

$$[jk, \alpha] \equiv \frac{1}{2}\left(\frac{\partial g_{j\alpha}}{\partial x^k} + \frac{\partial g_{k\alpha}}{\partial x^j} - \frac{\partial g_{jk}}{\partial x^\alpha} \right) \tag{88.20}$$

and the second kind by

$$\begin{Bmatrix} \alpha \\ jk \end{Bmatrix} \equiv [jk, \alpha] g^{\alpha i} \tag{88.21}$$

and note that both symbols are symmetric in j and k. By utilizing these definitions it can be shown that

$$\frac{\partial \mathbf{a}_j}{\partial x^k} = [jk, \alpha] \mathbf{a}^\alpha \tag{88.22}$$

so that the change in σ, $d\sigma$, is expressed completely in terms of the $\mathbf{a}_j$ base system, that is,

$$d\boldsymbol{\sigma} = \frac{\partial\sigma^j}{\partial x^k} dx^k\mathbf{a}_j + \sigma^\alpha \begin{Bmatrix} j \\ k\alpha \end{Bmatrix} dx^k\mathbf{a}_j \quad , \tag{88.23}$$

or, since dt is a scalar, we can write

$$\frac{d\sigma}{dt} = \left(\frac{\partial\sigma^j}{\partial x^k}\frac{dx^k}{dt} + \sigma^\alpha \begin{Bmatrix} j \\ k\alpha \end{Bmatrix} \frac{dx^k}{dt}\right)\mathbf{a}_j \quad . \tag{88.24}$$

We have succeeded in expressing $d\sigma/dt$ in terms of the $\mathbf{a}_j$, now we want to express $\partial H/\partial y^i\ \mathbf{e}_i$ in terms of the $\mathbf{a}_j$. For this, we write

$$\frac{\partial H}{\partial y^i} = \frac{\partial H}{\partial x^s}\frac{\partial x^s}{\partial y^i} + \frac{\partial H}{\partial\sigma^s}\frac{\partial\sigma^s}{\partial y^i} \quad , \tag{88.25}$$

and, according to eq. (88.6) we find,

$$\frac{\partial\sigma^s}{\partial y^i} = \sigma^m(y)\frac{\partial^2 x^s}{\partial y^m\partial y^i} \quad , \tag{88.26}$$

a result which follows when we consider that eq. (88.6) states that $\sigma^s(x)$ is considered as a function of the two independent quantities $\sigma^m(y)$ and y. Eq. (88.25) then becomes

$$\frac{\partial H}{\partial y^i} = \frac{\partial H}{\partial x^s}\frac{\partial x^s}{\partial y^i} + \sigma^m(y)\frac{\partial^2 x^s}{\partial y^m\partial y^i}\frac{\partial H}{\partial\sigma^s} \quad . \tag{88.27}$$

Under a change of coordinates, say from one curvilinear system to another, the Christoffel symbols transform according to the following rule,

$$\frac{\partial^2 x^s}{\partial y^m\partial y^i} = {}_y\begin{Bmatrix} r \\ mi \end{Bmatrix}\frac{\partial x^s}{\partial y^r} - {}_x\begin{Bmatrix} s \\ jk \end{Bmatrix}\frac{\partial x^s}{\partial y^m}\frac{\partial x^k}{\partial y^i} \quad , \tag{88.28}$$

where ${}_y\{\ \}$ means evaluated in the y-system, ${}_x\{\ \}$ in the x-system, If now we take the y-system as cartesian, ${}_y\{\ \} \equiv 0$ since all the g_{ij} are constants. By replacing the second derivative term in eq. (88.27), using eq. (88.28) we obtain,

$$\frac{\partial H}{\partial y^i} = \frac{\partial H}{\partial x^s}\frac{\partial x^s}{\partial y^i} - \sigma^m(y)\ {}_x\begin{Bmatrix} s \\ j\,k \end{Bmatrix}\frac{\partial x^j}{\partial y^m}\frac{\partial x^k}{\partial y^i}\frac{\partial H}{\partial \sigma^s} \quad . \tag{88.29}$$

Applying eq. (88.6), *i.e.*, $\sigma^j(x) = \sigma^m(y)\ (\partial x^j/\partial y^m)$, gives

$$\frac{\partial H}{\partial y^i} = \frac{\partial H}{\partial x^s}\frac{\partial x^s}{\partial y^i} - \sigma^j\ {}_x\begin{Bmatrix} s \\ j\,k \end{Bmatrix}\frac{\partial H}{\partial \sigma^s}\frac{\partial x^k}{\partial y^i} \quad . \tag{88.30}$$

Because s is a dummy index in the first term we can replace it by k and now write (dropping the subscript x on the Christoffel symbols)

$$\frac{\partial H}{\partial y^i} = \left(\frac{\partial H}{\partial x^k} - \sigma^\alpha \begin{Bmatrix} s \\ \alpha k \end{Bmatrix}\frac{\partial H}{\partial \sigma^s}\right)\frac{\partial x^k}{\partial y^i} \quad . \tag{88.31}$$

Now, we have, under a change of coordinates that

$$\left.\begin{aligned} \frac{d\sigma^i(y)}{dt}\,\mathbf{e}_i \text{ becomes } \frac{d\sigma^j(x)}{dt}\,\mathbf{a}_j \quad , \\ \frac{\partial H}{\partial y^i}\,\mathbf{e}_i \text{ becomes } \left(\frac{\partial H}{\partial x^k} - \sigma^\alpha \begin{Bmatrix} s \\ \alpha k \end{Bmatrix}\frac{\partial H}{\partial \sigma^s}\right)\frac{\partial x^k}{\partial y^i}\frac{\partial x^j}{\partial y^i}\,\mathbf{a}_j \quad , \end{aligned}\right\} \tag{88.32}$$

and a typical component say, the r-th is

$$\left(\frac{\partial \sigma^r}{\partial x^k}\frac{dx^k}{dt} + \sigma^\alpha \begin{Bmatrix} r \\ k\alpha \end{Bmatrix}\frac{dx^k}{dt}\right) + \left(\frac{\partial H}{\partial x^k} - \sigma^\alpha \begin{Bmatrix} s \\ k\alpha \end{Bmatrix}\frac{\partial H}{\partial \sigma^s}\right)\frac{\partial x^k}{\partial y^i}\frac{\partial x^r}{\partial y^i} = 0 \quad . \tag{88.33}$$

But,

$$g^{kr} = \frac{\partial x^k}{\partial y^i}\frac{\partial x^r}{\partial y^i} \quad , \tag{88.34}$$

so that if we multiply both terms of eq. (88.33) by g_{ir}, sum on r, and use the property that

$$g_{ir}g^{kr} = \delta^k_i \quad , \tag{88.35}$$

we obtain the covariant form of equation (88.33), namely,

$$g_{ir}\left(\frac{d\sigma^r}{dt} + \sigma^\alpha \begin{Bmatrix} r \\ k\alpha \end{Bmatrix} \frac{dx^k}{dt}\right) + \left(\frac{\partial H}{\partial x^i} - \sigma^\alpha \begin{Bmatrix} s \\ i\alpha \end{Bmatrix} \frac{\partial H}{\partial \sigma^s}\right) = 0 \ , \qquad (i = 1, 2, 3) \ , \tag{88.36}$$

where we have put

$$\frac{\partial \sigma^r}{\partial x^k}\frac{dx^k}{dt} \equiv \frac{d\sigma^k}{dt} \ .$$

For practical application we want to obtain $d\sigma^r/dt$ standing alone, in this case the form of eq. (88.33) is more useful. But we must examine the first equation of eqs. (88.7) and find its representation in the x-system. Since dy^i/dt is a contravariant vector, we can write

$$\frac{dx^j}{dt} = \frac{\partial x^j}{\partial y^i}\frac{dy^i}{dt} \ ,$$

also, $\partial H/\partial \sigma^i(x)$ is the covariant component of the vector $d\mathbf{r}/dt$. Therefore,

$$\frac{dy^i}{dt}\mathbf{e}_i = \frac{\partial H}{\partial \sigma^i(y)}\mathbf{e}^i \quad \text{in the } y\text{-system} \ ,$$

and,

$$\frac{dx^i}{dt}\mathbf{a}_i = \frac{\partial H}{\partial \sigma^i(x)}\mathbf{a}^i \quad \text{in the } x\text{-system} \ . \tag{88.37}$$

Taking the dot product of both sides of this equation with $\mathbf{a}^j$ gives,

$$\frac{dx^i}{dt}\mathbf{a}_i \cdot \mathbf{a}^j = \frac{\partial H}{\partial \sigma^i}\mathbf{a}^i \cdot \mathbf{a}^j$$

or,

$$\frac{dx^i}{dt}\delta^j_i = \frac{\partial H}{\partial \sigma^i} g^{ij} \ , \qquad \text{with} \quad g^{ij} = g^{ji} \ ,$$

so that we finally obtain

$$\frac{dx^j}{dt} = g^{ji} \frac{\partial H}{\partial \sigma^i} , \quad (j = 1, 2, 3) \quad . \tag{88.38}$$

If we solve for $d\sigma^r/dt$ from eq. (88.33), use eqs. (88.34) and (88.38), and employ the following identities:

$$\left. \begin{aligned} [ji, \alpha] &= \frac{\partial g_{j\alpha}}{\partial x^i} - [\alpha i, j] , \\ [jk, \alpha] &= \frac{\partial g_{j\alpha}}{\partial x^k} - [\alpha k, j] , \end{aligned} \right\} \tag{88.39}$$

and

$$\left. \begin{aligned} g^{s\alpha} [ji, \alpha] &= \left\{ \begin{matrix} s \\ ji \end{matrix} \right\} , \\ g^{m\alpha} [jk, \alpha] &= \left\{ \begin{matrix} m \\ jk \end{matrix} \right\} , \end{aligned} \right\} \tag{88.40}$$

then, after an obvious change of index notation, there results

$$\frac{d\sigma^j}{dt} = - g^{ij} \frac{\partial H}{\partial x^i} - g^{ij} g^{km} \sigma^l \frac{\partial H}{\partial \sigma^m} \left(\frac{\partial g_{li}}{\partial x^k} - \frac{\partial g_{kl}}{\partial x^i} \right) , \tag{88.41}$$

which must be considered along with

$$\frac{dx^j}{dt} = g^{ij} \frac{\partial H}{\partial \sigma^i} , \quad (j = 1, 2, 3) \quad . \tag{88.42}$$

Eqs. (88.41) and (88.42) constitute a simultaneous system of equations for the determination of the ray path in a general coordinate system. The general structure of this system is apparent if we put successively $u^1 = x^1$, $u^2 = x^2$, $u^3 = x^3$, $u^4 = \sigma^1$, $u^5 = \sigma^2$, $u^6 = \sigma^3$, then,

$$\frac{du^i}{dt} = f_i(u^1, u^2, u^3, u^4, u^5, u^6) , \quad (i = 1, 2, 3, \ldots, 6) , \tag{88.43}$$

which is a first order system of differential equations which in general is nonlinear. This system is closed in the sense that the parameter t does not appear in any of the $f_i(u)$. Consequently, it has a structure which is suitable for computation by numerical methods on an electronic computer.*

89. THE RAY PATH EQUATIONS IN TERMS OF THE PHYSICAL COMPONENTS

It is well known that in many physical problems which are formulated in a general curvilinear system we obtain, under coordinate transformations, only the components of the vectors. This means that we obtain entities which do not necessarily have the correct physical dimensions. In a rectangular cartesian frame the components do have the correct dimensions. Thus after finding the components in the general system, we must modify them to obtain the "physical components," *i.e.*, the components with the correct dimensions. These are easily obtained if we know the metric tensor of the space. That is, if g_{ij} is known, then the length of a vector, say σ, is defined by,

$$|\sigma|^2 = g_{ij}\sigma^i\sigma^j \quad . \tag{89.1}$$

Along the i-th coordinate line, we have (in what follows there is no sum on index i)

$$|\sigma|^2 = g_{ii}\sigma^i\sigma^i \quad , \tag{89.2}$$

hence, the physical components of σ are defined by

$$\sqrt{g_{ii}}\,\sigma^i \quad , \quad (i = 1, 2, 3) \quad . \tag{89.3}$$

Similarly, for dx^i/dt we have

$$\sqrt{g_{ii}}\,\frac{dx^i}{dt} \quad \text{as the physical components} \quad . \tag{89.4}$$

Let us define new variables

$$\rho_i = \sqrt{g_{ii}}\,\sigma^i \quad , \quad (i = 1, 2, 3) \quad , \tag{89.5}$$

* The computational considerations for such a system are treated elegantly and systematically in the paper by C. B. Haselgrove and Jenifer Haselgrove, "Twisted Ray Paths in the Ionosphere," Proc. Royal Society, Vol. LXXV, p. 357 (1960).

as the physical components of σ. If the coordinate system is orthogonal, $g_{ij} = 0$, for $i \neq j$, and we have

$$g^{ii} = \frac{1}{g_{ii}} . \tag{89.6}$$

We want to modify the system of equations (88.41) and (88.42) to obtain the expressions in terms of the physical components. To effect this we need the following formulas. If $f(x^1, x^2, x^3, \rho^1, \rho^2, \rho^3)$ is any differentiable function of the ρ^i and x^i; then

$$\left(\frac{\partial f}{\partial \sigma^i}\right)_{x^j} = \left(\frac{\partial f}{\partial \rho^i}\right)_{x^j} \frac{\partial \rho^i}{\partial \sigma^i} \tag{89.7}$$

where subscript x^j means that all x^j are kept constant in the differentiation process. Since, by eq. (89.5),

$$\frac{\partial \rho^i}{\partial \sigma^i} = \sqrt{g_{ii}} ,$$

$$\left(\frac{\partial f}{\partial \sigma^i}\right)_{x_j} = \left(\frac{\partial f}{\partial \rho^i}\right)_{x_j} \sqrt{g_{ii}} . \tag{89.8}$$

The other formula needed is derived as follows:

$$df = \sum_{k=1}^{3} \frac{\partial f}{\partial \rho^k} d\rho^k ; \tag{89.9}$$

and by definition,

$$\left(\frac{\partial f}{\partial x^i}\right)_{\sigma^j} = \sum_{k=1}^{3} \frac{\partial f}{\partial \rho^k} \frac{\partial \rho^k}{\partial x^i} \quad (i = 1, 2, 3) , \tag{89.10}$$

where subscript σ^j means to hold all σ^j constant in the differentiation process. With a similar meaning

$$\left(\frac{\partial f}{\partial x^i}\right)_{\rho^j} = \sum_{k=1}^{3} \frac{\partial f}{\partial \sigma^k}\frac{\partial \sigma^k}{\partial x^i} \quad , \quad (i = 1, 2, 3) \quad . \tag{89.11}$$

But, from eq. (89.5) again, and for a fixed value of k,

$$\frac{\partial \rho^k}{\partial x^i} = \sigma^k \frac{\partial}{\partial x^i}\sqrt{g_{kk}} + \sqrt{g_{kk}}\frac{\partial \sigma^k}{\partial x^i} \quad (i = 1, 2, 3) \quad , \tag{89.12}$$

so that

$$\left(\frac{\partial f}{\partial x^i}\right)_{\sigma^j} = \sum_{k=1}^{3} \frac{\partial f}{\partial \rho^k}\frac{\partial \rho^k}{\partial x^i} = \sum_{k=1}^{3} \frac{\partial f}{\partial \rho^k}\left(\sigma^k \frac{\partial}{\partial x^i}\sqrt{g_{kk}} + \sqrt{g_{kk}}\frac{\partial \sigma^k}{\partial x^i}\right) \quad , \tag{89.13}$$

and using both eqs. (89.5) and (89.8), eq. (89.13) becomes

$$\left(\frac{\partial f}{\partial x^i}\right)_{\sigma^j} = \sum_{k=1}^{3}\left(\frac{\partial f}{\partial \sigma^k}\frac{\partial \sigma^k}{\partial x^i} + \frac{\rho^k}{\sqrt{g_{kk}}}\frac{\partial \sqrt{g_{kk}}}{\partial x^i}\frac{\partial f}{\partial \rho^k}\right) \quad , \tag{89.14}$$

which by eq. (89.11) yields

$$\left(\frac{\partial f}{\partial x^i}\right)_{\sigma^j} = \left(\frac{\partial f}{\partial x^i}\right)_{\rho^j} + \sum_{k=1}^{3}\frac{\rho^k}{\sqrt{g_{kk}}}\frac{\partial \sqrt{g_{kk}}}{\partial x^i}\frac{\partial f}{\partial \rho^k} \quad , \quad (i = 1, 2, 3) \quad . \tag{89.15}$$

Equations (89.8) and (89.15) permit us to write the ray path equations in terms of the physical components.

90. THE RAY PATH EQUATIONS IN TERMS OF THE PHYSICAL COMPONENTS FOR AN ORTHOGONAL CURVILINEAR SYSTEM

The preceding formulas permit us to write the ray-path equations in an orthogonal curvilinear frame of reference. In this section also there will be no sum on the index i. The first of the set of ray path equations for an orthogonal system is obtained from eq. (88.42), and it becomes

$$\frac{dx^i}{dt} = g^{ii}\frac{\partial H}{\partial \sigma^i} = \frac{1}{g_{ii}}\frac{\partial H}{\partial \sigma^i} = \frac{1}{\sqrt{g_{ii}}}\frac{\partial H}{\partial \rho^i} \quad , \quad (i = 1, 2, 3) \quad . \tag{90.1}$$

The remaining equations of the set which is obtained from eq. (88.41) is analyzed in greater detail. We repeat this equation here for convenience and for an orthogonal reference frame,

$$\frac{d\sigma^i}{dt} = -g^{ii}\left(\frac{\partial H}{\partial x^i}\right)_{\sigma^j} - g^{ii}\sum_{k=1}^{3}\left(g^{kk}\sigma^i\frac{\partial H}{\partial\sigma^k}\frac{\partial g_{ii}}{\partial x^k} - g^{kk}\sigma^k\frac{\partial H}{\partial\sigma^k}\frac{\partial g_{kk}}{\partial x^i}\right) , \tag{90.2}$$

where $(\partial H/\partial x^i)_{\sigma^j}$ is the derivative in the (x, σ) system with all σ^j held constant. From eqs. (89.5), (89.8) and (89.15) with f now replaced by H, eq. (90.2) becomes in the (x, ρ) system

$$\frac{d\rho^i}{dt} = \sqrt{g_{ii}}\frac{d\sigma^i}{dt} + \sigma^i\sum_{k=1}^{3}\frac{\partial\sqrt{g_{ii}}}{\partial x^k}\frac{dx^k}{dt} . \tag{90.3}$$

If we replace dx^k/dt in this expression by its equivalent from eq. (90.1) and solve for $d\sigma^i/dt$, we find,

$$\frac{d\sigma^i}{dt} = \frac{1}{\sqrt{g_{ii}}}\frac{d\rho^i}{dt} - \frac{\sigma^i}{\sqrt{g_{ii}}}\sum_{k=1}^{3}\frac{\partial\sqrt{g_{ii}}}{\partial x^k}\frac{1}{\sqrt{g_{kk}}}\frac{\partial H}{\partial\rho^k} . \tag{90.4}$$

From the identities

$$\left.\begin{aligned}\frac{\partial g_{ii}}{\partial x^k} &= 2\sqrt{g_{ii}}\frac{\partial\sqrt{g_{ii}}}{\partial x^k} ,\\ \frac{\partial g_{kk}}{\partial x^i} &= 2\sqrt{g_{kk}}\frac{\partial\sqrt{g_{kk}}}{\partial x^i} ,\end{aligned}\right\} \tag{90.5}$$

and from eqs. (89.5), (89.8), (89.15) and (90.4) we obtain—after dropping the subscripts ρ^j since it is now understood that H is given as a function of the x^i and ρ^i—the ray path equations in terms of the physical components

$$\left.\begin{aligned}\frac{dx^i}{dt} &= \frac{1}{\sqrt{g_{ii}}}\frac{\partial H}{\partial\rho^i} ,\\ \frac{d\rho^i}{dt} &= -\frac{1}{\sqrt{g_{ii}}}\frac{\partial H}{\partial x^i} - \frac{1}{\sqrt{g_{ii}}}\sum_{k=1}^{3}\frac{1}{\sqrt{g_{kk}}}\frac{\partial H}{\partial\rho^k}\left(\rho^i\frac{\partial\sqrt{g_{ii}}}{\partial x^k} - \rho^k\frac{\partial\sqrt{g_{kk}}}{\partial x^i}\right) ,\end{aligned}\right\} \tag{90.6}$$

for $i = 1, 2, 3$. These equations are in a compact form, suitable for the determination of the ray path and clearly have the same basic structure as in eqs. (88.43). We emphasize again that the utility of describing the ray path in Hamiltonian form lies in the fact that there is no restriction on the medium, such as stratification, etc. Thus, such a formulation is quite general.

91. THE SPREAD OR DISPERSION OF THE RAYS BASED ON THE CONCEPT OF GEODESIC DEVIATION

The concept of the deviation between two geodesics is not new and has been thoroughly explored for a Riemanian space, *i.e.*, a space of n-dimensions for which the metric tensor g_{ij} is positive definite. The studies however utilize the second order Euler-Lagrange equations as the basis. It is possible however to carry over the concept of geodesic deviation for geodesics which are not based on a definite metric structure g_{ij} and also does not utilize directly the Euler-Lagrange equations.

The rays as we have defined them are geodesics in a wider sense and are characterized in the Hamiltonian formalism. The geodesic deviation between two rays when formulated in terms of the first order system of equations has a surprisingly simple structure and utility. It allows us to determine the spread of two rays whose frequencies differ by an amount say $\Delta\nu$. The differential equations defining the deviation can be integrated along with the ray path equations which together form a simultaneous system.

We shall assume that the Hamiltonian H is given as a function of $\mathbf{r}$, $\boldsymbol{\sigma}$ and frequency ν so that the ray path equations are given by

$$\left.\begin{aligned} \frac{dx^i}{dt} &= \frac{\partial H(\mathbf{r},\ \boldsymbol{\sigma};\ \nu)}{\partial \sigma_i} \ , \\ \frac{d\sigma_i}{dt} &= -\frac{\partial H(\mathbf{r},\ \boldsymbol{\sigma};\ \nu)}{\partial x^i} \ , \quad (i = 1,\ 2,\ 3) \ , \end{aligned}\right\} \qquad (91.1)$$

where the coordinates x^i are general and t is the parameter of time. Let us suppose that the solutions of these equations are exhibited in the following form,

$$\left.\begin{aligned} x^i &= x^i(t, \nu) \quad , \\ \sigma_i &= \sigma_i(t, \nu) \quad , \quad (i = 1, 2, 3) \quad , \end{aligned}\right\} \qquad (91.2)$$

so that the rays are a two-parameter family of geodesics arising from the variational principle

$$\delta \int_{P_1}^{P_2} \sigma_i dx^i = 0 \quad , \quad H(\mathbf{r}, \sigma; \nu) = 1 \quad . \qquad (91.3)$$

It is this two-parameter family which will be used to develop the concept of geodesic deviation. Consider two rays having a common initial point as shown in Fig. 26; denote one of these rays by C_ν and the other by $C_{\nu+d\nu}$. The meaning of the parameter t in this discussion is made clear as follows. Let the curve AA' cut the rays orthogonally and let t be the time of phase propagation measured along each ray from AA'. The curves ν = const. are rays in the three dimensional space. The points P and P' are corresponding points, that is, points which have the same value of the parameter when measured from a common point. The small distance between these corresponding points is called the deviation and the manner in which it varies is the geodesic deviation.

It is convenient when dealing with a parametric representation such as in eqs. (91.2) to introduce the notations

$$\left.\begin{aligned} \dot{x}^i &\equiv \frac{\partial x^i}{\partial t} \quad , \\ \eta^i &\equiv \frac{\partial x^i}{\partial \nu} d\nu \quad , \end{aligned}\right\} \qquad (91.4)$$

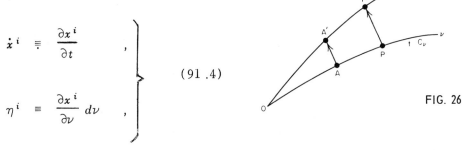

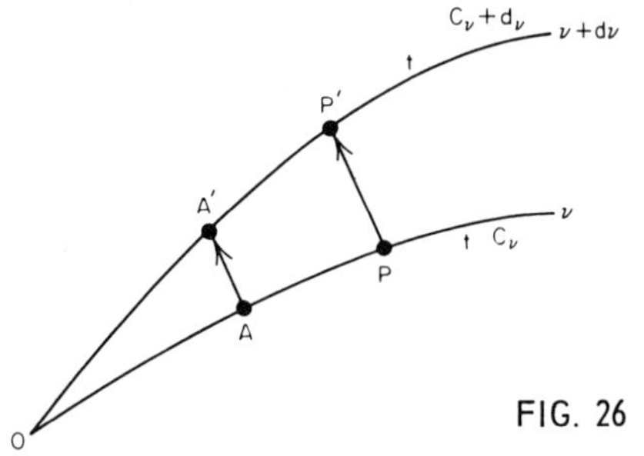

FIG. 26

so that $\dot{x}^i$ represents a field of tangent vectors to the rays, but which are not necessarily unit vectors unless t is the parameter of arc length. The vector η^i is the infinitesimal vector AA' which must be perpendicular to x^i at P since $C_{\nu+d\nu}$ is a neighboring geodesic. Let g_{ij} denote the metric tensor of the curvilinear reference frame in which the geodesics are imbedded, then since $\dot{x}^i$ and η^i are orthogonal by construction,

$$g_{ij}\dot{x}^i\eta^j = 0 \quad , \qquad (91.5)$$

where the summation convention is again invoked. We want to examine how η^i varies as we move along the geodesic C_ν. This is most conveniently done by calculating the absolute or intrinsic derivative of η^i with respect to the parameter t. The absolute derivative* is denoted by

$$\frac{\delta \eta^i}{\delta t} = \frac{\delta}{\delta t}\left(\frac{\partial x^i}{\partial \nu}\right) d\nu \quad , \tag{91.6}$$

the derivative applying only to quantity in parenthesis since $d\nu$ is a constant for the pair of rays C_ν and $C_{\nu+d\nu}$. The definition of the absolute derivative of a vector gives,

$$\frac{\delta}{\delta t}\frac{\partial x^i}{\partial \nu} = \frac{\partial}{\partial t}\frac{\partial x^i}{\partial \nu} + \begin{Bmatrix} i \\ mn \end{Bmatrix}\frac{\partial x^m}{\partial \nu}\frac{\partial x^n}{\partial t} = \frac{\delta}{\delta \nu}\frac{\partial x^i}{\partial t} \quad , \tag{91.7}$$

and from eq. (91.6), we can also write eq. (91.7) as

$$\frac{\delta \eta^i}{\delta t} = \frac{\delta}{\delta \nu}\dot{x}^i d\nu = \frac{\delta}{\delta \nu}\left(\frac{\partial H}{\partial \sigma_i}\right) d\nu \quad . \tag{91.8}$$

If we return to eq. (91.7), and write,

$$\frac{\delta \eta^i}{\delta t} = \left(\frac{\partial}{\partial \nu}\frac{\partial x^i}{\partial t} + \begin{Bmatrix} i \\ mn \end{Bmatrix}\frac{\partial x^m}{\partial \nu}\frac{\partial x^n}{\partial t}\right) d\nu \quad , \tag{91.9}$$

then according to eqs. (91.1) we also have,

$$\frac{\delta \eta^i}{\delta t} = \frac{\partial}{\partial \nu}\left(\frac{\partial H}{\partial \sigma_i}\right) d\nu + \begin{Bmatrix} i \\ mn \end{Bmatrix}\eta^m \frac{\partial H}{\partial \sigma_n} \tag{91.9$'$}$$

and since

$$\frac{\delta \eta^i}{\delta t} = \frac{d\eta^i}{dt} + \begin{Bmatrix} i \\ mn \end{Bmatrix}\eta^m \frac{dx^n}{dt} = \frac{d\eta^i}{dt} + \begin{Bmatrix} i \\ mn \end{Bmatrix}\eta^m \frac{\partial H}{\partial \sigma_n} \quad , \tag{91.10}$$

* The notion of absolute derivative is discussed in texts on tensor calculus. The concept of geodesic deviation is discussed in J. L. Synge and A. Schild, Tensor Calculus, Univ. of Toronto Press, p. 90-93 (1949). T. Leve-Civita, The Absolute Differential Calculus, p. 208-220, Blackie & Sons, London, (1947).

we obtain the relatively simple formula,

$$\frac{d\eta^i}{dt} = \frac{\partial}{\partial\nu}\left(\frac{\partial H}{\partial\sigma_i}\right)d\nu \quad , \quad (i = 1,\ 2,\ 3) \quad . \tag{91.11}$$

This formula shows that if we choose a given frequency ν, and $d\nu$, we can determine the spread between two rays which are separated by a frequency difference $d\nu$. As stated above this system of equations can be integrated along with the system determining the rays. We note however that in eq. (91.11) we have the description of $\partial H/\partial\sigma_i$ in terms of the covariant components of σ, namely σ_i. Consequently in order to be consistent with the description in the foregoing sections we should transform to a description in which we use the contravariant components of σ, namely σ^i. Finally after this is achieved, the physical components should be introduced. These transformations are left as an exercise for the reader.

Before concluding this chapter we should like to remark that although we based the development of the ray theory on an index of refraction characterization it would appear that this is the only way. This of course is not true. In the field of electron optics it is true that the study of the electron trajectories proceeds from a variational principle in which the integrand is interpreted as an index of refraction and the success of this approach has been aptly demonstrated.* But as we have seen in the section on the equivalent formulation, the theory of rays proceeds from a Hamiltonian which is properly normalized. The connection between rays and wave fronts has already been made clear in Chapter I and also in this chapter by deriving the Hamilton-Jacobi equation utilizing the characteristic function which is the spatial part of a wave front. The rays are curves in $\mathbf{r}$ space obtained by solving a system of ordinary differential equations in $(\mathbf{r},\ \sigma)$ space, *i.e.*, the canonical equations. The use of rays in the solution of propagation problems is of course well known. For example, as in Chapter III, if $S(t)$ represents a moving surface on which a set of physical quantities suffers a discontinuity, we may assume that it is given by the equation, $\psi(\mathbf{r}) - (t - t_0) = 0$, where t_0 is some initial reference time. Now suppose that we have found the Hamiltonian, $H(\mathbf{r},\ \sigma)$ where σ is normal to $\psi(\mathbf{r})$, by some means. Let $\mathbf{r}^0 = \mathbf{r}^0(\xi_1,\ \xi_2)$ be the equation of the initial manifold $S^0 = S(t_0)$ of the discontinuities, with $\sigma^0 = \sigma^0(\xi_1,\ \xi_2)$ denoting the wave normal. In

* See, for example, P. G. Sturrock, Static and Dynamic Optics.

principle then, we can exhibit the rays in the form $\mathbf{r} = \mathbf{r}(\xi_1, \xi_2, t - t_0)$, $\sigma = \sigma(\xi_1, \xi_2, t - t_0)$ for $t > t_0$, such that at $t = t_0$, $\mathbf{r}(\xi_1, \xi_2, 0) = \mathbf{r}^0(\xi_1, \xi_2)$ and $\sigma(\xi_1, \xi_2, 0) = \sigma(\xi_1, \xi_2)$. The equation $\mathbf{r} = \mathbf{r}(\xi_1, \xi_2, t - t_0)$ gives, for each value of t, the equation of the wave front in parametric form. By solving for the set $t - t_0$, ξ_1, ξ_2 in terms of the components of $\mathbf{r}$, the resulting expression for $t - t_0$ gives the equation of the wave front in the nonparametric form $\psi(\mathbf{r}) - (t - t_0) = 0$. The application of the Hamiltonian method described in this chapter to the problem of propagation of hydromagnetic discontinuities has recently been treated in some detail.*

92. THE APPROACH TO RAY PROPAGATION IN ANISOTROPIC MEDIA VIA MAXWELL'S EQUATIONS

As stated in the introduction to this chapter, the rigorous approach to a theory of ray propagation for electromagnetic fields is through Maxwell's equations. It is instructive to sketch here this approach and connect it with the exposition in the preceding sections. For harmonic time varying fields $e^{i\omega t}$, Maxwell's equations are,

$$\left.\begin{aligned} \nabla \times \mathbf{E} &= -i\omega \mathbf{B} \\ \nabla \times \mathbf{H} &= i\omega \mathbf{D} \end{aligned}\right\} , \qquad (92.1)$$

and for plane wave propagation, with spatial dependence $e^{-i\mathbf{K}\cdot\mathbf{r}}$, in an anisotropic homogeneous medium, these equations reduce to

$$\left.\begin{aligned} \omega \mathbf{B} &= \mathbf{K} \times \mathbf{E} \quad , \\ \omega \mathbf{D} &= -\mathbf{K} \times \mathbf{H} \quad . \end{aligned}\right\} \qquad (92.2)$$

In Chapter II, we showed that the vector product of two vectors can be written as the product of a skew-symmetric matrix and a vector. Therefore, we replace $\mathbf{K} \times \mathbf{E}$ by

$$\mathbf{K} \times \mathbf{E} = \begin{pmatrix} 0 & -k_3 & k_2 \\ k_3 & 0 & -k_1 \\ -k_2 & k_1 & 0 \end{pmatrix} \mathbf{E} \equiv \mathbf{K}\mathbf{E} \quad , \qquad (92.3)$$

* For a concrete application of the method, see J. Bazer and O. Fleischman, "Propagation of Weak Hydromagnetic Discontinuities," The Physics of Fluids, Vol. 2, No. 4, July-August, 1959.

and similarly for $\mathbf{K}\times\mathbf{H}$, thus,

$$\omega\mathbf{B} = \mathbf{K}\mathbf{E} \quad ,$$
$$\omega\mathbf{D} = -\mathbf{K}\mathbf{H} \quad . \tag{92.4}$$

If we have the constitutive relations,

$$\mathbf{B} = \mu\mathbf{H} \ ,$$
$$\mathbf{D} = \epsilon\mathbf{E} \ , \tag{92.5}$$

with both μ and ϵ tensors, and consider **B** and **D**, **E** and **H** as constituting column vectors, *i.e.*, $\begin{pmatrix}\mathbf{B}\\ \mathbf{D}\end{pmatrix}$, $\begin{pmatrix}\mathbf{E}\\ \mathbf{H}\end{pmatrix}$, the two constitutive relations can be combined into a single matrix relation. We write,

$$\begin{pmatrix}\mathbf{B}\\ \mathbf{D}\end{pmatrix} = \begin{pmatrix}0 & \mu\\ \epsilon & 0\end{pmatrix}\begin{pmatrix}\mathbf{E}\\ \mathbf{H}\end{pmatrix} \quad , \tag{92.6}$$

which is a 6 x 6 system. Eqs. (92.4) are likewise written in the form,

$$\omega\begin{pmatrix}\mathbf{B}\\ \mathbf{D}\end{pmatrix} = \begin{pmatrix}\mathbf{K} & 0\\ 0 & -\mathbf{K}\end{pmatrix}\begin{pmatrix}\mathbf{E}\\ \mathbf{H}\end{pmatrix} \quad , \tag{92.7}$$

and by substituting eq. (92.6) into (92.7) we obtain,

$$\left[\omega\begin{pmatrix}0 & \mu\\ \epsilon & 0\end{pmatrix} - \begin{pmatrix}\mathbf{K} & 0\\ 0 & -\mathbf{K}\end{pmatrix}\right]\begin{pmatrix}\mathbf{E}\\ \mathbf{H}\end{pmatrix} = 0$$

or,

$$\begin{pmatrix}-\mathbf{K} & \omega\mu\\ \omega\epsilon & \mathbf{K}\end{pmatrix}\begin{pmatrix}\mathbf{E}\\ \mathbf{H}\end{pmatrix} = 0 \quad . \tag{92.8}$$

For non-trivial $\begin{pmatrix}\mathbf{E}\\ \mathbf{H}\end{pmatrix}$ to exist, the determinant of this system must vanish, *i.e.*

$$\det\begin{pmatrix}-\mathbf{K} & \omega\mu\\ \omega\epsilon & \mathbf{K}\end{pmatrix} = 0 \quad . \tag{92.9}$$

This is a dispersion equation for **K**; it is the wave-normal equation since the vector **K** is proportional to the wave normal vector **n**. As we have seen already in Chapter II, this equation is of fourth order in the components of vector **K**; there are only two solutions in K^2, and four for vector **K**. The medium is birefringent in this case. If there is only one solution in K^2 the medium is non-birefringent, that is, in the language of crystal optics, the medium has an optical axis in the direction of **K**.

93. NON-HOMOGENEOUS MEDIA

For non-homogeneous media we assume solutions of the form (assymptotic representations, *i.e.*, as $\omega \to \infty$),

$$\left.\begin{aligned} \mathbf{E} &\sim \mathbf{E}_0 e^{-i\omega\psi(\mathbf{r})} , \\ \mathbf{H} &\sim \mathbf{H}_0 e^{-i\omega\psi(\mathbf{r})} , \end{aligned}\right\} \tag{93.1}$$

(see Chapter I, treatment of scalar wave equation). Here, $\mathbf{E}_0$, $\mathbf{H}_0$ are functions of position. Inserting eqs. (93.1) into (92.1) gives

$$\left.\begin{aligned} \mathbf{B} &\sim (\nabla\psi \times \mathbf{E}) + \frac{i}{\omega} (\nabla \times \mathbf{E}_0) \; e^{-i\omega\psi} , \\ \mathbf{D} &\sim -(\nabla\psi \times \mathbf{H}) - \frac{i}{\omega} (\nabla \times \mathbf{H}_0) \; e^{-i\omega\psi} , \end{aligned}\right\} \tag{93.2}$$

Put,

$$\mathbf{n} = \nabla\psi \tag{93.3}$$

then as $\omega \to \infty$, eqs. (93.2) reduce to

$$\left.\begin{aligned} \mathbf{B} &\sim \mathbf{n}\times\mathbf{E} , \\ \mathbf{D} &\sim -(\mathbf{n}\times\mathbf{H}) , \end{aligned}\right\} \tag{93.4}$$

and if **K** is defined as $\omega\mathbf{n}$, these are identical with eqs. (92.2) for the homogeneous medium. Consequently, as expected, we can treat the propagation in non-homogeneous media locally as a plane wave in a homogeneous medium. This is true in the asymptotic sense. With this result as a guide we can proceed to discuss rays in the non-homogeneous medium.

The determinental equation (92.9) implicitly contains the index of refraction and therefore can be identified as the Hamiltonian. Let us write this determinental equation in the form,

$$H(\sigma, \mathbf{r}) = 1 \quad , \tag{93.5}$$

where

$$\sigma \equiv \frac{\partial \psi}{\partial \mathbf{r}} \quad , \tag{93.6}$$

the phase function ψ is just the characteristic function. Even though eq. (93.5) is not necessarily a homogeneous function of degree one in σ we can still define "rays" by the system of equations,

$$\left.\begin{aligned} \frac{d\mathbf{r}}{du} &= \frac{\partial H}{\partial \sigma} \quad , \\ \frac{d\sigma}{du} &= -\frac{\partial H}{\partial \mathbf{r}} \quad , \end{aligned}\right\} \tag{93.7}$$

where u is some non-negative monotonic parameter. Let us examine this definition more closely. By substituting $\partial\psi/\partial\mathbf{r}$ for σ in eq. (94.5) we obtain a first order partial differential equation for the phase function $\psi(\mathbf{r})$. The result as we have already seen in a previous section is the Hamilton-Jacobi equation. We are then concerned with the problem of solving this equation subject to certain initial conditions. That is, ψ is assigned on some initial surface S. First suppose $H(\sigma, \mathbf{r})$ is any function of the six quantities $(\sigma, \mathbf{r})$ [not necessarily satisfying eq. (93.5)], the ordinary differential equations

$$\frac{d\mathbf{r}}{\dfrac{\partial H}{\partial \sigma}} = \frac{d\sigma}{-\dfrac{\partial H}{\partial \mathbf{r}}} \tag{93.8}$$

define a congruence of curves in the six dimensional space $(\sigma, \mathbf{r})$, one curve passing through any assigned point in that space. The system of equations (93.8) may also be written in the form of eqs. (93.7) defining the parameter u through

$$du = \frac{d\mathbf{r}}{\dfrac{\partial H}{\partial \sigma}} = \frac{d\sigma}{-\dfrac{\partial H}{\partial \mathbf{r}}} \quad . \tag{93.9}$$

Clearly, eqs. (93.7) imply

$$\frac{dH}{du} = 0 \quad . \tag{93.10}$$

Now consider the Hamilton-Jacobi equation,

$$H(\sigma, \mathbf{r}) = 1 \quad , \quad \sigma = \frac{\partial\psi}{\partial\mathbf{r}} \tag{93.11}$$

and look for a solution $\psi(\mathbf{r})$ which assumes values, say f on some surface S. Choose σ on S to satisfy

$$\sigma \cdot \delta\mathbf{r} = \delta f \quad , \quad H(\sigma, \mathbf{r}) = 1 \quad , \tag{93.12}$$

for every displacement in the surface S. There are two degrees of freedom in this displacement and we have three equations for the three quantities. So, even though the number of equations is right, there may be no σ which can be found. In order to examine this, consider a point $\mathbf{r}$ on S, and the space defined by σ, *i.e.*, the space in which the components of σ are the coordinates. The first equation of (93.12) determines the orthogonal projection of σ on the tangent plane of S, and the second equation constrains the end point of σ to lie on a surface defined by $H(\mathbf{r}, \sigma) = 1$. Equations (93.12) have a solution σ if and only if the orthogonal projection of $H(\mathbf{r}, \sigma) = 1$ on the tangent plane of S contains the assigned orthogonal projection of σ on the tangent plane of S. Moreover, if a solution exists, it is not necessarily unique.

To continue, suppose there exists a solution, then with the initial values of σ on S given by eqs. (93.12), draw the rays defined by eqs. (93.8). This congruence of rays emanates from S and at any point $\mathbf{r}$ in the region containing these rays we define $\psi(\mathbf{r})$ by the formula

$$\psi(\mathbf{r}) = f(\mathbf{r}_0) + \int_{\mathbf{r}_0}^{\mathbf{r}} \sigma \cdot d\mathbf{r} \tag{93.13}$$

where $\mathbf{r}_0$ is the point where the ray through $\mathbf{r}$ meets S, and the integral is taken along the ray. In this formula, $f(\mathbf{r}_0)$ is the assigned value on S, and consequently $\psi(\mathbf{r})$ satisfies the initial condition. We must now demonstrate that this construction of $\psi(\mathbf{r})$ satisfies the Hamilton-Jacobi equation. For this, we vary $\mathbf{r}$ and obtain

$$\frac{\partial \psi}{\partial \mathbf{r}} \cdot \delta \mathbf{r} = \delta f(\mathbf{r}_0) + \delta \int_{\mathbf{r}_0}^{\mathbf{r}} \sigma \cdot d\mathbf{r} \quad , \tag{93.14}$$

the variation being from the given ray to a neighboring ray. Since $H(\mathbf{r}, \sigma) = 1$ on S by assumption, it follows, from eq. (93.10) that $H(\mathbf{r}, \sigma) = 1$ everywhere, and therefore $\delta H = 0$. Thus, integrating (93.14) by parts, the last term in it is

$$\delta \int_{\mathbf{r}_0}^{\mathbf{r}} \sigma \cdot d\mathbf{r} = [\sigma \cdot \delta \mathbf{r}]_{\mathbf{r}_0}^{\mathbf{r}} + \int_{\mathbf{r}_0}^{\mathbf{r}} (\delta\sigma \cdot d\mathbf{r} - \delta \mathbf{r} \cdot d\sigma)$$

$$= [\sigma \cdot \delta \mathbf{r}]_{\mathbf{r}_0}^{\mathbf{r}} + \int_{\mathbf{r}_0}^{\mathbf{r}} \delta H du = [\sigma \cdot \delta \mathbf{r}]_{\mathbf{r}_0}^{\mathbf{r}} \quad , \tag{93.15}$$

hence,

$$\frac{\partial \psi}{\partial \mathbf{r}} \cdot \delta \mathbf{r} = \delta f(\mathbf{r}_0) + \sigma \cdot \delta \mathbf{r} - (\sigma \cdot \delta \mathbf{r})_S \quad , \tag{93.16}$$

the last term being evaluated on the surface S. By eqs. (93.12), we have therefore,

$$\frac{\partial \psi}{\partial \mathbf{r}} \cdot \delta \mathbf{r} = \sigma \cdot \delta \mathbf{r} \quad \text{or,} \quad \frac{\partial \psi}{\partial \mathbf{r}} = \sigma \quad , \tag{93.17}$$

and we conclude that $\psi(\mathbf{r}, \sigma)$ indeed satisfies $H(\mathbf{r}, \sigma) = 1$. Summarizing; to obtain the solution of the Hamilton-Jacobi equation with ψ assigned on S, we first determine the rays by solving eqs. (93.8) with initial values given by eqs. (93.12) and then construct $\psi(\mathbf{r})$ as in (93.13).

It is seen that the rays so defined satisfy the variational principle,

$$\delta \int \sigma \cdot d\mathbf{r} = 0 \quad , \quad \text{subject to } H(\mathbf{r}, \sigma) = 1 \quad , \tag{93.18}$$

for fixed end points and for σ arbitrary except for the constraint $H(\mathbf{r}, \sigma) = 1$. This is clear since the variational equation with this constraint leads to eqs. (93.8). What we have sketched in the foregoing is nothing more than the well known method of characteristics for solving the Hamilton-Jacobi partial differential equation. We note in particular, that if the equation of the initial surface is given by $S(\mathbf{r}) = 0$ and if $\partial H/\partial\sigma \cdot \partial S/\partial\mathbf{r} = 0$ on S, then the rays never leave the surface S. This is the exceptional case of ray propagation.

For the birefringent medium we know there are two possible initial values for eqs. (93.7) and therefore two corresponding solutions for $\psi(\mathbf{r})$ having the form of eq. (93.13).

If we define the index of refraction, m, in the direction of the ray $\partial H/\partial\sigma$, by the expression,

$$m = \frac{\sigma \cdot \dfrac{\partial H}{\partial \sigma}}{\left(\dfrac{\partial H}{\partial \sigma} \cdot \dfrac{\partial H}{\partial \sigma}\right)^{1/2}} , \tag{93.19}$$

the phase function $\psi(\mathbf{r})$ takes the form

$$\psi(\mathbf{r}) = \psi(0) + \int_0^s m\,ds , \tag{93.20}$$

where s is the parameter of arc length along the ray path. Suppose we define the vector

$$\mathbf{S} = \frac{\dfrac{\partial H}{\partial \sigma}}{\sigma \cdot \dfrac{\partial H}{\partial \sigma}} , \tag{93.21}$$

then

$$m = \frac{1}{|\mathbf{S}|} , \tag{93.22}$$

now asymptotically, the following relation holds,*

$$\mathbf{E} \cdot \mathbf{D} = \mathbf{H} \cdot \mathbf{B} \equiv W \tag{93.23}$$

*R. K. Luneberg, "Propagation of Electromagnetic Waves," Lectures at N.Y.U. 1947-8.

where W is the common value. Moreover, $\mathbf{S}$ can be expressed in the form,

$$\mathbf{S} = \frac{\mathbf{E} \times \mathbf{H}}{W} \quad . \tag{93.24}$$

The vector product of both sides of this relation with $\mathbf{B}$ and $\mathbf{D}$ respectively gives the two relations,

$$\left.\begin{aligned} \mathbf{S} \times \mathbf{B} &= \frac{1}{W}[(\mathbf{B} \cdot \mathbf{E})\mathbf{H} - (\mathbf{B} \cdot \mathbf{H})\mathbf{E}] \quad , \\ \mathbf{S} \times \mathbf{D} &= \frac{1}{W}[(\mathbf{D} \cdot \mathbf{E})\mathbf{H} - (\mathbf{D} \cdot \mathbf{H})\mathbf{E}] \quad , \end{aligned}\right\} \tag{93.25}$$

by using (93.23), and (93.4) which gives $\mathbf{B} \cdot \mathbf{E} = \mathbf{D} \cdot \mathbf{H} = 0$ assymptotically, replacing the vector products on the left side of (93.25) by their matrix equivalents, we find,

$$\begin{pmatrix} \mathbf{S} & \epsilon^{-1} \\ \mu^{-1} & -\mathbf{S} \end{pmatrix} \begin{pmatrix} \mathbf{B} \\ \mathbf{D} \end{pmatrix} = 0 \quad . \tag{93.26}$$

From this we have for non-trivial $\begin{pmatrix} \mathbf{B} \\ \mathbf{D} \end{pmatrix}$, the condition,

$$\det \begin{pmatrix} \mathbf{S} & \epsilon^{-1} \\ \mu^{-1} & -\mathbf{S} \end{pmatrix} = 0 \quad , \tag{93.27}$$

which is an alternative way of describing the propagation of rays. In retrospect we can describe the rays in a non-homogeneous anisotropic medium by the Hamilton-Jacobi equation, *i.e.*, through Hamilton's canonical equations, or by Fermat's principle, *i.e.*, $\delta \int m\,ds = 0$, or if we interpret $\mathbf{S}$ as the Poynting vector the rays are defined through $\mathbf{S}$ by means of eq. (93.27).

94. AMPLITUDE VARIATIONS--FIELD AND AMPLITUDE

In constructing a theory of ray propagation, it is natural to consider the next logical step, namely, the manner in which the fields which are being transported, vary. This means that in order to extend the utility of a ray theory it is desirable to construct an associated field theory to go along with it. This however is not easily done. Careful consideration has been given to this problem, particularly by the late R. K. Luneberg and his colleagues.

For anisotropic media we can only sketch here an approach following the lines of development set down by J. B. Keller for the isotropic case.*

If the field being transported is denoted by $u(s)$, this field is then associated with each ray, where s is some parameter along the ray, usually the arc length. The field consists of an amplitude $A(s)$ and a phase $\psi(s)$ in the form,

$$u(s) = A(s)e^{-ik\psi(s)} \tag{94.1}$$

with $k = \omega/V_0$ the propagation constant, ω the angular frequency of the field, V_0 the propagation speed in a reference medium. This construction is applicable to a time-harmonic field $e^{i\omega t}$. The total field at a point P is then the sum of the fields (94.1) on all rays through P. If the field under consideration is a vector field, $\mathbf{A}(s)$ is a vector. The theory is applicable to many diverse scalar fields.

We suppose first that if ψ is known at some point on the ray and if ψ increases in the direction of propagation of the ray it is determined by

$$\psi(P) = \psi(Q) + L \tag{94.2}$$

where L is the optical distance of the ray from P to Q. Obviously we must require ψ to be constant on some wavefront, *i.e.*, some initial surface of a normal congruence of rays. Assuming further that a conservation of energy principle is known for the field entity of interest, we consider a thin tube of rays. Assume the energy flux is the same at every cross section of the tube of rays. To calculate the amplitude variation we postulate that the energy flux is proportional to mA^2, where m is the group ray refractive index. Invoking the energy principle for the thin tube of rays, we have

$$mA^2 d\Sigma = m_0 A_0^2 d\Sigma_0 \quad . \tag{94.3}$$

---

* J. B. Keller, A Geometrical Theory of Diffraction; American Mathematical Society's Calculus of Variations and its Applications, 1958, McGraw-Hill Book Co.

In this formula m and A are evaluated at a point P on a ray in the tube, $d\Sigma$ is the cross-sectional area of the tube at P. The zero subscript quantities are evaluated at Q of the same ray. It follows from eq. (94.3) that,

$$A(s) = A_0 \sqrt{\frac{m_0}{m} \frac{d\Sigma_0}{d\Sigma}} \quad . \tag{94.4}$$

From this formula we see that if we know the amplitude A_0 at some point, A at any other point on the ray can be calculated. By considering the points in $d\Sigma$ (which are also points on the rays in the tube) as the maps of the points in $d\Sigma_0$ by virtue of the transformation $\mathbf{r} = \mathbf{r}\ (\mathbf{r}_0,\ s - s_0)$ it is evident that the ratio $d\Sigma/d\Sigma_0$ is just the Jacobian of the transformation. Consequently, the solution of the ray path equations gives the transformation and hence enables us to calculate the Jacobian, $J = \det\ (\partial\mathbf{r}/\partial\mathbf{r}_0)$. Now, in practice, the ray refractive index is not given or known so m must be expressed in terms of the phase refractive index and this can readily be effected.*

When $\mathbf{A}$ is a vector, we assume that its magnitude still satisfies eq. (94.4) but its direction is more complicated to calculate. If, for example, $\mathbf{A}$ is one of the electromagnetic field vectors, and if the medium is isotropic, the direction of $\mathbf{A}$ at P is obtained from its direction at Q by parallel displacement† in a space whose metric is given by $d\bar{s} \equiv m ds$, where m is a positive function of position only. In the anisotropic case m is a function of position and direction, so the notions of a Finsler space must be used to construct a suitable metric in order to define parallel propagation.§

The systematic study of using rays for the calculation of fields was employed by Luneberg, M. Kline, J. B. Keller, R. M. Lewis, I. Kay, F. G. Friedlander, H. Bremmer and many others. With the advent of the field of plasma physics, the use of ray theory in propagation investigations can be expected to yield fruitful results. This may be particularly true in the microwave region for which ray theory finds its natural settin

* J. L. Synge, loc. cit.

† For the concept of parallel displacement (or propagation) see any text on tensor calculus, e.g., Synge and Schild, Leve-Civita, loc. cit.

§ J. I. Horvath, Phys. Rev. Vol. 80, No. 5, p 901, Dec. 1950. See also, J. L. Synge, "Relativity, the Special Theory," (1956) and "Relativity, The General Theory," (1960), North-Holland Publishing Co.

BIBLIOGRAPHIES

1. Argence, E., loc, cit. Chapter VI.

2. Caratheodery, C., Geometrical Optics. Berlin, (1937).

3. Cartan, E., Finsler Spaces, Hermann and Co., Paris, (1934).

4. DeGroot, W., Some Remarks on The Analogy of Certain Cases of Propagation of Electromagnetic Waves and the Motion of a Particle in a Potential Field. Phil. Mag. Vol. 10, p. 521, (1930).

5. DeWitte, A. J., Equivalence of Huygen's Principle and Fermat's Principle in Ray Geometry. Amer. J. of Physics. Vol. 27, No. 5, pp. 293-301, (May 1959).

6. Eckersley, T. L., On the Connection Between the Ray Theory of Electric Waves and Dynamics. Proc. Roy. Soc. A, Vol. 132, p. 83, (1931).

7. Epstein, P.S., Geometrical Optics ..., loc. cit.

8. Forsgren, S. K. H., Some Calculations of Ray Paths in the Ionosphere. Chalmers Tek. Högsk. Hand. No. 104, (1951).

9. Furutsu, K., loc. cit. Chapter I.

10. Haselgrove, J., Ray Theory and a New Method of Ray Tracing. The Physics of the Ionosphere. Report of the Physical Soc. Confer. on the Physics of the Ionosphere, pp. 355-364, (1955).

11. Helliwell, R. A., and Morgan, M. G., Atmospheric Whistlers. Proc. IRE, Vol. 47, p. 200, (February 1959).

12. Horvath, J. I., New Geometrical Methods of the Theory of Physical Fields. Supplement to Vol. 9, Series 10, Il Nuovo Cimento, No. 2, 3rd Semester, pp. 444-496, (1958).

13. Horvath, J. I., Contribution to Stephenson-Kilmester's Unified Theory of Gravitation and Electromagnetism. Il Nuovo Cimento, Vol. 4, No. 3, pp. 571-576, (September 1956).

14. Lighthill, M. J., Studies in Magnetohydrodynamic Waves and Other Anisotropic Wave Motion. Philos. Trans. A, Vol. 252, pp. 397-430, (1960).

15. Maeda, K. and Kimura, I., A Theoretical Investigation on the Propagation Path of the Whistling Atmospherics. Rep. of Ionosph. Res. in Japan, Vol. 10, p. 105, (1956).

16. Maeda, K. and Kimura, I., Calculation of the Propagation Path of Whistling Atmospherics. R.R.S.I., XIIIth General Assembly, Boulder, (1957).

17. Poeverlein, H., Ray Path of Radiowaves in the Ionosphere. Sitz. Berich. bayer Akad. Wiss. p. 175, (1948).

18. Poeverlein, H., Ray Path of Radiowaves in the Ionosphere. Z. Angew. Phys. Vol. 1, p. 517, (1949).

19. Poeverlein, H., On Waves in Anisotropic Propagation Conditions. Z. Naturf. Vol. 5a, p. 492, (1950).

20. Poeverlein, H., Ray Path of Radio Waves in the Ionosphere. Z. Angew. Phyo. Vol. 2, p. 152, (1950).

21. Rund, H., The Application of the Methods of Generalized Metric Geometry to Dynamics. U.S.A.F. Res. and Dev. Com., p. 63, (1954).

22. Schiller, R., New Transition to Ray Optics. Phys. Rev. Vol. 97, No. 6, pp. 1421-1428, (March 15, 1955).

23. Shmoys, J., Proposed Diagnostic Method for Cylindrical Plasmas. J. Appl. Phys. Vol. 32, No. 4, pp. 689-695, (April 1961).

24. Smith, R. L., Helliwell, R. A., and Yabroff, I. W., A Theory of Trapping of Whistlers in Field-Aligned Columns of Enhanced Ionization. J. Geophys. Res., Vol. 65, No. 3, pp. 815-823, (March 1960).

25. Storey, L. R. O., Whistler Theory, U.R.S.I., XIIIth General Assembly London (1960).

26. Storey, L. R. O., An Investigation of Whistling Atmospherics. Phil. Trans. Roy. Soc., Vol. 246, p. 113, (1953).

27. Suchy, K., loc. cit.

28. Synge, J. L., Hamilton's Method in Geometrical Optics. (Univ. of Maryland Inst. for Fluid Dynamics and Appl. Math. Lecture Series No. 9), Lecture II, (1951).

29. Synge, J. L., Geometrical Mechanics and de Broglie Waves. Cambridge Univ. Press, (1954).

30. Synge, J. L., The Absolute Optical Instrument. Trans. Amer. Soc. Vol. 44, No. 1, pp. 32-46, (July 1938).

31. Synge, J. L., Hamilton's Characteristic Function and Brun's Eikonal. J. Optic. Soc. Amer. Vol. 27, No. 3, pp. 138-144, (March 1937).

32. Synge, J. L., Hamilton's Method in Geometrical Optics. J. Optic. Soc. Amer., Vol. 27, pp. 75-82, (February 1937).

33. Synge, J. L., Flux of Energy for Elastic Waves in Anisotropic Media. Proc. Roy. Irish. Acad., Vol. 58, Section A, No. 2, pp. 13-21, (1956).

34. Taylor, J. H., A Generalization of Levi-Civita Parallelism and the Frenet Formulas. Trans. Amer. Math. Soc. Vol. 27, pp. 61-67, (1925).

35. Taylor, J. H., Parallelism and Transversality in a Sub-Space of a General Finsler Space. Ann. of Math. Second Series, Vol. 28, No. 4, pp. 620-628, (September 1927).

36. Theoderesco, N., On the Geodesics of Null Length and Wave Propagation, Acad. Roumaine Bull. Sect. Sci. Vol. 23, pp. 132-137, (1940-41).

37. Theoderesco, N., Finsler Geometry and Wave Propagation, ibid. pp. 138-144, (1942).

38. Tucker, A. W., On Generalized Covariant Differentiation. Ann. of Math., Vol. 32, pp. 451-460, (1931).

39. Tucker, A. W., On Tensor Invariance in the Calculus of Variations. Ann. of Math., Vol. 35, No. 2, pp. 341-350, (Aprio 1934).

GENERAL BIBLIOGRAPHIES

1. Born, M., and Wolf, E.

2. Bremmer, H.

3. Courant, R. and Hilbert, D., Methods of Mathematical Physics, Vol. I, Interscience Pub. Co., N.Y., (1953).

4. Eisenhart, L. P., Continuous Groups of Transformations. Princeton Univ. Press, Princeton, (1933).

5. Friedlander, F. G., Sound Pulses. Cambridge Univ. Press, (1958).

6. Jeffreys, H. and B. S.

7. Landau and Lefshitz, Classical Theory of Fields.

8. Luneberg, R. K., The Mathematical Theory of Optics, Brown Univ. Notes, Providence, R.I., (1944).

9. Ollendorff, F., The World of Vectors, Springer-Verlag, Vienna, (1950).

10. Silver, S.

11. Sokolnikoff, I. S., Tensor Analysis, John Wiley & Sons, N.Y., (1951).

12. Sommerfeld, A., Optics.

13. Stratton, J. A.

14. Sturrock, P. A., Static and Dynamic Electron Optics, Cambridge Univ. Press, (1955).

15. Thomas, T. Y., Concepts from Tensor Analysis and Differential Geometry, Academic Press, N.Y., (1961).

CHAPTER VIII

PROPAGATION PHENOMENA BASED ON THE BOLTZMANN EQUATION—MICROSCOPIC CONSIDERATIONS

INTRODUCTORY REMARKS

In the previous chapters the analysis of propagation phenomena was based on a macroscopic description of the medium. It is natural to consider an analysis of propagation based on a more fundamental model of the plasma medium. By a more fundamental model we mean here a microscopic description from which the results obtained from the macroscopic model are recovered as a limiting or special case. It is inevitable therefore that such a description must fall back on an understanding of the statistical mechanics of a plasma. This is certainly clear since a microscopic description of a plasma is substantially a many-body problem. The means of dealing with such problems goes back to Gibbs and Boltzmann and their investigations of irreversible processes, and it is interesting to contrast their viewpoints.

Gibbs adopted the view that irreversibility was due to the fact that for systems containing many particles such as a gas or liquid the initial conditions of position and velocity of these particles are never really known. However, some average values are known and consequently the system can be described as a function of time by giving the probability distribution of the initial conditions. The rate of change of the distribution is then determined by the laws of mechanics and the resulting equation is known as the Liouville equation. Then according to Gibbs, if there exists two identical systems which deviate slightly in their initial conditions, this difference, in the course of time becomes larger and, as a consequence the probability distribution becomes uniform. The uniform distribution defines the equilibrium state of the system. What is involved in Gibbs's view is just a probabilistic statement about the state of the system and the laws of classical mechanics to describe its temporal evolution.

Boltzmann, on the other hand, viewed the irreversible behavior of gases as due to the randomness of the collisions between the particles.

Then, from *a priori* probabilities on the number of collisions he deduced the equation which bears his name and which describes the manner in which the distribution function of the state of the particles ultimately becomes Maxwellian in the course of time.

Gibbs's formulation is so broad and general that its usage is limited, whereas Boltzmann's equation has been applied with success to the calculation of transport coefficients of gases, etc. Attempts have been made to obtain the Boltzmann equation from Liouville's equation by various arguments, some of which are mathematical and some of which are philosophical. The inadequacy of the Boltzmann transport equation in describing irreversible processes in ionized gases has been known for many years and the core of a classical plasma problem is its non-equilibrium nature. The principal difficulty in applying the Boltzmann equation to ionized gases stems from the long-range Coulomb forces. In the Boltzmann theory of gases only binary collisions are important.

An important step toward a fundamental understanding of irreversible processes and the temporal evolution of dynamical systems was taken by Bogolubov.* This author develops a program from which the distribution function can be obtained by the solution of differential equations. The essence of Bogolubov's program can be described qualitatively and in this regard we follow Uhlenbeck.†

Bogolubov indicates that the randomizing or chaotization process of Gibbs occurs at different stages and this always, if in particular, the system contains a sequence of basic relaxation times of successively larger orders of magnitude. As a consequence, one can expect that at each stage the system in the course of time can be described by fewer parameters. These parameters in the corresponding stage vary in a secular manner (*e.g.*, as in planetary motion, non-linear oscillatory processes, etc.) whereas all other parameters have obtained their equilibrium value, and therefore a simpler description of the system is obtained, the simplest of which is for the equilibrium or thermodynamic state. Different systems have different relaxation times so no general theory of irreversible processes exist comparable to the general theory of thermodynamic equilibrium as given by Gibbs.

---

* N. Bogolubov, Kinetic Equations, Jour. of Physics (U.S.S.R.) *10*, No. 3, 256, 265 (1946); see also, Problemy Dynamicheskoi Teori V Statistichestoi Fizike, Tech. Press, Moscow, 1946.

† G. E. Uhlenbeck, Some Recent Progress in Statistical Mechanics, Vol. 13, No. 7. July 1960, Physics Today.

Each system, in its approach to the equilibrium state, and depending on the nature of the forces between particles behaves in an individual way. Thus, after a certain mixing time τ a first simplification or contraction of the description of the system occurs. Bogolubov calls this the "kinetic stage" or Boltzmann stage because the parameter which varies in a secular manner and determines the further time development of the system is just the distribution function of the states of a single particle as in the Boltzmann equation. It is hypothesized that the distribution function is in this stage a basic secular parameter because in the time period τ the distribution function is slowly varying while the other parameters (such as the pair-distribution function) are rapidly varying with respect to the distribution function and have already reached their equilibrium values. This can be considered as an asymptotic property of the solution of the initial value problem associated with the Liouville partial differential equation.

The further contraction after the kinetic stage is called the "hydrodynamic stage" in which the secular parameters are the macroscopic parameters such as temperature, density, and average velocity of the particles. The equations describing the further temporal evolution of the system are here the well known hydrodynamical equations given by either an Eulerian or Lagrangian description and the Navier-Stokes equations. This stage is assumed to result from the fact that during a time t_0, which is very short compared with macroscopic relaxation times which are determined by the spatial non-uniform distribution of the macroscopic parameters, the distribution function of the particles attains its equilibrium form with respect to the velocities and then slowly relaxes to the full equilibrium distribution by the slow uniformization of the density, temperature and and average velocity.

The preceding contraction processes can be conveniently summarized in the following way. For times $t > \tau$, the description in the phase space of the gas is given by Liouville's equation; for times $\tau > t > t_0$, the description in the phase space of the molecule is given by the kinetic equation of Boltzmann and for times $t_0 > t$, the description in ordinary space is given by the hydrodynamical equations of Euler and Stokes-Navier. These contraction processes are essentially successive approximations in which the parameter is the ratio of the two relaxation times and for short range forces in the kinetic stage this successive approximation is equivalent to the virial expansion in the kinetic theory of gases. The virial coefficients in the equilibrium theory are known almost exactly from the work of Mayer.

In the non-equilibrium state the kinetic equation is defined in terms of coefficients which depend on the dynamics of the collision processes.* These coefficients are the non-equilibria counterpart of the virial coefficients in the equilibrium theory.†

A development of the program of Bogolubov for an ionized gas has recently been given by Guernsey who actually gives a modification of the Bogolubov method.§ In this way the powerful methods of Bogolubov are brought to bear on systems with long range Coulomb forces analogous to gases where only short range forces exist. The analogue of the virial expansion is the Debye expansion (for the equilibrium theory). Here the basic parameter of expansion involves the reciprocal of the Debye length. Corresponding to the Debye correction to the ideal gas for a dilute plasma is an expansion of the kinetic equation for the non-equilibrium theory in terms of coefficients which depend functionally on the distribution functions of the charged species. It is shown that in the zero order approximation the effect of the Coulomb interaction on the distribution function results from the acceleration by the electric field which is produced by the average charge density. This charge density is defined by Poisson's equation which is defined through the distribution function. The zero order approximation coincides with the self-consistent field or Landau-Vlasov approximation. The next approximation in the development resembles the Fokker-Planck equation and results from the fluctuations in the charge distribution. The higher order approximations can in principle be determined but naturally are difficult to obtain in practice.

In the present chapter we treat the development of the Boltzmann equation on a purely classical basis so that the deductions from it can be easily understood. The role of the Debye shielding and its relation to plasma oscillations, *i.e.*, the collective behavior of the plasma, is treated first from an elementary point of view and later in a more fundamental way when we discuss propagation phenomena involving the Boltzmann equation.

---

* S. T. Choh, Dissertation, Univ. of Mich., 1958.

† Uhlenbeck, loc. cit.

§ R. L. Guernsey, The Kinetic Theory of Fully Ionized Gases, Tech. Report, Univ. of Mich., College of Engineering, Dept. of Physics.

A discussion of the Liouville equation and the hydrodynamic analogy of a phase fluid is given and here the material in Chapters III and VII is useful in understanding the development.

A variety of deductions from the Boltzmann equation are given including the conservation equations, equations of heat flux and stress, etc.

A detailed treatment of the development of the Fokker-Planck equation is given and considerable effort is devoted to the approximate solution of this equation for a Lorentz type gas. This approximate solution is then used to derive the dielectric tensor of the plasma and hence the propagation constants. Because of the limiting assumptions only the transverse waves which propagate can be discussed together with their polarization. The statistical meaning of the dielectric coefficients is also discussed and a comparison is made of the microscopic and macroscopic theories.

Although a parallel treatment of a microscopic theory for the low frequency case (heavy ion effects) is not carried out here we felt it worthwhile to consider collision effects on low frequency propagation from the macroscopic point of view.

There are large classes of plasma phenomena that are not treated in this chapter since otherwise the chapter would become too ponderous. One of these classes is the Landau damping phenomena theoretically deduced by L. Landau. A treatment of Landau damping in the presence of a magnetic field for a heavy ion medium would be most interesting from both a theoretical and practical point of view. But this and other topics have been purposefully neglected because they require a rigorous handling of the dispersion relations and involve the methods of complex variable theory which are beyond the scope of the present text.* In the same vein, nonlinear effects are not treated since this is a subject unto itself.

---

* See for example, K. Case, Annals of Physics, 7, 349.

95. PRELIMINARY CONCEPTS

It is well known in classical physics that the state of a complete dynamical system is characterized by the Liouville equation. Such a dynamical system includes a gas, or indeed any collection or group of particles. The Liouville equation is essentially an equation of continuity or conservation of volume, loosely speaking. In advanced mechanics or in statistical mechanics the term "extension" is used in place of volume. This conservation of volume or extension does not necessarily take place in the ordinary physical space but rather in a space called the phase space and which will be defined subsequently.

Let us recall that the fundamental feature of classical mechanics is its deterministic nature. That is, if we know the initial conditions, *i.e.*, the position and velocity (or momenta) at time $t = 0$, and all of the forces acting on a system, its future is precisely determined. Subject to certain conditions on the mathematical form of these forces, the future history is uniquely determined. The only uncertainty which arises in this classical picture stems from the initial conditions. However, this uncertainty in the initial conditions can be incorporated in a probability distribution of initial conditions and the resulting state of the system can be predicted with some degree of probability. That is, a distribution function for a single particle can be derived. Practically speaking, such an approach is difficult to execute. For this reason, the original problem of dealing with many particles is replaced by a somewhat more relaxed one, in which the initial conditions and the dynamic evolution of the system itself are described in a probabilistic manner.

One method of carrying out such a program is through the Boltzmann equation. This method assumes that the dynamical evolution of a particle can be described in terms of the collisions of one particle of the system with one other particle of the same system. Thus, only two particles are assumed to interact with each other. Then by solving the collision problem for only two particles, the motion of a single particle is obtained, and in this way, the history of the system is described. For systems which are of low enough density, such a description is plausible and has proved to be useful. Moreover, there is the underlying assumption that the forces which exist between the particles are of a short range nature. Consequently before and after collisions, the particles are relatively free.

This latter situation can not hold strictly in a plasma because a charged particle is always subjected to the long range forces of the other charges in the system. More specifically, the interactions responsible for collisions between charged particles are governed by Coulomb forces which vary inversely as the square of the distance. Since the number of particles at equal distance from any point is directly proportional to the square of the distance, the Coulomb interaction exhibits a very slow decrease with the distance. Consequently, the forces involved have a long range. It is not difficult to argue therefore that the effective diameter for collisions between charged particles is larger in magnitude than that between neutral particles. Because of the large magnitude of the effective diameter for collisions between charged particles, the collision frequencies should not be seriously affected by the presence of neutral particles unless the latter are extremely large in number.

Elementary physical considerations show that a charged body is generally surrounded by a space charge cloud which shields the bodies' charge within a certain distance which is called the Debye shielding length. This shielding is brought about by the Coulomb repulsion between similar charges and is determined by the balance of thermal and electrostatic energies of the interacting particles. This shielding distance is large for high temperature and low electron densities. The space charge is spherical for bodies at rest and becomes an ellipsoid for body speed less than the mean thermal speed of electrons and a paraboloid for body speeds exceeding the mean thermal speed of electrons.

Shielding—Historically, the term "plasma" was introduced by Langmuir, in his studies on oscillations in ionized gases; and who stated that except near boundaries or walls where there are sheaths containing very few electrons, the ionized gas contains electrons and ions about equal in number so that the resultant space charge is very small. Currently, the term plasma is defined to be the region containing balanced charges of electrons and ions. This definition differs little from Langmuir's earlier description. A typical term like the Debye radius enters into studies and discussions of plasmas as a "characteristic length." For, as we have asserted above, since unlike charges attract and like charges repel, there is a tendency for a given charged particle to be surrounded by an envelope which, on the average, contains one more unlike charge than like charge. The radius of this imaginary spherical envelope which includes the smallest number of charged particles to exactly give this charge neutrality is the Debye radius. It is a characteristic length of the plasma, since, by definition, the plasma is electrically neutral. Therefore, this radius is also called the plasma length. Another typical term that enters is "shielding" or "screening." This term has its origin in the concept of electrical neutrality in a plasma. From the fact that the net charge is almost zero at distances greater than the plasma length, the long range Coulomb forces are very nearly cancelled. This cancellation is referred to as a shielding or a screening of the long range forces. The distance at which the force is effectively zero is called the cut-off distance. We can make the foregoing more precise by giving an elementary derivation of the electrical potential created by an ion.

Consider a positive ion and a coordinate system whose origin coincides with the position of the ion. In the region about this ion there will exist on the average more electrons than ions since the positive ion repels like charges and attracts the lighter electrons. We now seek the equilibrium distribution of these electrons in the region about the ion. To find the equilibrium distribution we make the following assumptions. The electrons are in thermodynamic equilibrium at temperature T and that its average charge number density denoted by $N_e(\mathbf{r})$ is given by the Boltzmann formula

$$N_e(\mathbf{r}) = N_i \exp\left(\frac{e\varphi}{kT}\right) . \tag{95.1}$$

Here, e is the electronic charge taken negative, φ is the potential sought, k is Boltzmann's constant, and N_i is the average charge number density of the ions of the plasma, which is assumed constant throughout the plasma. The remaining assumption is that the density of the electrons is a slowly varying function in the neighborhood of the central ion, and that $N_e \neq N_i$ in this neighborhood, although the plasma as a whole is neutral. Because of the slowly varying character of the function we retain the first two terms of the exponential, *i.e.*,

$$N_e(\mathbf{r}) = N_i \left(1 + \frac{e\varphi}{kT}\right) . \tag{95.2}$$

But the static potential φ satisfies Poisson's equation,

$$\nabla^2\varphi = -(N_i - N_e)e \tag{95.3}$$

which according to (95.2) gives

$$\nabla^2\varphi = N_i \frac{e^2}{kT} \varphi \cdot \qquad (95.4)$$

The quantity h defined by

$$h^2 = \frac{kT}{N_i e^2} \qquad (95.5)$$

has the dimensions of length. Since the potential is on the average spherically symmetric about the central ion, we can write Poisson's equation as

$$\frac{1}{r^2}\frac{d}{dr}\left(r^2 \frac{d\varphi}{dr}\right) = \frac{\varphi}{h^2} \quad . \qquad (95.6)$$

The boundary conditions on φ are such that it vanishes at infinity and in the immediate neighborhood of the central ion it must reduce to the Coulomb field of this ion alone. Hence the spherically symmetrical solution is

$$\varphi = \frac{e_i}{r} \exp\left(-\frac{r}{h}\right) \qquad (95.7)$$

where e_i is the charge on the ion. We easily verify that for small enough values of r, the potential φ has the value e_i/r which is the Coulomb potential of the ion alone. This formula shows that the effect of the screen of electrons is to attenuate the potential of the central ion in an exponential manner. The significance of the quantity h is that it is a measure of the order of magnitude of the distance within which the attenuation is effective. It determines the size or radius of the spherical envelope about the central ion. Consequently, h is called the Debye radius or length. From its definition, it is clear that this length becomes small as the density N_i increases and gets larger as the temperature increases. These conclusions are in accord with our remarks made previously.

The elementary derivation just given, admittedly non-rigorous in many respects, nevertheless sheds some light on the concepts of screening or shielding and gives in a simple way a description of a mixture of charged particles. We shall not dwell on this aspect of the plasma here.

Equilibrium Considerations--In the standard works which consider the equilibrium of a gas, one of the principal problems which arise is the interaction between the constituents. The approach used in dealing with this problem is a statistical one. When quantum effects are negligible, classical statistics serve the purpose. As we have already implied in our opening remarks on the dynamical evolution of the system the underlying assumption is that of molecular chaos. By this assumption one considers the molecules of the gas to be rigid spheres and there is no interaction until the spheres actually collide. This hypothesis of molecular chaos is not completely valid if the molecules are assumed to have force fields of an inverse power law, that is, if the force is proportional to, say, r^{-n}. For sufficiently large values of the power n, however, the collision time is very small and the particle distribution function behaves very nearly like the Maxwell-Boltzmann distribution. Thus, in this case we have short range forces. On the other hand, for charged particles the forces are very long range; here the force field behaves like $n \approx 2$.

Since these forces are clearly going to influence the motion of the particles, some measure of their effect must be contrived. The simplest theory, or rather the most commonly used theory which considers the correlation is that of Debye. This theory which we have touched on in the previous section is asymptotically correct for large distances and approaches the Coulomb force field at short distances. Consequently the Coulomb force field overcorrelates the particles in the inner field, with the subsequent result that when calculating the thermodynamic properties of the gas by the Debye theory marked departures from the perfect gas law show up. These departures are too large, in general. The corrections required to take into account the influence of the force fields of the charged particles are normally small except for the total heat content of the system, *i.e.*, the enthalpy, and here the Debye theory yields the principal part of the correction.* Because of its simplicity despite the fact that it gives conservative estimates, the Debye theory is used in thermodynamic calculations.

---

* Landau-Lifshitz, Statistical Physics, p. 235 Addison-Wesley (1958). Feynman, R. P., Phys. Rev., Vol. 76, pp. 749, 769.

The existence of thermodynamic equilibrium is implied in the term "state of the system." This means that there exist measurable quantities which are called thermodynamic state variables which have the same value (or nearly so) at all points of the system under consideration. In the calculation of the state of a system in which there also exists charged particles, a consideration of both the electrical and mechanical aspects is of primary importance. For example, as we have already seen in an earlier chapter, a basic assumption was the separability of the electric energy and mechanical energy. That is, they were assumed to be additive. If the electrical part of the free energy is known, the equation of state can be written down. In fact if F is the free energy with $F = F_e + F_m$, electrical plus mechanical, the pressure p is

$$p = \left(\frac{\partial F}{\partial V}\right)_T \qquad (95.8)$$

where V is the volume, T is the temperature. The application of the Debye-Huckel theory then relates the thermodynamic variables, p, V, T to the density and charge of the constituents of the gas.* Once the equation of state is known, then together with the separability assumption above, the explicit calculation of the thermodynamics of a plasma can be carried out.

Non-Equilibrium Considerations—The results of detailed studies regarding the equilibrium properties of a plasma reveal the following principal conclusions. The thermodynamics of a gas can be represented by the perfect gas laws to a fair approximation, but with an additive correction for the electrical energy, which in many situations is not large. The effects of a magnetic field for a perfect gas has been given in Chapter V, and from it we find that the pressure is given by

$$p = NkT + \frac{1}{2}\mathbf{B}\cdot\mathbf{H} - \frac{1}{2}\rho\mathbf{H}\cdot\mathbf{H}\frac{\partial\mu}{\partial\rho} \qquad (95.9)$$

where ρ is the mass density of the gas and $\mu = \mu(\rho, T)$ is the magnetic permeability, **B**,**H** are the external fields. We also have,

---

* An explicit formula of this kind is given by Kaeppeler, J. H., and Baumann, G., Irreversible Stochastic Thermodynamics and the Transport Phenomena in a Reacting Plasma. AFOSR TR 57-20. Mitt Forsch. fur Physik und Strahlentriebe E. V. Stuttgart (1956).

$$dS = dS_m + dS_e = dS_m + d\left(\frac{\mathbf{H}\cdot\mathbf{H}}{2\rho}\frac{\partial\mu}{\partial T}\right) \tag{95.10}$$

which expresses the entropy of the system as the sum of the mechanical and electrical contributions. In this expression it is natural to inquire about the conditions which make dS_e an exact differential. According to P. Langevin,* this obtains if

$$B = |\mathbf{B}| = f\left(\frac{|\mathbf{H}|}{T}\right) \tag{95.11}$$

and the equations of state $p = p(T,V,B)$, $U(T,V,B)$ and $H = H(T,V,B)$ take the simpler forms, $U = U(T,V)$, $p = p(T,V)$. These are the forms of a system in the absence of a magnetic field. Accordingly, any medium which satisfies Langevin's condition is called a perfect magnetic material.

If the plasma is not in thermal equilibrium, the equation of state used for the equilibrium case can still be used. Its usage in the non-equilibrium case is justified by the following argument. If there are no inter-particle forces then according to elementary kinetic theory the pressure is $(2/3\ \rho)$ $\times$ translational energy. This amounts to writing the equation of state as

$$p = k\Sigma N_i T_i \quad , \tag{95.12}$$

with,

$$\frac{3}{2}kT_i = \frac{1}{2}m_i\langle v_i^2\rangle \quad , \tag{95.13}$$

for the *i*th constituent. The pressure is the thermodynamic pressure, a state variable. This definition of the pressure can be preserved in non-equilibrium flow if and only if there is energy in forms that are transferred more slowly than the translational energy. The details leading to this conclusion can be obtained from Chapter III, where the pressure is given in terms of the trace of the stress tensor. In other words, if the thermodynamic pressure is slightly larger than $1/3\ \tau_{ii}$ then the preceding conclusion holds and conversely.

---

* P. S. Epstein, Textbook of Thermodynamics, John Wiley & Sons, New York (1937).

The most successful approach for the description and computation of the non-equilibrium properties of a system thus far in classical physics has been by means of a distribution function. As is well known, this approach has been exploited in many areas, the kinetic theory of gases, solid state physics, neutron physics, to mention just a few.

The distribution function is the mathematical description of the probability of finding a particle of the system at a given point with a given velocity. More generally, it is the probability of finding a particle of the system at a given point with a given velocity together with the specification of the probability of finding the remaining particles at arbitrary points.

In general, the description and calculations are affected in a space of $6n$ dimensions, called the phase space. This phase space consists of the three position and the three momentum coordinates of each particle, and for a system of n particles we have $6n$ numbers or points. To obtain an equation that the distribution function must satisfy in this phase space it is convenient to use the analogy of fluid flow. We shall digress slightly in our discussion to explain this analogy.

Let us first recall that in classical mechanics a system satisfies the canonical equations of Hamilton, whose form has been given in the chapter on ray theory. Also, in mechanics we can describe a mechanical system in terms of "generalized coordinates" which are a set of independent parameters which specify the system and do not necessarily coincide with the actual physical coordinates of the system. We denote these generalized coordinates by $\mathbf{q} = \mathbf{q}(q_1, \ldots, q_n)$. Associated with these coordinates are the generalized momenta $\mathbf{p} = \mathbf{p}(p_1, p_2, \ldots, p_n)$. In this description the system has $2n$ degrees of freedom. The totality of the p_i and q_i together constitute the phase space. The mechanical system satisfies the equations,*

$$\left.\begin{aligned} \frac{d\mathbf{q}}{dt} &= \frac{\partial H(\mathbf{q},\mathbf{p})}{\partial \mathbf{p}} \\ \frac{d\mathbf{p}}{dt} &= -\frac{\partial H(\mathbf{q},\mathbf{p})}{\partial \mathbf{q}} \end{aligned}\right\} \qquad (96.1)$$

* The reader is urged to review Chapter VII.

A complete solution of these equations means that we can write the q_i and p_i as functions of $2n$ constants of integration and the time t, that is,

$$\left.\begin{aligned} \mathbf{q} &= \mathbf{q}(\mathbf{q}_0, \mathbf{p}_0; t) \quad , \\ \mathbf{p} &= \mathbf{p}(\mathbf{q}_0, \mathbf{p}_0; t) \quad . \end{aligned}\right\} \tag{96.2}$$

The analogy with fluid flow is obvious if we recall from Chapter III that in the Lagrangian or particle description, we follow the individual particle according to the description,

$$\mathbf{r} = \mathbf{r}(\mathbf{r}_0, t) \quad , \tag{96.3}$$

where $\mathbf{r}_0$ is the initial position; and in the Eulerian or field description we consider the velocity field,

$$\dot{\mathbf{r}} = \dot{\mathbf{r}}(\mathbf{r}, t) \quad . \tag{96.4}$$

The two descriptions are of course equivalent, since we can obtain (96.4) from (96.3) by differentiation and elimination, and (96.3) can be obtained from (96.4) by integration. Carrying this idea over into the phase space shows that the field description corresponds to the canonical equations. In this sense the description of the $2n$-dimensional phase fluid is entirely similar to that of the three dimensional fluid.

This analogy when still further exploited leads at once to Liouville's theorem. If an arbitrary volume of fluid is unchanged during its motion we describe the fluid as incompressible, *i.e.*, the dilatation is zero. In the Lagrangian description we can consider the function described by (96.3) as a mapping of the points $\mathbf{r}_0$ into the points $\mathbf{r}$ and the Jacobian or functional determinant of this mapping is

$$J \equiv \det\left(\frac{\partial \mathbf{r}}{\partial \mathbf{r}_0}\right) \quad . \tag{96.5}$$

If $J = 1$ at all points, the fluid is incompressible. In the Eulerian or field description, the vanishing of the dilatation implies

$$\operatorname{div} \dot{\mathbf{r}} = 0 = \frac{\partial v_1}{\partial x_1} + \frac{\partial v_2}{\partial x_2} + \frac{\partial v_3}{\partial x_3} \tag{96.6}$$

which describes the incompressibility, and where $\dot{\mathbf{r}} \equiv (v_1, v_2, v_3)$, in a rectangular cartesian reference frame. If we think of the totality of sets $(q_1, q_2, \ldots, q_n, p_1, p_2, \ldots, p_n)$ as representing a $2n$-dimensional rectangular cartesian system, then the totality of sets $(\dot{q}_1, \ldots, \dot{q}_n, \dot{p}_1, \ldots, \dot{p}_n)$ are the components of the velocity in the phase space of the phase fluid. Calculating the divergence of this fluid gives

$$\text{div } \mathbf{v} \equiv \left(\frac{\partial \dot{q}_i}{\partial q_i} + \frac{\partial \dot{p}_i}{\partial p_i}\right) \tag{96.7}$$

which according to (96.1) shows that it vanishes. By applying the divergence theorem extended to $2n$ dimensions we have the conclusion that the total flux of the phase fluid through any closed hyper-surface in phase space is always zero, and consequently the phase fluid behaves like an incompressible fluid. This is the famous Liouville theorem. If we consider an arbitrary volume in this phase space, we call this the extension defined by

$$\int dq_1, \ldots, dq_n, dp_1, \ldots, dp_n \quad , \tag{96.8}$$

this extension is an invariant during the motion of the system. Although the region becomes deformed, the extension remains constant.

Suppose that instead of writing the first integrals of the canonical equations in the form of eqs. (96.2) we write them in the alternative form,

$$f^{(k)}(\mathbf{q},\mathbf{p},t) = f^{(k)}(\mathbf{q}_0,\mathbf{p}_0,t) \quad , \quad (k = 1,2,\ldots,6n) \quad . \tag{96.9}$$

Eqs. (96.2), of course, are equivalent to (96.9), since they can, in principle be found from (96.9) by solving for the q_i and p_i. The first integrals (96.9), by their very definition (a typical one of which will be denoted by f) satisfies the following equation,

$$\frac{df}{dt} \equiv \dot{f} = \frac{\partial f}{\partial t} + \frac{\partial f}{\partial \mathbf{q}} \cdot \dot{\mathbf{q}} + \frac{\partial f}{\partial \mathbf{p}} \cdot \dot{\mathbf{p}}$$

$$= \frac{\partial f}{\partial t} + [f, H] = 0 \quad . \tag{96.10}$$

Here, $[A,B]$ is the "Poisson bracket" defined by

$$[A,B] \equiv \left(\frac{\partial B}{\partial \mathbf{p}} \cdot \frac{\partial A}{\partial \mathbf{q}} - \frac{\partial B}{\partial \mathbf{q}} \cdot \frac{\partial A}{\partial \mathbf{p}}\right) \tag{96.11}$$

and H is the Hamiltonian of the system. Eq. (96.10) is known as Liouville's equation, and is a first order linear partial differential equation. The general solution of an equation of this kind is determined by $6n$ particular independent solutions; for example, the $6n$ first integrals (96.9). It is therefore equivalent to describing the dynamical evolution of the state of the system. Any function $F(\mathbf{q},\mathbf{p},t)$ which depends either explicitly or not on t is called a mechanical quantity of the system. At any instant of time, its numerical value is determined by the mechanical state of the system defined by eqs. (96.2) and at this instant,

$$A(\mathbf{q},\mathbf{p},t) = A(\mathbf{q}(t),\mathbf{p}(t)) \quad . \tag{96.12}$$

This function satisfies an "equation of evolution" which is formed by writing the relation which defines the total time derivative of A, that is, A, and replacing the $\dot{\mathbf{q}}$ and $\dot{\mathbf{p}}$ by their values from the canonical eqs. (96.1); this gives

$$A = \frac{\partial A}{\partial t} + [A,H] \quad . \tag{96.13}$$

The canonical equations (96.1) and Liouville's equation (96.10) are special cases of eq. (96.13). In retrospect then, the mechanical state or phase of a system of n point particles of mass, m_1, m_2, ..., m_n, respectively is defined at a fixed time by the position coordinates q_1, ..., q_n and momentum p_1, ..., p_n of these particles. The position and momentum are considered as vectors in a space of three dimensions and phase $(\mathbf{q},\mathbf{p}) \equiv (q_1, \ldots, q_n, p_1, \ldots, p_n)$, and hence is a point in a space of $6n$ dimensions, the so-called phase space of the system.

The preceding discussion shows that Liouville's equation expresses a conservation equation for the points in phase space. Now denote by $\mathbf{v}_k$ the velocity of the kth particle, by $\nabla_{\mathbf{r}_k}$ the gradient operator in $\mathbf{r}_k$ space, $\nabla_{\mathbf{v}_k}$ the gradient operator in $\mathbf{v}_k$ space, $\mathbf{F}_{k,i}$ the force per unit mass on the particle at $\mathbf{r}_k$ due to all the other particles, by $\mathbf{F}_{ke}$ the external force per unit mass on the particle at $\mathbf{r}_k$ and by $f_{(n)}$ the probability distribution function, Liouville's equation then takes the form,*

$$\frac{\partial f_{(n)}}{\partial t} = \sum_{k=1}^{n} [(\mathbf{v}_k \cdot \nabla_{\mathbf{r}_k}) f_{(n)} + ((\mathbf{F}_{k,i} + \mathbf{F}_{k,e}) \cdot \nabla_{\mathbf{v}_k}) f_{(n)}] = 0 \quad . \tag{96.14}$$

This equation specifies the change for the complete distribution. Hence, for its complete specification the initial position in phase space must be given for all particles. This in general is not known and so we can eliminate this specification by reducing the order of the distribution function by integrating over the phase space. By integrating over $6(n - 1)$ coordinates of all but one particle we obtain,

$$\frac{\partial f'_s}{\partial t} + (\mathbf{v}_s \cdot \nabla_{\mathbf{r}_s}) f'_s + (\mathbf{F}_{s,e} \cdot \nabla_{\mathbf{v}_s}) f'_s = -\frac{1}{(n-1)!} \iint (\mathbf{F}_{s,i} \cdot \nabla_{\mathbf{v}_s}) f_{(n)} d\mathbf{r}^{(n-1)} d\mathbf{v}^{(n-1)} \ , \tag{96.15}$$

the integrals being carried out in the $6(n - 1)$ dimensional space. In this formula f'_s denotes the probability of finding a particle of type s in the phase space intervals $\mathbf{r}_s$, $\mathbf{r}_s + d\mathbf{r}_s$, and $\mathbf{v}_s$, $\mathbf{v}_s + d\mathbf{v}_s$. Following Hirschfelder *et al*,† the Maxwell-Boltzmann equation can be deduced under the following assumptions: (a) two-body interactions are the most important one; (b) the pair distribution function (denoted by f'_{ss}, f'_{sm}) is equal to the product of single distribution functions in the exterior of some small interaction neighborhood; (c) the time spent by the particles within the interaction region is small. By letting the collision time tend to zero, the following equation is obtained,

$$\frac{\partial f_s}{\partial t} + (\mathbf{v}_s \cdot \nabla_{\mathbf{r}_s}) f_s + (\mathbf{F}_{s,e} \cdot \nabla_{\mathbf{v}_s}) f_s = \sum_j \int (f'_s f'_j - f_s f_j) \sigma_{ij} v_{r_{sj}} d^2\Omega d^3\mathbf{v}_j \ , \quad (s = 1,2) \ , \tag{96.16}$$

where σ_{ij} is the collision cross section, $v_{r_{sj}}$ the relative velocity, $d\Omega$ the solid angle, $d^3\mathbf{v}_j$ is the volume in velocity space, the prime denotes the value of the functions after collision. A complete discussion in the general case of the right hand side of (96.16) is not possible here,§ but we

---

* Kaeppeler and Baumann, loc. cit. give a general formulation of Liouville's equation.

† Hirschfelder, J. O., Curtiss, C. F., and Bird, R. B. Molecular Theory of Gases and Liquids, J. Wiley & Sons, p. 451 (1954).

§ The influence of the duration of the collision is treated by Hirschfelder *et al*, loc. cit., p. 455.

shall take up this question later in connection with our principal concern, the propagation of waves. When considering a plasma it is clear that there exists at least three species of particles, positive and negative ions (including electrons) and neutrals, this entails the calculation of three distribution functions. The calculation of the collision integral in the Boltzmann equation is a principal problem in the theory of transport phenomena, there is a great body of literature on the subject and no doubt this will substantially increase.

The validity of the Boltzmann equation in the theory of ionized gases has been a subject of concern for many researchers. For example, Cowling, in a fundamental study states the following.* The Boltzmann equation assumes that the motion of a molecule can be divided into relatively brief instants of encounter separated by relatively long intervals during which the interaction forces with other molecules can be neglected in comparison with field forces. But, in an ionized gas, because of the slow attenuation of electrostatic forces with increasing distance, interaction forces are everywhere at least comparable with field forces. As an example, the interaction force between electrons is equal to the force experienced by an electron in a magnetic field of 1000 gauss at a distance which is less than the distance between particles. A majority of field forces are smaller than the above magnetic forces. The electrostatic forces however, which are large compared with field forces are not strong enough to produce large effects except at small distances compared with the average distance between particles.

The cumulative effect of electrostatic encounters producing small deflections is greater than those for large encounters. But in an encounter producing a small deflection the effects of the encounter and field forces are approximately additive, *i.e.*, the change in velocity can be expressed by supposing that the molecules normally move under field forces alone, but that at a given instant their velocities are suddenly changed by the full effect of the interaction forces. The motion then becomes the type to which the Boltzmann equation applies. It is these electrostatic forces which justify the validity of the Boltzmann equation for an ionized gas, according to Cowling's reasoning.

Any discussion of non-equilibrium flow must include the effects of both close and long range collisions. In an analysis on the structure of

---

* Cowling, T. G., Electrical Conductivity of an Ionized Gas in a Magnetic Field. Proc. Roy. Soc. *A*, 183, p. 478 (1944-1945).

plasma equations, Rosenbluth and Rostoker consider the collision terms to be due to short range forces, and the external acceleration is considered to be made up of those due to external forces and those forces due to the microscopic plasma fields.* These considerations when analyzed introduce an additional coupling which is consistent with Cowling's reasonings.

The conclusion reached from these and other studies of the effect of long range forces is that some allowance must be made for the fact that there is some order in the distribution function, *i.e.*, there exists correlations between the positions of the particles. The Debye theory which we have sketched above is in effect a statement of this correlation. Despite the fact that the inclusion of correlations is certainly important in the study of the microscopic analysis of a plasma, the use of the Boltzmann equation approach sans correlation has provided valuable insights in the investigation of the properties of a plasma, *e.g.*, conductivity, etc. We shall therefore focus our attention on the Boltzmann equation together with the implications resulting from its usage.

97. DEDUCTIONS FROM THE BOLTZMANN EQUATION

Suppose we are given a plasma consisting of a large number of different species of particles. The quantity defined by $f_s(\mathbf{r},\mathbf{v},t)$ is the velocity distribution function for particles of type s, and is such that $f_s(\mathbf{r},\mathbf{v},t)d^3\mathbf{r}d^3\mathbf{v}$ represents the number of particles of type s in a small volume element of the six-dimensional coordinate-velocity space. Here, the notation $d^3\mathbf{r}d^3\mathbf{v}$ stands for this volume element around the point $(\mathbf{r},\mathbf{v})$ at time t. Hereafter, we shall use only the term distribution function to denote velocity distribution function, unless otherwise stated, for the function

$$f(\mathbf{r},\mathbf{v},t) = \sum_s f_s(\mathbf{r},\mathbf{v},t) \quad . \tag{97.1}$$

This function is a density function in the $(\mathbf{r},\mathbf{v})$-space, since it gives the total number of particles per unit volume. When we write f_s as we have for each species we assume no individual correlation exists between the particle positions of each type. Each f_s is normalized by the following condition in velocity space,

---

* Rosenbluth, M. N., and Rostoker, N. Theoretical Structure of Plasma Equations. The Physics of Fluids, Vol. 2, No. 1, pp. 24-30 (January 1959). See also the article by R. S. Cohen, L. Spitzer, Jr., Paul Routly Mc, Phys. Rev. 80, 2, pp. 230-239 (1950) for another approach.

$$\int f_s(\mathbf{r},\mathbf{v},t)d^3\mathbf{v} = N_s(\mathbf{r},t) \qquad (96.2)$$

where $N_s(\mathbf{r},t)$ is the number density of particles of type s in coordinate space. The total particle density is then

$$N(\mathbf{r},t) = \sum_s N_s(\mathbf{r},t) \quad . \qquad (97.3)$$

Ultimately we want to know how a wave propagates in the plasma. This means we have to determine the propagation constants. We can not determine these constants without a knowledge of the behavior of the plasma under the influence of the electrodynamic field. in the wave. Since we are describing the plasma by the distribution function, this function must therefore be determined by the electrodynamic field.

In order to formulate this problem mathematically and also effect a solution, several simplifying hypotheses are made. These hypotheses fall into two classes, one class for the formulation, the other for the solution. Let us consider the former class; the assumptions are:

H_1. The plasma is of sufficient extent so that boundary effects are ignored.

H_2. Quantum and relativistic effects are ignored.

H_3. The plasma consists of spherically symmetric elastic particles.*

H_4. The only external field acting on the plasma is the magnetic induction **B** which is uniform in space and time.

H_5. The permeability of the plasma is the same as that of free space, μ_0. (For this condition to prevail the plasma temperature T must satisfy the condition $4NkT \ll B^2$).

H_6. Only plane waves are considered, and its magnetic field is negligible compared with the externally applied magnetic field.

Before we list the assumptions for the mathematical solution we want to derive the Boltzmann equation when electrical and magnetic fields are present and examine some of its implications. Under the assumptions

* An exhaustive description would take into account the position and velocity of the center of gravity of the particles, and also the motion of rotation about the centers of gravity. This kind of detail is neglected in the text.

listed above the path of a plasma particle is determined by (a) the force from the electric field in the electromagnetic wave which is given by $e_s\mathbf{E}$; (b) the Lorentz force due to the uniform magnetic field, $e_s(\mathbf{v}\mathrm{x}\mathbf{B})$; and (c) the force resulting from the mutual influence of the particles through their Coulomb fields.

Now consider the point $(\mathbf{r},\mathbf{v})$ and an element of volume $d^3\mathbf{r}d^3\mathbf{v}$ about this point. At a fixed time t the number of particles of type s in this volume will be given by $f_s(\mathbf{r},\mathbf{v},t)d^3\mathbf{r}d^3\mathbf{v}$. At time $t + dt$, these same particles will occupy an element of volume say $d^3\mathbf{r}'d^3\mathbf{v}'$, and the number of particles in this volume will now be given by

$$f_s(\mathbf{r} + \mathbf{v}dt \ , \quad \mathbf{v} + \frac{e_s}{m_s}[\mathbf{E} + \mathbf{v}\mathrm{x}\mathbf{B}]dt \ , \quad t + dt)d^3\mathbf{r}'d^3\mathbf{v}' \quad . \tag{97.3}$$

We can take the two elements of volume as approximately equal to each other since the difference will involve terms of order $(dt)^2$ and higher. For collisions between the particles we have

$$[f_s(\mathbf{r} + \mathbf{v}dt, \ \ldots, \ t + dt) - f_s(\mathbf{r},\mathbf{v},t)]d^3\mathbf{r}d^3\mathbf{v} = \left(\frac{\partial f_s}{\partial t}\right)_{\mathrm{coll}} d^3\mathbf{r}d^3\mathbf{v} \quad , \tag{97.4}$$

the term on the right side in parenthesis is the collision term. By applying the law of the mean to the left side we can write

$$\frac{\partial f_s}{\partial t} + \mathbf{v}\cdot\nabla_{\mathbf{r}}f_s + \frac{e_s}{m_s}[\mathbf{E} + \mathbf{v}\mathrm{x}\mathbf{B}]\cdot\nabla_{\mathbf{v}}f_s = \left(\frac{\partial f_s}{\partial t}\right)_{\mathrm{coll}} \quad . \tag{97.5}$$

From a mathematical point of view we have tacitly assumed in applying the law of the mean that f_s and its derivatives are continuous. This needs a justification and the connection between the physical model and the mathematical description involves some subtle points.* In our usage of the equation we shall assume the validity of the continuity hypothesis. The nature of the collision term will be examined later. Let us look at the continuity equation and write it in tensor notation.

---

* See for example, G. Ecker, Zeits. f. Phys. 140:274 (1955), ibid. 141:294 (1955).

In this notation we have

$$\frac{\partial f}{\partial t} + \frac{\partial}{\partial x_i}(f\dot{x}_i) + \frac{\partial}{\partial v_i}(f\dot{v}_i) = 0 \quad ; \tag{97.6}$$

carrying out the differentiations yields,

$$\frac{\partial f}{\partial t} + f\left(\frac{\partial \dot{x}_i}{\partial x_i} + \frac{\partial \dot{v}_i}{\partial v_i}\right) + \frac{\partial f}{\partial x_i}\dot{x}_i + \frac{\partial f}{\partial v_i}\dot{v}_i = 0 \quad . \tag{97.7}$$

Since x_i and v_i are independent variables, $\partial \dot{x}_i/\partial x_i = \partial v_i/\partial x_i = 0$, and similarly $\partial \dot{v}_i/\partial v_i = (1/m)(\partial F_i/\partial v_i) = 0$. The latter holds because F_i which is the force acting on a particle is independent of velocity for all but magnetic forces. Denoting the magnetic forces by $F_{i,m}$, and noting that the ith component of a cross product contains all components but the ith,

$$\frac{\partial F_{i,m}}{\partial v_i} = e\frac{\partial}{\partial v_i}(\mathbf{v x B})_i = 0 \tag{97.7'}$$

therefore,

$$\frac{\partial \dot{x}_i}{\partial x_i} + \frac{\partial \dot{v}_i}{\partial v_i} = 0 \tag{97.8}$$

which expresses the vanishing of the divergence of the six dimensional velocity vector. From this we find, together with eq. (97.7),

$$\frac{df}{dt} = \frac{\partial f}{\partial t} + \frac{\partial f}{\partial x_i}\dot{x}_i + \frac{\partial f}{\partial v_i}v_i = 0 \quad , \tag{97.9}$$

or

$$\frac{\partial f}{\partial t} + \frac{\partial f}{\partial x_i}v_i + \frac{F_i}{m}\frac{\partial f}{\partial v_i} = 0 \quad , \tag{97.10}$$

which is the collisionless Boltzmann equation.* Equation (97.9) simply characterizes the fact that the density in $(\mathbf{r},\mathbf{v})$ space is constant. We

* Also called the Boltzmann-Vlasov equation.

note that the only physical principle used in deriving the Boltzmann equation was the equation of motion in the derivation of eq. (97.8). Conversely, the Boltzmann equation implies the equation of motion and hence they are equivalent.

To handle collective phenomena it is useful to consider certain entities derivable from a knowledge of the distribution function. Thus the average plasma velocity is defined by

$$N(\mathbf{r},t)\langle\mathbf{v}\rangle = \int \mathbf{v}f(\mathbf{r},\mathbf{v},t)d^3\mathbf{v} = N\mathbf{u} \tag{97.11}$$

and in general for any quantity Q, its average value is defined by

$$N(\mathbf{r},t)\langle Q\rangle = \int Qf(\mathbf{r},\mathbf{v},t)d^3\mathbf{v} \quad . \tag{97.12}$$

The charge density is defined by

$$\rho(\mathbf{r},t) = \sum_s \rho_s \int f_s(\mathbf{r},\mathbf{v},t)d^3\mathbf{v} = \sum_s \rho_s N_s(\mathbf{r},t) \tag{97.13}$$

and the current density by

$$\mathbf{J}(\mathbf{r},t) = \sum_s \rho_s \int \mathbf{v}f_s d^3\mathbf{v} = \sum_s \rho_s N_s(\mathbf{r},t)\mathbf{v}_s(\mathbf{r},t) \tag{97.14}$$

where the sum is over all species of charged particles.

Self Consistent Formulation—From the preceding formalism it is possible to find the field quantities $\mathbf{E}(\mathbf{r},t)$, $\mathbf{B}(\mathbf{r},t)$ if the only forces acting on the system are electromagnetic. We can write for each type of particle

$$\frac{\partial f_s}{\partial t} + \mathbf{v}\cdot\frac{\partial f_s}{\partial \mathbf{r}} + \frac{\rho_s}{m_s}(\mathbf{E} + \mathbf{v}\mathrm{x}\mathbf{B})\cdot\frac{\partial f_s}{\partial \mathbf{v}} = 0 \tag{97.15}$$

and by using Maxwell's equations together with the expressions for $\mathbf{J}$ and ρ we have a complete set of self consistent equations. If we know $\mathbf{E}(\mathbf{r},t)$ and $\mathbf{B}(\mathbf{r},t)$ eqs. (97.15) determine f_s and via eqs. (97.13) and (97.14) lead to the plasma charges and currents; putting these charges and currents into Maxwell's equations we can then, in principle, find $\mathbf{E}$ and $\mathbf{B}$. These equations must be solved simultaneously. This procedure is called a self consistent formulation or solution.

Moments of the Boltzmann Equation—From a knowledge of the distribution function which is presumed to contain the "best" information of the system it is possible in principle to determine general laws concerning the system. This, of course, is done at the expense of losing or destroying information, so the term "general laws" has a restricted meaning. The method used to obtain these laws follows the pattern in ordinary statistics, namely we evaluate the moments resulting from the Boltzmann equation.

Since we must integrate over all $\mathbf{v}$ space the behavior of the distribution function for large values of the velocity is required. Because any particle velocity is bounded ($v < \infty$) we postulate that f is such that its value over an infinite sphere in velocity space causes all integrals over this sphere to vanish.

The moment of zero order is obtained by multiplying eq. (97.5) (dropping subscript s for convenience) by v^0 and integrating, thus in tensor notation we have

$$\int \left[\frac{\partial f}{\partial t} + v_i \frac{\partial f}{\partial x_i} + \frac{e}{m} (\mathbf{E} + \mathbf{v}\mathrm{x}\mathbf{B})_i \frac{\partial f}{\partial v_i} \right] d^3\mathbf{v} = \int \left(\frac{\partial f}{\partial t} \right)_{\text{coll.}} d^3\mathbf{v} \quad . \quad (97.16)$$

We obtain successively,

$$\int \left(\frac{\partial f}{\partial t} \right) d^3\mathbf{v} = \frac{\partial N}{\partial t} \quad , \quad (97.17)$$

$$\int v_i \frac{\partial f}{\partial x_i} d^3\mathbf{v} = \frac{\partial}{\partial x_i} \int v_i f d^3\mathbf{v} = \frac{\partial}{\partial x_i} N\langle v \rangle_i = \frac{\partial}{\partial x_i} N u_i \quad , \quad (97.18)$$

and from integration by parts

$$\int (\mathbf{E} + \mathbf{v}\mathrm{x}\mathbf{B})_i \frac{\partial f}{\partial v_i} d^3\mathbf{v} = \int \{ \quad \} d\Sigma + \int f \frac{\partial}{\partial v_i} (\mathbf{E} + \mathbf{v}\mathrm{x}\mathbf{B})_i d^3\mathbf{v} \quad ,$$

the integral involving $d\Sigma$ is an integral over the surface at infinity in **v**-space which vanishes because of our postulated behavior of f; the second integral vanishes because **E** is independent of **v** and

$$\frac{\partial}{\partial v_i}(\mathbf{v}\mathbf{x}\mathbf{B})_i = 0 \quad .$$

The collision integral vanishes because the collisions have the effect of just displacing points in **v**-space but leave the total number of points otherwise unchanged. Consequently, we have as a result

$$\frac{\partial N}{\partial t} + \frac{\partial}{\partial x_i}(Nu_i) = 0 \tag{97.19}$$

which is the *equation of continuity* in **r**-space. Another moment is obtained by multiplying the Boltzmann equation with (mv_k) and integrating again over **v**-space. As before we obtain successively,

$$\int m \frac{\partial}{\partial t} f v_k \, d^3\mathbf{v} = \frac{\partial}{\partial t}\int m f v_k \, d^3\mathbf{v} = \frac{\partial}{\partial t}(mNu_k) \tag{97.20}$$

using eq. (97.12),

$$m\int \frac{\partial}{\partial x_i} f v_i v_k \, d^3\mathbf{v} = m\frac{\partial}{\partial x_i}\int f v_i v_k \, d^3\mathbf{v} = \frac{\partial}{\partial x_i} mN\langle v_i v_k\rangle \, , \tag{97.21}$$

and if we put $F_i = e(\mathbf{E} + \mathbf{v}\mathbf{x}\mathbf{B})_i$, we can write for the third integral,

$$\int F_i \frac{\partial}{\partial v_i} v_k \, d^3\mathbf{v} = -\int f F_i \frac{\partial v_k}{\partial v_i} \, d^3\mathbf{v}$$

after integrating by parts. But $\partial v_k/\partial v_i = \delta_{ik}$, hence,

$$-\int f F_i \delta_{ik} \, d^3\mathbf{v} = -\int f F_k \, d^3\mathbf{v} = -N\langle F_k\rangle \tag{97.22}$$

collecting the results we obtain the equation expressing the *conservation of momentum*,

$$\frac{\partial}{\partial t}(Nmu_k) + \frac{\partial}{\partial x_i}(Nm\langle v_i v_k\rangle) = N\langle F_k\rangle \quad . \tag{97.23}$$

Each term here is simple to interpret and the reader is advised to review Chapter III.

To obtain an energy equation we multiply eqs. (97.17), (97.18) with $1/2\ mv^2$ and integrate obtaining now successively,

$$\frac{\partial}{\partial t}\int f\left(\frac{1}{2}mv^2\right)d^3\mathbf{v} = \frac{\partial}{\partial t}\left(N\frac{1}{2}mv^2\right) \quad , \tag{97.24}$$

$$\frac{\partial}{\partial x_i}\int fv_i\left(\frac{1}{2}mv^2\right)d^3\mathbf{v} = \frac{\partial}{\partial x_i}\left(N\frac{1}{2}mv^2 v_i\right) \quad , \tag{97.25}$$

$$\frac{1}{2}\int\frac{\partial f}{\partial v_i}F_i v^2 d^3\mathbf{v} = -\frac{1}{2}\int fF_i\frac{\partial v^2}{\partial v_i}d^3\mathbf{v} \quad , \tag{97.26}$$

but

$$\frac{\partial}{\partial v_i}v^2 = \frac{\partial}{\partial v_i}v_k v_k = \partial v_k \delta_{ik}$$

and therefore

$$\frac{1}{2}\int\frac{\partial}{\partial v_i}F_i v^2 d^3\mathbf{v} = -\int fF_i v_k \delta_{ik} d^3\mathbf{v} = -Ne\langle E_i v_i\rangle = -NeE_i u_i \quad . \tag{97.27}$$

The collision integral vanishes again here since kinetic energy is unchanged by collisions. The final result is the *law of conservation of energy*,

$$\frac{\partial}{\partial t}\left(N \frac{1}{2} m v^2\right) + \frac{\partial}{\partial x_i}\left(N \frac{1}{2} m v^2 v_i\right) = NeE_i u_i \qquad (97.28)$$

here, the first term is the rate of change of energy density, the second represents the loss per unit volume from energy flux or the heat transfer, and the right side is the power fed into the system by the electric field only since the work done by the magnetic field is zero.

Unfortunately the higher order moments do not have a simple physical interpretation. Moreover, there are no entities which involve third or higher powers of v which are conserved by collisions and therefore the collision terms do not vanish for such equations.

The conservation laws derived above, although useful in a general way, do not form a closed system of plasma equations. More specifically, the mass or continuity equation contains the two unknown functions N and $\mathbf{u}$; the momentum equation contains besides these unknowns also $\langle v_i v_k \rangle$, and the energy equation contains also $\langle v^2 v_i \rangle$. Thus, the number of unknowns always is greater than the number of equations and this sequence of equations can not be closed by forming the higher order moment equations.

Equations of Stress and Heat Flux—Before we continue with our program of finding self consistent laws involving Maxwell's equations a slight digression is in order. The conservation laws for an ionized mixture as a whole give the same equations as those of ordinary magneto-gas dynamics but with arbitrary stress tensor and heat flux vector. If we assume a linear relation between the stress and rate of strain and between heat flux and temperature gradient the equations of magneto-gas dynamics in the continuum sense are obtained (see Chapter V).

The stress and heat flux vector can be specified by taking higher moments of the Boltzmann equation which then give constitutive equations of stress and heat flux. These equations hold for each type, they contain third and fourth moments which in turn require higher moments to govern. In order to close the system, the distribution function must be approximated such that these third and fourth moments are represented in terms of the physically significant lower moments of stress and heat flux. Then by summing over all species we obtain the constitutive equations of the stress and heat flux for the whole gas. In general this procedure leads to equations which are quite complicated.*

In order to obtain a simpler description, *i.e.*, simpler stress and heat flux equations, we resort to a single-fluid description of the whole mixture, which is physically realizable if the gas is weakly ionized. For sake of discussion we shall consider here a monatomic gas and write the Boltzmann equation for each type in the form,

$$\frac{\partial f_s}{\partial t} + v_i \frac{\partial f_s}{\partial x_i} + \frac{F_{s,i}}{m_s} \frac{\partial f_s}{\partial v_i} = I_s \tag{97.29}$$

where I_s is a collision integral whose form can be determined for binary collisions. The external force $F_{s,i}$ is the same as before and we can also include an additional gravitational force $m_s g_i$ where g_i is the component of gravitational acceleration. To carry out our program we make the following hypothesis:

(a) The gas is monatomic with no rotational or vibrational degrees of freedom, and hence the ratio of specific heats is given by

$$\gamma = \frac{C_p}{C_V} = \frac{5}{3} \tag{97.30}$$

(b) The collision between particles is binary, *i.e.*, a dilute gas.

(c) Molecular chaos holds for the gas.

(d) The distribution function is uniform within a distance comparable to the size of the particle, but varies over a distance comparable to the mean free path.

(e) Ionization and recombination processes are neglected.

(f) The gas density is low but the temperature is high, hence collisions between charged particles are mostly of a binary type.

---

* Kolodner, I. I., "Moment Description of Gas Mixtures," AEC Res. and Dev. Report NYO-7980, Inst. of Math. Sciences, N.Y.U., Sept. 1957; Burgers, J. M., "The Application of Transfer Equations to the Calculation of Diffusion, Heat Conduction, Viscosity and Electrical Conductivity," Inst. for Fluid Dynamics and Applied Math., Univ. of Maryland, Tech. Note BN-124, May 1958.

(g) The magnetic field strength is such that the minimum Larmor radius is large compared with the mean collision distance. Thus the conduction current is due to the diffusion of the charged particles.

We introduce the following notations; the mass density of type s is

$$\rho_{m,s}(\mathbf{r},t) = m_s N_s(\mathbf{r},t) \tag{97.31}$$

The total mass density is

$$\rho_m = \sum_s \rho_{m,s} \tag{97.32}$$

the mass velocity $\mathbf{V}$ is defined by

$$\rho_m \mathbf{V} = \sum_s \rho_{m,s} \mathbf{u}_s \tag{97.33}$$

where

$$N_s \mathbf{u}_s = \int \mathbf{v} f_s(\mathbf{r},\mathbf{v},t) d^3\mathbf{v} \tag{97.34}$$

defines the flow velocity of type s. The diffusion velocity of type s with respect to the mean mass flow is defined by

$$\mathbf{W}_s = \mathbf{u}_s - \mathbf{V} \tag{97.35}$$

from which we find

$$\sum_s \rho_{m,s} \mathbf{W}_s = \sum_s \rho_{m,s} \mathbf{u}_s - \mathbf{V} \sum_s \rho_{m,s} = 0 \ . \tag{97.36}$$

We define the higher moments of type s in terms of the thermal velocity with respect to the mean mass flow,

$$\mathbf{C} = \mathbf{v} - \mathbf{V} \ . \tag{97.37}$$

The pressure tensor of type s is defined through

$$\begin{aligned} P_{s,ij} &= m_s \int C_i C_j f_s(\mathbf{r},\mathbf{v},t) d^3\mathbf{v} \\ &= p_s \delta_{ij} + p_{s,ij} \end{aligned} \tag{97.38}$$

where p_s is the hydrostatic pressure, $p_{s,ij}$ the viscous stress tensor and

$$P_{s,ii} = 3p_s + p_{s,ii} = 0 \quad , \quad \text{(see Chapter III)} \quad . \qquad (97.39)$$

The heat flux vector of type s is defined by

$$q_{s,i} = \frac{1}{2} m_s \int C_i C^2 f_s(\mathbf{r},\mathbf{v},t) d^3\mathbf{v} \qquad (97.40)$$

and the temperature T_s is taken to be proportional to the mean kinetic energy of particles of type s measured with respect to the mixture flow velocity $\mathbf{V}$. For point particles, the kinetic energy per unit volume is $3/2\ N_s kT_s$, where k is Boltzmann's constant. Consequently we can write, using (97.38) and (97.39),

$$\frac{3}{2} N_s kT_s = \frac{1}{2} m_s \int C^2 f\ d^3\mathbf{v}$$

$$= \frac{3}{2} p_s \qquad (97.41)$$

hence,

$$p_s = N_s kT_s \qquad (97.42)$$

an equation of state for type s. Therefore, for the entire mixture we have,

$$P_{ij} = \sum_s P_{s,ij} \quad , \quad \text{the pressure tensor,} \qquad (97.43)$$

$$p = \sum_s p_s \quad , \quad \text{the hydrostatic pressure,} \qquad (97.44)$$

$$p_{ij} = \sum_s p_{s,ij} \quad , \quad \text{the viscous stress tensor,} \qquad (97.45)$$

from which we conclude,

$$P_{ii} = 3p + p_{ii} = 0 \quad . \qquad (97.46)$$

The heat flux vector for the whole mixture is

$$q_i = \sum_s q_{s,i} \tag{97.47}$$

and from eqs. (97.42) and (97.44) we have Dalton's Law, hence

$$p = k \sum_s N_s T_s = NkT \tag{97.48}$$

an equation of state for the whole gas, with temperature T defined by

$$NT = \sum_s N_s T_s \quad . \tag{97.49}$$

Finally we complete our definitions with

$$\rho_s = N_s e_s \quad , \quad \text{the charge density} , \tag{97.50}$$

$$\mathbf{J}_s = N_s e_s \mathbf{u}_s \quad , \quad \text{current density} , \tag{97.51}$$

and for the whole mixture,

$$\rho = \sum_s \rho_s \quad , \tag{97.52}$$

$$\mathbf{J} = \sum_s \mathbf{J}_s \quad . \tag{97.53}$$

The total current $\mathbf{J}$ is rewritten as

$$\mathbf{J} = \sum_s e_s N_s (\mathbf{V} + \mathbf{W}_s)$$

$$= \rho \mathbf{V} + \mathbf{J}_C \quad , \tag{97.54}$$

where,

$$\mathbf{J}_C = \sum_s e_s N_s \mathbf{W}_s \quad , \quad \text{the conduction current,}$$

$$= \sum_s \mathbf{J}_{C,s} \tag{97.55}$$

with

$$\mathbf{J}_{C,s} = e_s N_s \mathbf{W}_s \quad , \quad \text{conduction current of type } s. \tag{97.56}$$

The transfer equation for a particle property Q_s is obtained by multiplying the Boltzmann equation by Q_s and integrating over velocity space to obtain,

$$\int \left(Q_s \frac{\partial f_s}{\partial t} + Q_s v_i \frac{\partial f_s}{\partial x_i} - \frac{F_{s,i}}{m_s} f_s \frac{\partial Q_s}{\partial v_i} \right) d^3\mathbf{v} = \int Q_s I_s d^3\mathbf{v} \quad . \tag{97.57}$$

The conservation of mass, momentum and energy result from putting successively $Q_s = m_s$, $m_s C_i$, and $1/2\ m_s C^2$ into eq. (97.57) and summing over all types to obtain respectively for the whole mixture,

$$\frac{\partial \rho_m}{\partial t} + \frac{\partial}{\partial x_i} (\rho_m V_i) \tag{97.58}$$

$$\rho_m \left(\frac{\partial V_i}{\partial t} + V_j \frac{\partial V_i}{\partial x_j} \right) + \frac{\partial p}{\partial x_i} + \frac{\partial p_{ij}}{\partial x_j} - \rho_s E_i - (\mathbf{J} \mathbf{x} \mathbf{B})_i = 0 \quad , \tag{97.59}$$

$$\frac{3}{2} \left(\frac{\partial p}{\partial t} + V_i \frac{\partial p}{\partial x_i} \right) + \frac{5}{2} p \frac{\partial V_i}{\partial x_i} + p_{ij} \frac{\partial V_j}{\partial x_i} + \frac{\partial q_i}{\partial x_i} - (\mathbf{J}_C)_i (\mathbf{E} + \mathbf{V} \mathbf{x} \mathbf{B})_i = 0 \tag{97.59'}$$

the latter is the energy equation for $\gamma = 5/3$.

In the following paragraphs we shall sketch the development of the stress and heat flux equations. As expected, higher moments than stress and heat flux will appear in these two equations. The system can be closed by approximating them by lower moments, then by summing over all types, stress and heat flux equations result for the whole gas. By introducing the assumption of weak ionization a simpler single-fluid description is obtained and finally the stress and heat flux equations for magneto-gas dynamics are derived. Together with the conservation equations these stress and heat flux equations then constitute a determinate system and can be used to describe the dynamics of a rarefied conducting gas in the presence of an electrodynamic field.

Stress Equation—Put $Q_s = m_s C_i C_j$ and introduce the notation

$$\{A_{ij}\} = \frac{1}{2} (A_{ij} + A_{ji}) - \frac{1}{3} \delta_{ij} A_{kk}$$

which is a divergenceless tensor. From eq. (97.57) and some formidable calculations and summing over all species it can be shown that,

$$\frac{\partial p_{ij}}{\partial t} + \frac{\partial}{\partial x_k}(V_k p_{ij}) + \frac{\partial}{\partial x_k}(P_{ijk}) - \frac{2}{3}\delta_{ij}\frac{\partial q_k}{\partial x_k} + 2\left\{p_{ik}\frac{\partial q_k}{\partial x_k}\right\}$$

$$+ 2p\left\{\frac{\partial V_i}{\partial x_j}\right\} - 2\,\{J_{C,i}(\mathbf{E} + \mathbf{VxB})_j\} - \sum_s \frac{\rho_s}{\rho_{m,s}}\,[(\mathbf{P}_s\mathbf{xB})_{ij} + (\mathbf{P}_s\mathbf{xB})_{ji}]$$

$$= \sum_s \{I_s\} \quad , \qquad (97.60)$$

$$(\mathbf{PxB})_{ij} \equiv m_s \int C_i(\mathbf{C}f_s d^3\mathbf{vxB})_j \quad , \qquad (97.61)$$

and

$$P_{ijk} = \sum_s P_{s,ijk} \quad . \qquad (97.62)$$

Note that in order to determine the third moment $P_{s,ijk}$ we need to take further moments, etc; hence to close the system we must approximate this moment by lower moments.

Heat Flux Equations—Now we put $Q_s = 1/2\ m_s C^2 C_i$ into eq. (97.57) and a similar tedious calculation, and summing over s yields for the whole gas,

$$\frac{\partial q_i}{\partial t} + \frac{\partial}{\partial x_j}(V_j q_i) + \frac{1}{2}\frac{\partial}{\partial x_j}(P_{ijkk}) + q_j\frac{\partial V_i}{\partial x_j} + P_{ijk}\frac{\partial V_k}{\partial x_j} - \frac{5}{2}\frac{p}{\rho_m}\left(\frac{\partial p}{\partial x_i} + \frac{\partial p_{ij}}{\partial x_j}\right)$$

$$-\frac{p_{ij}}{\rho_m}\left(\frac{\partial p}{\partial x_j} + \frac{\partial p_{jk}}{\partial x_k}\right) - \sum_s \frac{\rho_s}{\rho_{m,s}}(\mathbf{q}_s\mathbf{xB})_i + \frac{5}{2}\frac{\rho}{\rho_m}E_i p - \frac{5}{2}(\mathbf{E} + \mathbf{VxB})_i \sum_s \frac{\rho_s}{\rho_{m,s}} p_s$$

$$+ \frac{\rho}{\rho_{m,s}}E_j p_{ij} - (\mathbf{E} + \mathbf{VxB})_j \sum_s \frac{\rho_s}{\rho_{m,s}} p_{s,ij} + \frac{5}{2}p\,\frac{(\mathbf{JxB})_i}{\rho_m} + p_{ij}\,\frac{(\mathbf{JxB})_j}{\rho_m}$$

$$= \frac{1}{2}\sum_s I_s^{ijj} \quad , \qquad (97.63)$$

with

$$\frac{1}{2}\sum_s I_s^{ijj} = \frac{1}{2}\int m_s C^2 C_i \sum_s I_s d^3\mathbf{v} \tag{97.64}$$

and,

$$P_{ijkk} = \sum_s P_{s,\,ijkk} \quad . \tag{97.65}$$

Subject to the hypothesis made at the outset the stress and heat flux equations given by (97.60) and (97.63) are completely general. In order to approximate the higher moments that occur in these equations and to evaluate the collision term we need to know the form of the distribution function.

The Distribution Function—For an electrically neutral mixture, Grad* takes the distribution function in the form,

$$f = \frac{N}{\pi^{3/2}\left(2\frac{k}{m}T\right)^{3/2}} \exp\left(-\frac{C^2}{2\frac{k}{m}T}\right)\left[1 + \frac{p_{jk}}{\rho_m}\frac{C_j C_k}{2\frac{k}{m}T} - \frac{2q_j C_j}{p\left(2\frac{k}{m}T\right)}\left(1 - \frac{2}{3}\frac{C^2}{2\frac{k}{m}T}\right)\right] \quad . \tag{97.66}$$

Here the first two factors in f describe a local Maxwellian distribution, *i.e.*, a description of a gas in local equilibrium. For a non-equilibrium state, there is a transport of mass, momentum and energy, or as we say, there exists currents. These currents exhibit themselves respectively as diffusion velocity, viscous stresses, and heat flux. For a single component gas there are, clearly, no mass concentration differences; consequently the only non-vanishing currents are the stress p_{ij} and the heat flux q_i. We see from eq. (97.66) that the term in brackets is linear in both the stress and the heat flux. This bracketed term therefore represents the small deviation from equilibrium.

Following Grad, Kolodner takes the distribution function for a component in the following form,*

---

* H. Grad, "On the Kinetic Theory of Rarefied Gases," Comm. on Pure and Applied Math., Vol. 2, No. 4, pp. 331-407, Dec. 1949; also, H. Grad, "Principles of the Kinetic Theory of Gases," Encyc. of Physics, Vol. 12, pp. 205-294, Springer-Verlag, 1958.

$$f_s = \frac{N_s}{\pi^{3/2}\left(2\frac{k}{m_s}T_s\right)^{3/2}} \exp\left(-\frac{C^2}{2\frac{k}{m_s}T_s}\right)\left[1 + \left(7 - 2\frac{C^2}{2\frac{k}{m_s}T_s}\right)\frac{\mathbf{W}_s\cdot\mathbf{C}}{2\frac{k}{m_s}T_s} + \frac{p_{s,jk}}{p_s}\frac{C_jC_k}{2\frac{k}{m_s}T_s}\right.$$

$$\left. - \frac{2\mathbf{q}_s\cdot\mathbf{C}}{p_s 2\frac{k}{m_s}T_s}\left(1 - \frac{2}{5}\frac{C^2}{2\frac{k}{m}T_s}\right)\right] \quad . \qquad (97.67)$$

The difference in the distribution functions is seen to be in the inclusion of the non-vanishing diffusion velocity $\mathbf{W}_s$ in (97.67). In this equation as in (97.66), the whole gas deviates little from its equilibrium state. Equation (97.67) would not be valid for fast flows (*i.e.*, strong shock waves). There are still other representations for the distribution function but we shall not list them here.* If Kolodner's form of the distribution is used the resulting stress and heat flux equations can be given explicitly; however, they are very complicated and we shall not write them down. Rather, we now invoke the assumption of weak ionization. This means that the number of charged particles is small compared with the electrically neutral atoms. Therefore, the momentum and energy transport of these charged particles is negligible compared with that of the neutrals. This assumption implies

$$\sum_s \frac{\rho_s}{\rho_{m,s}}\left[(\mathbf{P}_s\mathbf{xB})_{ij} + (\mathbf{P}_s\mathbf{xB})_{ji}\right] \approx 0 \qquad (97.68)$$

and the following,

$$\left.\begin{aligned} \sum_s \frac{p_s}{\rho_{m,s}}\frac{\partial p_{s,ij}}{\partial x_j} &\approx \frac{p}{\rho_m}\frac{\partial p_{ij}}{\partial x_j} \quad , \\ \sum_s p_{s,ij}\frac{\partial}{\partial x_j}\left(\frac{p_s}{\rho_{m,s}}\right) &\approx p_{ij}\frac{\partial}{\partial x_j}\left(\frac{p}{\rho_m}\right) \quad , \end{aligned}\right\} \qquad (97.69)$$

---

* See for example, Burgers, J., loc. cit.

$$\left.\begin{aligned}
\sum_s p_s \frac{\partial}{\partial x_i}\left(\frac{p_s}{\rho_{m,s}}\right) &\approx p \frac{\partial}{\partial x_i}\left(\frac{p}{\rho_m}\right) ,\\
\sum_s \frac{p_s}{\rho_{m,s}} \frac{\partial p_s}{\partial x_i} &\approx \frac{p}{\rho_m}\frac{\partial p}{\partial x_i} ,\\
\sum_s \frac{\rho_s}{\rho_{m,s}} \mathbf{q}_s &\approx 0 ,\\
\sum_s \frac{\rho_s}{\rho_{m,s}} p_s &\approx 0 ,\\
\sum_s \frac{\rho_s}{\rho_{m,s}} p_{s,ij} &\approx 0 .
\end{aligned}\right\} \qquad (97.69)$$

For a weakly ionized gas we shall take as the force law* between the particles to be

$$F = \frac{K}{r^{\nu}} , \qquad (97.70)$$

with r as the distance between two particles, K a constant, and ν is an integer such that $5 < \nu < \infty$. With all these assumptions and using Kolodner's form of the distribution function it can be shown that for the weakly ionized gas the stress equation and heat flux equation become respectively,

$$\frac{\partial p_{ij}}{\partial t} + \frac{\partial}{\partial x_k}(V_k p_{ij}) + \frac{4}{5}\left\{\frac{\partial q_i}{\partial x_j}\right\}' + 2\left\{p_{ik}\frac{\partial V_j}{\partial x_k}\right\}' + 2p\left\{\frac{\partial V_i}{\partial x_j}\right\}' - 2\left\{J_{C,i}(\mathbf{E} + \mathbf{VxB})_j\right\}' = -\frac{p}{\mu} p_{ij} , \qquad (97.71)$$

* In a weakly ionized gas the predominant collisions are between neutrals and between one neutral and one charged particle.

$$\frac{\partial q_i}{\partial t} + \frac{\partial}{\partial x_k}(V_k q_i) + \frac{7}{5} q_k \frac{\partial V_i}{\partial x_k} + \frac{2}{5} q_K \frac{\partial V_k}{\partial x_i} + \frac{2}{5} q_i \frac{\partial V_k}{\partial x_k} + \frac{p}{\rho_m} \frac{\partial p_{ik}}{\partial x_k} + \frac{7}{2} p_{ik} \frac{\partial}{\partial x_k}\left(\frac{p}{\rho_m}\right)$$

$$- \frac{p_{ik}}{\rho_m}\left(\frac{\partial p}{\partial x_k} + \frac{\partial p_{kj}}{\partial x_j}\right) + \frac{5}{2} p \frac{\partial}{\partial x_i}\left(\frac{p}{\rho_m}\right) + \frac{5}{2}\frac{\rho}{\rho_m} E_i p + \frac{\rho}{\rho_m} E_k p_{ik} + \frac{5}{2}\frac{p}{\rho_m}(\mathbf{J x B})_i + \frac{p_{ik}}{\rho_m}(\mathbf{J x B})_k$$

$$= -\frac{2}{3}\frac{p}{\mu} q_i \tag{97.72}$$

where μ is here the coefficient of viscosity. Thus, even under the simplifying assumptions we have made, the stress and heat flux equations for the single fluid model are not simple. If the fluid is at rest and is electrically neutral, we can put $\partial q_i/\partial t = 0$, $\rho = \mathbf{V} = 0$ and $p_{ik} \approx 0$ and eq. (97.72) simplifies to

$$\frac{5}{2} p \frac{\partial}{\partial x_i}\left(\frac{p}{\rho_m}\right) + \frac{5}{2}\frac{p}{\rho_m}(\mathbf{J x B})_i = -\frac{2}{3}\frac{p}{\mu} q_i \quad . \tag{97.73}$$

It follows from eq. (97.48) and the definition $C_p\mu/\lambda \mp 2/3$ where λ is the coefficient of heat conduction that the above equation can be written as

$$\mathbf{q} = -K \operatorname{grad} T - \frac{15}{4}\frac{\mu}{\rho_m}(\mathbf{J x B}) \quad . \tag{97.74}$$

The first term on the right is recognized as Fourier's law for heat conduction and the second term gives a heat flux in the direction normal to **J** and **B**, which is the Ettinghausen effect.

The development above of the stress and heat flux equations serves to indicate the complexity inherent in descriptions involving the higher moments. However any program which seeks to be comprehensive in its physical description of plasma phenomena must allow for such complexity.*

* For some of the detailed calculations see H. T. Yang, "Moment Equations and Boundary Conditions for Magneto-Gas Dynamics," Univ. of Southern California, Rept. 56-216 (1960).

Alternative Representations of the Conservation Laws—We return now to our original program of finding self consistent laws. For this we rewrite the first and second moments of Boltzmann's equation by expressing the self fields via Maxwell's equations. By summing over all species the momentum equation (97.23) now reads

$$\frac{\partial}{\partial t}\sum_s N_s m_s u_{s,k} + \frac{\partial}{\partial x_i}\sum_s N_s m_s <v_i v_k>_s = \sum_s N_s <F_k>_s \quad . \qquad (97.75)$$

The second term on the left side is the divergence of an expression which has the dimensions of a pressure, its dependence on the two indices suggests a tênsor character and therefore we put

$$P_{ik} = \sum_s N_s m_s <v_i v_k>_s \quad . \qquad (97.76)$$

In the elementary kinetic theory of gases the distribution function is isotropic in velocity space. This means that it has the form $f(\mathbf{r}, v^2, t)$ which implies $v_1^2 = v_2^2 = v_3^2 = v^2/3$ so that eq. (97.78) becomes, in this case

$$P_{ik} = \sum_s \frac{1}{3} N_s m_s <v^2>_s \delta_{ik} \qquad (97.77)$$

which we recognize as just the usual scalar pressure. Because of this fact we shall adopt P_{ik} as defining a pressure tensor. Let us now relate the right side of eq. (97.75) directly with the electromagnetic field. By definition,

$$\sum_s N_s <\mathbf{F}>_s = \sum_s \rho_s \int (\mathbf{E} + \mathbf{v x B}) f_s d^3\mathbf{v} = \sum_s [\rho_s N_s \mathbf{E}_s + \rho_s \int f_s \mathbf{v} d^3\mathbf{v x B}]$$

$$= \rho\mathbf{E} + \mathbf{J x B} \quad . \qquad (97.78)$$

Here, ρ and $\mathbf{J}$ are the charge and current densities which arise only from the plasma. By using Maxwell's equations we can write

$$\mu_0 \mathbf{J x B} = (\nabla \mathbf{x B})\mathbf{x B} - \mu_0 \frac{\partial \mathbf{D}}{\partial t}\mathbf{x B} = (\mathbf{B}\cdot\nabla)\mathbf{B} - \nabla\frac{B^2}{2} - \mu_0 \frac{\partial \mathbf{D}}{\partial t}\mathbf{x B} \qquad (97.79)$$

but since div $\mathbf{B} = 0$, we have for the first term on the right,

$$\mu_0 B_i \frac{\partial B_k}{\partial x_i} = \frac{\partial}{\partial x_i} B_i B_k \qquad (97.80)$$

and therefore,

$$(\mathbf{JxB})_i = \frac{\partial}{\partial x_k}\left(\frac{B_i B_k}{\mu_0} - \frac{B^2}{2\mu_0}\delta_{ik}\right) - \left(\frac{\partial \mathbf{D}}{\partial t}\mathbf{xB}\right)_i , \qquad (97.81)$$

which expresses the electromagnetic force density as the divergence of a stress tensor plus a radiation term (cf. also Chapter V). The analogous result for the electric force density is,

$$\rho E_i = \frac{\partial}{\partial x_k}\left(\epsilon_0 E_i E_k - \frac{\epsilon_0 E^2}{2}\delta_{ik}\right) - \left(\mathbf{Dx}\frac{\partial \mathbf{B}}{\partial t}\right)_i . \qquad (97.82)$$

The superposition of the two force densities give

$$(\rho\mathbf{E} + \mathbf{JxB})_i = -\left(\frac{\partial \tau_{ik}}{\partial x_k} + \frac{\partial \mathbf{g}}{\partial t}\right) \qquad (97.83)$$

with the electromagnetic stress tensor given by,

$$\tau_{ik} = \left(\frac{\epsilon_0 E^2}{2} + \frac{B^2}{2\mu_0}\right)\delta_{ik} - \left(\epsilon_0 E_i E_k + \frac{B_i B}{\mu_0}\right) , \qquad (97.84)$$

and the momentum density of the electromagnetic field given by

$$\mathbf{g} = \epsilon_0 \mu_0 (\mathbf{ExH}) . \qquad (97.85)$$

Therefore the alternative representation of eq. (97.75) incorporates the external forces into the self consistent fields in the form,

$$\frac{\partial}{\partial t}(\pi_i + g_i) + \frac{\partial}{\partial x_k}(P_{ik} + \tau_{ik}) = 0 \qquad (97.86)$$

with the momentum density of the plasma defined by

$$\pi_i = \sum_s N_s m_s u_{s,i} \quad . \tag{98.87}$$

The interpretation of eq. (97.86) has already been given in Chapter V but for convenience here we shall interpret it anew. First note that in the stationary state we are left with

$$\frac{\partial}{\partial x_k} (P_{ik} + \tau_{ik}) = 0 \quad , \tag{97.88}$$

which expresses the vanishing of the divergence of the total tensor, *i.e.*, plasma plus the electromagnetic, and can therefore be considered as a pressure balance equation. Another way of looking at this balance equation is to integrate it throughout a fixed volume of the plasma and apply the divergence theorem, hence

$$\int_\Sigma (P_{ik} + \tau_{ik})\, d\Sigma = 0 \quad , \tag{97.89}$$

where Σ is the surface bounding the volume. In this form the dependence of both P_{ik} and τ_{ik} on each other is clearly seen.

Plasma Diamagnetism—The concept of plasma diamagnetism stems from the following simple case. Let P_{ik} be a scalar, set the electric field equal to zero, and consider the magnetic field lines to be straight parallel lines but not necessarily homogeneously distributed. Equation (97.88) then reduces to

$$\frac{\partial}{\partial x_k} \left(P + \frac{B^2}{2\mu_0}\right) \delta_{ik} = \frac{\partial}{\partial x_i} \left(P + \frac{B^2}{2\mu_0}\right) = 0 \quad , \tag{97.90}$$

which implies that $[P + (B^2/2\mu_0)]$ is independent of position, *i.e.*, uniform in space. Thus the pressure balance equation for this case asserts that the plasma plus the magnetic pressure is constant. In the region outside the plasma the material pressure $P = 0$, the magnetic field is larger than inside the plasma. This is known as plasma diamagnetism.

Let us now consider an alternative representation of the law of conservation of energy, that is, in a self consistent form. By summing over all species eq. (97.28) becomes

$$\frac{\partial}{\partial t}\sum_s N_s\left\langle\frac{1}{2}mv^2\right\rangle_s + \frac{\partial}{\partial \boldsymbol{x}_i}\sum_s N_s\left\langle\frac{1}{2}mv^2 v_i\right\rangle_s = \mathbf{J}\cdot\mathbf{E}, \quad (97.91)$$

and from Maxwell's equations we have the identity,

$$\mathbf{J}\cdot\mathbf{E} = -\frac{\partial}{\partial t}\left(\frac{\epsilon_0}{2}E^2 + \frac{B^2}{2\mu_0}\right) + \nabla\cdot(\mathbf{ExH}), \quad (97.92)$$

which upon substitution into eq. (97.91) gives

$$\frac{\partial}{\partial t}\left(\sum_s N_s\left\langle\frac{1}{2}mv^2\right\rangle_s + \frac{\epsilon_0}{2}E^2 + \frac{B^2}{2\mu_0}\right) + \nabla\cdot\left(\sum_s N_s\left\langle\frac{1}{2}mv^2 v_i\right\rangle_s + \mathbf{ExH}\right) = 0, \quad (97.93)$$

and is easily interpreted as the rate of change of the kinetic energy of the plasma plus electromagnetic energy density equals the negative of the divergence of the plasma material plus electromagnetic energy flow.

An alternative representation of the momentum conservation law is obtained by introducing the average velocity of the whole plasma as in the discussion of the stress and heat flux equations [see eq. (97.33)], and expressing the fluid pressure tensor in the local moving coordinate system. Thus,

$$\mathbf{V} = \frac{\sum_s m_s N_s \mathbf{u}_s}{\sum_s m_s N_s} \quad (97.94)$$

and,

$$p_{ik} = \sum_s m_s N_s \langle (v_i - V_i)(v_k - V_k)\rangle_s = P_{ik} - V_i V_k \sum_s m_s N_s, \quad (97.95)$$

by substituting eqs. (97.94), (97.95) into eq. (97.23) we obtain,

$$\frac{\partial}{\partial t} \sum_s m_s N_s V_i + \frac{\partial}{\partial x_k} (p_{ik} + V_i V_k) \quad m_s N_s = \sum_s N_s \langle F_i \rangle_s , \tag{97.96}$$

or,

$$V_i \frac{\partial}{\partial t} \sum_s m_s N_s + \sum_s m_s N_s \frac{\partial V_i}{\partial t} + \frac{\partial p_{ik}}{\partial x_k} + V_i \frac{\partial}{\partial x_k} \sum_s m_s N_s V_k + \sum_s m_s N_s V_k \frac{\partial V_i}{\partial x_k} = \sum_s N_s \langle F_i \rangle_s . \tag{97.97}$$

Now the equation of continuity is used in the form

$$\frac{\partial}{\partial t} \sum_s m_s N_s + \frac{\partial}{\partial x_k} \sum_s m \, N_s V_k = 0 , \tag{97.98}$$

together with eq. (97.97) to yield,

$$\sum_s m_s N_s \left(\frac{\partial V_i}{\partial t} + V_k \frac{\partial V_i}{\partial x_k} \right) + \frac{\partial p_{ik}}{\partial x_k} = \sum_s N_s \langle F_i \rangle_s . \tag{97.99}$$

The term in parenthesis is just the total time derivative of $\mathbf{V}(\mathbf{r}, t)$, so that eq. (97.99) can finally be written as

$$\sum_s m_s N_s \frac{dV_i}{dt} + \frac{\partial p_{ki}}{\partial x_k} = \sum_s N_s \langle F_i \rangle_s , \tag{97.100}$$

which can be interpreted as an equation of motion of the plasma as a whole if $\mathbf{V}$, the local average velocity of the particles, is associated with a "fluid velocity." When the pressure tensor is a scalar quantity, eq. (97.100 becomes the usual Euler equation for a fluid.

A Virial Theorem—Eq. (97.100) is not in a self consistent form and in order to cast it into such a form we use eq. (97.83) for the force density term,

$$\sum_s m_s N_s \frac{dV_i}{dt} + \frac{\partial}{\partial x_k} (p_{ik} + \tau_{ik}) + \frac{\partial}{\partial t} \mathbf{g} = 0 . \tag{97.101}$$

By multiplying this equation with x_i and integrating over a volume which moves with the plasma the first term can be written as

$$\sum_s \int m_s N_s x_i \frac{dV_i}{dt} d^3\mathbf{r} = \int x_i \frac{dV_i}{dt} d^3 m \qquad (97.102)$$

where $d^3\mathbf{r}$ indicates integration in configuration space and d^3m denotes integration over the mass (see Chapter V). Replacing V_i by its equivalent dx_i/dt and since the elements of mass do not vary with time because they move with the fluid

$$\int x_i \frac{d^2x_i}{dt^2} d^3m = \frac{1}{2}\frac{d^2}{dt^2}\int x_i x_i d^3m - \int \left(\frac{dx_i}{dt}\right)^2 d^3m \equiv \frac{1}{2}\frac{d^2I}{dt^2} - 2T \quad . (97.103)$$

where„ by definition, $\int x_i x_i d^3m$ is the moment of inertia of the fluid and $1/2 \int (dx_i/dt)^2 d^3m$ is the kinetic energy of the fluid. Let us look at the second term of eq. (97.101) and the divergence theorem, denoting by Σ the surface bounding the volume V,

$$\int_V x_i \frac{\partial}{\partial x_k}(p_{ik} + \tau_{ik})d^3\mathbf{r} = \int_\Sigma x_i(p_{ik} + \tau_{ik})d\Sigma - \int_V \delta_{ik}(p_{ik} + \tau_{ik})d^3\mathbf{r} \quad . \qquad (97.104)$$

By using eq. (97.95) we can rewrite the first term in the volume integral as

$$\sum_s m_s \int_V N_s \langle(\mathbf{v} - \mathbf{V})^2\rangle_s d^3\mathbf{r} \equiv 2U_R \quad , \qquad (97.105)$$

where U_R is the random thermal energy of the plasma. By using eq. (97.84) we also find

$$\int_V \delta_{ik}\tau_{ik} d^3\mathbf{r} = \int_V \left(\frac{\epsilon_0 E^2}{2} + \frac{B^2}{2\mu_0}\right) d^3\mathbf{r} = U_e + U_m \quad , \qquad (97.106)$$

and finally from eqs. (97.84), (97.86), (97.87) and (97.101) we obtain the virial theorem in the form

$$\frac{1}{2}\frac{d^2I}{dt^2} + \int_V x_k \frac{\partial g_k}{\partial t} d^3\mathbf{r} = 2(T + U_R) + U_e + U_m + \int_\Sigma x_k(p_{ik} + \tau_{ik})d\Sigma \quad . \qquad (97.107)$$

Self Confinement of a Plasma—The virial theorem above permits us to discuss briefly the possibility of self confinement of a bounded plasma. More precisely stated, can a bounded finite plasma generate an electromagnetic field(s) which act on the self charges and currents to yield a stationary configuration? To answer this question we let the volume V enclose the entire plasma and field. Hence the surface integral vanishes since the torque due to p_{ik} exactly balances that of τ_{ik}. The time derivative also vanishes for a stationary configuration and therefore eq. (97.107) reduces to

$$2(T + U_R) + U_e + U_m = 0 \quad . \tag{97.108}$$

But since all the terms on the left are clearly positive this equation can not hold and we conclude that no self confinement is possible. Moreover, in eq. (97.107) we can usually neglect the volume integral on the left side and we obtain the further result that the finite plasma must expand, that is,

$$\frac{d^2 I}{dt^2} > 0 \quad . \tag{97.109}$$

Consequently the more energy (all kinds) contained in the plasma, the larger is d^2I/dt^2, and the faster is the expansion.

98. THE COLLISION TERM

We shall now discuss the collision term that occurs in the Boltzmann equation. To aid us in the discussion we consider the following diagram which represents a collision (more generally speaking, an encounter) between the elastic and charged particles denoted by 1 and 2, and for simplicity of discussion we shall assume they are identical. In the usual discussions on collisions two coordinate systems are used. One of these coordinate systems considers the common center of mass at rest and therefore the two particles move along trajectories which are hyperbolic in a plane, the "orbital plane" (see Fig. 27). The other system is the laboratory system, a system in which the measurements of scattering are performed.*

* H. C. Corben, P, Stehle, "Classical Mechanics," pp. 61-63, second edition, John Wiley & Sons, Inc. (1960); R. B. Leighton, "Principles of Modern Physics," Chapter XIV, McGraw-Hill Co., New York, 1959.

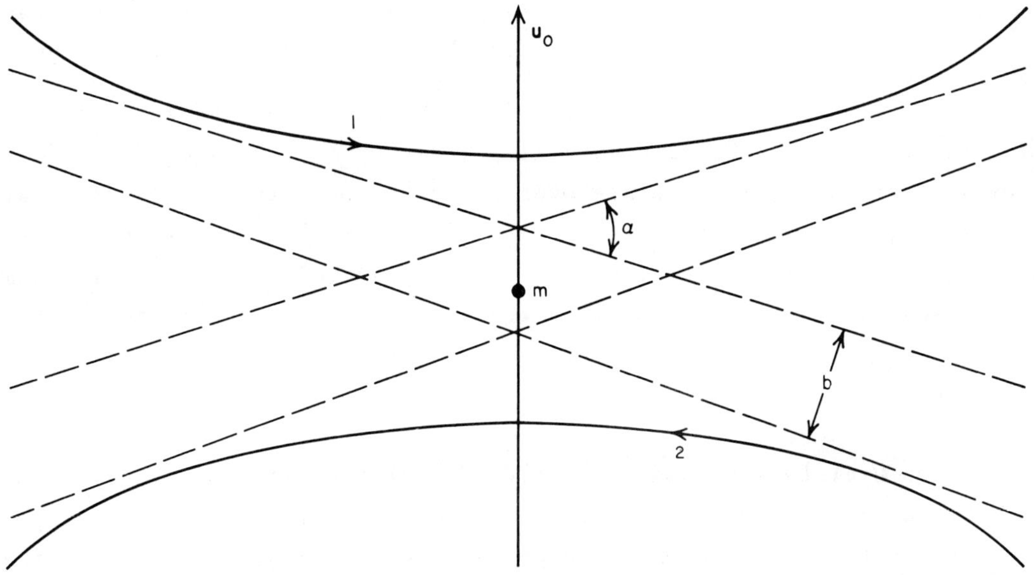

FIG. 27

In the figure b denotes the impact parameter, which is the distance of closest approach of the particles when the particles do not mutually influence each other. The deflection angle is denoted by α, and $\mathbf{u}_0$ denotes a unit vector along the line of closest approach connecting the two particles. It is in the direction of deflection of particle 1. We introduce also the angle β which is the angle between the orbital plane and an arbitrary fixed plane in space. Thus, the geometry of the collision is described by α and β.

Prior to a discussion of collisions we want to consider some "characteristic lengths" which will play a significant role. The impact parameter "b" corresponding to a deflection of $\alpha = \pi/2$ will be denoted by b_0. If a collision takes place between an ion of charge e_i and an electron charge e, the well known dispersion formula of Rutherford yields

$$b_0 = \frac{|e_i e|}{m_e V_R^2} , \tag{98.1}$$

where m_e is the electron mass, V_R^2 is the square of the relative velocities of the particles.

The next characteristic length is the mean distance between the particles denoted here by $d = (1/N)^{1/3}$ where N is the number density of particles

The Debye shielding distance, "h" is the remaining characteristic length which was already discussed previously, given by $h = (kT/N_s e_s)^{1/2}$ and indicates approximately the distance over which the negative charge can deviate significantly from the positive charge. This formula, in the strict sense, is valid only in the presence of one type of particle. But, the formula may be used if there are several positive species at the same temperature if we denote the density of positive charges by N_s and their average charge by e_s.

Plasma Oscillations and Collective Coordinates—It is apropos to discuss the concept of plasma oscillations and collective coordinates together. According to the description given previously on the significance of the Debye length we recognized that the Coulomb interaction, which is a long range force, is capable of organizing the behavior of the electrons into a collective motion on which the individual motions are superposed. Now suppose that by some means a gap or cavity appears in an electron cloud. Besides the neighboring electrons which tend to fill up this gap, the entire cloud of electrons contracts inward , say, by some small amount in order to keep the density uniform. But in contracting to maintain this uniform state, kinetic energy is acquired by the cloud and therefore overshoots the mark. This overshoot creates a relative excess of charge at the center. This excess can be nullified by an expansion of the cloud, etc. Therefore, the result of some perturbing force which causes small changes in the motion of electrons which are separated by large distances is a long-wavelength oscillation in the density of the electron cloud. Such oscillations are called plasma oscillations. The frequency of such oscillations can be calculated in an elementary way. Let N denote the volume density of an electron charge cloud and suppose these charges undergo a displacement $\mathbf{r}$ from their equilibrium positions. This gives rise to a polarization defined by $\mathbf{P} = Ne\mathbf{r}$, where e is the charge, and hence to an electrical field, $\epsilon_0\mathbf{E} = -\mathbf{P}$. The force returning the charges to their equilibrium position is $e\mathbf{E}$ and the equation of motion is therefore given by

$$m\ddot{\mathbf{r}} = e\mathbf{E} = -\frac{e}{\epsilon_0}\mathbf{P} = -\frac{Ne^2}{\epsilon_0}\mathbf{r} \tag{98.2}$$

which describes a simple harmonic motion with frequency

$$\omega_p = \left(\frac{Ne^2}{\epsilon_0 m}\right)^{1/2} . \tag{98.3}$$

Suppose now that we want to separate out the "collective modes of vibration" of the plasma from the motions of the individual particles themselves. The Debye radius then comes into consideration. For, the plasma can only screen out the Coulomb field of the individual charges outside a radius equal to the Debye radius "h", and hence this radius must be the smallest wavelength of an organized collective mode of vibration, *i.e.*, it is the cut-off point of the plasma spectrum. Following Bohm and Pines we derive the means by which we can actually count these collective modes.* For a free electron gas the Hamiltonian in terms of the momenta $\mathbf{p}_i$ and coordinates $\mathbf{r}_i$ of the individual electrons is given by

$$H(\mathbf{r},\mathbf{p}) = \sum_i \frac{|\mathbf{p}_i|^2}{2m} + \frac{1}{2} e^2 \sum_{i,j} \frac{1}{|\mathbf{r}_i - \mathbf{r}_j|} . \tag{98.4}$$

We Fourier analyze the Coulomb interaction potential inside a finite volume V, that is, we represent $1/r$ by the formula

$$\frac{1}{r} = \frac{4\pi}{V} \sum_{\mathbf{K}}{}' \frac{1}{\mathbf{K}^2} \exp\,(i\mathbf{K} \cdot \mathbf{r}) , \tag{98.5}$$

where the sum is over all allowable values of $\mathbf{K}$ inside V subject to periodic boundary conditions.† The summation however excludes $\mathbf{K} = 0$ which corresponds physically to the effect of the average charge density of the electrons in the medium cancelled by an equal and opposite fixed positive charge distribution, an ion as discussed previously.

---

* Bohm, D. and Pines, D., Phys. Rev. 82, 625 (1951), ibid. 85, 338 (1952), 92, 609 (1953); see also, Hubbard, J., Proc. Phys. Soc. A, 68, 441 (1955).

† The finite volume is required since for such regions we obtain a discrete representation and therefore countable. The reader will recall that for an infinite region the Fourier analysis of a nonperiodic function leads to the Fourier integral, a continuous spectrum and therefore noncountable.

Substituting eq. (98.5) into eq. (98.4) gives

$$H = \sum_i \frac{|\mathbf{p}_i|^2}{2m} + \frac{2\pi e^2}{V} \sum_{i,j} \sum_{\mathbf{K}}{}' \frac{\exp\,[i\mathbf{K}\cdot(\mathbf{r}_i - \mathbf{r}_j)]}{\mathbf{K}^2} - 2\pi N e^2 \sum_{\mathbf{K}}{}' \frac{1}{\mathbf{K}^2} \,, \tag{98.6}$$

where the infinite self energy of the electrons has been subtracted from the total energy H. Since a point particle can be considered defined in terms of a delta function, we expand the density $N(\mathbf{r})$ as a sum of delta functions, one for each particle,

$$N(\mathbf{r}) = \sum_i \delta(\mathbf{r} - \mathbf{r}_i) \quad . \tag{98.7}$$

A collective coordinate $Q_{\mathbf{K}}$ is defined by

$$Q_{\mathbf{K}} = \left(\frac{4\pi e^2}{\mathbf{K}^2}\right)^{\frac{1}{2}} N_{\mathbf{K}} \,, \tag{98.8}$$

that is, they are proportional to the Fourier components of the electron density. But,

$$N_{\mathbf{K}} \equiv \int N(\mathbf{r}) \exp\,(-i\mathbf{K}\cdot\mathbf{r})\,d^3\mathbf{r} = \sum_i \exp\,(-i\mathbf{K}\cdot\mathbf{r}_i) \tag{98.9}$$

so that,

$$Q_{\mathbf{K}} = \left(\frac{4\pi e^2}{\mathbf{K}^2 V}\right)^{\frac{1}{2}} \sum_i \exp\,(-i\mathbf{K}\cdot\mathbf{r}_i) \quad . \tag{98.10}$$

We note that the Coulomb term in eq. (98.6) can be cast in the form $\sum'_{\mathbf{K}} Q_{\mathbf{K}} Q^*_{\mathbf{K}}$ which seems to imply that all of the electron motion is contained in the collective coordinates, and is therefore inconsistent with the kinetic energy term. To remove this inconsistency we allow the collective modes to enter only with values of $\mathbf{K}$ less than some fixed value, say $\mathbf{K}_C$ and write,

$$\frac{2\pi e^2}{V} \sum_{i,j} \sum_{\mathbf{K}} \frac{\exp\,[i\mathbf{K}\cdot(\mathbf{r}_i - \mathbf{r}_j)]}{\mathbf{K}^2} = \frac{1}{2} \sum_{K<K_C} Q_{\mathbf{K}} Q^*_{\mathbf{K}} + \frac{2\pi e^2}{V^2} \sum_{i,j} \sum_{K>K_C} \frac{\exp\,[i\mathbf{K}\cdot(\mathbf{r}_i - \mathbf{r}_j)]}{\mathbf{K}^2} \,. \tag{98.11}$$

By doing this however, we obtain a mixture of coordinates and the Hamiltonian loses its meaning. For, some of the coordinates describe the individual particle motions and some the large scale fluctuations of the electron density. The coordinates $Q_{\mathbf{K}}$ are not independent of the position $\mathbf{r}_i$ of the particles. The way out of this is to introduce the momenta $P_{\mathbf{K}}$ which are canonically conjugate to the $Q_{\mathbf{K}}$ and note that the Hamiltonian is unchanged if we add to it the term,

$$H_T = \frac{1}{2} \sum_{K<K_C} P_{\mathbf{K}} P_{\mathbf{K}}^* - i \sum_{K<K_C} P_{\mathbf{K}} \left(\frac{4\pi e^2}{\mathbf{K}^2 V} \right)^{1/2} N_{\mathbf{K}} \quad . \tag{98.12}$$

The Hamiltonian can now be written as

$$H = \sum_i \frac{|\mathbf{p}_i|^2}{2m} + \frac{1}{2} \sum_{K<K_C} \left[P_{\mathbf{K}}^* - i \left(\frac{4\pi e^2}{\mathbf{K}^2 V} \right)^{1/2} N_{\mathbf{K}} \right] \cdot \left[P_{\mathbf{K}} + i \left(\frac{4\pi e^2}{\mathbf{K}^2 V} \right)^{1/2} N_{\mathbf{K}}^* \right]$$

$$- 2\pi N e^2 \sum_{K<K_C}' \frac{1}{\mathbf{K}^2} + \frac{2\pi e^2}{V} \sum_{i,j} \sum_{K>K_C}' \frac{\exp\,[i\mathbf{K} \cdot (\mathbf{r}_i - \mathbf{r}_j)]}{\mathbf{K}^2} \quad , \tag{98.13}$$

but since all the real kinetic energy is still contained in the first term we shall separate it out among the collective and individual coordinates by putting

$$\mathbf{p}_i = \mathbf{p}_i' + \sum_{K<K_C} Q_{\mathbf{K}} \left(\frac{4\pi e^2}{\mathbf{K}^2 V} \right)^{1/2} \mathbf{K} \exp\,(i\mathbf{K} \cdot \mathbf{r}_i) \quad . \tag{98.14}$$

Here, $\mathbf{p}_i'$ is the momentum of the ith electron after taking account of its participation in the different collective motions, each with amplitude $Q_{\mathbf{K}}$ and polarized longitudinally which is demonstrated by the vector $\mathbf{K}$ in eq. (98.14). In order to utilize correctly the above separation of $\mathbf{p}_i$ we must also separate the corresponding collective momenta,

$$P_{\mathbf{K}} = P_{\mathbf{K}}' - i \left(\frac{4\pi e^2}{\mathbf{K}^2 V} \right)^{1/2} N_{\mathbf{K}}^* \, , \tag{98.15}$$

and now write the Hamiltonian H' as a function of the primed quantities,

$$H' = \sum_i \frac{|\mathbf{p}_i'|^2}{2m} + H_p + \frac{2\pi e^2}{V} \sum_{\substack{i,j \\ K>K_C}} \frac{\exp\,[i\mathbf{K}\cdot(\mathbf{r}_i - \mathbf{r}_j)]}{\mathbf{K}^2} - 2\pi N e^2 \sum_{K<K_C} \frac{1}{\mathbf{K}^2}$$

$$+ H_{e,p} + H_{C,i} \quad . \tag{98.16}$$

In this representation, it is clear that

$$H_p = \frac{1}{2} \sum_{K<K_C} (P_{\mathbf{K}}'^{\,*} P_{\mathbf{K}}' + \omega_p^2 Q_{\mathbf{K}}^* Q_{\mathbf{K}}) \tag{98.17}$$

gives collective vibrations of the pure plasma frequency ω_p. The sum of the first, third and fourth terms on the right side of eq. (98.16) represents the motion of the individual electrons but with a modified electron-electron interaction force. The term $H_{C,i}$ represents interactions between collective and individual coordinates and actually vanishes when averaged over a large number of particles in the volume. Finally, the term $H_{e,p}$ represents an electron-plasma interaction.

The justification of the transformations leading to H' depends naturally on how well it separates the Hamiltonian into terms which correspond to independent motions of the collective coordinates $Q_{\mathbf{K}}$ and the individual electron coordinates $\mathbf{r}_i$. The separation can hardly ever be expected to be precise because the electrons are prevented from exactly following the collective motion on a small scale by their individual random motions.*

Following Spitzer and Härm, in many actual cases the three parameters b_0, d and h satisfy the following inequality,

$$b_0 \ll d \ll h \,, \tag{98.18}$$

and therefore we should distinguish between four intervals for the impact parameter.† Interval 1 is defined by $b < b_0$, and most collisions satisfying

* For other theories of collective behavior including the one given above, see D. TerHaar, Introduction to the Physics of Many-Body Systems, Chapter 6, Interscience Tracts on Physics and Astronomy, Number 5, Interscience Publishers, Inc., N.Y. (1958).

† Spitzer, L., Jr., and Härm, R., Phys. Rev. 89, 977 (1953).

this inequality involve only two particles. This follows from the fact that the smallest distance between the particles b is much smaller than the mean distance d between the particles. The second interval 2 is defined by $d \geqq b \geqq b_0$, and collisions between several particles often occur in this interval. This is an intermediate group between the well defined interval 1 and interval 3. Interval 3 is defined by $h \gtrsim b > d$ and in this interval we can not consider the collisions as independent since several particles will affect each other simultaneously. For this interval we must consider deflections in the trajectory of a particle as arising from the fluctuations in the charge density inside a spherical shell of radius h. The effect of such fluctuations can be considerable and can completely outweigh the effect of collisions where $b < b_0$.* Finally, interval 4 is defined by $b > h$, and according to our discussion on plasma oscillations and collective coordinates, we see that particles with this parameter will participate in an organized oscillating motion. These plasma oscillations propagate in the plasma with wavelengths greater than h. For this region the concept of collisions loses its meaning and the mutual influence of the particles results in density variations which can be included in the left side of the Boltzmann equation (97.5). Consequently, in the collision term in this equation we must consider particles for which the impact parameters are bounded above by the Debye radius or shielding distance h.

Because of the classification just given we shall separate the collision term into two parts as follows,

$$\left(\frac{\partial f_s}{\partial t}\right)_{\text{coll.}} = \left(\frac{\partial f_s}{\partial t}\right)_c + \left(\frac{\partial f_s}{\partial t}\right)_d \tag{98.19}$$

the first term on the right represents the effect of the close collisions defined by $b \leqq b_0$ and the second term the effect of other influences defined through $h \gtrsim b > b_0$.

The Close Collision Term—The term $(\partial f_s/\partial t)_c$ is relatively easy to evaluate for particles which are both spherically symmetric and elastic. The derivation will not be given here; we discuss only the principal features.

* Cohen, R. S., Spitzer, L., Jr., McR. Routly, P., Phys. Rev. 80, 230 (1950).

Let two particles with masses given respectively by m_s and $m_{s'}$ move respectively with velocities $\mathbf{v}_s$ and $\mathbf{v}_{s'}$ before collision; $\mathbf{v}'_s$ and $\mathbf{v}'_{s'}$ after collision. Define the relative velocity before collision by

$$\mathbf{v}_r \equiv \mathbf{v}_s - \mathbf{v}_{s'} \quad . \tag{98.20}$$

Let $\mathbf{u}_0$ be in the direction of deflection of $m_{s'}$, then for the velocities of the particles after collision we have

$$\mathbf{v}'_s = \mathbf{v}_s - 2M_s(\mathbf{v}_r \cdot \mathbf{u}_0)\mathbf{u}_0 \, , \tag{98.21}$$

$$\mathbf{v}'_{s'} = \mathbf{v}_{s'} - 2M_{s'}(\mathbf{v}_r \cdot \mathbf{u}_0)\mathbf{u}_0 \, , \tag{98.22}$$

where,

$$M_s = \frac{m_s}{m_s + m_{s'}} \, , \qquad M_{s'} = \frac{m_{s'}}{m_s + m_{s'}} \quad . \tag{98.23}$$

From eqs. (98.21), (98.22), it is clear that if $\mathbf{u}_0$ is known, the velocity changes are determined. The vector $\mathbf{u}_0$ however is determined by the geometric parameters b and β in such a way that the right side of eqs. (98.21) and (98.22) can be considered as a function of these parameters. Chapman and Cowling give the result

$$\left(\frac{\partial f_s}{\partial t}\right)_c = \sum_{s'} \iiint (f'_s f'_{s'} - f_s f_{s'}) v_r \, b \, db \, d\beta \, d^3 v_s \tag{98.24}$$

where the integration is taken over all values of β and $\mathbf{v}_{s'}$, and to the upper limit b_0 of b; the summation is over all species of particles, the distribution functions f'_s and $f'_{s'}$ are defined by

$$f'_s = f_s(\mathbf{r}, \mathbf{v}'_s, t) \quad , \tag{98.25}$$

$$f'_{s'} = f_{s'}(\mathbf{r}, \mathbf{v}'_{s'}, t) \quad , \tag{98.26}$$

with $\mathbf{v}'_s, \mathbf{v}'_{s'}$ defined by (98.21) and (98.22).* The integral in eq. (98.24) represents the net addition to the number of type s particles in the volume element $d^3\mathbf{r}d^3\mathbf{v}$ due to collisions with particles of type s'. The total net increase is obtained by summing over all types of particles s', In the integrand, the primed terms represent the number of particles entering the volume element $d^3\mathbf{r}d^3\mathbf{v}$ per unit time from collisions, while the unprimed terms give the number lost from the same volume element by collisions.

The Fokker-Planck Term—To discuss the term $(\partial F_s/\partial t)_d$ we shall follow a method used by Chandrasekhar in his treatment of Brownian motion.† This term is treated in a much different manner than the close collision term. The basic idea is to consider a particle, a so-called test particle, moving through the plasma subjected to many small deflections caused by those particles in the interval $h > b > b_0$.

We define a function $\psi_s(\mathbf{v},\Delta\mathbf{v})$ which is the probability that a particle of type s with velocity $\mathbf{v}$ will undergo a change in velocity $\Delta\mathbf{v}$ in a unit time. This function will therefore describe the fluctuations of the test particle. Following Cohen, we shall carry over Chandrasekhar's treatment to plasmas.§ Consider now particles of type s at some instant of time t. These particles have a distribution given by $f_s(\mathbf{r},\mathbf{v},t)$. At a time $t + \Delta t$, where Δt is very much larger than the time period for small fluctuations, but small compared with the period for macroscopic changes, the distribution is given by $f_s(\mathbf{r},\mathbf{v},t+\Delta t)$. By hypothesis, there is no variation in the spatial dependence of the distribution function during the time interval Δt. Consequently, the distribution functions at time t and $t + \Delta t$ are related through the function $\psi_s(\mathbf{v},\Delta\mathbf{v})$ by the formula,

$$f_s(\mathbf{r},\mathbf{v},t + \Delta t) = \int f_s(\mathbf{r},\mathbf{v} - \Delta\mathbf{v},t)\psi_s(\mathbf{v} - \Delta\mathbf{v},\Delta\mathbf{v})\Delta t d^3\Delta\mathbf{v} \quad . \quad (98.27)$$

If we assume that f_s is analytic in t we can expand it in terms of Δt by means of a Taylor series; similarly we shall expand the right side in terms of $\Delta\mathbf{v}$. Interpreting $\psi_s(\mathbf{v},\Delta\mathbf{v})$ as $(\partial f_s/\partial t)_d$ and since

---

* Chapman, S. and Cowling, T. G., The Mathematical Theory of Non-Uniform Gases, Cambridge (1958). The situation for inelastic collisions and its effect on the electrical conductivity of ionized gases has also been treated by P. S. Epstein, "On the Electrical Conductivity of Ionized Gases," GMD42-247, Appl. Phys. Dept, Space Tech. Labs., Los Angeles, Calif., May 1957.

† Chandrasekhar, S., Rev. of Mod. Phys., 15, 1 (1943), Astrophys. J., 97, 255 (1943).

§ Cohen, R. S., et al, loc. cit.

$$\int \psi_s(\mathbf{v},\Delta\mathbf{v})\,d^3\Delta\mathbf{v} = 1 \qquad (98.28)$$

we can therefore write, neglecting terms of order $(\Delta t)^2$ and higher and also terms of order higher than $(\Delta v_j)^2$,

$$\left(\frac{\partial f_s}{\partial t}\right)_d = -\sum_j \frac{\partial}{\partial v_j}\left[f_s \int \psi_s \Delta v_j d^3\Delta v\right] + \frac{1}{2}\sum_j \frac{\partial^2}{\partial v_j^2}\left[f_s \int \psi_s (\Delta v_j)^2 d^3\Delta v\right]$$

$$+\frac{1}{2}\sum_{j\neq i} \frac{\partial^2}{\partial v_i \partial v_j}\left[f_s \int (\Delta v_i \Delta v_j)\psi_s d^3\Delta v\right] \quad . \qquad (98.29)$$

Let us now define the average quantities with respect to the function ψ_s by

$$\langle\Delta v_j\rangle_s = \int \Delta v_j \psi_s d^3\Delta v \ , \qquad (98.30)$$

$$\langle(\Delta v_j)^2\rangle_s = \int (\Delta v_j)^2 \psi_s d^3\Delta v \ , \qquad (98.31)$$

$$\langle(\Delta v_i \Delta v_j)\rangle_s = \int \Delta v_i \Delta v_j \psi_s d^3\Delta v \ , \qquad (98.32)$$

with these designations we can rewrite eq. (98.29)

$$\left(\frac{\partial f_s}{\partial t}\right)_d = -\sum_j \frac{\partial}{\partial v_j}\left[f_s\langle\Delta v_j\rangle\right] + \frac{1}{2}\sum \frac{\partial^2}{\partial v}\left[f_s\langle(\Delta v_j)^2\rangle\right] + \frac{1}{2}\sum_{j\neq i}\frac{\partial^2}{\partial v_j \partial v_i}\left[f_s\langle\Delta v_j \Delta v_i\rangle\right] \ , \qquad (98.33)$$

this is called the Fokker-Planck term. The quantities defined by eqs. (98.30)-(98.32) are called the "diffusion coefficients." To make use of these results in a specific situation, the function ψ_s must be determined. This, however, may not be an easy task. The actual determination of ψ_s can be circumvented by following an alternative scheme due to Chandrasekhar.* This scheme amounts to an alternative definition of

* Chandrasekhar, S., Astrophys. J., loc. cit.

the diffusion coefficients in the two-two particle approximation. Let $<D>$ denote any one of the diffusion coefficients, then in the two-two particle approximation we have

$$<D>_s = \iiint fDbv_r db d\beta d^3v_s , \qquad (98.34)$$

the integration is extended over all values of β and $\mathbf{v}$ as in eq. (98.24),, and the b integration extends from b_0 to h, the lower and upper limits of b. Since $f = \sum_s f_s$, eq. (98.34) yields

$$<D>_s = \sum_{s'} <D_{s'}>_s \qquad (98.35)$$

where

$$<D_{s'}>_s = \iiint f_{s'} Dbv_r db d\beta d^3v_s \quad . \qquad (98.36)$$

The distinction between the terms $<D>_s$ and $<D_{s'}>_s$ is as follows. The first quantity is the average value of D caused by collisions with all types of particles, and the second quantity represents only the part of the average value due to collisions with a fixed type s' of particles. The sum in eq. (98.35) is over all types s' including $s' = s$. We shall interpret the diffusion coefficients more specifically, later.

The Spherical Polar Representation of Boltzmann's Equation—Now that we have a representation of the collision term as the sum of close and distant collision terms, it will prove useful to transform Boltzmann's equation into a spherical polar form. Thus, we write,

$$\frac{\partial f_s}{\partial t} + \mathbf{v} \cdot \frac{\partial f_s}{\partial \mathbf{r}} + \frac{e_s}{m_s} (\mathbf{E} + \mathbf{v x B}) \cdot \frac{\partial f_s}{\partial \mathbf{v}} = \sum_{s'} \iiint (f'_s f'_{s'} - f_s f_{s'}) v_r b db d\beta d^3v_s$$

$$- \sum_j \frac{\partial}{\partial v_j} [f_s <\Delta v_j>_s] + \frac{1}{2} \sum_j \frac{\partial^2}{\partial v_j^2} [f_s <\Delta v_j^2>_s]$$

$$+ \frac{1}{2} \sum_{j \neq i} \frac{\partial^2}{\partial v_j \partial v_i} [f_s <\Delta v_j \Delta v_i>] , \qquad (98.37)$$

because of the integral term on the right side this form is an integro-differential equation. To date there does not exist an exact solution of this equation. But with some restricted hypothesis it is possible to simplify the equation, and the methods selected clearly depend on the class of problems considered.

Let us first suppose that $\mathbf{v} \cdot (\partial f_s/\partial \mathbf{r})$ and $\mathbf{E}$ are sufficiently small compared with the other terms so that the distribution function is approximately spherically symmetrical in the velocity space. With this assumption we can develop the distribution function formally in spherical harmonics in velocity space,

$$f_s(\mathbf{r},\mathbf{v},t) = \sum_{l=0}^{\infty} \sum_{m=-l}^{+l} f_{l,s}^m(\mathbf{r},\mathbf{v},t) Y_l^m(\theta,\varphi) \quad , \tag{98.38}$$

here, v, θ and φ denote spherical polars in velocity space, and Y_l^m are the normalized spherical harmonics; the $f_{l,s}^m$ are the expansion coefficients. By introducing rectangular cartesians in velocity space, we can write,

$$\left.\begin{aligned} v_1 &= v \sin\theta \cos\varphi \\ v_2 &= v \sin\theta \sin\varphi \\ v_3 &= v \cos\theta \end{aligned}\right\} \tag{98.39}$$

Now

$$Y_l^m = (-1)^m \left[\frac{(2l+1)(l-m)!}{4\pi(l+m)!}\right]^{\frac{1}{2}} \sin^m\theta \frac{d^m}{d(\cos\theta)^m} P_l(\cos\theta) e^{im\varphi} \, , \tag{98.40}$$

where $P_l(\cos\theta)$ is the Legendre polynomial, and

$$(Y_l^m)^* = (-1)^m Y_l^{-m} \tag{98.41}$$

while the conditions of reality require

$$(f_{l,s}^m)^* = (-1)^m f_{l,s}^{-m} \quad . \tag{98.42}$$

Let us choose the first four spherical harmonics Y_0^0, Y_1^{-1}, Y_1^0 and Y_1^1, then by using eqs. (98.39) and substituting the results in eq. (98.38) we can write the expansion in the form,

$$f_s(\mathbf{r},\mathbf{v},t) = f_{0,s}(\mathbf{r},v,t) + \frac{\mathbf{v}}{v} \cdot \mathbf{f}_{1,s}(\mathbf{r},v,t) + \sum_{l+2\ m} f_{l,s}^m Y_l^m , \tag{98.43}$$

where,

$$f_{0,s} = \left(\frac{1}{4\pi}\right)^{1/2} \cdot f_{0,s}^0(\mathbf{r},v,t) , \tag{98.44}$$

and

$$\mathbf{f}_{1,s} = \left(\frac{3}{4\pi}\right)^{1/2} [f_{1,s}^1 \mathbf{e}_1 + f_{1,s}^0 \mathbf{e}_2 + f_{1,s}^{-1} \mathbf{e}_3] , \tag{98.45}$$

the $\mathbf{e}_i$ constitute an orthonormal set of vectors in velocity space.* Following the usual pattern we retain the first two terms of the expansion (98.43). The validity of truncating the expansion after the second term of course depends on the terms truncated and comparing them with the preceding ones. This is not known *a priori* and therefore one must also calculate these terms in order to estimate the utility of a given expansion.

If we consider the first term in eq. (98.43) as the dominant term, the next term constitutes a perturbation. The first term is clearly symmetrical in velocity space, the second term provides the non-symmetrical features. Such an asymmetry is necessary on physical grounds since it is the source of the so-called currents; the symmetrical term, on the average, yields a zero net current. The principal task is to evaluate the coefficients, $f_{0,s}^0$, $f_{1,s}^1$, etc. in eqs. (98.44) and (98.45).

---

* Another and more interesting approach to the representation of f_s in spherical harmonics makes use of the fact that for a fixed l, the Y_l^m constitute an irreducible spherical tensor of rank l with $2l + 1$ components. The expansion coefficients $f_{l,s}^m$ also constitute a spherical tensor of rank m and the sum $\sum_{m=-l}^{+l}$ yields the contraction of these two tensors which is a scalar. See in this connection, R. Jancel and Theo. Kahan, "Étude Théorique De La Distribution Électronique Dans Un Plasma Lorentzien Hétérogéne Et Anisotrope," Le Journal De Physique Et Le Radium, Tome 20, Janvier 1959, pp. 35-42. See also, "Theorie Des Groups En Physiques Classique et Quantique," Septième Partie, Groupe Des Rotations, by R. Nataf, Ed. Th. Kahan, Dunod, Paris (1960).

In order to effect these calculations, we need to transform the left side of eq. (98.37). By substituting eq. (98.43) into eq. (98.37) we find

$$\frac{\partial f_s}{\partial t} = \frac{\partial f_{0,s}}{\partial t} + \frac{\mathbf{v}}{v} \cdot \frac{\partial \mathbf{f}_{1,s}}{\partial t} , \tag{98.46}$$

$$\mathbf{v} \cdot \frac{\partial f_s}{\partial \mathbf{r}} = \mathbf{v} \cdot \frac{\partial f_{0,s}}{\partial \mathbf{r}} + \mathbf{v} \cdot \frac{\partial}{\partial \mathbf{r}} \frac{\mathbf{v}}{v} f_{1,s} , \tag{98.47}$$

and since,

$$\frac{\partial}{\partial \mathbf{v}} = \frac{\mathbf{v}}{v} \frac{\partial}{\partial v} ,$$

then,

$$\frac{e_s}{m_s} [\mathbf{E} + \mathbf{vxB}] \cdot \frac{\partial f_s}{\partial \mathbf{v}} = \frac{e_s}{m_s} \mathbf{E} \cdot \frac{\mathbf{v}}{v} \left[\frac{\partial f_{0,s}}{\partial v} + \mathbf{v} \cdot \frac{\partial}{\partial v} \left(\frac{\mathbf{f}_{1,s}}{v} \right) \right]$$

$$+ \frac{e_s}{m_s} [\mathbf{E} + \mathbf{vxB}] \cdot \frac{\mathbf{f}_{1,s}}{v} \tag{98.48}$$

We now consider the right side of eq. (98,37) and examine the close collision term. If we substitute eq. (98.43) into eq. (98.24) we obtain an expression which is quite formidable and difficult to evaluate. Let us therefore limit ourselves for the present to a special type of plasma, a "Lorentz gas." This gas consists of only two species, electrons and one type of ion, and only the electrons are influenced by collisions. Moreover, the collisions are assumed to take place only between electrons and ions, with the ions considered at rest. Under these assumptions we rewrite eq. (98.24),

$$\left(\frac{\partial f_e}{\partial t} \right)_c = \iiint (f'_e f'_i - f_e f_i) v_r \, b db d\beta d^3 v_i \tag{98.49}$$

where subscripts e and i now refer to electrons and ions. The details of the calculations will not be given here, only the result.* We have

$$\left(\frac{\partial f_e}{\partial t}\right)_c = \frac{m_e}{m_i v^2}\frac{\partial}{\partial v}(\nu_e v^3 f_{0,e}) + \frac{kT_e}{m_i v^2}\frac{\partial}{\partial v}\left(\nu_e v^2 \frac{\partial f_{0,e}}{\partial v}\right) + \nu_e \frac{\mathbf{v}}{v}\cdot \mathbf{f}_{1,e}, \quad (98.50)$$

where,

$$\nu_e = \frac{2\pi N_i (e)^4}{m_e^2 v^3} \ln\left[1 + \frac{b_0 m_e^2 v^4}{(e)^4}\right] \quad (98.51)$$

is the collision frequency of the electrons.†

The transformation of the Fokker-Planck term by means of eq. (98.43) gives rise to a rather complicated expression. To achieve some simplification we shall use only the first term of the expansion, *i.e.*, the symmetrical part of eq. (98.43) in evaluating the "diffusion coefficients." Since at any time t the "test particle" has a velocity $\mathbf{v}$ we define a rectangular cartesian frame in velocity space with the v_3 axis directed along $\mathbf{v}$. Because of the approximate symmetry of the field particle distribution about the test particle, the average deflections of the test particle in the v_1 and v_2 directions must be zero. Moreover, since the deflections in the three directions v_1, v_2, and v_3 are not correlated, the diffusion coefficients $<\Delta v_1>_s = <\Delta v_2>_s = <\Delta v_1 \Delta v_3>_s = <\Delta v_2 \Delta v_3>_s = 0$, and by symmetry all directions in the v_2, v_2 plane are equally probable, $<(\Delta v_1)^2>_s = <(\Delta v_2)^2>_s$. This leaves only the three independent diffusion coefficients,§

$$\left.\begin{aligned} <\Delta v_3>_s &\equiv <\Delta v_{11}>_s \,, \\ <(\Delta v_3)^2>_s &\equiv <(\Delta v_{11})^2>_s \,, \\ 2<(\Delta v_1)^2>_s &= 2<(\Delta v_2)^2>_s = <(\Delta v_1)^2>_s \,. \end{aligned}\right\} \quad (98.52)$$

* See for example, W. P. Allis, "Motions of Ions and Electrons," Encyclop. of Physics, Springer-Verlag, Berlin (1956). Also, Chapman and Cowling, loc. cit.; B. J. Davydov, Zh. eksper. teor. fiz., 7, 1065 (1937).

† This formula for the collision frequency is given by A. V. Gurevich, Sov. Phys. JETP, 3, 895 (1957).

§ The following designations are also given to these coefficients respectively; slowing-down coefficient, longitudinal dispersion coefficient, transverse dispersion coefficient. See for example, J. L. Delcroix, Introduction to the Theory of Ionized Gases, Interscience Tracts on Physics and Astronomy, No. 8, P107, Interscience Publishers, Inc., New York, 1960.

The first quantity of this set is in general negative, and is called the "coefficient of dynamical friction," since it represents a measure by which the test particle speed is attenuated by the field particles, *i.e.*, those particles which contribute to the deflection of the test particle. The remaining coefficients represent the mean square change in the velocity in directions parallel and perpendicular to the initial direction.

The Fokker-Planck Term in Spherical Polars—Instead of transforming eq. (98.33) directly into spherical polars in velocity space we can start with the function ψ_s in the form

$$\psi_s = \psi_s(\mathbf{v}, \Delta v, \Delta\theta, \Delta\varphi) \tag{98.53}$$

which represents the probability of deflections Δv, $\Delta\theta$, and $\Delta\varphi$ of a particle in a unit of time. Let us also transform f_s by the formula

$$g_s(\mathbf{r},\mathbf{v},t) = f_s(\mathbf{r},\mathbf{v},t)v^2 \sin^2\theta \quad , \tag{98.54}$$

where g_s represents the number of particles of type s in an element $dv d\theta d\varphi$ around the point v, θ and φ. Now in the same way that eq. (98.33) was derived we find,

$$\left(\frac{\partial f_s}{\partial t}\right)_d = -\frac{1}{v^2 \sin\theta}\left\{\sum_j \frac{\partial}{\partial x_j}[e_s\langle\Delta x_j\rangle_s] - \frac{1}{2}\sum_j \frac{\partial^2}{\partial x_j^2}[g_s\langle(\Delta x_j)^2\rangle_s] - \frac{1}{2}\sum_{j\neq i}\frac{\partial^2}{\partial x_j \partial x_i}[g_s\langle\Delta x_j \Delta x_i\rangle_s]\right\} \tag{98.55}$$

where

$$x_1 = v \quad , \quad x_2 = \theta \quad , \quad x_3 = \varphi \quad .$$

We shall now evaluate the above diffusion coefficients in spherical polars in terms of the coefficients in cartesians because the latter can be evaluated in the binary collision approximation.* For the symmetrical distribution in our case this easily is established. Consider Fig. 28 in velocity space.

---

* Cohen, *et al.*, loc. cit., have done this for a more general non-symmetrical distribution function of the field particles.

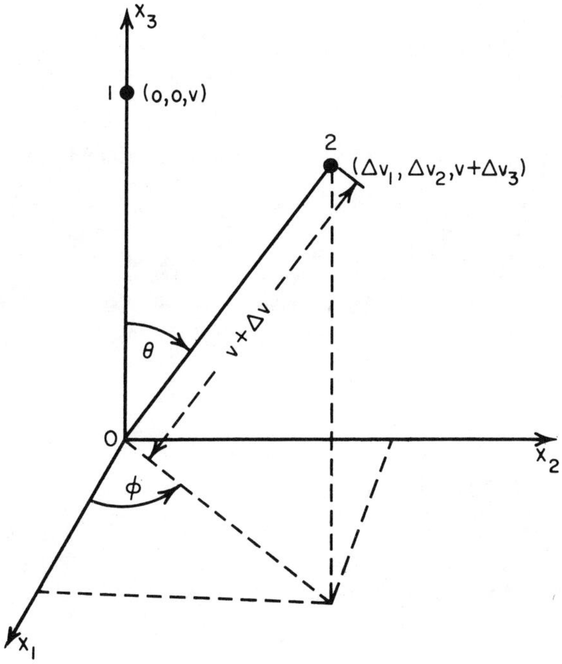

FIG. 28

For simplicity of discussion, the velocity of the particle is taken in the x_3 direction before the deflection. If we assume that both $\Delta\theta$ and Δv are sufficiently small so that $\sin\theta \approx \Delta\theta$, and $\cos\theta \approx 1 - [1/2(\Delta\theta)^2]$, eqs. (98.39) give

$$\left.\begin{aligned} \Delta v_1 &= (v + \Delta v)\Delta\theta \cos\varphi , \\ \Delta v_2 &= (v + \Delta v)\Delta\theta \sin\varphi , \\ \Delta v_3 &= \Delta v - \frac{1}{2}(\Delta\theta)^2 v . \end{aligned}\right\} \tag{98.56}$$

But,

$$(\Delta v_1)^2 + (\Delta v_2)^2 = (v + \Delta v)^2(\Delta\theta)^2 , \tag{98.57}$$

together with the third equation of the set (98.52) yields,

$$(\Delta\theta)^2 = \frac{(\Delta v_\perp)^2}{v^2} , \tag{98.58}$$

keeping just the second order terms. From the third of eqs. (98.56) we obtain

$$\Delta v = \Delta v_{11} + \frac{1}{2}\frac{(\Delta v_\perp)^2}{v} , \tag{98.59}$$

and squaring,

$$(\Delta v)^2 = (\Delta v_{11})^2 . \tag{98.60}$$

In a unit time the average value of eqs. (98.58)-(98.60) gives the diffusion coefficients

$$<(\Delta\theta)^2> = \frac{1}{v^2} <(\Delta v_\perp)^2> , \tag{98.61}$$

$$<\Delta v> = <\Delta v_{11}> + \frac{1}{2v} <(\Delta v_\perp)^2> , \tag{98.62}$$

$$<(\Delta v)^2> = <(\Delta v_{11})^2> . \tag{98.63}$$

Substituting these results into eq. (98.55) we obtain the following form for the Fokker-Planck term

$$\left(\frac{\partial f_s}{\partial t}\right)_d = -\frac{1}{v^2}\frac{\partial}{\partial v}\left[f_s v^2\left(<\Delta v_{11}>_s + \frac{1}{2}\frac{<\Delta v_\perp>_s}{v}\right)\right] + \frac{1}{2v^2}\frac{\partial^2}{\partial v^2}\,[f_s v^2<(\Delta v_{11})^2>_s] . \tag{98.64}$$

This expression may be simplified by writing

$$<\Delta V>_s = <\Delta v_{11}>_s + \frac{<(\Delta v_\perp)^2>_s}{2v} - \frac{1}{2v^2}\frac{\partial}{\partial v}\,[v^2<(\Delta v_{11})^2>_s] , \tag{98.65}$$

and by using eq. (98.43) there results,

$$\left(\frac{\partial f_s}{\partial t}\right)_d = -\frac{1}{v^2}\frac{\partial}{\partial v} v^2\left[<\Delta V>_s f_{0,s} - \frac{1}{2}<(\Delta v_{11})^2>_s \frac{\partial f_{0,s}}{\partial v}\right]$$

$$-\frac{\mathbf{v}}{v^3}\cdot\frac{\partial}{\partial v} v^2\left[<\Delta V>_s - \frac{1}{2}<(\Delta v_{11})^2>_s \frac{\partial f_{1,s}}{\partial v}\right] \quad . \quad (98.66)$$

With all terms now evaluated in Boltzmann's equation, let us substitute eqs. (98.46)-(98.48), (98.50) and (98.66) into eq. (98.37) to obtain

$$\frac{\partial f_{0,s}}{\partial t} + \frac{\mathbf{v}}{v}\cdot\frac{\partial \mathbf{f}_{1,s}}{\partial t} + \mathbf{v}\cdot\frac{\partial f_{0,s}}{\partial \mathbf{r}} + \frac{\mathbf{v}}{v}\cdot\frac{\partial(\mathbf{v}\cdot\mathbf{f}_{1,s})}{\partial \mathbf{r}} + \frac{e_s}{m_s}\mathbf{E}\cdot\frac{\mathbf{v}}{v}\frac{\partial f_{0,s}}{\partial v}$$

$$+\frac{e_s}{m}[\mathbf{E} + \mathbf{v x B}]\cdot\frac{\mathbf{f}_{1,s}}{v} + \frac{e_s}{m}\mathbf{E}\cdot\left(\mathbf{v}\cdot\frac{\partial \mathbf{f}_{1,s}}{\partial v}\right)\frac{\mathbf{v}}{v}$$

$$= \left\{\frac{m_e}{m_i v^2}\frac{\partial}{\partial v}[\nu_e v^3 f_{0,e}] + \frac{kT_e}{m_i v^2}\frac{\partial}{\partial v}\left[\nu_e v^2\frac{\partial f_{0,e}}{\partial v}\right] + \nu_e\frac{\mathbf{v}}{v}\cdot\mathbf{f}_{1,e}\right\}\delta_{se}$$

$$-\frac{1}{v^2}\frac{\partial}{\partial v} v^2\left[<\Delta V>_s f_{0,s} - \frac{1}{2}<(\Delta v_{11})^2>_s\frac{\partial f_{0,s}}{\partial v}\right]\delta_{se}$$

$$-\frac{\mathbf{v}}{v^3}\cdot\frac{\partial}{\partial v} v^2\left[<\Delta V>_s \mathbf{f}_{1,s} - \frac{1}{2}<(\Delta v_{11})^2>\frac{\partial \mathbf{f}_{1,s}}{\partial v}\right]\delta_{se} , \quad (98.67)$$

where δ_{se} is the Kronecker delta symbol, and since we have postulated a Lorentz type gas it means that we do not consider any form of collision on any of the ions with respect to the close and distant collision terms, *i.e.*, for $s = i$, $\delta_{ie} = 0$, and for $s = e$, $\delta_{ee} = 1$.

To carry the analysis further, we make use of the following orthogonality property of eqs. (98.39),

$$\int_0^{\pi}\int_0^{2\pi} v_i v_j \sin\theta d\theta d\varphi = \frac{4\pi}{3} v^2 \delta_{ij} \quad ; \qquad (98.68)$$

now multiply eq. (98.67) by $\sin\theta d\theta d\varphi$ and integrate over θ and φ to obtain the following result

$$\frac{\partial f_{0,s}}{\partial t} + \frac{e_s}{3m_s v^2}\frac{\partial}{\partial v}(v^2\mathbf{E}\cdot\mathbf{f}_{1,s}) + \frac{\mathbf{v}}{3}\cdot\frac{\partial \mathbf{f}_{1,s}}{\partial \mathbf{r}} = \frac{1}{v^2}\frac{\partial}{\partial v}v^2\left[\left(\frac{m_e\nu_e v}{m_i} - \langle\Delta V\rangle_s\right)f_{0,s} + \left(\frac{kT_e\nu_e}{m_i} + \frac{1}{2}\langle(\Delta v_{11})\rangle_s\right)\frac{\partial f_0}{\partial v}\right]\delta_{se} \quad .$$

(98.69)

Multiplying eq. (98.69) by $\mathbf{v}\sin\theta d\theta d\varphi$ and integrating over θ and φ again gives

$$\frac{\partial \mathbf{f}_{1,s}}{\partial t} + \frac{e_s}{m_s}\mathbf{E}\frac{\partial f_{0,s}}{\partial v} + v\frac{\partial f_{0,s}}{\partial \mathbf{r}} + \frac{e_s}{m_s}\mathbf{B}\mathrm{x}\mathbf{f}_{1,s}$$

$$= \left\{-\nu_e\mathbf{f}_{1,e} - \frac{1}{v^2}\frac{\partial}{\partial v}v^2\left[\langle\Delta V\rangle_s\mathbf{f}_{1,s} - \frac{1}{2}\langle(\Delta v_{11})^2\rangle\frac{\partial \mathbf{f}_{1,s}}{\partial v}\right]\right\}\delta_{se} \quad .$$

(98.70)

Equations (98.69) and (98.70) are two linearly independent equations, the first is a scalar equation for the zero order approximation and the second is a vector equation equivalent to three scalar equations for the components of $\mathbf{f}_{1,s}$. The right side of eq. (98.70) is zero for $s = i$. Even with the simplifications made these equations are quite formidable. In order not to lose sight of what we have done let us summarize briefly the assumptions leading to these two independent equations.

For the Lorentz gas neglecting ion-ion collisions, we do not have to write the equations for this plasma component. By introducing the Kronecker symbol an artificial mode of expression for the ions enters into the description. This form of expression results from being able to transform the close collision term into a differential form. This was not required for the Fokker-Planck term which arises from an averaging process.

If collision terms are further neglected, and by retaining only the diffusion terms, it is possible to obtain a system of equations in a symmetrical form. For this, on the right side of both eqs. (98.69) and (98.70) we put $\delta_{se} = 1$ and neglect terms not containing diffusion coefficients. Here too, we remark that the resulting set of equations is still complicated. Rather than attempt to discuss the nature and properties of such a system we shall consider a solution which results from neglecting the terms containing the diffusion coefficients.

Although this is apparently unsatisfactory from a complete physical point of view, nevertheless it is plausible to expect that the effects of distant collisions will outweigh those of close collisions because of the cumulative effect of the large number of distant encounters as compared with the rare number of close encounters. Before we proceed however to find a solution for our particular case it will be worthwhile to digress and discuss the solutions of Boltzmann's equation in the collisionless case.

99. SOLUTIONS OF BOLTZMANN'S EQUATION

Let us first recall that the collisionless Boltzmann equation is a first order partial differential equation. If the force $\mathbf{F}(\mathbf{r},\mathbf{v},t)$ is given and if the initial and boundary conditions for $f(\mathbf{r},\mathbf{v},t)$ are also known, a solution can be found. The theory of partial differential equations shows that any function $f(\mathbf{r},\mathbf{v},t)$ which is a function of the constants of motion, say $f(a_1,\ldots)$ is a solution of Boltzmann's equation. Indeed, we find by differentiation

$$\frac{df}{dt} = \frac{\partial f}{\partial a_i}\frac{\partial a_i}{\partial t} = 0 \qquad (99.1)$$

which follows from the definition of the constants of motion. So, if we have the constants of the motion of the system, particular solutions are known at once. Since Boltzmann's equation is equivalent to the equation of motion of the particles of the system, each particle follows a path in the $(\mathbf{r},\mathbf{v})$-space so as to maintain the constants of motion, *i.e.*, constant. Consequently, any function of the constants of motion only satisfies the equation of motion and is a solution of the Boltzmann equation.

We may ask how f becomes a function of the constants of motion. The answer is clear when we recall that the constants of motion are functions of the $(\mathbf{r},\mathbf{v})$-space and of time, that is, $a_i = a_i(\mathbf{r},\mathbf{v},t)$ and this implies $f = f(a_i,\ldots)$. If the a_i are independent of time we then obtain the stationary solutions of Boltzmann's equation. As an example in clarifying the concepts let us restrict ourselves to a one dimensional motion whose constant of motion is time independent. We have $a(x_1,v) = \text{const.}$, which represents a family of curves in the (x_1,v)-plane. Each particle is therefore restricted to move along such a curve. Now consider any region between two neighboring curves of the family which is filled by a uniform point density f. The points must move so as to behave like an incompressible fluid which yields a stationary solution of Boltzmann's equation. But this manner of filling the plane with points is nothing more than asserting that $f(x_1,v) = f(a)$.

For an actual three dimensional motion, the space $(\mathbf{r},\mathbf{v})$ is six dimensional. If we know only one constant of the motion we are constrained to a five dimensional subspace. If we know only two constants of the motion, the motion of the phase points is constrained to the four dimensional space which is the space common to the two five dimensional subspaces. The more constants known, the lesser the number of degrees of freedom, *i.e.*, the more we know about the motion. Thus, by knowing six independent constants of the motion, which can be obtained from the initial conditions, the motion is completely determined. The more constants we know the more general solutions of Boltzmann's can be found. On the other hand, if we do not know any constants of the motion we still have the trivial solution $f(\mathbf{r},\mathbf{v},t) = \text{const.}$, *i.e.*, the distribution uniform in $\mathbf{r}$, in $\mathbf{v}$ and in time. The general solution is $f = f(a_1,a_2,\ldots,a_6)$.

As mentioned above, the initial conditions provide a possible set of constants, and these can be adjusted to fit any initial distribution $f(\mathbf{r},\mathbf{v},0) = f(\mathbf{r}_0,\mathbf{v}_0)$ which then gives the solution of any initial value problem. This procedure however is deceptive since in order to use this solution we must know $a_i = a_i(\mathbf{r}, \mathbf{v}, t)$, for each i. But if we know the a_i we know the solution of the problem. If we know the five stationary constants of the motion we can find the general stationary solution.

Thermodynamic Considerations—Since $df/dt = 0$ for the collisionless Boltzmann equation we have the interpretation that the probability of finding a particle in a unit volume of the $(\mathbf{r}, \mathbf{v})$ space is constant. This, of course refers to the *a priori* probability. If we take the entropy of a system as a measure of its thermodynamic probability then it is also a constant. In elementary statistical mechanics it is shown that this entropy is given by

$$S = -k \int f \log f d^3\mathbf{r} d^3\mathbf{v} + \text{const.} \quad , \tag{99.2}$$

and by taking the total time derivative of this function it can be proved that S = const. if f satisfies the collisionless Boltzmann equation. Entropy preserving processes in the thermodynamics are also adiabatic, hence those processes which involve collisionless plasmas in any sort of electromagnetic field, even self fields can be considered as adiabatic. Suppose now that we have a plasma whose particles are contained in some volume say V, and also assume that the distribution function in velocity space is isotropic. Now if the particles participate in some collisionless process such that the velocity distribution remains isotropic we conclude that

$$4\pi v^2 dv V = \text{const.} = 4\pi v_0^2 dv_0 V_0 \quad , \tag{99.3}$$

because the phase volume is invariant. By setting $v^3 V = v_0^3 V_0$ we can satisfy eq. (99.3); for the two dimensional case the relation analogous to eq. (99.3) is

$$2\pi v dv V = 2\pi v_0 dv_0 V_0 \tag{99.4}$$

which is satisfied by setting $v^2 V = v_0^2 V_0$. Let us define a temperature T which is proportional to v^2, then

$$T = T_0 \left(\frac{V_0}{V}\right)^{2/3} \tag{99,5}$$

obtains for the three-dimensional plasma, while

$$T = T_0 \left(\frac{V_0}{V}\right) \qquad (99.6)$$

holds for the two-dimensional case. The temperature so defined is the kinetic temperature. To show that eqs. (99.5) and (99.6) correspond to the adiabatic equation of state when $\gamma = 5/3$ and $\gamma = 2$ respectively, we simply recall that for a Maxwellian distribution the kinetic temperature becomes the ordinary definition of temperature.* The same conclusions can not be made for the case of collisions. In general the entropy of a system increases when collisions take place until thermal equilibrium result.

Returning now to eqs. (98.69) and (98.70) we note that if these two equations could be solved simultaneously we would obtain a first order approximate solution of Boltzmann's equation. Because of their complexity we shall assume the following.

(1) $(\partial f_s/\partial t)_d = 0$, which amounts to neglecting the diffusion coefficients. Also, we shall replace the value b_0 by the shielding distance d in eq. (98.50) which means that $(\partial f_s/\partial t)_c$ represents the effect of the collisions by itself. Thus, the integration over b in eq. (98.24) is extended to the upper limit h rather than just to b_0, thereby compensating a bit for the neglect of the Fokker-Planck term.

(2) Neglect the spatial gradient terms, $[(\mathbf{v}/3) \cdot (\partial \mathbf{f}_{1,s}/\partial \mathbf{r})]$ and $[\mathbf{v} \cdot (\partial f_{0,s}/\partial \mathbf{r})]$. This assumption forces us to exclude the important class of waves, the longitudinal oscillations. Hence, f_s is independent of $\mathbf{r}$ and may be written as $f_s(\mathbf{v}, t)$.†

(3) The motion of the ions is negligible, hence we shall put $s = e$ and drop the summation over s.

Consequently, eqs. (98.69) and (98.70) become respectively

$$\frac{\partial f_{0,e}}{\partial t} + \frac{e}{3m_e v^2}\frac{\partial}{\partial v}(v^2 \mathbf{E} \cdot \mathbf{f}_{1,e}) = \frac{1}{v^2}\frac{\partial}{\partial v} v^2 \left(\frac{m_e \nu_e v}{m_i} f_{0,e} + \frac{kT_e \nu_e}{m_i}\frac{\partial f_{0,e}}{\partial v}\right), \qquad (99.7)$$

---

* Landau and Lifshitz, "Statistical Physics," loc. cit.

† Jancel and Kahan, loc. cit., treat the inhomogeneous plasma. See also, K. Rawer and K. Suchy, Annalen der Physik. 7. Folge. Band 2, 1958; ibid. 7. Folge. Band 3, 1959; C.R. 1958, 1st Semestre (Tome 246, No. 25) 23 June 1958, pp. 3428-3430.

and

$$\frac{\partial \mathbf{f}_{1,e}}{\partial t} + \frac{e}{m_e}\mathbf{E}\frac{\partial f_{0,e}}{\partial v} + \frac{e}{m_e}\mathbf{B}\mathbf{x}\mathbf{f}_{1,e} = -\nu_e \mathbf{f}_{1,e} \quad . \tag{99.8}$$

We follow Gurevich in attempting to solve eqs. (99.7) and (99.8).* We expand

$$f_{0,s} = f^0_{0,s} + f^1_{0,s} + \cdots \quad , \tag{99.9}$$

$$f_{1,s} = f^0_{1,s} + f^1_{1,s} + \cdots \quad , \tag{99.10}$$

and we further consider that the zero order approximation of the symmetrical part of the distribution is independent of time, *i.e.*, $\partial f^0_{0,s}/\partial t = 0$. Now define the operator

$$L\left(\nu_e, \frac{\partial}{\partial t}, \mathbf{B}\right) = \nu_e^2 + 2\nu_e\frac{\partial}{\partial t} + \frac{\partial^2}{\partial t^2} - \nu_e\frac{e}{m_e}\mathbf{B}\mathbf{x} - \frac{e}{m_e}\frac{\partial}{\partial t}\mathbf{B}\mathbf{x} + \frac{e}{m_e}\mathbf{B}[\mathbf{B}\cdot\;] \quad . \tag{99.11}$$

and apply it to the left side of eq. (99.8), to obtain

$$\frac{\partial^3}{\partial t^3}\mathbf{f}^0_{1,e} + 3\nu_e\frac{\partial^2}{\partial t^2}\mathbf{f}^0_{1,e} + \left[3\nu_e^2 + \left(\frac{e}{m_e}\right)^2\mathbf{B}\cdot\mathbf{B}\right]\frac{\partial}{\partial t}\mathbf{f}^0_{1,e} + \left[\nu_e^3 + \nu_e\left(\frac{e}{m_e}\right)^2\mathbf{B}\cdot\mathbf{B}\right]\mathbf{f}^0_{1,e}$$

$$= \frac{e}{m_e}\frac{\partial f^0_{0,e}}{\partial v}\left[-\frac{\partial^2}{\partial t^2}\mathbf{E} - 2\nu_e\frac{\partial}{\partial t}\mathbf{E} - \nu_e^2\mathbf{E} + \frac{e}{m_e}\mathbf{B}\mathbf{x}\frac{\partial}{\partial t}\mathbf{E} + \nu_e\frac{e}{m_e}\mathbf{B}\mathbf{x}\mathbf{E} - \left(\frac{e}{m_e}\right)^2\mathbf{B}(\mathbf{B}\cdot\mathbf{E})\right] \quad . \tag{99.12}$$

For harmonically varying fields,

$$\left.\begin{aligned} \frac{\partial}{\partial t}\mathbf{E} &= i\omega\mathbf{E} \\ \text{and} \qquad & \\ \frac{\partial}{\partial t}\mathbf{f}^0_{1,e} &= i\omega\mathbf{f}_{1,e} \end{aligned}\right\} \tag{99.13}$$

---

* A. V. Gurevich, loc. cit., in this paper the following assumption is made for rapidly varying electric fields, $(2m_c/m_i)\langle v\rangle \ll \omega$ where $\langle \nu_e\rangle$ is the average value of ν_e.

from which we derive

$$\mathbf{f}^0_{1,e} = -\frac{e}{m_e}\frac{\partial f_{0,e}}{\partial v}\frac{(\nu_e + i\omega)^2\mathbf{E} - \omega_{c,e}(\nu + i\omega)\mathbf{B}_0\mathbf{x}\omega^2(\mathbf{E}\cdot\mathbf{B}_0)\mathbf{B}_0}{(\nu_e + i\omega)[\omega^2_{c,e} + (\nu_e + i\omega)^2]} \tag{99.14}$$

recalling from Chapter II that $\omega_{c,e} = eB/m_e$ is the gyro-frequency of the electron, and $B_0 = \mathbf{B}/B$. To obtain an explicit expression for $f^0_{0,e}$ we substitute eq. (99.9) into eq. (99.7) and obtain

$$\frac{\partial f^1_{0,e}}{\partial t} = -\frac{e}{3m_e v^2}\frac{\partial}{\partial v}(v^2\mathbf{E}\cdot\mathbf{f}^0_{1,e}) + \frac{1}{v^2}\frac{\partial}{\partial v}v^2\left(\frac{m_e\nu_e v}{m_i}f^0_{0,e} + \frac{kT_e\nu_e}{m_i}\frac{\partial f^0_{0,e}}{\partial v}\right). \tag{99.15}$$

The scalar product of $\mathbf{E} = \mathbf{E}_0 \exp(i\omega t)$ with $\mathbf{f}^0_{1,e}$ yields

$$\mathbf{E}\cdot\mathbf{f}^0_{1,e} = -E^2_0\frac{e}{m_e}\frac{\partial f_{0,e}}{\partial v}[\nu_e A_1\cos^2\omega t - \omega B_1\sin\omega t\cos\omega t]$$

$$+ \text{time independent term.}^* \tag{99.16}$$

If θ_0 represents the angle between $\mathbf{E}_0$ and the magnetic field $\mathbf{B}_0$, the coefficients A_1 and B_1 are given by

$$\left.\begin{aligned} A_1 &= \frac{\sin^2\theta_0(\omega^2_{c,e} + \omega^2 + \nu^2_e)}{[(\omega_{c,e} + \omega)^2 + \nu^2_e][(\omega_{c,e} - \omega)^2 + \nu^2_e]} + \frac{\cos^2\theta_0}{\omega^2 + \nu^2_e} \\ B_1 &= \frac{\sin^2\theta_0(\omega^2_{c,e} + \omega^2 - \nu^2_e)}{[(\omega_{c,e} + \omega)^2 + \nu^2_e][(\omega_{c,e} - \omega)^2 + \nu^2_e]} - \frac{\cos^2\theta_0}{\omega^2 + \nu^2_e} \end{aligned}\right\}. \tag{99.17}$$

By substituting eq. (99.16) into eq. (99.15) and integrating with respect to time from 0 to t, we find,

---

* The neglect of the time independent term entails no serious limitation in the final results. Equation (99.16) represents the real part of the scalar product.

$$f^1_{0,e}(v,0) - f^1_{0,e}(v,t) = \left\{\frac{1}{v^2}\frac{\partial}{\partial v}v^2\left[\left(\frac{e^2\nu_e}{6m_e^2}E_0^2A_1 + \frac{kT_e\nu_e}{m_i}\right)\frac{\partial f_{0,e}}{\partial v} + \frac{m_e\nu_e v}{m_i}f_{0,e}\right]\right\}t$$

$$+ \frac{1}{v^2}\frac{\partial}{\partial v}\left[v^2\,\frac{e}{6m_e^2}\,\frac{\partial f_{0,e}}{\partial v}\,E_0^2(\nu_e A_1 \sin\omega t + \omega B_1 \cos\omega t)\sin\omega t\right]$$

$$+ \text{constant of integration} \quad . \qquad (99.18)$$

Since $f^1_{0,e}(v,t)$ must be bounded as $t \to \infty$, the coefficient of t in eq. (99.18) must vanish. This implies

$$\frac{\partial}{\partial v}v^2\left[\left(E_0^2\,\frac{e}{6m_e^2}\,\nu_e A_1 + kT_e\frac{\nu_e}{m_i}\right)\frac{\partial f^0_{0,e}}{\partial v} + \frac{m_e\nu_e}{m_i}vf^0_{0,e}\right] = 0 \quad , \qquad (99.19)$$

and integrating with respect to v gives

$$v^2\left[\left(E_0^2\,\frac{e}{6m_e^2}\,\nu_e A_1 + kT_e\frac{\nu_e}{m_i}\right)\frac{\partial f^0_{0,e}}{\partial v} + \frac{m_e\nu_e}{m_i}vf^0_{0,e}\right] = C \quad . \qquad (99.20)$$

Again we invoke the condition that both $f^0_{0,e}$ and $\partial f_{0,e}/\partial v$ be bounded at $v = 0$ from which it follows that $C = 0$.

Integrating again with respect to v we obtain

$$f^0_{0,e} = C_0 \exp\left(-\int\frac{m_e v}{E_0A_1e\dfrac{m_i}{6m_e} + kT_e}\,dv\right) \qquad (99.21)$$

where C_0 is determined by

$$\int f_s(\mathbf{r},\mathbf{v},t)d^3\mathbf{v} = N_s(\mathbf{r},t)$$

which in our case, after dropping the perturbation terms is

$$4\pi^2 \int f^0_{0,e}v^2dv = N_e \qquad (99.22)$$

the integration over θ and φ having been performed.* From eq. (99.20) with $C = 0$ we have the following expression for $\mathbf{f}^0_{1,e}$;

$$\mathbf{f}^0_{1,e} = v\left(\frac{6m_e}{kT_e + A_1E_0^2}\right)\frac{f^0_{0,e}}{m_i}\left\{\frac{(\nu_e + i\omega)^2\mathbf{E} - \omega_{c,e}\mathbf{B}_0\mathbf{x}\mathbf{E} + \omega_{c,e}(\mathbf{B}_0 \cdot \mathbf{E})\mathbf{B}_0}{(\nu_e + i\omega)[\omega^2_{c,e} + (\nu_e + i\omega)^2]}\right\} \quad (99.23)$$

with $f^0_{0,e}$ given by eq. (99.21). It is possible but not without a great deal of computation to find $f^1_{0,e}$, $f^1_{1,e}$, etc. Consequently we can not say anything further about the convergence of the expansions in eqs. (99.9) and (99.10).†

In arriving at the non-symmetrical perturbation, eq. (99.23) of the symmetrical distribution $f^0_{0,e}$ in the zero order approximation several assumptions have been made besides the hypothesis made for the formulation which have already been listed. We shall now summarize the hypothesis made in effecting the solution. They are;

H_7. Only electrons make up the plasma, *i.e.*, we neglect the ion motion.

H_8. Electron-electron collisions are neglected. The close collision term represents the collisions all by itself and this term is only approximated.

H_9. Spatial gradients have been neglected in the distribution functions. Thus the distribution is effectively homogeneous in **r**-space. This neglect implies the neglect of both longitudinal waves and coupling between transverse and longitudinal waves.

H_{10}. The solution of Boltzmann'equation holds only for those rapidly fluctuating **E** fields which satisfy

$$\sqrt{\frac{2}{3}}\,\frac{eE_0}{\sqrt{kT_e m_i}} + \frac{2m_e}{m_i} \ll \omega \quad .$$

H_{11}. Only two terms in the spherical harmonic solution of Boltzmann's equation have been evaluated, and these only in a zero order approximation in the development with respect to time.

---

* According to Gurevich, loc. cit., eq. (99.21) holds if $\sqrt{2/3}\left[(eE_0/\sqrt{kT_e m_i}) + (2m_e/m_i)\right] \ll \omega$.

† Analogous formulas have derived by Jancel and Kahan, C.R. 236, 788 (1953), ibid, 238, 995 (1954); Jour. Phys. Radium 16, 136 (1955); and for the inhomogeneous case, ibid, Tome 20, Jan. 1955; Tome 20, Oct. 1959. See Also, V. M. Fain, Sov. Phys. JETP 1, 205 (1955); Margenau, H. and Kelly, O. C., Rendiconti Terzo Congr. intern. sui fenom. d'ionizzazione nei gas, Venezie, p. 508 (1957).

We emphasize in connection with H_7, that the results obtained hold only for those frequency regions where the effect of ionic motions on the wave is negligible. Thus, for high frequencies the above hypothesis will be satisfied.

100. PROPAGATION CONSIDERATIONS

In this section we shall consider the propagation of transverse electromagnetic waves in an unbounded medium which can be described by the distribution function previously obtained.

From Chapter II for harmonically varying fields we recall that the effective displacement vector $\mathbf{D}_e$ is

$$\mathbf{D}_e = -\frac{i}{\omega}\mathbf{J} + \epsilon_0\mathbf{E} \qquad (100.1)$$

we shall now write

$$\mathbf{D}_e = \epsilon_0 \boldsymbol{\epsilon}_e \mathbf{E} \qquad (100.2)$$

where $\boldsymbol{\epsilon}_e$ is the effective dielectric tensor of the medium, and from these two equations we have

$$-\frac{i}{\omega}\mathbf{J} = \epsilon_0[\boldsymbol{\epsilon}_e - \mathbf{I}]\mathbf{E} \qquad (100.3)$$

For convenience we shall drop the subscript e in what follows. The conduction tensor is defined through $\mathbf{J} = \boldsymbol{\sigma}\mathbf{E}$ hence

$$\boldsymbol{\sigma} = i\omega\epsilon_0[\boldsymbol{\epsilon} - \mathbf{I}] \qquad (100.4)$$

and from the two Maxwell's equations we obtain,

$$\nabla \mathbf{x} \nabla \mathbf{x} \mathbf{E} = -\frac{1}{V_0^2}\boldsymbol{\epsilon}\frac{\partial^2\mathbf{E}}{\partial t^2} \qquad (100.5)$$

where $\mu_0\epsilon_0 = (1/V_0)^2$. From the form $\mathbf{E} = \mathbf{E}_0 \exp\{i[\omega t - (M/V_0)\mathbf{r}\cdot\mathbf{n}]\}$ we have

$$\nabla \mathbf{x} \mathbf{E} = \frac{i\omega M}{V_0} \mathbf{E} \mathbf{x} \mathbf{n} \tag{100.6}$$

also since

$$\nabla \mathbf{x} \nabla \mathbf{x} \mathbf{E} = \left(\frac{\omega M}{V_0}\right)^2 [\mathbf{E} - (\mathbf{E} \cdot \mathbf{n})\mathbf{n}] \tag{100.7}$$

and

$$\frac{\partial^2 \mathbf{E}}{\partial t^2} = -\omega^2 \mathbf{E} \tag{100.8}$$

eq. (100.3) becomes

$$(M^2 \mathbf{I} - \epsilon)\mathbf{E} = M^2 (\mathbf{E} \cdot \mathbf{n})\mathbf{n} \quad . \tag{100.9}$$

Equations (100.3) and (100.9) with an equation for $\mathbf{J}$ will determine the index M and ϵ. The expression for $\mathbf{J}$ in the plasma is obtained from

$$\mathbf{J} = \sum_s \mathbf{J}_s \tag{100.10}$$

with $\mathbf{J}_s$ defined through

$$\mathbf{J}_s = e_s \int f_s(\mathbf{v}, t)\mathbf{v} d^3\mathbf{v} \quad . \tag{100.11}$$

For the plasma under consideration, $f_s = f_{0,s} + (\mathbf{v}/v) \cdot \mathbf{f}_{1,s}$, but since as already stated the symmetrical part $f_{0,s}$ contributes no current we write

$$\mathbf{J} = e \int \left(\frac{\mathbf{v}}{v} \cdot \mathbf{f}^0_{1,e}\right) \mathbf{v} d^3\mathbf{v} \tag{100.12}$$

i.e., the total contribution to the current comes only from the electrons. Using eqs. (98.39) and integrating over θ and φ we obtain

$$\mathbf{J} = \frac{4\pi}{3} e \int v^3 \mathbf{f}^0_{1,e}(v, t) dv \quad . \tag{100.13}$$

Substituting eq. (99.23) into (100.13) and the result into eq. (100.3), setting $\mathbf{B}_0 = \mathbf{e}_3$, we find, after equating coefficients of the unit vectors $\mathbf{e}_1, \mathbf{e}_2, \mathbf{e}_3$, the relations

$$\left.\begin{aligned}
(\epsilon_{11}-1)E_{01}+\epsilon_{12}E_{02}+\epsilon_{13}E_{03} &= i\,\frac{4\pi}{3}\,\frac{e^2}{m_e\epsilon_0\omega}\int\frac{v^4 f_e[(\nu_e+i\omega)^2E_{01}+\omega_{c,e}(\nu_e+i\omega)E_{02}]}{(\nu_e+i\omega)[\omega_{c,e}^2+(\nu_e+i\omega)^2]}\,dv\\
\epsilon_{21}E_{01}+(\epsilon_{22}-1)E_{02}+\epsilon_{23}E_{03} &= i\,\frac{4\pi}{3}\,\frac{e^2}{m_e\epsilon_0\omega}\int\frac{v^4 f_e[(\nu_e+i\omega)^2E_{02}-\omega_{c,e}(\nu_e+i\omega)E_{01}]}{(\nu_e+i\omega)[\omega_{c,e}^2+(\nu_e+i\omega)^2]}\,dv\\
\epsilon_{31}E_{01}+\epsilon_{32}E_{02}+(\epsilon_{33}-1)E_{03} &= i\,\frac{4\pi}{3}\,\frac{e^2}{m_e\epsilon_0\omega}\int\frac{v^4 f_e[(\nu_e+i\omega)^2+\omega_{c,e}^2]E_{03}\,dv}{(\nu_e+i\omega)[\omega_{c,e}^2+(\nu_e+i\omega)^2]}
\end{aligned}\right\} \tag{100.14}$$

where,

$$f_e \equiv \frac{6(m_e)^2}{kT_e + A_1E_0^2}\,\frac{f_{0,e}^0}{em_i} \quad . \tag{100.15}$$

Since $\mathbf{E}_0$ is an arbitrary vector, we can now equate the coefficients of its components on both sides of eqs. (100.14) to obtain the further relations,

$$\epsilon_{11}-1 = \epsilon_{22}-1 = i\,\frac{4\pi}{3}\,\frac{e^2}{m_e\epsilon_0}\int\frac{v^4 f_e(\nu_e+i\omega)\,dv}{\omega[\omega_{c,e}^2+(\nu_e+i\omega)^2]} \quad , \tag{100.16}$$

$$\epsilon_{33}-1 = i\,\frac{4\pi}{3}\,\frac{e^2}{m_e\epsilon_0}\int\frac{v^4 f_e\,dv}{\omega(\nu_e+i\omega)} \quad , \tag{100.17}$$

$$\epsilon_{12} = -\epsilon_{21} = i\,\frac{4\pi}{3}\,\frac{e^2}{m_e\epsilon_0}\int\frac{v^4 f_e\,dv}{[\omega_{c,e}^2+(\nu_e+i\omega)^2]} \quad , \tag{100.18}$$

and

$$\epsilon_{13} = \epsilon_{23} = \epsilon_{31} = \epsilon_{32} = 0 \quad . \tag{100.19}$$

As in Chapter IV, we define the quantities ϵ_1, ϵ_2 and ϵ_3 by the formulas

$$\epsilon_1 = \epsilon_{11} + i\epsilon_{12} \tag{100.20}$$

$$\epsilon_2 = \epsilon_{22} - i\epsilon_{12} = \epsilon_{22} + i\epsilon_{21} \quad , \tag{100.21}$$

$$\epsilon_3 = \epsilon_{33} \quad , \tag{100.22}$$

using eqs. (100.16)-(100.18) we find the explicit diclcctric coefficients

$$\epsilon_1 = 1 - \frac{4\pi}{3}\frac{\omega_e^2}{N_e}\int \frac{f_e v^4 dv}{\omega[\omega - (\omega_{c,e} + i\nu_e)]} \quad , \tag{100.23}$$

$$\epsilon_2 = 1 - \frac{4\pi}{3}\frac{\omega_e^2}{N_e}\int \frac{f_e v^4 dv}{\omega[\omega + (\omega_{c,e} - i\nu_e)]} \quad , \tag{100.24}$$

$$\epsilon_3 = 1 - \frac{4\pi}{3}\frac{\omega_e^2}{N_e}\int \frac{f_e v^4 dv}{\omega[\omega - i\nu_e]} \tag{100.25}$$

where ω_e is the plasma frequency of the electrons. If θ denotes the angle between the applied magnetic field and the vector $\mathbf{n}$,

$$\mathbf{n} \cdot \mathbf{e}_3 = \cos\theta \tag{100.26}$$

we may assume without loss of generality (as in Chapter IV) that the wave normal direction $\mathbf{n}$ lies in the $x\ x$ -plane. From eq. (100.26)

$$(\mathbf{E}_0 \cdot \mathbf{n})\mathbf{n} = (\sin^2\theta E_{02} + \sin\theta\cos\theta E_{03})\mathbf{e}_2 + (\sin\theta\cos\theta E_{02} + \cos^2\theta E_{03})\mathbf{e}_3 \tag{100.27}$$

by substituting this result into eq. (100.9) yields a system of equations from which the index of refraction M^2 can be determined,

$$\left.\begin{aligned} (M^2 - \epsilon_{11})E_{01} - \epsilon_{12}E_{02} &= 0 \\ -\epsilon_{21}E_{01} + (M^2\cos^2\theta - \epsilon_{22})E_{02} - M^2\sin\theta\cos\theta E_{03} &= 0 \\ -M^2\sin\theta\cos\theta E_{02} + (M^2\sin^2\theta - \epsilon_{33})E_{03} &= 0 \quad . \end{aligned}\right\} \tag{100.28}$$

For nontrivial solutions to exist we must have the determinant,

$$(\epsilon_{33}\cos^2\theta + \epsilon_{11}\sin^2\theta)M^2 - [2\epsilon_{11}\epsilon_{33}\cos^2\theta + (\epsilon_{11}\epsilon_{33} + \epsilon_{11}^2 + \epsilon_{12}^2)\sin^2\theta]M^2$$

$$+ (\epsilon_{11}^2 + \epsilon_{12}^2)\epsilon_{33} = 0 \qquad (100.29)$$

or in terms of the dielectric coefficients ϵ_i this dispersion relation becomes,

$$\left\{\epsilon_3(\epsilon_1\epsilon_2 - \epsilon_2 - \epsilon_1 + 1) + \left[\frac{1}{2}(\epsilon_3 - 1)(\epsilon_2 + \epsilon_1 - 2) - (\epsilon_2 - 1)(\epsilon_1 - 1)\right]\sin^2\theta\right\}\left(\frac{1}{M^2 - 1}\right)$$

$$-\left\{\epsilon_3(\epsilon_2 + \epsilon_1 - 2) + \left[\epsilon_3 - \frac{1}{2}(\epsilon_2 + \epsilon_1) - \frac{1}{2}(\epsilon_3 - 1)(\epsilon_2 + \epsilon_1 - 2) + (\epsilon_2 - 1)(\epsilon_1 - 1)\right]\sin^2\theta\right\}\left(\frac{1}{M^2 - 1}\right)$$

$$+ \epsilon_3 - \left[\epsilon_3 - \frac{1}{2}(\epsilon_2 + \epsilon_1)\right]\sin^2\theta = 0 \ . \qquad (100.30)$$

We introduce the notations

$$\left.\begin{aligned}
P_1 &= \frac{1}{\epsilon_2 - 1} + \frac{1}{\epsilon_1 - 1} \\
P_2 &= -\frac{1}{\epsilon_3}\left[1 - \frac{1}{2}(\epsilon_3 - 1)\left(\frac{1}{\epsilon_2 - 1} + \frac{1}{\epsilon_1 - 1}\right)\right] \\
P_3 &= \frac{1}{\epsilon_3}\left\{\frac{\epsilon_3 - 1}{(\epsilon_2 - 1)(\epsilon_1 - 1)} - \frac{1}{2}\left[\frac{1}{(\epsilon_2 - 1)} + \frac{1}{(\epsilon_1 - 1)}\right]\right\} \\
P_4 &= -\frac{1}{\epsilon_2 - 1} + \frac{1}{\epsilon_1 - 1}
\end{aligned}\right\} \qquad (100.31)$$

and express eq. (100.30) in the form

$$M^2 = 1 + \frac{2(1 + P_2 \sin^2\theta)}{P_1 + (P_3 - P_2)\sin^2\theta \pm \sqrt{(P_2 + P_3)^2 \sin^4\theta + P_4^2 \cos^2\theta}} \ . \tag{100.32}$$

Polarization—We choose besides the unit vectors $\mathbf{e}_i$ a new set of vectors $\mathbf{e}_\xi$, $\mathbf{e}_\eta$, and $\mathbf{e}_\zeta$ such that

$$\left.\begin{aligned} \mathbf{e}_\xi &= \mathbf{e}_1 \ , \\ \mathbf{e}_\eta &= \sin\theta\mathbf{e}_2 + \cos\theta\mathbf{e}_3 = \mathbf{n} \ , \\ \mathbf{e}_\zeta &= \cos\theta\mathbf{e}_2 - \sin\theta\mathbf{e}_3 \ , \end{aligned}\right\} \tag{100.33}$$

and

$$\left.\begin{aligned} E_{01} &= E_{0\xi} \ , \\ E_{02} &= E_{0\zeta}\cos\theta \ , \\ E_{03} &= E_{0\zeta}\sin\theta \ . \end{aligned}\right\} \tag{100.34}$$

By substituting the first two equations of (100.34) into the first equation of (100.28) we find

$$(M^2 - \epsilon_{11})E_{0\xi} - \epsilon_{12}E_{0\zeta}\cos\theta = 0 \ , \tag{100.35}$$

the polarization is by definition (see Chapter II),

$$Q' = -\frac{E_{0\xi}}{E_{0\zeta}} = \frac{\frac{1}{2}(\epsilon_2 - \epsilon_1)\cos\theta}{M^2 - \frac{1}{2}(\epsilon_2 + \epsilon_1)} \tag{100.36}$$

where we have used the definitions (100.20) and (100.21).

Computational Considerations—A glance at the polarization Q' above shows that in principle its computation is simple if we have M^2, ϵ_1 and ϵ_2.

But this simplicity is deceptive when we look at the formulas defining these quantities. The integrals defining these quantities are themselves not simple. Similar statements hold for the calculation of all of the properties of a plane electromagnetic wave, *i.e.*, phase velocity, refraction, attenuation, etc. Thus in order not to render the theory already developed useless we shall make some further assumptions in addition to those already made. These assumptions permit us to find alternative expressions for the ϵ_i and hence to effect the required computations.

We assume first that ν_e can be considered as constant. More precisely, ν_e is some average collision frequency so chosen that the ϵ_i obtained from it is the "best" approximation in some sense, to the ϵ_i found by using the more exact expressions (100.23)-(100.25). Since A_1 is also a function of v through ν_e, it now becomes independent of v. Therefore eq. (99.21) reduces to

$$f^0_{0,e} = C_0 \exp\left[-\left(\frac{\frac{1}{2} m_e v^2}{kT'_e}\right)\right] \tag{100.37}$$

where,

$$T'_e = T_e + \frac{m_i e}{6km_e} AE_0^2 \tag{100.38}$$

with $A = A_1$ when ν_e = constant. With this assumption we see that the symmetrical part of the distribution function is now Maxwellian with temperature T'_e which is called the effective temperature.

From the normalization eq. (99.2) we evaluate C_0 by

$$C_0 = \left(\frac{m_e}{2\pi kT'_e}\right)^{3/2} N_e \tag{100.39}$$

and substituting both eq. (100.37) and (100.39) into eq. (100.15) we obtain

$$f_e = 2\pi N_e \left(\frac{m_e}{2\pi kT'_e}\right)^{5/2} \exp\left[-\left(\frac{\frac{1}{2} m_e v^2}{kT'_e}\right)\right]. \tag{100.40}$$

From this form we easily evaluate

$$\int v^4 f_e dv = \frac{3}{2\pi}\left(\frac{m_e}{2\pi k T'_e}\right)^{-5/2} \tag{100.41}$$

and therefore eqs. (100.23)-(100.25) become

$$\epsilon_1 = 1 - \frac{\omega_e^2}{\omega[\omega - \omega_{c,e} - i\nu_e]} , \tag{100.42}$$

$$\epsilon_2 = 1 - \frac{\omega_e^2}{\omega[\omega + \omega_{c,e} - i\nu_e]} , \tag{100.43}$$

$$\epsilon_3 = 1 - \frac{\omega_e^2}{\omega[\omega - i\nu_e]} . \tag{100.44}$$

Statistical Meaning of the Dielectric Coefficients--It is worthwhile to explore the statistical significance of the dielectric coefficients ϵ_i. For this we consider eq. (99.8), first multiply both sides by the tensor $[(v_i v_j)/v]d^3\mathbf{v} \equiv (\mathbf{vv}/v)d^3\mathbf{v}$ and then integrate over all $\mathbf{v}$. Using eq. (98.43) we can write the average value of $\mathbf{v}_s$ as

$$N_s\langle\mathbf{v}_s\rangle = \int \mathbf{v}\left(\frac{\mathbf{v}}{v}\cdot \mathbf{f}_{1,s}\right) d^3\mathbf{v} \tag{100.45}$$

since $f_{0,s}$ contributes no net value, *i.e.*, it is symmetrical. Moreover if we put

$$\langle v_{1,s}^2\rangle = \langle v_{2,s}^2\rangle = \langle v_{3,s}^2\rangle = \frac{1}{3}\langle v_s^2\rangle \tag{100.46}$$

it follows that

$$\frac{1}{N_s}\int (\mathbf{vv})E_0 f_{0,s} d^3\mathbf{v} = \sum_{i=1}^{3}\langle v_{i,s}^2\rangle E_{0i}\mathbf{e}_i = \frac{1}{3}\langle v_s^2\rangle\mathbf{E}_0 . \tag{100.47}$$

Now put $(1/2)m_e\langle v_e^2\rangle = (3/2)kT'_e$, utilize both eq. (100.45) and (100.47), then eq. (99.8) can be replaced by the following

$$\frac{\partial}{\partial t}\langle\mathbf{v}_s\rangle - \frac{e_s}{m_s}\mathbf{E} - \frac{e_s}{m_s}\langle\mathbf{v}_s\rangle\mathbf{x}\mathbf{B} = -\nu_s\langle\mathbf{v}_s\rangle \qquad (100.48)$$

an equation which holds for each type s. But this equation is just the equation of motion for each type of particle when subjected to the forces due to the other particles and given by $m_s\nu_s\langle\mathbf{v}_s\rangle$. Here ν_s is a constant average collision frequency for particle of type s. Using this interpretation we can consider our plasma medium now to contain an arbitrary number of types instead of only two. Neutral particles are also included in this description. Since eq. (100.48) has the same form as eq. (99.8) and the solution can be obtained from eq. (99.14) if we make the following replacements

$$\mathbf{f}^0_{1,e} \rightarrow \langle\mathbf{v}_s\rangle \quad , \quad \text{and} \quad \frac{\partial f^0_{0,e}}{\partial v} \rightarrow -1 \quad . \qquad (100.49)$$

From eqs. (100.10) and (100.12) we can write

$$\mathbf{J} = \sum_s N_s e_s\langle\mathbf{v}_s\rangle \qquad (100.50)$$

and following the pattern which led to eqs. (100.23)-(100.25), we obtain in the new approximation

$$\epsilon_1 = 1 - \sum_s \frac{\omega_s^2}{\omega[\omega - \omega_{c,s} - i\nu_s]} \quad , \qquad (100.51)$$

$$\epsilon_2 = 1 - \sum_s \frac{\omega_s^2}{\omega[\omega + \omega_{c,s} - i\nu_s]} \quad , \qquad (100.52)$$

$$\epsilon_3 = 1 - \sum_s \frac{\omega_s^2}{\omega[\omega - i\nu_s]} \quad , \qquad (100.53)$$

where ω_s is the plasma frequency of type s particle. The ϵ_i given by by eqs. (100.51)-(100.53) are substantially the same as those obtained in Chapter II, but here we have the effect of collisions. These values of ϵ_i now enter into the calculation of the index of refraction M and the polarization Q'.

In order to use the results just obtained the following additional hypothesis must be given. We shall denote them by

H_{12}. All species affect each other, *i.e.*, mutually influence each other. For each type s, this effect is contained in the factor $\nu_s\langle\mathbf{v}_s\rangle$ which appears in the equation of motion (100.48).

H_{13}. We neglect longitudinal and coupled wave phenomena, that is, the particle densities N_s are assumed uniform in space.

Thus H_{12} replaces H_7, H_8 and H_{10}, H_{11}, since H_{10} is concerned with the solution of Boltzmann's equation it does not enter at all in the above treatment.

We want next to examine the validity of our last hypothesis and to assess its utility. This entails a comparison of the microscopic and macroscopic theories. Since we only know the results of the microscopic theory for a restricted region the comparison will be carried out for it.*

Microscopic versus Macroscopic Theory—Let us denote by $\boldsymbol{\epsilon}^{(M)}$ and $\boldsymbol{\epsilon}^{(s)}$ respectively, the dielectric tensors obtained from the macroscopic and statistical theories. From eqs. (100.23)-(100.25) and the preceding hypothesis we can write

$$\boldsymbol{\epsilon}^{(s)} = 1 - \frac{4\pi}{3}\int \frac{\omega_e^2 v^4 f_e dv}{N_e \omega[\omega - i\nu_e]} \tag{100.54}$$

while from eqs. (100.42)-(100.44),

$$\boldsymbol{\epsilon}^{(M)} = 1 - \frac{\omega_e^2}{\omega[\omega - i\nu_e]} \tag{100.55}$$

---

* Gurevich, loc. cit., carries out a comparison for zero magnetic field and for electrons; collisions take place between electrons and ions.

Assuming the statistical theory to be the more accurate one we introduce a correction factor κ and relate the quantities $\epsilon^{(s)}$ and $\epsilon^{(M)}$ by

$$(\epsilon^{(s)} - 1) = \kappa(\epsilon^{(M)} - 1) \qquad (100.56)$$

which essentially corrects $\epsilon^{(M)}$. Now this correction parameter is not an independent variable but should be a function of the impressed frequency ω. Following Gurevich we consider two situations; (a) weak electric fields; (b) strong electric fields. Thus for (a): $E_0^2 << 6kT_e(\omega^2 + \nu_e^2)(m_e^2/m_i)$, Gurevich shows graphically that for $\omega \lesssim 5\nu$, κ differs markedly from unity which implies that in this region $\epsilon^{(M)}$ is not a good approximation, and differs from the correct value by at least one order of magnitude. A comparison at the low frequencies is not complete because ω is restricted by the condition $\omega >> \sqrt{2/3}\ (eE_0/\sqrt{kT_e m_i}) + (2m_e/m_i)$. For the second case (b), Gurevich finds that for $\omega > 5\nu_e$, the value of κ is closer to unity than in case (a), and therefore the microscopic theory is a more valid approximation.

The implications which follow from the above comparisons based on the parameter κ are the following. For sufficiently high frequencies ω, the tensor $\boldsymbol{\epsilon}$ is essentially independent of the two descriptions and since the macroscopic description is the simpler one, its use in this frequency region is justified. The same conclusions can not be made for the low frequency case because the deviations between the two descriptions yield results which can differ by an order of magnitude. The use of a macroscopic description at low frequencies is questionable. Our remarks in this case however should be qualified. At low temperatures the motion of ions must enter into the description and according to the comments above a comparison between the two theories is not rigorously possible for this situation. Thus, where the gyro-frequency effects become important we can say practically nothing about the agreement of the two descriptions. We note further that in the comparisons between the two theories the effect of a strong magnetic field has not entered.

Collision Effects at Low Frequency—Despite the lack of a simple microscopic description for the low frequency case we can still gain some insight by using the macroscopic theory to study propagation.* Let us apply the results just developed to examine the effects of collisions on low frequency propagation of transverse electromagnetic waves along the magnetic field. For simplicity we shall deal with a two component plasma, electrons and one type of positive ion, with the plasma being over-all neutral. With these assumptions we make use of eq. (100.32) and put $\theta = 0$, then P_1 and P_4 are the only quantities which enter and from eqs. (100.31) we have

$$\left.\begin{aligned} M_1^2 &= \epsilon_1 \\ M_2^2 &= \epsilon_2 \end{aligned}\right\} \qquad (100.57)$$

where the subscripts 1 and 2 refer respectively to the positive sign of the square root, that is, the extraordinary mode, and the negative sign, which yields the ordinary mode. From eqs. (100.51), (100.52) we obtain

$$M_1^2 = 1 - \frac{1}{\omega}\left[\frac{(\omega - \omega_{c,e})\omega_e^2}{(\omega-\omega_{c,e})^2 + \nu_e^2} + \frac{(\omega - \omega_{c,i})\omega_i^2}{(\omega-\omega_{c,i})^2 + \nu_i^2}\right] + \frac{i}{\omega}\left[\frac{\nu_e\omega_e^2}{(\omega-\omega_{c,e})^2 + \nu_e^2} + \frac{\nu_i\omega_i^2}{(\omega-\omega_{c,i})^2 + \nu_i^2}\right], \qquad (100.58)$$

$$M_2^2 = 1 - \frac{1}{\omega}\left[\frac{(\omega + \omega_{c,e})\omega_e^2}{(\omega+\omega_{c,e})^2 + \nu_e^2} + \frac{(\omega + \omega_{c,i})\omega_i^2}{(\omega+\omega_{c,i})^2 + \nu_i^2}\right] + \frac{i}{\omega}\left[\frac{\nu_e\omega_e^2}{(\omega+\omega_{c,e})^2 + \nu_e^2} + \frac{\nu_i\omega_i^2}{(\omega+\omega_{c,i})^2 + \nu_i^2}\right], \qquad (100.59)$$

where ω_i, $\omega_{c,i}$ and ν_i are the plasma, gyro and collision frequencies of the ions, respectively. Since M_2^2 is obtained from M_1^2 by replacing $\omega_{c,e}$ by $-\omega_{c,e}$ and $\omega_{c,i}$ by $-\omega_{c,i}$, we need only to treat M_1^2. Now put

$$M_1^2 = p_1 - iq_1 , \qquad (100.60)$$

and since the charge neutrality implies

$$\omega_{c,i}\omega_e^2 + \omega_{c,e}\omega_i^2 = 0 , \qquad (100.61)$$

* We do not wish to imply that a statistical theory does not exist, but rather the resulting formulas which arise are cumbersome and complex without simplifying approximations. See for example, I. M. Vilensky, The Influence of the Earth's Magnetic Field on the Interaction of Radio Waves in the Ionosphere, Zh. Eksper i Teoret. Fiz. Vol. 26, No. 1, pp. 42-56 (1954).

we find by equating the real and imaginary parts of eq. (100.58) with eq. (100.60),

$$p_1 = 1 - \frac{(\omega-\omega_{c,e})(\omega-\omega_{c,i})\omega_p^2}{[(\omega-\omega_{c,e})^2+\nu_e^2][(\omega-\omega_{c,i})^2+\nu_i^2]} - \frac{(\omega-\omega_{c,e})\nu_i^2\omega_e^2 + (\omega-\omega_{c,i})\nu_e^2\omega_e^2}{\omega[(\omega-\omega_{c,e})^2+\nu_e^2][(\omega-\omega_{c,i})^2+\nu_i^2]} , \qquad (100.62)$$

$$q_1 = -\frac{\nu_e\omega_{c,i}^2\omega_e^2 + \nu_i\omega_{c,e}^2\omega_e^2 + \nu_e\nu_i[\nu_i^2\omega_e^2 + \nu_e^2\omega_i^2]}{\omega[(\omega-\omega_{c,e})^2+\nu_e^2][(\omega-\omega_{c,i})^2+\nu_i^2]} , \qquad (100.63)$$

where

$$\omega_p^2 = \omega_e^2 + \omega_i^2 . \qquad (100.64)$$

The Magneto-Hydrodynamic Approximation, Low Collision Frequency— We shall assume that $\omega << \omega_{c,i}$ and $\nu_i << \omega_{c,i}$ and that the collision frequencies satisfy approximately the relation

$$\frac{\nu_i}{\nu_e} \sim \left(\frac{m_e}{m_i}\right)^{1/2} \qquad (100.65)$$

which yield simpler relations for p_1 and q_1 above, namely

$$p_1 \approx 1 - \frac{\omega_p^2}{\omega_{c,i}\omega_{c,i}}\left(1 - \frac{\nu_i^2}{\omega\omega_{c,i}}\right) , \qquad (100.66)$$

$$q_1 \approx -\frac{\nu_i}{\omega\omega_{c,i}^2}\omega_i^2 , \qquad (100.67)$$

where $\omega_p^2 \approx \omega_e^2$ has also been used.* If we set

---

* There are a variety of different expressions given for electron-ion collision frequency, some of which are more complex than that above. See for example, M. Nicolet, J. Atmos. Terr. Physics, Vol. 3, p. 200 (1953); T. G. Cowling, Proc. Roy. Soc. (London) Vol. A 183, p. 453 (1945); R. C. Mazumdar, Zo. f. fysik, Vol. 107, p. 599 (1937).

$$M_1 = \alpha_1 - i\beta_1 \tag{100.68}$$

we find,

$$\alpha_1 = \left\{\frac{1}{2}\left[1 - \frac{\omega_p^2}{\omega_{c,i}\,\omega_{c,e}}\left(1 - \frac{\nu_i^2}{\omega\omega_{c,i}}\right)\right]\left(\sqrt{1 + \frac{\nu_i^2\omega_i^4}{\omega^2\omega_{c,i}^4\left[1 - \frac{\omega_p^2}{\omega\omega_{c,i}}\left(1 - \frac{\nu_i^2}{\omega\omega_{c,i}}\right)\right]^2}} + 1\right)\right\}^{1/2}$$

(100.69)

$$\beta_1 = \left\{\frac{1}{2}\left[1 - \frac{\omega_p^2}{\omega_{c,e}\,\omega_{c,i}}\left(1 - \frac{\nu_i^2}{\omega\omega_{c,i}}\right)\right]\left(\sqrt{1 + \frac{\nu_i^2\omega_i^4}{\omega^2\omega_{c,i}^4\left[1 - \frac{\omega_p^2}{\omega\omega_{c,i}}\left(1 - \frac{\nu_i^2}{\omega\omega_{c,i}}\right)\right]^2}} - 1\right)\right\}^{1/2}$$

(100.70)

while for α_2, β_2 defined by

$$M_2 = \alpha_2 - i\beta_2 \quad , \tag{100.71}$$

there results the same expressions except that the factors $[1 - (\nu_i^2/\omega\omega_{c,i})]$ are replaced by $[1 + (\nu_i^2/\omega\omega_{c,i})]$. Introduce the mass density

$$\rho = N_e m_e + N_i m_i \tag{100.72}$$

and the exact expressions for the quantities ω_p^2, Ω_i, and Ω_e to obtain

$$-\frac{\omega_p^2}{\omega_{c,e}\omega_{c,i}} = \frac{\rho V_0^2}{BH} \tag{100.73}$$

where $V_0^2 = (\mu_0\epsilon_0)^{-1}$. Assume that $\rho V_0^2 >> BH$ and since $[1 + (\nu_i^2/\omega\omega_{c,i})] \geqq 1$, the expressions for α_2 and β_2 simplify to

$$\alpha_2 = \frac{V_0}{V_A}\left\{\frac{1}{2}\left(1 + \frac{\nu_i^2}{\omega\omega_{c,i}}\right)\left[\sqrt{1 + \frac{\nu_i^2}{\omega^2\left(1 + \frac{\nu_i^2}{\omega\omega_{c,i}}\right)^2}} + 1\right]\right\}^{1/2} \tag{100.74}$$

$$\beta_2 = \frac{V_0}{V_A}\left\{\frac{1}{2}\left(1 + \frac{\nu_i^2}{\omega\omega_{c,i}}\right)\left[\sqrt{1 + \frac{\nu_i^2}{\omega^2\left(1 + \frac{\nu_i^2}{\omega\omega_{c,i}}\right)^2}} - 1\right]\right\}^{1/2} \tag{100.75}$$

where we have used the expression for the Alfvén velocity

$$V_A = V_0\sqrt{\frac{BH}{\rho}} \tag{100.76}$$

and also used,

$$\omega_i^2|\omega_{c,e}| = \omega_e^2\omega_{c,i} \quad . \tag{100.77}$$

The polarization is obtained from eqs. (100.36) and (100.57),

$$Q_1' = -1 \quad , \quad \text{and} \quad Q_2' = 1 \quad , \tag{100.78}$$

hence both waves are circularly polarized. This conclusion is seen to be independent of the number of species in the plasma regardless of collisions. Let us however compare the α_i, β_i just found with the collision free case. For this we consider the interval

$$\Omega_i \gg \omega \gtrsim 10\,\frac{\nu_i^2}{\omega_{c,i}}$$

for this interval

$$\omega \gg \frac{\nu_i^2}{\omega_{c,i}} \quad , \tag{100.79}$$

we have approximately

$$\alpha_1 = \alpha_2 = \frac{V_0}{V_A}\sqrt{\frac{1}{2}\left[\sqrt{1 + \left(\frac{\nu_i}{\omega}\right)^2} + 1\right]} \quad , \tag{100.80}$$

$$\beta_1 = \beta_2 = \frac{V_0}{V_A}\sqrt{\frac{1}{2}\left[\sqrt{1 + \left(\frac{\nu_i}{\omega}\right)^2} - 1\right]} \quad . \tag{100.81}$$

This shows that for the two waves, the propagation constants are equal and hence their phase velocity is given by

$$V = V_A\left\{\frac{1}{2}\left[\sqrt{1 + \left(\frac{\nu_i}{\omega}\right)^2} + 1\right]\right\}^{-1/2} \quad ; \tag{100.82}$$

eq. (100.79) holds only for a restricted interval and for this interval both waves have a phase velocity equal to the Alfvén velocity but modified by the presence of collisions, namely the ion collision frequency and also the wave frequency. This result should be contrasted with those obtained in Chapter II, in the absence of collisions. The next interval to consider is defined by

$$10\,\frac{\nu_i^2}{\omega_{c,i}} \gtrsim \omega \gtrsim 10^{-1}\,\frac{\nu_i^2}{\omega_{c,i}}$$

For this interval the full expressions (100.69), (100.70), (100.74) and (100.75), are to be used. In an interval about

$$\omega = \frac{\nu_i^2}{\omega_{c,i}} \tag{100.83}$$

the values of α_1 and α_2, β_1 and β_2 differ significantly. Substituting eq. (100.83) in the above stated expressions leads to

$$V_1 = V_0\left[\frac{1}{2}\left(\sqrt{1 + \frac{\omega_i^4}{\nu_i^2\omega_{c,i}^2}} + 1\right)\right]^{-1/2} \tag{100.84}$$

for the phase velocity and

$$\beta_1 = V_0\left[\frac{1}{2}\left(\sqrt{1+\frac{\omega_i^4}{\nu_i^2\omega_{c,i}^2}}-1\right)\right]^{1/2} \quad ; \tag{100.85}$$

using the fact that $\omega_{c,i} >> \nu_i$ we obtain

$$V_2 = V_A\sqrt{\frac{2\nu_i}{\omega_{c,i}}} \quad , \tag{100.86}$$

$$\beta_2 = \frac{V_0}{V_A}\sqrt{\frac{\omega_{c,i}}{2\nu_i}} \quad . \tag{100.87}$$

For this interval we note the distinction in the phase velocity for the two waves, one of them is a modified Alfvén velocity while for the other it is V_0 which is modified. It is not difficult to show from eqs. (100.69) and (100.74) that $V_1 > V_2$.

The last interval to examine is $10^{-1}(\nu^2/\omega_{c,i}) \gtrsim \omega \geqq 0$, and we have

$$\alpha_1 = \frac{V_0}{V_A}\left\{\frac{1}{2}\frac{\nu_i^2}{\omega\omega_{c,i}}\left[\sqrt{1+\left(\frac{\omega_{c,i}}{\nu_i}\right)^2}-1\right]\right\}^{1/2} \tag{100.88}$$

$$\alpha_2 = \frac{V_0}{V_A}\left\{\frac{1}{2}\frac{\nu_i^2}{\omega\omega_{c,i}}\left[\sqrt{1+\left(\frac{\omega_{c,i}}{\nu_i}\right)^2}+1\right]\right\}^{1/2} \tag{100.89}$$

which implies $\alpha_2 > \alpha_1$ or $V_1 > V_2$, as already asserted. If we further invoke the condition $\nu_i << \omega_{c,i}$, we find $\alpha_1 \approx \alpha_2$ and also,

$$V_1 = V_2 = V = V_A\left(\frac{2\omega}{\nu_i}\right)^{1/2} \quad , \tag{100.90}$$

$$\beta_1 = \beta_2 = \beta = \frac{V_0}{V_A}\left(\frac{\nu_i}{2\omega}\right)^{1/2} \quad . \tag{100.91}$$

Summarizing, we have in the magneto-hydrodynamic approximation, $\omega \ll \omega_{c,i}$, when collisions are considered (low collision frequency) the following statements.

(1) The polarization is the same as in the collisionless case.

(2) In the frequency region, $\omega_{c,i} \gg \omega \gtrsim 10\ (\nu_i^2/\omega_{c,i})$, the phase velocity of both waves approximately equal to the Alfvén velocity, and the low collision frequency is not a significant effect.

(3) In the interval, $10\ (\nu_i^2/\omega_{c,i}) \gtrsim \omega \gtrsim 10^{-1}\ (\nu_i^2/\omega_{c,i})$, the effects of collisions deviates markedly from the collisionless case. Here the different polarized waves have distinct phase velocities. The wave with polarization defined by $Q' = -1$ has a phase velocity which is greater than for polarization defined by $Q' = 1$ and its velocity differs least from the Alfvén velocity.

(4) In the interval, $10^{-1}(\nu_i^2/\omega_{c,i}) \gtrsim \omega \gtrsim 0$, the phase velocity of both waves tends toward zero as $\omega \to 0$. But if $\nu_i = 0$, the phase velocity approaches the Alfvén velocity. Also, as $\omega \to 0$, the waves are heavily damped since the damping constants increase without limit.

BIBLIOGRAPHIES

1. Akhiezer, A. I. and Lyubarskii, Y. G., On the nonlinear theory of electron plasma oscillations, Dokl. Akad. Nauk. SSSR, Vol. 80, p. 193 (1951).

2. Akhiezer, A. I. and Fainberg, Y. B., High frequency oscillations of an electron plasma, Zh. eksper. teor. Fiz. Vol. 21, p. 1262 (1951).

3. Akhiezer, A. I. and Polovin, R. V., Plasma oscillations in crossed electric and magnetic fields, ibid, Vol. 22, p. 794 (1952).

4. Allis, W. P., Motion of ions and electrons, Tech. Rep. 299, Res. Lab. of Electronics, M.I.T. Cambridge, Mass. (1956).

5. Bayet, M., Electromagnetic properties of a plasma, J. Phys. Rad., Vol. 13, p. 579 (1952).

6. Bayet, M., et al., On the conductivity tensor of electron plasmas in the presence of a constant magnetic field, Comptes Rendus. Vol. 237, p. 1503 (1953).

7. Bayet, M., Delcroix, J. L., and Denisse, J. F., Kinetic theory of weakly ionized homogeneous plasmas, I, J. Phys. Rad. Vol. 15, p. 795 (1954).

8. Bayet, M., Delcroix, J. L., and Denisse, J. F., Distribution function of electrons in a discharge, Appl. Sci. Res. B., Vol. 5, p. 331 (1955).

9. Bayet, M., Delcroix, J. L., and Denisse, J. F., Kinetic theory of weakly ionized homogeneous plasmas III: The collision operator in the case of an imperfect Lorentz gas, J. Phys. Radium, Vol. 17, p. 923 (1956).

10. Bayet, M., Delcroix, J. L., and Denisse, J. F., Kinetic theory of weakly ionized homogeneous plasmas IV: Study of the evolution of the isotropic part of the distribution function, J. Phys. Radium, Vol. 17, p. 1005 (1956).

11. Berz, F., On the theory of plasma waves, Proc. Phys. Soc., Vol. 69B, p. 939 (1956).

12. Berz, F., Electronic oscillations in a plasma, Le Vide (Paris), Vol. 11, p. 338 (1956).

13. Bernstein, I. B., Waves in a plasma in a magnetic field, Phys. Rev. Vol. 109, p. 10 (1958).

14. Bernstein, I. B., Greene, J. M., and Kruskal, M. D., Exact non-linear plasma oscillations, Phys. Rev., Vol. 108, p. 546 (1957).

15. Bohm, D. and Gross, E. P., Theory of Plasma Oscillations. A: Origins of Medium-like Behavior, Phys. Rev. Vol. 75, p. 1851 (1959).

16. Bohm, D. and Gross, E. P., Theory of Plasma Oscillations; B: Excitation and Damping of Oscillations, Phys. Rev., Vol. 75, p. 1864 (1949).

17. Bohm, D. and Gross, E. P., Effect of Plasma Boundaries on Plasma Oscillations, Phys. Rev., Vol. 79, p. 992 (1950).

18. Bohm, D. and Pines, D., A Collective Description of Electron Interactions I: Magnetic Interactions, Phys. Rev., Vol. 82, p. 625 (1951).

19. Bohm, D. and Pines, D., A Collective Description of Electron Interactions III: Coulomb Interactions in a Degenerate Electron Gas., Phys. Rev., Vol. 92, p. 609 (1953).

20. Braginskii, S. I., On the Types of Plasma Oscillations in a Magnetic Field, Dokl. Akad. Nauk SSSR, Vol. 115, p. 475 (1957).

21. Brittin, W. E., Statistical Mechanical Theory of Transport Phenomena in a Fully Ionized Gas, Phys. Rev. Vol. 106, No. 5, pp. 843-847 (June 1, 1957).

22. Brueckner, K. A. and Watson, K. M., Use of Boltzmann equation for the study of ionized gases of low density II, Phys. Rev., Vol. 102, p. 12 (1956).

23. Chandrasekhar, S., Kaufmann, A. N., and Watson, K. M., Properties of an Ionized Gas at Low Density in a Magnetic Field III, Ann. Phys. (N.Y.), Vol. 2, p. 435 (1957).

24. Clemmow, P. C. and Willson, A. V., The Dispersion Equation in Plasma Oscillations, Proc. Roy. Soc. A, Vol. 237, p. 117 (1956).

25. Clemmow, P. C. and Wilson, A. J., The Dispersion Equation in Plasma Oscillations, Proc. Roy. Soc. A, Vol. 237, pp. 117-131, London (1956).

26. Desloge, E. A. and Matthysse, S. W., Collision term in the Boltzman transport equation, Amer. J. Phys. Vol. 28, No. 1, pp. 1-11 (Jan. 1960).

27. Dittmer, A. F., Experiments on the Scattering of Electrons by Ionised Mercury Vapor, Phys. Rev. Vol. 28, p. 507 (1926).

28. Drummond, J., Microwave propagation in hot magneto-plasmas, Phys. Rev., Vol. 112, pp. 1460-1464 (Dec. 1958).

29. Dungey, J. W., The Attenuation of Alfvén Waves, J. Geophys. Res., Vol. 59, p. 323 (1954).

30. Emeléus, K. G. and Allen, T. K., Note on Plasma-Electron Oscillations, Austral. J. Phys., Vol. 8, p. 305 (1955).

31. Emeléus, K. G., Plasma Electron Oscillations, Appl. Sci. Res. B, Vol. 5, p. 66 (1955).

32. Emeléus, K. G., Oscillations and Fluctuations in Gas Discharges, Nuovo Cimento Suppl. (10), Vol. 3, p. 490 (1956).

33. Gabor, D., Electrostatic Theory of the Plasma, Z. Physik, Vol. 84, p. 474 (1933).

34. Gabor, D., Wave Theory of Plasmas, Proc. Roy. Soc. A, Vol. 213, p. 73 (1952).

35. Gabor, D., Ash, E. A. and Dracott, D., Langmuir's Paradox, Nature, Vol. 176, p. 916 (1955).

36. Gasiorowicz, S., Neuman, M. and Riddel, R. J., Dynamics of Ionized Media, Phys. Rev. Vol. 101, No. 3, pp. 922-934 (1956).

37. Gersham, B. N., Notes concerning waves in a homogeneous magnetoactive plasma, Zh. eksper teor Fiz, Vol. 31, p. 707 (1956).

38. Gertsenshtein, M. E., On the longitudinal waves in an ionized medium (Plasma). Zh. eksper teor Fiz, Vol. 22, p. 303,(1952).

39. Ginzburg, V. L., Magnetohydrodynamic Waves in Gases, Zh. eksper teor Fiz, Vol. 21 p. 788 (1951).

40. Gold, L., Non-linear Phenomenological Theory of Plasma Oscillations, J. Electronics and Control, Vol. 4, p. 219 (1958).

41. Gold, L., Oscillations in a Plasma with Oriented (D.C.) Magnetic Field, J. Electronics and Control, Vol. 4, p. 409 (1958).

42. Gold, L., Current-Voltage Behavior in a Plasma, J. Electronics and Control, Vol. 5, p. 432 (1958).

43. Gordeyev, G. V., Plasma Oscillations in a Magnetic Field, Zh. eksper teor Fiz, Vol. 23, p. 660 (1952).

44. Gordeyev, G. V., Low-Frequency Plasma Oscillations, Zh. eksper teor Fiz, Vol. 27, p. 19 (1954)

45. Green, H. S., Propagation of disturbances at high frequencies in gases, liquids, and plasmas, The Physics of Fluids, Vol. 2, No. 1, pp. 31-39 (Jan.-Feb. 1959).

46. Gross, E. P., Plasma Oscillations in a Static Magnetic Field, Phys. Rev., Vol. 82, p. 232 (1951).

47. Gutton, H., Ionised Gases in High-Frequency Fields, Comptes Rendus, Vol. 188, p. 156 (1929).

48. Gutton, H., Effect of a Magnetic Field on Resonance Phenomena in Ionised Gases, Comptes Rendus, Vol. 188, p. 385 (1929).

49. Harris, E. G., Unstable Plasma Oscillations in a Magnetic Field, Phys. Rev. Letters, Vol. 2, No. 2, pp. 34-36 (Jan. 15, 1959).

50. Holter, O., On the propagation of transverse electromagnetic waves in a plasma in a magnetic field, Inst. of Theoretical Astrophysics, Univ. of Oslo, Oslo (1959).

51. Ionescu, T. V. and Mihul, C., Free Electrons in Ionised Gases in a Magnetic Field, Comptes Rendus, Vol. 194, p. 1330 (1932).

52. Ionescu, T. V., Sur les Periodes Propres des vibrationes des gaz ionisée dans. le Champs magnétique, Comptes Rendus, Vol. 203, p. 57 (1936).

53. Jancel, R. and Kahan, T., Analysis of the Coupling of Ordinary and Extraordinary Electromagnetic Waves in a Lorentzian Plasma and Its Applications to the Ionosphere, Physics of the Ionosphere (Cambridge) pp. 374-383 (1955).

54. Jancel, R. and Kahan, T., Statistical Mechanics of Plasmas: Applications of the Boltzmann and Fokker-Planck equations, Cahiers De Physique, Vol. 13, (107/8), pp. 289-308 (July/Aug. 1959).

55. Jancel, R. and Kahan, T., On the theory of plasmas in the presence of a constant magnetic field of arbitrary intensity superposed on an oscillating electric field, Comptes Rendus (Paris) Vol. 238, pp. 995-6 (March 1, 1954).

56. Jancel, R. and Kahan, T., Propagation of Plane Electromagnetic Waves in a Homogeneous Plasma (Ionosphere), J. Phys. Rad., Vol. 15, p. 26 (1954).

57. Jancel, R. and Kahan, T., Maxwellian approximation of the general magneto-ionic theory of ion plasmas in an electric field, ibid; p. 382 (1954).

58. Jancel, R. and Kahan, T., Non Maxwellian theory of homogeneous and anisotropic plasmas, Il Nuovo Cumento, Vol. 12, p. 573 (1954).

59. Jancel, R. and Kahan, T., Statistical Mechanics of Lorentzian electron plasmas and then application to the ionosphere, Phys. of the Ionosphere, p. 365, Cambridge (1955).

60. Jancel, R. and Kahan, T., Development of a general solution of the transport equation of Boltzmann in the presence of an electric and magnetic field, Comptes Rendus, Vol. 244, p. 1333 (1957).

61. Jancel, R. and Kahan, T., On a generalized theory of Lorentzian plasmas under the action of a non-periodic force and taking account of the processes of inelastic collisions, Comptes Rendus, Vol. 244, p. 2583 (1957).

62. Jancel, R. and Kahan, T., Conditions for discharge in an electromagnetic cavity and traveling waves in Lorentzian plasmas, Comptes Rendus, Vol. 244, p. 2894 (1957).

63. Jancel, R. and Kahan, T., Magneto-ionic theory of a weakly ionized gas in the presence of an oscillating electric and constant magnetic field, L. Journal de Physique et la Radium, Vol. 10, p. 533 (1953).

64. Jancel, R. and Kahan, T., Analysis of the coupling of ordinary and extraordinary electromagnetic waves in a Lorentzian plasma and its applications to the ionosphere, Physics of the Ionosphere, pp. 374-383, Cambridge (1955).

65. Kahn, F. D., Long-range interactions in ionized gases in thermal equilibrium, Astrophys. J., Vol. 129, pp. 205-216 (1959).

66. Kischel, K., Zur Theorie Electrischer Wellen in homogeneous Plasmen, Ann. d. Physik (Leipzig) (6), Vol. 19, p. 309 (1956).

67. Kischel, K., On the theory of electric waves in inhomogeneous plasmas, Ann. der Physik, Vol. 19, series 6, pp. 309-321 (1957).

68. Kober, H., Absorption in a mixed electron gas, Ann. der Physik, Vol. 11, series 6, pp. 1-11 (1952).

69. Landau, L., On the vibrations of the electronic plasma, Zh. tekh. Fiz. SSSR., Vol. 10, p. 25 (1946).

70. Langmuir, I., Oscillations in Ionized Gases, Proc. Nat. Acad. Sci., Vol. 14, p. 627 (1928).

71. Margenau, H., Conductivity of Plasmas to Microwaves, Phys. Rev., Vol. 109, No. 1, pp. 6-9 (Jan. 1958).

72. Molmud, P., Langevin equation and the AC conductivity of Non-Maxwellian plasmas, Phys. Rev. Vol. 114, No. 1, pp. 29-32 (April 1, 1959).

73. Nozieres, P. and Pines, D., Electron interaction in solids, General Formulation, Phys. Rev. Vol. 109, No. 3, pp. 741-761 (Feb. 1, 1958).

74. Nozieres, P. and Pines, D., Electron interaction in solids, Collective approach to the dielectric constant, ibid, pp. 762-777 (Feb. 1, 1958).

75. Pradhan, T., Plasma oscillations in a steady magnetic field: circularly polarized electromagnetic waves, Phys. Rev., Vol. 107, p. 1222 (1957).

76. Rawer, K. and Suchy, K., Statistical derivation of the dispersion formula of Lorentzian plasmas of finite temperature, Ann. der Physik, Vol. 2, series 7, pp. 313-325 (1958).

77. Rawer, K. and Suchy, K., Longitudinal and transverse waves in a Lorentz plasma, ibid, Vol. 3, series 7, pp. 155-170 (1959).

78. Rostoker, N. and Rosenbluth, Test particles in a completely ionized plasma, ibid, Vol. 3, No. 1, pp. 1-14 (Jan.-Feb. 1960).

79. Schermer, H. and Friedrick, J., The electrical conductivity of plasmas, I, Zeit. f. Physik., Vol. 151, pp. 174-186 (1958).

80. Schermer, H. and Friedrick, J., ibid, pp. 375-384 (1958).

81. Tehen, C. H., Kinetic Equation for a Plasma with Unsteady Correlations, Phys. Rev. Vol. 114, No. 2, pp. 394-411 (April 15, 1959).

82. Temko, S. V., On the deduction of the Fokker-Planck equation for a plasma, Zh. eksper teor. Fiz., Vol. 31, p. 1021 (1956).

83. Tonks, L. and Langmuir, I., Oscillations in Ionized Gases, Phys. Rev., Vol. 33, p. 195 (1929)

84. Van Kampen, N. G., On the theory of stationary waves in plasmas, Physica. XXI, pp. 949-963 (1955).

85. Van Kampen, N. G., The dispersion equation for plasma waves, Physica XXIII, pp. 641-650 (1957).

86. Watson, K. M., Use of Boltzmann equation for the study of ionized gases of low density, I. Phys. Rev., Vol. 102, p. 12 (1956).

87. Weibel, E. S., Oscillations of a non-uniform plasma, ibid, Vol. 3, No. 3, pp. 399-407 (May-June 1960).

88. Westfold, K. C., Collisional effects and the conduction current in an ionized gas, Philosophical Mag., Vol. 44, pp. 712-724.

89. Yankov, V. V., On the ponderomotive force in localized plasma in the electromagnetic field of a plane wave, Zh. eksper. teor. Fiz., Vol. 32, p. 926 (1957).

GENERAL BIBLIOGRAPHIES

1. Alfvén, Hannes, Cosmical Electrodynamics, Clarendon Press, Oxford, First edition, 1950: Second edition, 1953.

2. Balescu, R., Irreversible processes in a plasma; Effect of Long Range Forces, Dynamics of Conducting Gases, Northwestern Univ. Press, Evanston, Ill. (1960).

3. Beer, Arthur (Editor), Vistas in Astronomy, Pergamon Press, London and New York, Vol. 3 (1959).

4. Bishop, Amasa S., Project Sherwood - The U.S. Program in Controlled Fusion, Addison-Wesley, Reading, Mass. (1958).

5. Chandrasekhar, S., Plasma Physics.

6. Chapman, S. and Cowling, T. G., The Mathematical Theory of Non-Uniform Gases, Cambridge Univ. Press (2nd Ed. 1953).

7. Chapman, Sidney, and Cowling, Thomas G., The Mathematical Theory of Non-Uniform Gases, University Press, Cambridge (1939).

8. Chapman, Sidney and Bartels, Julius, Geomagnetism, Clarendon Press, Oxford (1940) (2 volumes).

9. Corben, H. and Stehle, P.

10. Cowling, Thomas G., Magnetohydrodynamics, Interscience Publishers, New York (1957).

11. Delcroix, J. L., Introduction á la Théorie des Gas Ionisés, Dunod, Paris, (1959).

12. Drummond, J. (Ed.), Plasma Physics

13. Eisenschitz, R., Statistical Theory of Irreversible Processes, Oxford Univ. Press, N.Y. (1958).

14. Fisher, H., and Mansur, L. C. (Editors), Conference on Extremely High Temperatures, John Wiley (1958).

15. Francis, G., Ionization Phenomena in Gases, Acad. Press, London (1960).

16. Goldstein, H.

17. Grad. H., Thermodynamics of Gases, Encycl. of Phys., Vol. XII, Springer-Verlag (1958).

18. Guthrie, A. and Wakerling, R. K. (Editors), The Characteristics of Electrical Discharges in Magnetic Fields, McGraw-Hill, New York (1949).

19. Heitler, Walter, The Quantum Theory of Radiation, Clarendon Press, Oxford, First Edition, 1936; Second Edition, 1944; Third Edition, 1954.

20. Hill, T. L., Statistical Mechanics, McGraw-Hill Book Co. N.Y. (1956).

21. Hirschfelder, Joseph O., Curtiss, Charles F., and Bird, R. Byron, Molecular Theory of Gases and Liquids, John Wiley (1954).

22. Joos, G.

23. Landau and Lifshitz, Statistical Physics.

24. Landshoff, R. K. (Editor), Magnetohydrodynamics, Stanford University Press, (1957). Proceedings of Symposium sponsored by Lockheed held on December 29, 1956.

25. Linhart, J. G., Plasma Physics.

26. Nottingham, Wayne B., and Staff, Bibliography of Electronics, Massachusetts Institute of Technology, Research Laboratory of Electronics, Addison-Wesley (1954).

27. Physical Society, London, The Physics of the Ionosphere, Physical Society, London (1955). Report of Physical Society Conference on Physics of the Ionosphere held at Cavendish Laboratory, Cambridge, September 1954.

28. Prigogine, I., The Statistical Mechanics of the Approach to Equilibrium in Gases, ibid.

29. Rosseland, S., Theoretical Astrophysics, Clarendon Press, Oxford (1936).

30. Rozhdestvensky, D. S., Anomalous Dispersion, Press of the Academy of Science, USSR (1951).

31. Smith, M. L. (Editor), Electromagnetically Enriched Isotropes and Mass Spectrometry, Academic Press, New York and London (1956).

32. Sommerfeld, A., Thermodynamics and Statistical Mechanics, Academic Press, N.Y. (1956).

33. Spitzer, Lyman, Jr., Physics of Fully Ionized Gases, Interscience Publishing Co. (1956).

34. Synge, John Lighton, The Relativistic Gas, North Holland Publishing Company (1957).

35. ter Haar, D., Introduction to the Physics of Many-Body Systems, Interscience Publishers, New York (1958).

36. Thomson, J. J. and Thomson, G. P., Conduction of Electricity Through Gases, Electrical Discharges Through Gases, Vol. 1. Ionization of Gases, Vol. 2, University Press, Cambridge (1928-1933).

37. Townsend, John S. E., Electricity in Gases, Clarendon Press, Oxford (1915).

38. Tolman, R. C.

39. Van de Hulst, H. C. and Burgers, J. M. (Editors), Gas Dynamics of Cosmic Clouds, Symposium on Cosmical Gas Dynamics held at Cambridge, July 6-11, 1953. Interscience Publishing Co. (1955).

40. Vlasov, A. A., Many Body Theory, State Technical and Theoretical Literature Press, USSR (1950).

41. von Engel, Alfred, Ionized Gases, Clarendon Press, Oxford (1955).

42. Ziman, J., Electrons and Phonons, Oxford Univ. Press (1960).

CHAPTER IX

RADIATION IN A PLASMA

INTRODUCTORY REMARKS

Radiation phenomena has been and no doubt will continue to be the subject of intense investigations for a long time. Its scope is vast, ranging from atmos to cosmos, and its philosophical foundations are still being probed. The technological importance of the subject is impossible to assess completely.

The study of electromagnetic radiation in isotropic homogeneous media is still proceeding at a fast rate, particularly in applications, *e.g.*, antennae, etc. Studies of radiation phenomena in anisotropic media have just recently received more attention, the motivations arising from controlled fusion experiments, astrophysics, ionospheric phenomena, *e.g.*, the sources of natural very low frequency phenomena, Cerenkov radiation and a multitude of other natural and man made phenomena, *e.g.*, high altitude nuclear bursts. The qualitative aspects of some of these phenomena are well understood but still more are not.

It is desirable therefore to seek a better understanding of the radiation due to sources in anisotropic medium which is also lossy. Radiation properties in such media have been explored considerably by Soviet scientists in connection with the phenomena of Cerenkov radiation mentioned above. An excellent account of this phenomena is found in Jelley. Later, scientists in the United States, Great Britain, Australia undertook a serious study of radiation processes in ionized gasses in order to understand better the complex phenomena which take place in these so-called plasmas. The possibility of extracting useful devices from such studies also provide a strong motivation for the continuance of these studies.

However, radiation phenomena in anisotropic media is not limited to just plasmas. Anisotropy is present in ferrites, crystals (as we have already seen in Chapter II), artificial dielectrics, photo-elastic materials in which stress birefringence is present, and in semi-conductors to mention just a few.

In the present chapter we consider first, from an elementary point of view, the radiative processes in an ionized gas in the absence of a magnetic field, following the work of Westfold. This part of the chapter is given because it provides an insight into the connection between the scattering processes and the macroscopic index of refraction.

Following this we formulate the radiation problem in a general macroscopic anisotropic medium in which we assume that both electric and magnetic current densities are the sources of radiation. The media which are considered are restricted to be linear, and the anisotropy is subsumed under a dielectric and magnetic tensor, whose elements are in general complex valued. It is shown that the calculation of the resultant fields requires the construction of a Green's dyadic or tensor which is a generalization of the Green's scalar function in the case of an isotropic medium. This Green's tensor for an unbounded region is, in the case of an electric and magnetic medium, given by a super matrix. That is, a matrix whose elements are matrices themselves and indicates the coupling of the electric and magnetic properties of the medium. The calculation of the Green's tensor is facilitated by use of the Fourier transform and explicit formulae are developed.

A brief discussion is given on power dissipation and some related quadratic forms as preparation for a later section in which these concepts are applied.

The interesting and important problem of wave excitation due to a distribution of oscillating electric dipoles constrained to a plane of arbitrary orientation is treated in some detail.

The radiated power from both electric and magnetic dipoles is discussed and formulae are given for the calculation of the wave impedance of these dipoles. Here, it is important to mention that only the real part of the impedance has physical significance.

We then consider the formulation of the problem of electromagnetic scattering and reflection indicating the potential applications to low frequency phenomena.

Finally, we sketch the solution to the problem of a slot radiator and magnetic current sheet embedded in a non-isotropic medium, both of which are treated as boundary value problems.

Particular and interesting problems which are direct applications of the theory are relegated to problems for the reader.

We have not calculated radiation patterns as these are tedious and difficult to treat in the general case, nor have we discussed radiation from relativistic charges since these topics have been treated elsewhere.

An extensive bibliography is given at the end of the chapter of the pertinent work on radiation in non-iostropic media and in particular we mention here the works of Kogelnik and Abraham.

101. RADIATIVE PROCESSES IN AN IONIZED GAS

In this section we shall consider briefly the microscopic processes of absorption and emission and the electromagnetic scattering by the other particles of the ionized gas. The electromagnetic scattering is substantially the process which implies the macroscopic refractive index of the medium.

Although Hartree, Darwin and others have considered in great detail this relation between the refractive index and electromagnetic scattering it seems appropriate here to discuss it on a more elementary level than that given by the above-mentioned. In an ionized gas, the scattering, absorption and emission associated with the electron motion dominates over the same processes associated with ion motions.

We recall that the average motion for a free electron of mass m, charge e under the influence of an electromagnetic field (the externally applied uniform magnetic field is absent in this discussion) is given by

$$m(\dot{\mathbf{v}} + \nu\mathbf{v}) = e(\mathbf{E} + \mathbf{v}\mathbf{x}\mathbf{B}) \tag{101.1}$$

where $\mathbf{v}$ is the average velocity of the electron induced by the field $(\mathbf{E},\mathbf{B})$ and ν is the average collision frequency.

Provided that $v << V_0$ (where V_0 is the speed of light in a vacuum reference medium), the scattered field which results from the induced motion of the electron is equivalent to a current density $e\mathbf{v}$. If N is the electron density, the coherent scattered fields of all the electrons, which are affected by the induced field, are equivalent to an induced current distribution of density

$$\mathbf{J} = Ne\mathbf{v} \quad , \tag{101.2}$$

and this is the only source distribution of the field. The scattered field consequently is identical with the induced field and hence must satisfy the field equations

$$\left.\begin{aligned} \operatorname{curl} \mathbf{E} + \frac{\partial \mathbf{B}}{\partial t} &= 0 \quad , \\ \operatorname{curl} \mathbf{H} - \frac{\epsilon_0 \partial \mathbf{E}}{\partial t} &= \mathbf{J} \quad . \end{aligned}\right\} \tag{101.3}$$

For time harmonic fields, we find from eqs. (101.1)-(101.3),* the wave equation for $\mathbf{E}$ (in rectangular cartesians),

$$\nabla^2 \mathbf{E} + \mu_0 \epsilon_0 \omega^2 M^2 \mathbf{E} = 0 \quad , \tag{101.4}$$

where

$$M^2 = p - iq \quad , \tag{101.5}$$

$$\left.\begin{aligned} p &= 1 - \frac{\omega_0^2}{\omega^2 + \nu^2} \quad , \\ q &= \frac{\nu}{\omega} \frac{\omega_0^2}{\omega^2 + \nu^2} \quad , \end{aligned}\right\} \tag{101.6}$$

ω_0 is the electron plasma frequency. Now,

$$\epsilon_0 \dot{\mathbf{E}} + Ne\mathbf{v} = \left[\epsilon_0 i\omega + \frac{Ne^2}{m} \frac{(\nu - i\omega)}{\nu^2 + \omega^2} \right] \mathbf{E} \tag{101.7}$$

so that,

$$\mathbf{J} = \sigma \mathbf{E} \tag{101.8}$$

with

$$\sigma = \frac{Ne^2}{m} \frac{(\nu - i\omega)}{\nu^2 + \omega^2} \quad . \tag{101.9}$$

---

* For $v \ll V_0$, eq. (101.1) reduces to $v + \nu v = (e/m)E$, a result easily obtained when it is written in Gaussian units.

Let us now write,

$$\mathbf{E} = \mathbf{E}_0 \exp\left[i\omega\left(t - \frac{M}{V_0} \mathbf{n} \cdot \mathbf{r} \right)\right] , \qquad (101.10)$$

and put

$$M = \mu - i\chi , \quad \text{(complex index of refraction)}, \qquad (101.11)$$

hence,

$$M^2 = (\mu - i\chi)^2 = p - iq \qquad (101.12)$$

which implies,

$$\left.\begin{aligned} \mu^2 - \chi^2 &= p, \\ 2\mu\chi &= q. \end{aligned}\right\} \qquad (101.13)$$

Here, μ is the real refractive index, and χ defines the absorption index. Both **E** and **H** are related by

$$\mathbf{H} = \frac{M}{\mu_0 V_0} \mathbf{nxE} , \qquad (101.14)$$

which shows that **H** is transverse to **n**, likewise for **E**.

Cross-Section for Absorption by a Free Electron—The Absorption Coefficient—We shall now derive the expression for the absorption coefficient from the concept of absorption cross section of a free electron of the ionized gas in a radiation field, by considering the scattering properties of the medium.

Now the energy of the radiation field plus the magnetic energy of the current distribution is the total energy of the electromagnetic field.* The energy density of the current distribution can be expressed in terms of the current density and the vector potential **A**, of which it is the source function. Any radiation field is a linear superposition of plane monochromatic waves of all frequencies and propagating in all directions, hence we

---

* G. Burkhardt, loc. cit.

can consider plane wave fields of the form of eq. (101.10). We shall denote quantities corresponding to a frequency $f = \omega/2\pi$ by subscript f. Thus the energy density expressed in terms of the field quantities, current $\mathbf{J}$ and vector potential $\mathbf{A}$ is given by*

$$<U_f> = \frac{1}{4}\left(\epsilon_0|\mathbf{E}|^2 + \mu_0|\mathbf{H}|^2\right) + \frac{1}{4}Re(\mathbf{J}\cdot\mathbf{A}^*) \tag{101.15}$$

for time averages over a period $1/f$. For the Poynting vector we already know it is given by

$$<\mathbf{s}_f> = \frac{1}{2}Re(\mathbf{E}\mathrm{x}\mathbf{H}^*) \quad . \tag{101.16}$$

By definition,

$$\mathbf{E} = -\frac{\partial\mathbf{A}}{\partial t} = -i\omega\mathbf{A} \tag{101.17}$$

or,

$$\mathbf{A} = \frac{i}{\omega}\mathbf{E} \quad , \tag{101.18}$$

hence,

$$\mathbf{A}^* = -\frac{i}{\omega}\mathbf{E}^* \quad , \tag{101.19}$$

using $\mathbf{H}$ from eq. (101.14), and $\mathbf{J}$ from eq. (101.8) all quantities are now in terms of $\mathbf{E}$. Therefore,

$$<U_f> = \frac{1}{4}\left(\epsilon_0|\mathbf{E}|^2 + \mu_0\left|\frac{M_f}{\mu_0 V_0}\,\mathbf{n}\mathrm{x}\mathbf{E}\right|^2\right) + \frac{1}{4}Re\left[(\sigma_f\mathbf{E})\cdot\left(-\frac{i}{\omega}\mathbf{E}^*\right)\right] \quad , \tag{101.20}$$

but since $\mathbf{n}$ is real and $\mathbf{E}$ is transverse to $\mathbf{n}$ we have

$$\left(\frac{M_f}{\mu_0 V_0}\,\mathbf{n}\mathrm{x}\mathbf{E}\right)\cdot\left(\frac{M_f^*}{\mu_0 V_0}\,\mathbf{n}\mathrm{x}\mathbf{E}^*\right) = \left(\frac{M_f}{\mu_0 V_0}\right)^2|\mathbf{E}|^2 \quad , \tag{101.21}$$

* Stratton, loc. cit., pp. 134, 457.

also,

$$\sigma_f \mathbf{E} \cdot \left(-\frac{i}{\omega}\mathbf{E}^*\right) = -i\frac{\sigma_f}{\omega}|\mathbf{E}|^2 \qquad (101.22)$$

and using eq. (101.9) for σ, and eq. (101.12) for M_f^2 we obtain,

$$<U_f> = \frac{\epsilon_0\mu_f^2}{2}|\mathbf{E}|^2 \quad . \qquad (101.23)$$

Similarly,

$$<\mathbf{s}_f> = \frac{1}{2}Re\left[\mathbf{E}\mathbf{x}\left(\frac{M_f^*}{\mu_0 V_0}\mathbf{n}\mathbf{x}\mathbf{E}^*\right)\right]$$

$$= \frac{1}{2\mu_0 V_0}Re[(\mathbf{E}\cdot\mathbf{E}^*)M_f^*\mathbf{n} - (\mathbf{E}\cdot M_f^*\mathbf{n})\mathbf{E}^*] \quad , \qquad (101.24)$$

but since $\mathbf{E}\cdot\mathbf{n} = 0$, we find that

$$<\mathbf{s}_f> = \frac{1}{2\mu_0 V_0}Re[|\mathbf{E}|^2(\mu_f + i\chi_f)\mathbf{n}]$$

$$= \frac{\mu_f}{2\mu_0 V_0}|\mathbf{E}|^2\mathbf{n} = \frac{V_0}{\mu_f}\left(\frac{1}{2}\epsilon_0\mu_f^2|\mathbf{E}|^2\right)\mathbf{n} \quad , \qquad (101.25)$$

or, by eq. (101.23),

$$<\mathbf{s}_f> = \frac{V_0}{\mu_f}<U_f>\mathbf{n} \quad . \qquad (101.26)$$

According to this formula we see that since V_0/μ_f is the phase velocity in a medium of dielectric constant defined by (p,q), hence this is the velocity with which the energy propagates.

The average rate of absprption of energy by an electron from the field is given by

$$<W_f> = \frac{1}{2}eRe(\dot{\mathbf{r}})\cdot Re(\mathbf{E})$$

$$= \frac{1}{4}eRe(\dot{\mathbf{r}}\cdot\mathbf{E}^*) \quad . \qquad (101.27)$$

For an average electron the current is given by

$$\frac{\mathbf{J}}{N} = e\dot{\mathbf{r}} = \frac{\sigma_f}{N}\mathbf{E} = \frac{e^2}{m}\frac{(\nu - i\omega)}{\nu^2 + \omega^2}\mathbf{E} \qquad (101.28)$$

hence,

$$<W_f> = \frac{1}{4} Re\left[\frac{e^2}{m}\frac{(\nu - i\omega)}{\nu^2 + \omega^2}\mathbf{E}\cdot\mathbf{E}^*\right] \qquad (101.29)$$

or.

$$<W_f> = \frac{e^2}{4m}\frac{\nu}{\nu^2 + \omega^2}|\mathbf{E}|^2 \quad . \qquad (101.30)$$

This formula shows that there is an over-all extraction of energy from the field only due to collisions of the electron with other particles of the gas. Also, during a part of any period the rate of absorption of electromagnetic energy is negative, and this represents the emission stimulated by the field. In the absence of a collision, it is balanced by an equal amount of energy absorbed from the field during the other part of the period. Consequently $<W_f>$ is the net absorption over a period, and on the average, is transferred to the heavier ions with which the electron collides.

The absorption cross section for a free electron denoted by a_f is defined by

$$<W_f> = a_f <s_f> \quad , \qquad (101.31)$$

where $<s_f>$ is the magnitude of $<\mathbf{s}_f>$. From eqs. (101.26) and (101.30) we find,

$$a_f = \frac{e^2}{2\mu_f \epsilon_0 V_0 m}\frac{\nu}{\nu^2 + \omega^2} \quad . \qquad (101.32)$$

The energy absorption coefficient is by definition,

$$K_f = Na_f = \frac{Ne^2}{\epsilon_0 m}\frac{1}{2\mu_{f\ 0}}\frac{\nu}{\nu^2 + \omega^2} = \frac{1}{2}\frac{\nu}{\mu_f V_0}\frac{\omega_0^2}{\nu^2 + \omega^2} \quad . \qquad (101.33)$$

102. RADIATION IN ANISOTROPIC MEDIA

In this section we shall consider the problem of radiation in an unbounded homogeneous anisotropic medium. First we shall give a general formulation of the problem and then apply the results to some situations of both theoretical and practical interest.

It is desirable to start with Maxwell's equations for the time harmonic case and include in the description external magnetic current densities denoted here by **M**. The complex amplitudes **E**,**H**,**J** and **M** are then bound by the relations

$$\left.\begin{aligned} \nabla\mathbf{x}\mathbf{E} &= -i\omega\mu_0\mu\mathbf{H} - \mathbf{M} \quad , \\ \nabla\mathbf{x}\mathbf{H} &= i\omega\epsilon_0\epsilon\mathbf{E} + \mathbf{J} \quad , \end{aligned}\right\} \tag{102.1}$$

here **J** is the external impressed current density. In what follows **J** and **M** are assumed to be given. The quantities ϵ and μ are respectively the dielectric and magnetic tensors. The elements of these tensors are in general complex quantities. If the externally applied uniform magnetic field is parallel to the x_3 axis we know that the structure of the dielectric tensor is

$$\epsilon = \begin{pmatrix} \epsilon_1 & -i\epsilon_2 & 0 \\ i\epsilon_2 & \epsilon_1 & 0 \\ 0 & 0 & \epsilon_3 \end{pmatrix} \quad , \tag{102.2}$$

an exactly similar structure holds for media which are magnetically anisotropic, that is, for a ferrite with a permanent applied magnetic field in the x_3 direction,

$$\mu = \begin{pmatrix} \mu_1 & -i\mu_2 & 0 \\ i\mu_2 & \mu_1 & 0 \\ 0 & 0 & \mu_3 \end{pmatrix} \quad . \tag{102.3}$$

We remind the reader that even though a magnetic current density is not exactly a physical reality but rather a mathematical artifice it is useful in exploring the formal duality between dielectric and magnetic media.*

For $\mathbf{J} = \mathbf{M} = 0$, plane wave solutions of the form $\mathbf{E} = \mathbf{E}_0 e^{-iK\mathbf{n}\cdot\mathbf{r}}$ yield,

$$\mathbf{K}\mathrm{x}\mathbf{E} = \omega\mu_0\mu\mathbf{H} \equiv \omega\mathbf{B} \quad , \tag{102.4}$$

$$\mathbf{K}\mathrm{x}\mathbf{H} = -\omega\epsilon_0\epsilon\mathbf{E} = -\omega\mathbf{D} \quad , \tag{102.5}$$

where K is complex. This form of Maxwell's equations can be rewritten in the form of matrix equations when we recall that the vector product of two vectors is equivalent to a skew-symmetric matrix times a vector. Hence,

$$\mathbf{K}\mathrm{x}\mathbf{E} = \begin{pmatrix} 0 & -K_3 & K_2 \\ K_3 & 0 & -K_1 \\ -K_2 & K_1 & 0 \end{pmatrix} \mathbf{E} \equiv \mathbf{K}\mathbf{E} \quad , \tag{102.6}$$

and we now write,

$$\mathbf{K}\mathbf{E} = \omega\mathbf{B} \quad , \tag{102.7}$$

$$\mathbf{K}\mathbf{H} = -\omega\mathbf{D} \ . \tag{102.8}$$

The scalar product of $\mathbf{n}$ with both sides of these equations shows that $\mathbf{B}$ and $\mathbf{D}$ are transverse to $\mathbf{n}$. We also find that†

$$\mathbf{B}\cdot\mathbf{E} = \mathbf{D}\cdot\mathbf{H} = 0 \tag{102.9}$$

From eqs. (102.4) and (102.5) we have,

$$\mathbf{H} = \frac{1}{\omega\mu_0}\mu^{-1}\mathbf{K}\mathbf{E} \quad , \tag{102.10}$$

---

* M. E. Durand, General Theory of Magnetic Masses at rest and in motion, (in French). Revue Génerale De L'Electricité, Tome 64, No. 7, pp. 350-356, (1955). See also Chapter V.

† We use the term transverse when the scalar product of two complex vectors (or at least one is complex) is zero. If both vectors are real we use perpendicular. The term transverse in the more general sense arises from the definition of inner product as in the calculus of variations. Thus transversality does not coincide with geometric perpendicularity. If the fields $\mathbf{E}(t)$, *etc.* were linearly polarized we would have perpendicularity, but since we have in general, elliptic polarization we use the term "transverse."

$$\mathbf{E} = \frac{-1}{\omega\epsilon_0}\epsilon^{-1}\mathbf{KH} \quad , \tag{102.11}$$

we note that the matrix **K** can not be inverted because it is skew-symmetric of odd order which has zero determinant. By substituting **H** from the first equation into the second and **E** from the second into the first we obtain,

$$(\mathbf{K}\epsilon^{-1}\mathbf{K} + k_0^2\mu)\mathbf{H} = 0 \quad , \tag{102.12}$$

$$(\mathbf{K}\mu^{-1}\mathbf{K} + k_0^2\epsilon)\mathbf{E} \equiv 0 \quad , \tag{102.13}$$

where,

$$k_0^2 = \omega^2\mu_0\epsilon_0 \quad , \tag{102.14}$$

We define,

$$\mathbf{W}_H \equiv \mathbf{K}\epsilon^{-1}\mathbf{K} + k_0^2\mu \tag{102.15}$$

as the magnetic wave matrix, and

$$\mathbf{W}_E \equiv \mathbf{K}\mu^{-1}\mathbf{K} + k_0^2\epsilon \tag{102.16}$$

as the electric wave matrix. By arguments similar to those used in Chapters II and VII, it is not difficult to show that

$$\det \mathbf{W}_H = \det \mathbf{W}_E = 0 \tag{102.17}$$

is quadratic in K^2 and we designate these roots by K_1^2, K_2^2. The value K^2 is related to M^2 by

$$K^2 = k_0^2 M^2 \quad . \tag{102.18}$$

If, as in a non magnetic medium $\mu = \mathbf{I}$ the identity matrix, we find

$$\mathbf{W}_E = \mathbf{KK} + k_0^2\epsilon \quad , \tag{102.18'}$$

but since $\mathbf{K}$ is skew-symmetric, $\mathbf{KK}$ is symmetric and we can decompose it as follows,

$$\mathbf{KK} = \begin{pmatrix} K_1^2 - K^2 & K_1K_2 & K_1K_3 \\ K_1K_2 & K_2^2 - K^2 & K_2K_3 \\ K_1K_3 & K_2K_3 & K_3^2 - K^2 \end{pmatrix} = \begin{pmatrix} K_1 \\ K_2 \\ K_3 \end{pmatrix} (K_1 \quad K_2 \quad K_3) - K^2\mathbf{I} \tag{102.19}$$

where,

$$K_1^2 + K_2^2 + K_3^2 = K^2 \quad , \tag{102.20}$$

denoting now by $\mathbf{K}$ the column vector with components K_i, and by $\mathbf{K}'$ the transpose or row vector, we can now write,

$$\mathbf{W}_E = \mathbf{KK}' - K^2\mathbf{I} + k_0^2\boldsymbol{\epsilon} \quad . \tag{102.21}$$

It follows from eqs. (102.13) and (102.21) when $\mu = \mathbf{I}$ that the condition for propagation, *i.e.*, non-trivial $\mathbf{E}$, is the vanishing of the determinant of (102.21). Recalling from Chapter II, that $\mathbf{n} = (\sin\theta\cos\phi, \sin\theta \sin\phi, \cos\theta)$, we find

$$\det \mathbf{W}_E = k_0^2(\epsilon_1 \sin^2\theta + \epsilon_3 \cos^2\theta)(K^2 - K_1^2)(K^2 - K_2^2) \quad , \tag{102.21'}$$

with

$$M_{1,2}^2 = \frac{K_{1,2}^2}{k_0^2} = \frac{(\epsilon_1^2 - \epsilon_2^2)\sin^2\theta + \epsilon_1\epsilon_3(1 + \cos^2\theta)}{2(\epsilon_1 \sin^2\theta + \epsilon_3\cos^2\theta)} \pm \frac{\sqrt{(\epsilon_1^2 - \epsilon_2^2 - \epsilon_1\epsilon_3)^2 \sin^4\theta + 4\epsilon_2^2\epsilon_3^2\cos^2\theta}}{2(\epsilon_1 \sin^2\theta + \epsilon_3\cos^2\theta)} \quad . \tag{102.22}$$

The vanishing of the determinant W_E of course is nothing more than the Appleton-Hartree equation and eq. (102.22) gives the refractive indices for the ordinary and extraordinary waves respectively. We note that for real $\epsilon_1, \epsilon_2, \epsilon_3$ the indices are real (a lossless medium), but if ϵ_1 and/or ϵ_3 are negative, and if $\epsilon_2^2 > \epsilon_1^2$, both M_1^2 and/or M_2^2 can be negative for some range of θ, hence the indices become imaginary. In this case we say that the waves are cut off (at a certain frequency), *i.e.*, the plane waves cannot propagate.

Let us note that if we did not assume plane wave propagation, the same formalism that was used in deriving the wave matrix W_E can be used to derive the wave equation. We simply replace **K** by ∇ and K^2 by ∇^2 and thus obtain

$$\left(\nabla\nabla' - \nabla^2 \mathbf{I} - \frac{\omega^2}{V_0^2}\epsilon\right)\mathbf{E} = 0 \quad , \tag{102.23}$$

the elements of the matrix $\nabla\nabla'$ corresponding to $\mathbf{KK}'$, *i.e.*, K_1K_2 corresponds to $\partial^2/\partial x_i \partial x_j$.

Eqs. (102.1) for $\mu = \mathbf{I}$ then yield when $\mathbf{J} \neq 0$, $\mathbf{M} \equiv 0$, the form

$$(\nabla\nabla' - \nabla^2 \mathbf{I} - k_0^2 \epsilon)\mathbf{E} = -i\omega\mu_0 \mathbf{J} \quad , \tag{102.24}$$

103. THE TENSOR (OR DYADIC) GREEN'S FUNCTIONS

Let us return to eqs. (102.1) and note that since Maxwell's equations are linear we can seek the solution of the inhomogeneous system (102.1) in the form,

$$\begin{bmatrix} \mathbf{E}(\mathbf{r}) \\ \mathbf{H}(\mathbf{r}) \end{bmatrix} = \int \mathbf{G}(\mathbf{r},\mathbf{r}') \begin{bmatrix} \mathbf{J}(\mathbf{r}') \\ \mathbf{M}(\mathbf{r}') \end{bmatrix} d\mathbf{r}' \tag{103.1}$$

where,

$$\mathbf{G}(\mathbf{r},\mathbf{r}') = \begin{bmatrix} \mathbf{G}_{EJ}(\mathbf{r},\mathbf{r}') & \mathbf{G}_{EM}(\mathbf{r},\mathbf{r}') \\ \mathbf{G}_{HJ}(\mathbf{r},\mathbf{r}') & \mathbf{G}_{HM}(\mathbf{r},\mathbf{r}') \end{bmatrix} \quad , \tag{103.2}$$

and each element of the super matrix $\mathbf{G}(\mathbf{r},\mathbf{r}')$ is itself a dyadic Green's function. The integral in (103.1) is taken over all space, *i.e.*,

$$\int d\mathbf{r}' \equiv \iiint_{-\infty}^{\infty} dx_1' dx_2' dx_3' \quad .$$

It is advantageous at this point to consider the Fourier transform of the expression (103.1); denoting by $\mathbf{E}(\mathbf{K})$ etc. the Fourier transform of $\mathbf{E}(\mathbf{r})$,

$$\mathbf{E}(\mathbf{r}) = \frac{1}{8\pi^3}\int \mathbf{E}(\mathbf{K})e^{-i\mathbf{K}\cdot\mathbf{r}}d\mathbf{K} \tag{103.3}$$

then,*

$$\mathbf{E}(\mathbf{K}) = \int \mathbf{E}(\mathbf{r})e^{i\mathbf{K}\cdot\mathbf{r}}d\mathbf{r} \quad , \tag{103.4}$$

the integration over $\mathbf{K}$ is three-dimensional as for $\mathbf{r}$-space. We want now to utilize the δ-function and its Fourier Transform in a formal manner. Recall that by definition

$$\int_{-\infty}^{\infty} f(x_1')\delta(x_1 - x_1')dx_1' = f(x_1) \quad , \tag{103.5}$$

and

$$\delta(x_1) = \frac{1}{2\pi}\int_{-\infty}^{\infty} e^{-iK_1x_1}dK_1 \tag{103.6}$$

the three dimensional transform is defined by

$$\delta(\mathbf{r}) \equiv \delta(x_1)\delta(x_2)\delta(x_3) = \frac{1}{8\pi^3}\int e^{-i\mathbf{K}\cdot\mathbf{r}}d\mathbf{K} \quad . \tag{103.7}$$

The Fourier Transform of the matrices $\mathbf{G}_{EJ}$, etc. will be denoted by $\mathbf{g}_{EJ}$, etc., hence,

$$\mathbf{G}_{EJ}(\mathbf{r},\mathbf{r}') = \frac{1}{8\pi^3}\int \mathbf{g}_{EJ}(\mathbf{K})e^{-i\mathbf{K}\cdot(\mathbf{r}-\mathbf{r}')}d\mathbf{K} \quad , \text{ etc.} \tag{103.8}$$

From the relations (103.3), (103.4), (103.8) substituted into eq. (103.1) and assuming the validity of interchanging the order of integration of $\mathbf{r}$ and $\mathbf{K}$ space, we obtain

$$\begin{bmatrix} \mathbf{E}(\mathbf{K}) \\ \\ \mathbf{H}(\mathbf{K}) \end{bmatrix} = \mathbf{g}(\mathbf{K})\begin{bmatrix} \mathbf{J}(\mathbf{K}) \\ \\ \mathbf{M}(\mathbf{K}) \end{bmatrix} \quad , \tag{103.9}$$

* We are defining here the Fourier Transform with the factor $1/8\pi^3$ for reasons which will become apparent later when we use the δ-function. Thus, we depart from the symmetrical form used in Chapter I. This departure should offer no conceptual difficulty for the alert reader.

where

$$\mathbf{g}(\mathbf{K}) \equiv \begin{bmatrix} \mathbf{g}_{EJ}(\mathbf{K}) & \mathbf{g}_{EM}(\mathbf{K}) \\ \\ \mathbf{g}_{HJ}(\mathbf{K}) & \mathbf{g}_{HM}(\mathbf{K}) \end{bmatrix} . \tag{103.10}$$

To understand the above formalism better it is instructive to consider the case of only one external current density vector $\mathbf{J} \neq 0$, $\mathbf{M} \equiv 0$. From eqs. (102.24) and (103.5) we see that $\mathbf{E}$ satisfies the wave equation if $\mathbf{G}_{EJ}(\mathbf{r},\mathbf{r})$ satisfies

$$(\nabla\nabla' - \nabla^2\mathbf{I} - k_0^2\epsilon)\mathbf{G}_{EJ}(\mathbf{r},\mathbf{r}') = -i\omega\mu_0\mathbf{I}\delta(\mathbf{r} - \mathbf{r}') \tag{103.11}$$

where the operators ∇,∇' and ∇^2 operate only on $\mathbf{r}$. We assume also that interchange of $\mathbf{r}$ and $\mathbf{r}'$ in the order of integration is valid. The connection between $\mathbf{G}_{EJ}$ and the wave matrix $\mathbf{W}_E$ is obtained as follows. From the identity

$$(\nabla\nabla' - \nabla^2\mathbf{I} - k_0^2\epsilon)e^{-i\mathbf{K}\cdot\mathbf{r}} = -\mathbf{W}_E e^{-i\mathbf{K}\cdot\mathbf{r}} , \tag{103.12}$$

we multiply both sides by $\mathbf{W}_E^{-1}$, then by $e^{i\mathbf{K}\cdot\mathbf{r}'}$ and integrate over $\mathbf{K}$ space and find that

$$\mathbf{G}_{EJ} = \frac{i\omega\mu_0}{8\pi^3}\int \mathbf{W}_E^{-1}e^{-i\mathbf{K}\cdot(\mathbf{r}-\mathbf{r}')}d\mathbf{K} \tag{103.13}$$

satisfies eq. (103.11). This is the Green's tensor for the unbounded anisotropic medium with no extenal magnetic current densities. For future use it is desirable to calculate explicitly $\mathbf{W}_E^{-1}$ when $\mu = \mathbf{I}$. At this point it is worth mentioning that the use of the mathematical system employed in Chapter II so fruitfully is not directly applicable for the inversion of $\mathbf{W}_E$. A detailed calculation yields, [for ϵ given by eq. (102.2)],

$$\det(\mathbf{W}_E)\mathbf{W}_E^{-1} = K^4\mathbf{nn}'$$

$$-K^2k_0^2\begin{bmatrix} \epsilon_1(n_1^2+n_2^2)+\epsilon_3(n_1^2+n_3^2) & i\epsilon_2(n_1^2+n_2^2)+\epsilon_3 n_1 n_2 & \epsilon_1 n_1 n_3 + i\epsilon_2 n_2 n_3 \\ -i\epsilon_2(n_1^2+n_2^2)+\epsilon_3 n_1 n_2 & \epsilon_1(n_1^2+n_2^2)+\epsilon_3(n_2^2+n_3^2) & \epsilon_1 n_2 n_3 - i\epsilon_2 n_1 n_3 \\ \epsilon_1 n_1 n_3 - i\epsilon_3 n_2 n_3 & \epsilon_1 n_2 n_3 + i\epsilon_2 n_1 n_3 & \epsilon_1(1+n_3^2) \end{bmatrix}$$

$$+ k_0^4\begin{pmatrix} \epsilon_1\epsilon_3 & i\epsilon_2\epsilon_3 & 0 \\ -i\epsilon_2\epsilon_3 & \epsilon_1\epsilon_3 & 0 \\ 0 & 0 & \epsilon_1^2-\epsilon_2^2 \end{pmatrix}$$

$$= K^4\mathbf{nn}' - K^2k_0^2\mathbf{L} + k_0^4\mathbf{e} \qquad (103.14)$$

or,

$$\mathbf{W}_E^{-1} = \text{adjoint of } \frac{\mathbf{W}_E}{\det \mathbf{W}_E} = \frac{\mathbf{D}_E}{\det \mathbf{W}_E}, \qquad (103.15)$$

where $\mathbf{D}_E$ is the matrix on the right side of eq. (103.14). Thus we have,

$$\mathbf{G}_{EJ}(\mathbf{r},\mathbf{r}') = \frac{i\omega\mu_0}{8\pi^3}\int_{-\infty}^{\infty} \mathbf{D}_E \frac{e^{-i\mathbf{K}\cdot(\mathbf{r}-\mathbf{r}')}}{\det \mathbf{W}_E}\, d\mathbf{K}, \qquad (103.16)$$

since $\mathbf{D}_E$ is not a constant matrix it can not be brought outside the integral. Denoting the integrand by $\mathbf{I}_{EJ}(\mathbf{r},\mathbf{r}')$ we write more compactly

$$\mathbf{G}_{EJ}(\mathbf{r},\mathbf{r}') = \frac{i\omega\mu_0}{8\pi^3}\int_{-\infty}^{\infty} \mathbf{D}_E\mathbf{I}_{EJ}(\mathbf{r},\mathbf{r}')\, d\mathbf{K} \qquad (103.17)$$

and we see that the problem of determining the field $\mathbf{E}$ is therefore reduced to evaluating the integral (103.17). We shall return to this problem later, after we determine the elements of $\mathbf{D}_E$.

104. GENERAL CASE

Returning now to the more general case, we shall calculate the transforms of the elements of $\mathbf{G}$. By taking the Fourier Transform of Maxwell's equations (102.1) we obtain,

$$
\left.
\begin{aligned}
- i\mathbf{K}\mathbf{E}(\mathbf{K}) &= - i\omega\mu_0\mu\mathbf{H}(\mathbf{K}) - \mathbf{M}(\mathbf{K}) \quad ,\\
- i\mathbf{K}\mathbf{H}(\mathbf{K}) &= i\omega\epsilon_0\epsilon\mathbf{E}(\mathbf{K}) + \mathbf{J}(\mathbf{K}) \quad ,
\end{aligned}
\right\} \tag{104.1}
$$

from which we further obtain,

$$
\left.
\begin{aligned}
\mathbf{E}(\mathbf{K}) &= - \frac{\epsilon^{-1}}{i\omega\epsilon_0} [i\mathbf{K}\mathbf{H}(\mathbf{K}) + \mathbf{J}(\mathbf{K})] \quad ,\\
\mathbf{H}(\mathbf{K}) &= \frac{\mu^{-1}}{i\omega\mu_0} [i\mathbf{K}\mathbf{E}(\mathbf{K}) - \mathbf{M}(\mathbf{K})] \quad .
\end{aligned}
\right\} \tag{104.2}
$$

By substituting these expressions back into eqs. (104.1) and some suitable rearrangements there results,

$$
\left.
\begin{aligned}
(\mathbf{K}\mu^{-1}\mathbf{K} + k_0^2\epsilon)\ \mathbf{E}(\mathbf{K}) &= i\omega\mu_0\mathbf{J}(\mathbf{K}) - i\mathbf{K}\mu^{-1}\mathbf{M}(\mathbf{K}) \quad ,\\
(\mathbf{K}\epsilon^{-1}\mathbf{K} + k_0^2\mu)\ \mathbf{H}(\mathbf{K}) &= i\mathbf{K}\epsilon^{-1}\mathbf{J}(\mathbf{K}) + i\omega\epsilon_0\mathbf{M}(\mathbf{K})
\end{aligned}
\right\} \tag{104.3}
$$

or in matrix form,

$$
\begin{pmatrix} \mathbf{W}_E & 0 \\ 0 & \mathbf{W}_H \end{pmatrix}
\begin{bmatrix} \mathbf{E}(\mathbf{K}) \\ \mathbf{H}(\mathbf{K}) \end{bmatrix}
=
\begin{pmatrix} i\omega\mu_0\mathbf{I} & - i\mathbf{K}\mu^{-1} \\ i\mathbf{K}\epsilon^{-1} & i\omega\epsilon_0\mathbf{I} \end{pmatrix}
\begin{bmatrix} \mathbf{J}(\mathbf{K}) \\ \mathbf{M}(\mathbf{K}) \end{bmatrix} \quad . \tag{104.4}
$$

The inverse of the matrix on the left is easily established since it is diagonal, therefore,

$$
\begin{bmatrix} \mathbf{E}(\mathbf{K}) \\ \mathbf{H}(\mathbf{K}) \end{bmatrix}
=
\begin{pmatrix} \mathbf{W}_E^{-1} & 0 \\ 0 & \mathbf{W}_H^{-1} \end{pmatrix}
\begin{pmatrix} i\omega\mu_0\mathbf{I} & - i\mathbf{K}\mu^{-1} \\ i\mathbf{K}\epsilon^{-1} & i\omega\epsilon_0\mathbf{I} \end{pmatrix}
\begin{bmatrix} \mathbf{J}(\mathbf{K}) \\ \mathbf{M}(\mathbf{K}) \end{bmatrix} \quad . \tag{104.5}
$$

By comparing eq. (103.9) with eq. (104.5) and using eq. (103.10) we find

$$\begin{bmatrix} \mathbf{g}_{EJ}(\mathbf{K}) & \mathbf{g}_{EM}(\mathbf{K}) \\ \\ \mathbf{g}_{HJ}(\mathbf{K}) & \mathbf{g}_{HM}(\mathbf{K}) \end{bmatrix} \equiv \begin{pmatrix} i\omega\mu_0 \mathbf{W}_E^{-1} & -i\mathbf{W}_E^{-1}\mathbf{K}\mu^{-1} \\ \\ i\mathbf{W}_H^{-1}\mathbf{K}\epsilon^{-1} & i\omega\epsilon_0 \mathbf{W}_H^{-1} \end{pmatrix} , \qquad (104.6)$$

which establishes the relations between $\mathbf{g}_{EJ}(\mathbf{K})$, etc. and the wave matrices, *i.e.*,

$$\begin{aligned} \mathbf{g}_{EJ}(\mathbf{K}) &= i\omega\mu_0 \mathbf{W}_E^{-1} , \\ \mathbf{g}_{EM}(\mathbf{K}) &= -i\mathbf{W}_E^{-1}\mathbf{K}\,\mu^{-1} , \text{ etc.} \end{aligned} \qquad (104.7)$$

We now want to calculate $\mathbf{g}_{EJ}$ and $\mathbf{g}_{HM}$ when $\mu = \mathbf{I}$. From the basic equations (102.15) and (102.16) we can establish the identities,

$$\left.\begin{aligned} k_0^2\mathbf{W}_E^{-1} &= \epsilon^{-1} - \epsilon^{-1}\mathbf{K}\mathbf{W}_H^{-1}\mathbf{K}\epsilon^{-1} , \\ \mathbf{W}_E^{-1}\mathbf{K}\mu^{-1} &= \epsilon^{-1}\mathbf{K}\mathbf{W}_H^{-1} , \\ \mu^{-1}\mathbf{K}\mathbf{W}_E^{-1} &= \mathbf{W}_H^{-1}\mathbf{K}\epsilon^{-1} , \\ k_0^2\mathbf{W}_H^{-1} &= \mu^{-1} - \mu^{-1}\mathbf{K}\mathbf{W}_E^{-1}\mathbf{K}\mu^{-1} . \end{aligned}\right\} \qquad (104.8)$$

We have already calculated $\mathbf{W}_E^{-1}$ for $\mu = \mathbf{I}$, and from the last identity of eqs. (104.8) we find,

$$\begin{aligned} k_0^2\mathbf{W}_H^{-1} &= \mathbf{I} - \mathbf{K}\mathbf{W}_E^{-1}\mathbf{K} \\ &= \frac{k_0^2}{\det \mathbf{W}_E} \left[(\mathbf{n}'\epsilon\mathbf{n})K^4\mathbf{n}\mathbf{n}' - K^2k_0^2\mathbf{S} + k_0^4\mathbf{I} \det \epsilon \right] \end{aligned} \qquad (104.9)$$

where $\mathbf{n}$ is a column vector, $\mathbf{n}'$ its transpose is therefore a row vector and hence the scalar, *i.e.*, quadratic form,

$$\mathbf{n}'\epsilon\mathbf{n} = (n_1^2 + n_2^2)\epsilon_1 + n_3^2\epsilon_3 , \qquad (104.10)$$

$$\det \epsilon = \epsilon_3(\epsilon_1^2 - \epsilon_2^2) \quad ; \qquad (104.11)$$

the matrix $\mathbf{S}$ is more involved.

$$
\mathbf{S} = \begin{bmatrix} \epsilon_1\epsilon_3 + n_1^2(\epsilon_1^2 - \epsilon_2^2) & -in_3^2\epsilon_2\epsilon_3 + n_1n_2(\epsilon_1^2 - \epsilon_2^2) & in_2n_3\epsilon_2\epsilon_3 + n_1n_3\epsilon_1\epsilon_3 \\ in_3^2\epsilon_2\epsilon_3 + n_1n_2(\epsilon_1^2 - \epsilon_2^2) & \epsilon_1\epsilon_3 + n_2^2(\epsilon_1^2 - \epsilon_2^2) & n_2n_3\epsilon_1\epsilon_3 - in_1n_3\epsilon_2\epsilon_3 \\ -in_2n_3\epsilon_2\epsilon_3 + n_1n_3\epsilon_1\epsilon_3 & n_2n_3\epsilon_1\epsilon_3 + in_1n_3\epsilon_2\epsilon_3 & 2n_3^2\epsilon_1\epsilon_3 + (n_1^1 + n_2^2)(\epsilon_1^2 - \epsilon_2^2) \end{bmatrix} \tag{104.12}
$$

From eq. (104.6) we obtain

$$
\mathbf{g}_{EJ} = \frac{i\omega\mu_0}{\det \mathbf{W}_E} [K^4\mathbf{nn}' - K^2k_0^2\mathbf{L} + k_0^4\mathbf{e}] \quad , \tag{104.13}
$$

$$
\mathbf{g}_{HM} = \frac{i\omega\mu_0}{\det \mathbf{W}_E} [(\mathbf{n}'\epsilon\mathbf{n})K^4\mathbf{nn}' - K^2k_0^2\mathbf{S} + k_0^4\mathbf{I}\epsilon_3(\epsilon_1^2 - \epsilon_2^2)] \quad . \tag{104.14}
$$

Power Dissipation and Quadratic Forms—Before we proceed further with the application of the formal apparatus developed in the foregoing we should consider the connection between power dissipation and some related quadratic forms. These quadratic forms permit us to systematically classify the dissipative properties of the propagating media, *i.e.*, media which can support propagation.

To fix the ideas here we shall at the risk of repeating ourselves (see Chapter 5) first consider the expression for the Poynting vector in vacuum. We further assume $\mathbf{J} = \mathbf{M} = \rho = 0$, where ρ is here the charge density, *i.e.*, we take div $\mathbf{D} = 0$. Thus,

$$
\mathbf{s} = \mathbf{E}\mathbf{x}\mathbf{H} \quad ,
$$

and in a time interval dt, the influx of energy per unit volume is given by

$$
-\operatorname{div} \mathbf{s}\, dt = \left(\mathbf{H} \cdot \frac{\partial \mathbf{B}}{\partial t} + \mathbf{E} \cdot \frac{\partial \mathbf{D}}{\partial t}\right) dt \quad , \tag{104.15}
$$

whose interpretation has already been given. For a lossless medium in which the process of building up an electromagnetic field is a reversible one (an idealized situation) we can establish the mathematical criterion for it quite simply. This criterion is used in thermodynamics, mechanics, etc. and is nothing more than the statement that the right side of eq. (104.15) is an exact differential. This means that there exists a function $u(t)$ such that

$$\left(\mathbf{H} \cdot \frac{\partial \mathbf{B}}{\partial t} + \mathbf{E} \cdot \frac{\partial \mathbf{D}}{\partial t}\right) dt = du \quad , \tag{104.16}$$

in which $u(t)$ is a function of the time derivatives of the field but not an explicit function of t. The net energy absorbed is therefore in this case,*

$$-\int_{t_0}^{t} \operatorname{div} \mathbf{s}\, dt = u(t_0) - u(t) \quad . \tag{104.17}$$

For isotropic media, in which $\mathbf{B} = \mu\mathbf{H}$, $\mathbf{D} = \epsilon\mathbf{E}$ with ϵ, μ scalar functions of position only, eq. (104.16) gives,

$$\frac{1}{2} \frac{d}{dt} (\mathbf{H} \cdot \mathbf{B} + \mathbf{E} \cdot \mathbf{D})\, dt = du$$

or,

$$\frac{1}{2} (\mathbf{H} \cdot \mathbf{B} + \mathbf{E} \cdot \mathbf{D}) = u \quad . \tag{104.18}$$

For anisotropic media, in which μ, ϵ are tensors whose elements are functions of position only the following expression can be verified,

$$-\operatorname{div} \mathbf{s}\, dt = \frac{1}{2} d(\mathbf{H} \cdot \mathbf{B} + \mathbf{E} \cdot \mathbf{D}) + \frac{1}{2}\left[\mathbf{H} \cdot (\mu - \mu') \frac{\partial \mathbf{H}}{\partial t} + \mathbf{E} \cdot (\epsilon - \epsilon') \frac{\partial \mathbf{E}}{\partial t}\right] dt \tag{104.19}$$

where the prime indicates the transpose of the tensors. It is clear from this expression that only if the second term on the right side vanishes the left side will be an exact differential. Consequently, the necessary and sufficient condition for this to hold is that both

$$\left.\begin{aligned} \mu &= \mu' \quad , \\ \epsilon &= \epsilon' \quad , \end{aligned}\right\} \tag{104.20}$$

---

* For fields such that the values of **E**, **D**, **H**, **B** and their time derivatives are equal at t_0 and t, the net energy absorbed is clearly zero. So, for a complete cycle of field variation the power absorbed is zero. See, A. Tonning, *loc. cit.*

i.e., the tensors are symmetrical,* which is the condition for a lossless medium, and the energy density is then also expressed by eq. (104.18).

A more general type of linear medium can be conceived than those given above, namely one in which, say $\mathbf{D}$ depends on its previous history,

$$\mathbf{D}(t) = \int_{-\infty}^{t} \mathbf{K}(t-\tau)\mathbf{E}(\tau)d\tau \quad . \tag{104.21}$$

If we put $\mathbf{E}(t) = Re(\mathbf{E}e^{i\omega t})$ with $\mathbf{E}$ now complex, and if $\epsilon(\omega)$ is the Fourier Transform of $\mathbf{K}(\tau)$ we can write,

$$\mathbf{D} = \epsilon(\omega)\mathbf{E} \tag{104.22}$$

all quantities are now complex, *i.e.*, ($\mathbf{E}$, $\mathbf{H}$, $\mathbf{B}$, $\mathbf{D}$) and $\epsilon(\omega)$. We can, without introducing any specific constitutive relations deduce conditions for a lossless medium. We use time harmonic fields for the discussion, and complex amplitudes. Thus,

$$\left.\begin{aligned} -\operatorname{div}\overline{\mathbf{s}} &= -\frac{1}{2} Re \operatorname{div}(\mathbf{ExH}^*)dt \quad , \\ &= -\frac{1}{2} Re \operatorname{div}(\mathbf{ExH}e^{2i\omega t})dt \quad , \end{aligned}\right\} \tag{104.23}$$

if this is to be an exact differential the integral over one cycle must vanish. Because of the periodicity of the fields in time, we have after integrating over one period the result,

$$Re \operatorname{div}(\mathbf{ExH}^*) = 0 \tag{104.24}$$

as the condition for a lossless medium. Now recall that Maxwell's equations

$$\nabla\mathbf{xE} + i\omega\mathbf{B} = 0 \quad ,$$

$$\nabla\mathbf{xH} - i\omega\mathbf{D} = 0 \quad ,$$

imply

$$\operatorname{Im}(\mathbf{E}^* \cdot \mathbf{D} + \mathbf{H}^* \cdot \mathbf{B}) = 0 \quad , \tag{104.25}$$

* We have in mind here crystalline media.

and we can state, for a lossless medium,

$$\frac{1}{4}(\mathbf{E}^* \cdot \mathbf{D} + \mathbf{H}^* \cdot \mathbf{B}) \equiv \overline{u} \qquad (104.26)$$

is real for arbitrary complex fields and arbitrary real ω. If now we introduce the constitutive relations defined through tensors, ϵ, μ, a lossless medium implies $\epsilon = (\epsilon')^*$, $\mu = (\mu')^*$, that is, the tensors are Hermitian, and conversely.*

We want to construct now the quadratic forms which characterize the loss properties of a plasma medium. We start with the expression for the average complex power fluxing from a unit volume enclosing the sources of the field. For convenience we repeat the expression here,

$$\frac{1}{2}\,\mathrm{div}\,(\mathbf{E}\mathrm{x}\mathbf{H}^*) = \frac{1}{2}(\mathbf{H}^* \cdot \mathrm{curl}\,\mathbf{E} - \mathbf{E} \cdot \mathrm{curl}\,\mathbf{H}^*) \quad , \qquad (104.27)$$

and from eqs. (102.1), we can write,

$$\mathrm{div}\,(\mathbf{E}\mathrm{x}\mathbf{H}^*) = i\omega[\mathbf{E} \cdot \epsilon_0 \epsilon^* \mathbf{E}^* - \mathbf{H}^* \cdot \mu_0 \mu \mathbf{H}] - \mathbf{E} \cdot \mathbf{J}^* - \mathbf{H}^* \cdot \mathbf{M} \quad . \qquad (104.28)$$

Let us consider this expression in matrix form, and note that

$$\mathbf{E} \cdot \epsilon^* \mathbf{E}^* = \mathbf{E}'\epsilon^*\mathbf{E}^* ; \quad \mathbf{H}^* \cdot \mu\mathbf{H} = \mathbf{H}^{*\prime}\mu\mathbf{H} \quad ,$$
$$\mathbf{E} \,.\, \mathbf{J}^* = \mathbf{E}'\mathbf{J}^*, \quad \mathbf{H}^* \cdot \mathbf{M} = \mathbf{H}^{*\prime}\mathbf{M} \quad , \qquad (104.28')$$

since eq. (104.28) is a scalar equation its value is not changed by taking the transpose, hence we can write

$$\mathrm{div}\,(\mathbf{E}\mathrm{x}\mathbf{H}^*) = i\omega[\epsilon_0 \mathbf{E}^{*\prime}\epsilon^{*\prime}\mathbf{E} - \mu_0 \mathbf{H}^{*\prime}\mu\mathbf{H}] - \mathbf{J}^{*\prime}\mathbf{E} - \mathbf{M}'\mathbf{H}^* \quad . \qquad (104.29)$$

First put $\mathbf{J} = \mathbf{M} = 0$ and introduce Q as the power dissipated per unit volume; also define

---

* Strictly speaking, if the energy density of a lossless medium is defined as the energy absorbed by the medium during the build up of the field, the procedure given above is not valid for harmonic time varying fields. This is so, because at $t = -\infty$, the fields do not vanish. By a suitable modification of replacing the real frequency by $\omega + i\nu$, $\nu \ll \omega$, a more general expression can be derived for the energy density, corresponding to u.

$$\left.\begin{aligned} \epsilon^{*\prime} &= \epsilon_1 + i\epsilon_2; \quad \mu = \mu_1 - i\mu_2 ; \\ \epsilon_1 &= \frac{1}{2}(\epsilon + \epsilon^{*\prime}); \quad \mu_1 = \frac{1}{2}(\mu + \mu^{*\prime}) ; \\ \epsilon_2 &= \frac{1}{2i}(\epsilon^{*\prime} - \epsilon); \quad \mu_2 = \frac{1}{2i}(\mu^{*\prime} - \mu) ; \end{aligned}\right\} \tag{104.30}$$

where ϵ_1, ϵ_2, μ_1, μ_2 are Hermitian matrices, that is, $\epsilon_1 = \epsilon_1^{*\prime}$ etc.,* hence

$$\begin{aligned} \mathrm{div}\,(\mathbf{E}\mathrm{x}\mathbf{H}^*) &= i\omega[\epsilon_0\mathbf{E}^{*\prime}(\epsilon_1 + i\epsilon_2)\mathbf{E} - \mu_0\mathbf{H}^{*\prime}(\mu_1 - i\mu_2)\mathbf{H}] \\ &= \omega[-\epsilon_0\mathbf{E}^{*\prime}\epsilon_2\mathbf{E} + i\epsilon_0\mathbf{E}^{*\prime}\epsilon_1\mathbf{E} - \mu_0\mathbf{H}^{*\prime}\mu_2\mathbf{H} - i\mu_0\mathbf{H}^{*\prime}\mu_1\mathbf{H}] \ . \end{aligned} \tag{104.31}$$

We define Q by,

$$Q = \frac{\omega}{2}[\epsilon_0\mathbf{E}^{*\prime}\epsilon_2\mathbf{E} + \mu_0\mathbf{H}^{*\prime}\mu_2\mathbf{H}] \tag{104.32}$$

which is a real quantity because ϵ_2 and μ_2 are Hermitian, that is, $Q = Q^*$. We recognize Q as a quadratic form in **E**, **H**.

For a lossless medium $Q = 0$ for all **E**, **H** and it follows that both $\epsilon_2 = \mu_2 = 0$, therefore ϵ and μ are Hermitian.

For a lossy medium, Q must be positive, *i.e.*, $Q > 0$ for all non-zero values of **E**, **H**. The conditions for this are easier to see if we cast Q into a more general form. We define the matrix

$$\gamma = \begin{pmatrix} \epsilon_0\epsilon_2 & 0 \\ 0 & \mu_0\mu_2 \end{pmatrix} \tag{104.33}$$

and put,

$$\mathbf{F} = \begin{pmatrix} \mathbf{E} \\ \mathbf{H} \end{pmatrix} \quad , \tag{104.34}$$

---

* The fact that these matrices are Hermitian can be verified directly from the structure of ϵ and μ as given by eqs. (102.2) and (102.3). Of course the theorem is true for any matrix.

then Q takes the form

$$Q = \frac{\omega}{2}\mathbf{F}^{*\prime}\gamma\mathbf{F} \equiv \frac{\omega}{2}\gamma_{ij}F_i^*F_j \quad (\text{sum on } i,j = 1,2, \ldots, 6) \quad . \tag{104.35}$$

Now we recall a basic theorem on quadratic forms which says that a quadratic form is positive definite if and only if all of its principal minors are positive. This means that the determinants

$$\gamma_{11} > 0, \quad \begin{vmatrix} \gamma_{11} & \gamma_{12} \\ \gamma_{21} & \gamma_{22} \end{vmatrix} > 0, \quad \begin{vmatrix} \gamma_{11} & \gamma_{12} & \gamma_{13} \\ \gamma_{21} & \gamma_{22} & \gamma_{23} \\ \gamma_{31} & \gamma_{32} & \gamma_{33} \end{vmatrix} > 0 \quad ,$$

$$\det \gamma > 0. \tag{104.36}$$

an analogous theorem applied to quadratic forms of Hermitian matrices as in the above we find that for a lossy plasma, (non-magnetic),

$$\text{Im}\ \epsilon_1 < 0, \quad \text{Im}\ \epsilon_3 < 0, \quad (\text{Im}\ \epsilon_1)^2 > (\text{Im}\ \epsilon_2)^2 \quad . \tag{104.37}$$

If the medium is characterized by both ϵ, μ, the inequalities (104.37) are supplemented by the same ones with ϵ replaced everywhere by μ.

If we consider as a special case now plane wave propagation and put $\mathbf{K} = \mathbf{K}_1 - i\mathbf{K}_2$, where $\mathbf{K}$ represents either the ordinary or extraordinary mode we find from eq. (104.31) that

$$2|\mathbf{K}_2|\mathbf{n} \cdot \frac{1}{2}\text{Re}(\mathbf{ExH}^*) = Q \tag{104.38}$$

and for a lossy medium in which $Q > 0$, we must have

$$\text{sign}\ |\mathbf{K}_2| = \text{sign}\ \mathbf{n} \cdot \frac{1}{2}\text{Re}\ (\mathbf{ExH}^*) \quad . \tag{104.39}$$

If the medium is lossless, $Q = 0$, eq. (104.38) implies that either $|\mathbf{K}_2| = 0$ or $\mathbf{n}$ is perpendicular to the mean Poynting vector. In the first case there is no extinction of the wave and in the latter case the wave is cut off, *i.e.*, it does not transport any power.

105. WAVE EXCITATION

In a great many fields of application it is important to know quantitatively what happens when a bounded charge distribution in space is set into motion. In particular, we should like to know what modes will be excited in a magneto-ionic medium. For this, we examine the electric field resulting from a system of oscillating electric dipoles of equal dipole moment and constrained to lie in a plane.* We can calculate the $\mathbf{E}(\mathbf{r})$ field from a knowledge of $\mathbf{G}_{EJ}$ which is now given explicitly by

$$\mathbf{G}_{EJ}(\mathbf{r},\mathbf{r}') = \frac{i}{8\pi^3\omega\epsilon_0}\int d\mathbf{K}\,\frac{K^4\mathbf{n}\mathbf{n}' - k_0^2K^2\mathbf{L} + k_0^2\mathbf{e}}{\mathbf{n}'\epsilon\mathbf{n}(K^2 - K_1^2)(K^2 - K_2^2)}\exp\left[-i\mathbf{K}\cdot(\mathbf{r}-\mathbf{r}')\right], \tag{105.1}$$

but for the case at hand it is preferable to use the transform, namely $\mathbf{g}_{EJ}$. For simplicity of calculation we assume that the plane continuous dipole configuration is represented by a current distribution of the form,

$$\mathbf{J}(\mathbf{r}) = \mathbf{I}\delta(\mathbf{m}\cdot\mathbf{r}) . \tag{105.2}$$

Here, $\delta(\mathbf{m}\cdot\mathbf{r})$ is the delta function, $\mathbf{m}$ defines the normal to the plane (which contains the origin) of the dipole distribution and $\mathbf{I}$ is a complex constant vector whose value is determined by the dipoles polarization and amplitude density. Eqs. (103.1) and (103.8) give

$$\mathbf{E}(\mathbf{r}) = \frac{1}{8\pi^3}\int \mathbf{g}_{EJ}(\mathbf{K})\mathbf{I}e^{-i\mathbf{K}\cdot(\mathbf{r}-\mathbf{r}')}\delta(\mathbf{m}\cdot\mathbf{r}')d\mathbf{r}'d\mathbf{K} . \tag{105.3}$$

At this point we utilize the property of the δ-function,†

$$\delta(\alpha x) = \frac{1}{|\alpha|}\delta(x) , \tag{105.4}$$

which when applied to $\delta(\mathbf{m}\cdot\mathbf{r}')$ leads to

$$\delta(\mathbf{m}\cdot\mathbf{r}') = \frac{1}{|m_3|}\delta\left(\frac{m_1}{m_3}x_1' + \frac{m_2}{m_3}x_2' + x_3'\right) \tag{105.5}$$

---

* R. Q. Twiss and J. A. Roberts have analyzed the electromagnetic radiation from electrons rotating in an ionized medium, (magneto-ionic) under the action of a uniform magnetic field. They show that although the radiation is emitted predominantly in the extraordinary mode the ordinary mode is also weakly excited even for a vanishingly small electron density background plasma. The methods employed however are mathematically intricate. Austr. J. Physics, Vol. 11, pp. 424-496, (1958).

† Landau and Lifshitz, Quantum Mechanics, Non Relativistic Theory, p. 17, Addison-Wesley, 1958.

where $m_3 \neq 0$, which is equivalent to assuming that the dipole distribution does not lie in a plane containing the x_3' axis. Substituting this quantity (105.5) into eq. (105.3);

$$\mathbf{E}(\mathbf{r}) = \frac{1}{8\pi^3|m_3|}\int \mathbf{g}_{EJ}(\mathbf{K})\mathbf{I}\delta\left(\frac{m_1}{m_3}x_1' + \frac{m_2}{m_3}x_2' + x_3'\right)e^{-i\mathbf{K}\cdot(\mathbf{r}-\mathbf{r}')}d\mathbf{r}'d\mathbf{K} ,$$

$$= \frac{1}{8\pi^3|m_3|}\int \mathbf{g}_{EJ}(\mathbf{K})\mathbf{I}e^{-i\mathbf{K}\cdot\mathbf{r}}d\mathbf{K}\int_{-\infty}^{\infty}\delta\left(\frac{m_1}{m_3}x_1' + \frac{m_2}{m_3}x_2' + x_3'\right)e^{i\mathbf{K}\cdot\mathbf{r}'}d\mathbf{r}' , \tag{105.6}$$

the last integral can be written as

$$\frac{1}{4\pi^2}\iint_{-\infty}^{\infty}dx_1'dx_2'\int_{-\infty}^{\infty}\delta\left(\frac{m_1}{m_3}x_1' + \frac{m_2}{m_3}x_2' + x_3'\right)e^{i\mathbf{K}\cdot\mathbf{r}'}dx_3'$$

$$= \frac{1}{4\pi^2}\iint_{-\infty}^{\infty}dx_1'dx_2'e^{i\{[K_1-(m_1/m_3)K_3]x_1'+[K_2-(m_2/m_3)K_3]x_2'\}}$$

$$= \delta\left(K_1 - \frac{m_1}{m_3}K_3\right)\delta\left(K_2 - \frac{m_2}{m_3}K_3\right) ,$$

by eqs. (103.5) and (103.6), and by defining

$$K_m = \frac{K_3}{m_3} \tag{105.7}$$

and a repeated application of eq. (103.5) we can finally express eq. (105.6) in the form,

$$\mathbf{E}(\mathbf{r}) = \frac{1}{2\pi}\int_{-\infty}^{\infty}\mathbf{g}_{EJ}(K_m\mathbf{m})\mathbf{I}e^{-iK_m\mathbf{m}\cdot\mathbf{r}}\,dK_m , \tag{105.8}$$

the argument in all functions is now K_m. From the expression for $\mathbf{g}_{EJ}$ from eq. (104.13), and from eq. (103.14) we must now express all of the quantities as functions of $\mathbf{m}$ and K_m, hence

$$\mathbf{g}_{EJ}(K_m\mathbf{m}) = \frac{i\omega\mu_0}{\det.\mathbf{W}_E}[K_m^4\mathbf{mm}' - K_m^2k_0^2\mathbf{L}(\mathbf{m}) + k_0^4\mathbf{e}] \quad ,$$

now from eq. (102..21') we can easily verify that if $\mathbf{n} = (\sin\theta\cos\varphi, \sin\theta\sin\varphi, \cos\theta)$ we can write $\epsilon_1\sin^2\theta + \epsilon_3\cos^2\theta = \mathbf{n}'\epsilon\mathbf{n}$ so that

$$\det\mathbf{W}_E = k_0^2\mathbf{n}'\epsilon\mathbf{n}(K^2 - K_1^2)(K^2 - K_2^2)$$

and in terms of K_m and $\mathbf{m}$ we can now assert that

$$\mathbf{E}(\mathbf{r}) = \frac{i}{2\pi\omega\epsilon_0\mathbf{m}'\epsilon\mathbf{m}}\int_{-\infty}^{\infty}\frac{(K_m^4\mathbf{mm}' - K_m^2k_0^2\mathbf{L}(\mathbf{m}) + k_0^4\mathbf{e})e^{-iK_m\mathbf{m}\cdot\mathbf{r}}\mathbf{I}}{(K_m^2 - K_{m1}^2)(K_m^2 - K_{m2}^2)}dK_m \quad . \tag{105.9}$$

In this formula K_{m1}, K_{m2} are the propagation constants of the ordinary and extraordinary modes with wave normal $\mathbf{m}$, defined by eq. (102.22). This integral is best evaluated by using the calculus of residues from complex function theory. It is however instructive to carry out some of the detail for this situation. We make use of an elementary theorem in complex function theory which states that if $f(K_m)$ is an analytic function in the complex K_m-plane whose only singularities are simple poles at points K_{m1}, K_{m2}, ... with respective residues a_1, a_2, ... etc., then*

$$f(K_m) = f(0) + \sum_1^{\infty}\left(\frac{a_j}{K_m - K_{mj}} + \frac{a_j}{K_{mj}}\right) \quad . \tag{105.10}$$

In our case we consider separately the functions K_m^4/Δ, K_m^2/Δ and Δ^{-1}, where $\Delta \equiv (K_m^2 - K_{m1}^2)(K_m^2 - K_{m1}^2)$; in each case the expansion of $f(K_m)$ is finite so that we have the representation in partial fractions.

By definition, the residue of K_m^4/Δ at a pole K_{mj} is $\lim\,(K_m - K_{mj})K_m^4/\Delta$ as $K_m \to K_{mj}$. Since the poles are at $\pm K_{m1}$, $\pm K_{m2}$ in all of these functions the residues are respectively at these points, for

$$\left.\begin{array}{llll} K_m^4/\Delta: & K_{m1}^3/2\Delta_{1,2} \;, & -K_{m1}^3/2\Delta_{1,2} \;, & -K_{m2}^3/2\Delta_{1,2} \;, & +K_{m2}^3/2\Delta_{1,2} \\ K_m^2/\Delta: & K_{m1}/2\Delta_{1,2} \;, & -K_{m1}/2\Delta_{1,2} \;, & -K_{m2}/2\Delta_{1,2} \;, & +K_{m2}/2\Delta_{1,2} \\ 1/\Delta: & 1/K_{m1}2\Delta_{1,2} \;, & -1/K_{m1}2\Delta_{1,2} \;, & -1/K_{m2}2\Delta_{1,2} \;, & +1/K_{m2}2\Delta_{1,2} \end{array}\right\} \tag{105.11}$$

where $\Delta_{1,2} = (K_{m1}^2 - K_{m2}^2)$.

* Morse and Feshbach, Methods of Theoretical Physics, Vol. I, p. 383 McGraw-Hill Co., 1953.

Hence, by eq. (105.10),

$$\left.\begin{aligned}
\frac{K_m^4}{\Delta} &= \frac{1}{2\Delta_{1,2}}\left(\frac{K_{m1}^3}{K_m - K_{m1}} - \frac{K_{m1}^3}{K_m + K_{m1}} - \frac{K_{m2}^3}{K_m - K_{m2}} + \frac{K_{m2}^3}{K_m + K_{m2}}\right) + 1 \quad , \\
\frac{K_m^2}{\Delta} &= \frac{1}{2\Delta_{1,2}}\left(\frac{K_{m1}}{K_m - K_{m1}} - \frac{K_{m1}}{K_m + K_{m1}} - \frac{K_{m2}}{K_m - K_{m2}} + \frac{K_{m2}}{K_m + K_{m2}}\right) \quad , \\
\frac{1}{\Delta} &= \frac{1}{2\Delta_{1,2}}\left(\frac{1/K_{m1}}{K_m - K_{m1}} - \frac{1/K_{m1}}{K_m + K_{m1}} - \frac{1/K_{m2}}{K_m - K_{m2}} + \frac{1/K_{m2}}{K_m + K_{m2}}\right) \quad ,
\end{aligned}\right\} \tag{105.12}$$

we note that in the second equation of (105.12) there is no constant term in the expansion as in the first equation of this set, likewise for the third equation. The appearance of the constant term in the first equation, as we shall see, gives rise to a delta function source of the resultant $\mathbf{E}(\mathbf{r})$ field.

We can now apply the residue theorem, but first noting that since the medium is assumed lossy this implies that the imaginary parts of K_{m1} and K_{m2} are negative. Thus to effect the integration of eq. (105.9) we close the contour by a semicircle of infinite radius in the lower half of the complex K_m-plane. Thus the only poles of interest are K_{m1} and K_{m2}, the remaining poles $-K_{m1}$, $-K_{m2}$ are now excluded, they lie outside the contour of integration, in the upper half plane. The case in which the imaginary parts of K_{m1} and K_{m2} are positive is interesting in the sense of growing waves, but we shall not discuss this here. The residue theorem now reads,

$$\int_{-\infty}^{\infty} e^{-i(\mathbf{m}\cdot\mathbf{r})} dK_m + \int_{-\infty}^{\infty} \frac{K_m^4}{\Delta} e^{-iK_m(\mathbf{m}\cdot\mathbf{r})} dK_m = 2\pi i \sum \text{Residue of } \frac{K_m^4}{\Delta} e^{-iK_m(\mathbf{m}\cdot\mathbf{r})} \text{ at } K_{mj} \quad .$$

and similarly for the remaining functions, except for the first integral above. The theorem applies either for $(\mathbf{m}\cdot\mathbf{r}) \gtrless 0$ and so we shall replace $\mathbf{m}\cdot\mathbf{r}$ by $|\mathbf{m}\cdot\mathbf{r}|$, also there are no singularities of any of the integrands on the real axis of the K_m plane. Carrying out the integrations and replacing $\int_{-\infty}^{\infty} e^{-iK_m(\mathbf{m}\cdot\mathbf{r})} dK_m$ by $2\pi\delta(\mathbf{m}\cdot\mathbf{r})$ we finally have,

$$\mathbf{E}(\mathbf{r}) = \frac{1}{2\omega\epsilon_0 \mathbf{m}'\epsilon\mathbf{m}} \left\{ 2i\delta(\mathbf{m}\cdot\mathbf{r})\mathbf{m}\mathbf{m}' + \frac{1}{(K_{m1}^2 - K_{m2}^2)} \left[\mathbf{D}_{EJ}(K_{m1}\mathbf{m}) \frac{e^{-iK_{m1}\,\mathbf{m}\cdot\mathbf{r}}}{K_{m1}} - \mathbf{D}_{EJ}(K_{m2}\mathbf{m}) \frac{e^{-iK_{m2}\,\mathbf{m}\cdot\mathbf{r}}}{K_{m2}} \right] \right\} \mathbf{I} \qquad (105.13)$$

where,

$$\mathbf{D}_{EJ}(K_m\mathbf{m}) \equiv K_m^4\mathbf{m}\mathbf{m}' - K_m^2 k_0^2 \mathbf{L}(\mathbf{m}) + k_0^4 \mathbf{e} \quad .$$

This result shows that both the ordinary and extraordinary modes, *i.e.*, plane waves with wave normal **m** and −**m** are excited. The amplitude of the field $\mathbf{E}(\mathbf{r})$ is determined by the amplitude and polarization of **I**. We mention that the plane of polarization of **I** itself need not coincide with the plane of the dipole distribution. The excited waves decay with distance from the dipole source since the K_{mi} are in general complex. The polarization of the excited waves, however, depend only on the constants of the medium and the wave normal but not on the polarization of the source.

106. RADIATED POWER

In this section we shall consider the power radiated by alternating current distributions, both electric and magnetic. From equation (104.29) the average complex power radiated by a volume element $dx_1 dx_2 dx_3$ with source distributions $\mathbf{J}(\mathbf{r}),\mathbf{M}(\mathbf{r})$ is

$$dP = -\frac{1}{2}(\mathbf{J}^{*\prime}\mathbf{E} + \mathbf{H}^{*\prime}\mathbf{M})dx_1 dx_2 dx_3 \tag{106.1}$$

and the total power radiated is

$$P = -\frac{1}{2}\int(\mathbf{J}^{*\prime}\mathbf{E} + \mathbf{H}^{*\prime}\mathbf{M})d\mathbf{r} \quad . \tag{106.2}$$

Eqs. (103.1) and (103.2) lead to

$$P = -\frac{1}{2}\int d\mathbf{r}d\mathbf{r}'\int[\mathbf{J}^{*\prime}(\mathbf{r})\mathbf{G}_{EJ}\mathbf{J}(\mathbf{r}') + \mathbf{J}^{*\prime}(\mathbf{r})\mathbf{G}_{EM}\mathbf{M}(\mathbf{r}') + \mathbf{J}^{*\prime}(\mathbf{r}')\mathbf{G}^{*\prime}\mathbf{M}(\mathbf{r}) + \mathbf{M}^{*\prime}(\mathbf{r}')\mathbf{G}^{*\prime}\mathbf{M}(\mathbf{r})] \tag{106.3}$$

by utilizing the Fourier Transforms of $\mathbf{J}$, $\mathbf{M}$ and the Green's tensors we can write,

$$P = -\frac{1}{16\pi^3}\int d\mathbf{r}d\mathbf{r}'d\mathbf{K}d\mathbf{K}'d\mathbf{K}''\mathbf{J}^{*\prime}(\mathbf{K})\mathbf{g}_{EJ}(\mathbf{K})\mathbf{J}(\mathbf{K}'')e^{-i[\mathbf{r}\cdot(\mathbf{K}-\mathbf{K}')-\mathbf{r}'\cdot(\mathbf{K}-\mathbf{K}'')]} + . \tag{106.4}$$

where the dashes indicate the other integrals. In all there exist fifteen integrals, but if the integrals over $\mathbf{r}$ and $\mathbf{r}'$ are evaluated by the use of the delta function, *e.g.*, by equations of the form,

$$\int d\mathbf{r}e^{-i\mathbf{r}\cdot[\mathbf{K}-\mathbf{K}']} = 8\pi^3\delta(\mathbf{K}-\mathbf{K}') \quad ;$$

the fifteen integrals are reduced to only three, by the further integrations over $\mathbf{K}'$ and $\mathbf{K}''$. The result of these operations yields

$$P = -4\pi^3\int d\mathbf{K}[\mathbf{J}^{*\prime}(\mathbf{K})\mathbf{g}_{EJ}\mathbf{J}(\mathbf{K}) + \mathbf{J}^{*\prime}(\mathbf{K})\mathbf{g}_{EM}\mathbf{M}(\mathbf{K}) + (\mathbf{M}^{*\prime}(\mathbf{K})\mathbf{g}_{HJ}\mathbf{J}(\mathbf{K}))^* + (\mathbf{M}^{*\prime}(\mathbf{K})\mathbf{g}_{HM}\mathbf{M}(\mathbf{K}))^*] \quad . \tag{106.5}$$

This formula for the radiated power from both electrical and magnetic current distributions simplifies when $\mathbf{M} \equiv 0$ or $\mathbf{J} \equiv 0$. Hence for $\mathbf{M} \equiv 0$, we have

$$P = -4\pi^3 \int \mathbf{J}^{*\prime}(\mathbf{K})\mathbf{g}_{EJ}\mathbf{J}(\mathbf{K})\,d\mathbf{K} \tag{106.6}$$

and for $\mathbf{J} \equiv 0$,

$$P = -4\pi^3 \int (\mathbf{M}^{*\prime}(\mathbf{K})\mathbf{g}_{HM}\mathbf{M}(\mathbf{K}))^*\,d\mathbf{K} \quad . \tag{106.7}$$

Thus the power is expressed in terms of the Fourier transforms of the current distributions and the elements of the super matrix $\mathbf{g}$. This form of the result is not unexpected when we consider it in the light of Parseval's relation.* Let us apply the preceding results to the case of an oscillating elementary dipole of moment $\mathbf{p}$ and located at the origin of the coordinate system. We can then write

$$\mathbf{J}(\mathbf{r}) = i\omega\mathbf{p}\delta(\mathbf{r}) \quad . \tag{106.8}$$

The Fourier Transform of this distribution is

$$\mathbf{J}(\mathbf{K}) = \frac{i\omega\mathbf{p}}{8\pi^3} \tag{106.9}$$

and by substitution into eq. (106.6) we obtain,

$$P = -\frac{\omega^2}{16\pi^3}\int (\mathbf{p}^{*\prime}\mathbf{g}_{EJ}\mathbf{p})\,d\mathbf{K} \tag{106.10}$$

now define the matrix

$$\mathbf{Z} = \mathbf{R} + i\mathbf{X} = -\frac{1}{8\pi^3}\int \mathbf{g}_{EJ}\,d\mathbf{K} \tag{106.11}$$

so we can write

$$P = \frac{\omega^2}{2}\,\mathbf{p}^{*\prime}\mathbf{Z}\mathbf{p} \quad . \tag{106.12}$$

---

* Morse and Feshbach, loc. cit. Vol. I, p 456.

Note that the decomposition of $\mathbf{Z}$ is such that $\mathbf{R}$ is Hermitian and $i\mathbf{X}$ is skew or anti-Hermitian ($\mathbf{X}$ is Hermitian). The expression for the power becomes

$$P = \frac{\omega^2}{2} [\mathbf{p}^{*\prime}(\mathbf{R} + i\mathbf{X})\mathbf{p}] \tag{106.13}$$

in which both $\mathbf{p}^{*\prime}\mathbf{R}\mathbf{p}$ and $\mathbf{p}^{*\prime}\mathbf{X}\mathbf{p}$ are real numbers.* To evaluate $\mathbf{Z}$ we consider its explicit form,

$$\mathbf{Z} = -\frac{1}{16\pi^3} \int \frac{i\omega\mu_0 \mathbf{D}_{EJ}(\mathbf{K})}{k_0^2 \mathbf{n}'\boldsymbol{\epsilon}\mathbf{n}(K^2 - K_1^2)(K^2 - K_2^2)} d\mathbf{K} \quad . \tag{106.14}$$

Now introduce spherical coordinates in $\mathbf{K}$ space with volume element

$$d\mathbf{K} = K^2 \sin\theta d\theta dK d\varphi \tag{106.15}$$

and in order to cover all $\mathbf{K}$-space the ranges of K, θ, and φ are respectivel $(-\infty, +\infty)$, $(0, \pi/2)$, $(0, 2\pi)$. Therefore we can write

$$\mathbf{Z} = -\frac{i\omega\mu_0}{8\pi^3 k_0^2} \int_0^{\pi/2} \sin\theta d\theta \int_{-\infty}^{\infty} dK \int_0^{2\pi} d\varphi \frac{K^2 \mathbf{D}_{EJ}(\mathbf{K})}{\mathbf{n}'\boldsymbol{\epsilon}\mathbf{n}(K^2 - K_1^2)(K^2 - K_2^2)} \tag{106.16}$$

and the expansion of the integrand is

$$\frac{K^2 \mathbf{D}_{EJ}(K\mathbf{n})}{(K^2 - K_1^2)(K^2 - K_2^2)} = K^2 \mathbf{n}\mathbf{n}' + (K_1^2 + K_2^2)\mathbf{n}\mathbf{n}' - k_0^2 \mathbf{L} + \frac{1}{(K_1^2 - K_2^2)} \left(\frac{K_1^2 \mathbf{D}_{EJ}(K_1\mathbf{n})}{K^2 - K_1^2} - \frac{K_2^2 \mathbf{D}_{EJ}(K_2\mathbf{n})}{K^2 - K_2^2} \right) . \tag{106.17}$$

Let us also define the matrices

$$\mathbf{N} = \frac{1}{\pi} \int_0^{2\pi} \mathbf{n}\mathbf{n}' d\varphi \quad , \quad \mathbf{M} = \frac{1}{\pi} \int_0^{2\pi} \mathbf{L} d\varphi \ , \tag{106.18}$$

which is permissible since both K_1, K_2 are functions of ω and θ and not of φ. The integration over K is effected by the residue theorem, in which

* This is a direct result of the properties of an Hermitian matrix.

we assume as before that the imaginary parts of K_1, K_2 are negative. The contour is again closed by a semi-circle in the lower half of the complex K-plane. The integrals over K of the terms in the brackets of eq. (106.17) are $-\pi i K_1 \mathbf{D}_{EJ}(K_1\mathbf{n})$, $+\pi i K_2 \mathbf{D}_{EJ}(K_2\mathbf{n})$ respectively. The integrals of the first three terms of eq. (106.17) over K do not exist either in the ordinary sense or in the Cauchy principle value sense. This mathematical fact corresponds to the physical fact that the reactive power defined through the matrix $\mathbf{X}$ for an elementary dipole becomes unbounded as the dimensions of the region containing the dipole tend toward zero. Thus for the elementary dipole, the reactive power loses its meaning. Let us therefore drop these terms since they contribute to $\mathbf{X}$. We shall proceed formally with the remaining terms and later drop all further contributions to the reactive power, therefore retaining only the real power.

We examine the φ integration,

$$\int_0^{2\pi} [K_1\mathbf{D}_{EJ}(K_1\mathbf{n}) - K_2\mathbf{D}_{EJ}(K_2\mathbf{n})]\,d\varphi = \int_0^{2\pi} [(K_1^5 - K_2^5)\mathbf{nn}' - k_0^2(K_1^3 - K_2^3)\mathbf{L}(\mathbf{n}) + k_0^4(K_1 - K_2)\mathbf{e}]\,d\varphi$$

but,

$$\int_0^{2\pi} \mathbf{nn}'\,d\varphi = \pi\mathbf{N} = \pi\begin{pmatrix} \sin^2\theta & 0 & 0 \\ 0 & \sin^2\theta & 0 \\ 0 & 0 & 2\cos^2\theta \end{pmatrix} \qquad (106.19)$$

and,

$$\int_0^{2\pi} \mathbf{L}\,d\varphi = \pi\begin{pmatrix} 2\epsilon_1\sin^2\theta + \epsilon_3(1+\cos^2\theta) & 2i\epsilon_2\sin^2\theta & 0 \\ -2i\epsilon_2\sin^2\theta & 2\epsilon_1\sin^2\theta + \epsilon_3(1+\cos^2\theta) & 0 \\ 0 & 0 & 2\epsilon_1(1+\cos^2\theta) \end{pmatrix}$$

$$= \pi\mathbf{M} \qquad (106.20)$$

note that if the medium is lossless, all ϵ_i are real and hence both $\mathbf{M}$ and $\mathbf{N}$ are Hermitian. The matrix $\mathbf{e}$ is neither a function of θ nor φ [see eq. (103.14)]. The result of the φ integration is $\pi\mathbf{F}$, where,

$$\mathbf{F} = (K_1^5 - K_2^5)\mathbf{N} - k_0^2(K_1^3 - K_2^3)\mathbf{M} + 2k_0^4(K_1 - K_2)\mathbf{e} \qquad (106.21)$$

so that

$$\mathbf{Z} = -\frac{\omega\mu_0}{8\pi k_0^2}\int_0^{\pi/2}\frac{\mathbf{F}\sin\theta}{\mathbf{n}'\epsilon\mathbf{n}(K_1^2 - K_2^2)}\,d\theta \quad . \tag{106.22}$$

If we introduce a new variable $u = \cos\theta$, then since $\mathbf{n}'\epsilon\mathbf{n} = \epsilon_1 \sin^2\theta + \epsilon_3 \cos^2\theta = \epsilon_1 + (\epsilon_3 - \epsilon_1)u^2$ and from eq. (102.22) we find

$$K_1^2 - K_2^2 = \frac{k_0^2\sqrt{(\epsilon_1^2 - \epsilon_2^2 - \epsilon_1\epsilon_3)^2(1 - u^2)^2 + 4\epsilon_2^2\epsilon_3^2u^2}}{\mathbf{n}'\epsilon\mathbf{n}}$$

hence

$$\mathbf{Z} = -\frac{\omega\mu_0}{8\pi k_0^4}\int_0^1\frac{\mathbf{F}(u)}{h(u)}\,du \tag{106.23}$$

where the elements of the matrix $\mathbf{F}$ are now functions of u, and $h(u)$ is the scalar function $\sqrt{\ }$ above. If we multiply numerator and denominator by $[h(u)]^*$ we can write the result as

$$\mathbf{Z} = -\frac{\omega\mu_0}{8\pi k_0^4}\int_0^1\frac{[h(u)]^*\mathbf{F}(u)}{|h(u)|^2}\,du \tag{106.24}$$

and finally, by introducing the characteristic impedance $Z_0 = \sqrt{\mu_0/\epsilon_0}$

$$\mathbf{R} = -\frac{-Z_0}{8\pi k_0^3}\int_0^1\frac{1}{|h(u)|^2}\,\mathrm{Re}\{[h(u)]^*\mathbf{F}(u)\}\mathrm{d}u \quad . \tag{106.25}$$

This is the matrix which must be used to obtain the real power radiated by the elementary dipole. It is clear that in the general case as presented here the problem of calculating the real power is reduced to evaluating the integrals to obtain the matrix elements R_{ij} of $\mathbf{R}$. This is not a trivial task, the difficulty arises from the complicated form of the roots of the Appleton-Hartree equation (102.22).

When the medium is lossless, **M**, **N** and **e** are Hermitian and by introducing the characteristic wavelength $\lambda_0 = 2\pi/k_0$, the result is written in the form,

$$\mathbf{R} = -\frac{\pi}{2}\frac{Z_0}{\lambda_0^2}\int_0^1 \frac{\text{Hermitian part of } \mathbf{F}}{k_0^3[\epsilon_1 + (\epsilon_3 - \epsilon_1)u^2](K_1^2 - K_2^2)}\, du \tag{106.26}$$

by the Hermitian part we mean that in **F** we put all terms with imaginary K_1 or K_2 equal to zero. By looking at the form of the matrices **M**, **N** and **e** we see that **R** has the following form,

$$\mathbf{R} = \begin{pmatrix} R_1 & -iR_2 & 0 \\ iR_2 & R_1 & 0 \\ 0 & 0 & R_3 \end{pmatrix} \tag{106.27}$$

and the elements R are calculated from the formulas,

$$R_i = -\frac{\pi}{2}\frac{Z_0}{\lambda_0^2}\int_0^1 \frac{F_i(u)du}{k_0^3[\epsilon_1 + (\epsilon_3 - \epsilon_1)u^2](K_1^2 - K_2^2)} \qquad (i = 1,2,3)\ , \tag{106.28}$$

where,

$$\left.\begin{aligned} F_1(u) &= \mathrm{Re}\{(K_1^5 - K_2^5)(1 - u^2) - k_0^2(K_1^3 - K_2^3)[2\epsilon_1(1 - u^2) + \epsilon_3(1 + u^2)] \\ &\quad + 2k_0^4(K_1 - K_2)\epsilon_1\epsilon_3\} \\ F_2(u) &= \mathrm{Re}\{- 2k_0^4(K_1^3 - K_2^3)\epsilon_2(1 - u^2) + 2k_0^4(K_1 - K_2)\epsilon_2\epsilon_3\} \\ F_3(u) &= \mathrm{Re}\{2(K_1^5 - K_2^5)u^2 - 2k_0^2(K_1^3 - K_2^3)\epsilon_1(1 + u^2) + 2k_0^4(K_1 - K_2)(\epsilon_1^2 - \epsilon_2^2)\}. \end{aligned}\right\} \tag{106.29}$$

We consider now the radiation from an elementary magnetic dipole. Such a dipole is equivalent to an oscillating current in a small closed loop of a conducting wire. This problem is important from both a theoretical and practical point of view. For this case we take the magnetic current distribution $\mathbf{M}(\mathbf{r})$ which is given by

$$\mathbf{M}(\mathbf{r}) = i\omega\mathbf{p}_m\delta(\mathbf{r}) \tag{106.30}$$

where $\mathbf{p}_m$ is the magnetic dipole moment. As in the case of the electric dipole we first calculate the spatial Fourier transform,

$$\mathbf{M}(\mathbf{K}) = \frac{i\omega\mathbf{p}_m}{8\pi^3} . \quad (106.31)$$

From eq. (106.7) we find analogous to eq. (106.12), the complex conjugate of the power,

$$P^* = \frac{\omega^2}{2}\mathbf{p}^{*\prime}\mathbf{Z}_m\mathbf{p}_m \quad (106.32)$$

where the complex impedance matrix is defined by

$$\mathbf{Z}_m = -\frac{1}{8\pi^3}\int \mathbf{g}_{HM}d\mathbf{K} \equiv \mathbf{R}_m + i\mathbf{X}_m \quad (106.33)$$

which is a decomposition into a Hermitian and skew-Hermitian part. The real power radiated is again obtained from $\mathbf{R}_m$. The matrix $\mathbf{g}_{HM}$ is given by eq. (104.14) and we obtain

$$\mathbf{Z}_m = \frac{-i\omega\epsilon_0}{8\pi^3k_0^2}\int_0^{\pi/2}\sin\theta d\theta\int_{-\infty}^{\infty}dK\int_0^{2\pi}d\varphi\,\frac{K^2(\mathbf{n}'\epsilon\mathbf{n}K^4\mathbf{n}\mathbf{n}' - k_0^2K^2\mathbf{S} + k_0^4\mathbf{I}\epsilon_3(\epsilon_1^2 - \epsilon_2^2))}{\mathbf{n}'\epsilon\mathbf{n}(K^2 - K_1^2)(K^2 - K_2^2)} . \quad (106.34)$$

The integration over φ can be carried out as before and analogous to $\mathbf{M}$ we define

$$\mathbf{M}_m = \frac{1}{\pi}\int_0^{2\pi}\mathbf{S}d\varphi = \begin{pmatrix} 2\epsilon_1\epsilon_3 + (\epsilon_1^2-\epsilon_2^2)\sin^2\theta & -2i\epsilon_2\epsilon_3\cos^2\theta & 0 \\ 2i\epsilon_2\epsilon_3\cos^2\theta & 2\epsilon_1\epsilon_3 + (\epsilon_1^2-\epsilon_2^2)\sin^2\theta & 0 \\ 0 & 0 & 4\epsilon_1\epsilon_3\cos^2\theta + 2(\epsilon_1^2-\epsilon_2^2)\sin^2 \end{pmatrix} \quad (106.35)$$

The matrix $\mathbf{N}$ is as before, the partial fraction expansion of the integrand of eq. (106.34) and an application of the residue theorem permits the integration over K to be performed. Finally, by introducing the transformations from the θ variable to u and expressing the results in terms of the free space impedance and λ_0, yields as in the electric dipole case,

$$\mathbf{F}_m = \mathbf{n}'\epsilon\mathbf{n}(K_1^5 - K_2^5)\mathbf{N} - k_0^2(K_1^3 - K_2^3)\mathbf{M}_m + 2k_0^4(K_1 - K_2)\mathbf{I}\epsilon_3(\epsilon_1^2 - \epsilon_2^2) \quad . \tag{106.36}$$

Therefore,

$$\mathbf{Z}_m = -\frac{\pi}{2}\frac{1}{Z_0\lambda_0^2}\int_0^1 \frac{du\mathbf{F}_m(u)}{k_0^3[\epsilon_1 + (\epsilon_3 - \epsilon_1)u^2](K_1^2 - K_2^2)} \tag{106.37}$$

and to find $\mathbf{R}_m$ we take the Hermitian part of $\mathbf{F}_m$. It is clear from the structure of $\mathbf{M}_m$, that for the lossless case, this matrix is Hermitian. The structure of the matrix $\mathbf{R}_m$ is

$$\mathbf{R}_m = \begin{pmatrix} R_{m1} & -iR_{m2} & 0 \\ iR_{m2} & R_{m1} & 0 \\ 0 & 0 & R_{m3} \end{pmatrix} \tag{106.38}$$

where in the lossless case,

$$R_{mi} = -\frac{\pi}{2}\frac{1}{Z_0\lambda_0^2}\int_0^1 \frac{F_{mi}(u)du}{k_0^3[\epsilon_1 + (\epsilon_3 - \epsilon_1)u^2](K_1^2 - K_2^2)} \quad , \quad (i = 1,2,3) \quad , \tag{106.39}$$

with

$$\left.\begin{aligned} F_{m1}(u) &= \mathrm{Re}\,\{\mathbf{n}'\epsilon\mathbf{n}(K_1^5 - K_2^5)(1 - u^2) - k_0^2(K_1^3 - K_2^3)[2\epsilon_1\epsilon_3 + (\epsilon_1^2 - \epsilon_2^2)(1 - u^2)] \\ &\quad + 2k_0^4(K_1 - K_2)\epsilon_3(\epsilon_1^2 - \epsilon_2^2)\} \quad , \\ F_{m2}(u) &= \mathrm{Re}\,\{-2k_0^2(K_1^3 - K_2^3)\epsilon_2\epsilon_3u^2\} \quad , \\ F_{m3}(u) &= \mathrm{Re}\,\{2\mathbf{n}'\epsilon\mathbf{n}(K_1^5 - K_2^5)u^2 - 2k_0^2(K_1^3 - K_2^3)[2\epsilon_1\epsilon_2u^2 + (\epsilon_1^2 - \epsilon_2^2)(1 - u^2)] \\ &\quad + 2k_0^4(K_1 - K_2)\epsilon_3(\epsilon_1^2 - \epsilon_2^2)\} \quad . \end{aligned}\right\} \tag{106.40}$$

107. ELECTROMAGNETIC SCATTERING AND REFLECTION

In this section we shall formulate the problem of electromagnetic scattering and reflection in terms of the Green's tensor. We assume that the infinite homogeneous medium contains a collection of scatterers and that these scatterers occupy a finite region of space. The basis of the formulation is the inhomogeneous source equation for the electric field

$$\nabla\mathbf{x}(\nabla\mathbf{x}\mathbf{E}) - k_0^2\epsilon\mathbf{E} = -i\mu_0\omega\mathbf{J} \tag{107.1}$$

and the definition of the Green's function

$$\nabla\mathbf{x}(\nabla\mathbf{x}\mathbf{G}) - k_0^2\epsilon\mathbf{G} = -i\mu_0\omega\mathbf{I}\delta(\mathbf{r} - \mathbf{r}') \tag{107.2}$$

where $\mathbf{I}$ is here the unit tensor δ_{ij}, and $\mathbf{G}$ is a function of both $\mathbf{r}$ and $\mathbf{r}'$. To give a meaning to the above equation we recall that the Green's tensor defines three vectors, either its columns or rows. We consider the vectors formed from its columns so that $\mathbf{G}_i$ stands for the vector from the i-th column, and the j-th component of this vector is denoted by G_{ji}. We also consider the complex conjugate of eq. (107.2) namely

$$\nabla\mathbf{x}(\nabla\mathbf{x}\mathbf{G}_i^*) - k_0^2\epsilon^*\mathbf{G}_i^* = i\mu_0\omega\mathbf{I}\delta(\mathbf{r} - \mathbf{r}') \quad . \tag{107.3}$$

Now take the scalar product of eq. (107.3) with $\mathbf{E}$, and that of eq. (107.1) with $\mathbf{G}_i^*$ and subtract giving

$$\mathbf{E}\cdot[\nabla\mathbf{x}(\nabla\mathbf{x}\mathbf{G}_i^*)] - \mathbf{G}_i^*\cdot[\nabla\mathbf{x}(\nabla\mathbf{x}\mathbf{E})] + k_0^2[\mathbf{G}_i^*\cdot\epsilon\mathbf{E} - \mathbf{E}\cdot\epsilon^*\mathbf{G}_i^*] = i\mu_0\omega[E_i\delta(\mathbf{r}-\mathbf{r}') + \mathbf{J}\cdot\mathbf{G}_i^*] \quad . \tag{107.4}$$

But we can also write

$$\left.\begin{aligned} \mathbf{E}\cdot\epsilon^*\mathbf{G}_i^* &= \epsilon_{kj}^* G_{ik}^* E_j \\ \mathbf{G}_i^*\cdot\epsilon\mathbf{E} &= \epsilon_{kj} E_k G_{ij}^* \quad , \text{ sum on } k, j, \end{aligned}\right\} \tag{107.5}$$

and since k and j are dummy indices, we can write the difference of these bilinear forms as $(\epsilon_{kj}^* - \epsilon_{jk})G_{ik}^* E_j$ from which we can conclude that if $\mathbf{E}$ is Hermitian $\epsilon_{kj}^* = \epsilon_{jk}$ and so the difference would vanish for this case.

A further simplification results if we use the following identity for any two vectors **A**, **B**,

$$\mathbf{A} \cdot [\nabla\mathbf{x}(\nabla\mathbf{x}\mathbf{B})] = (\nabla\mathbf{x}\mathbf{A}) \cdot (\nabla\mathbf{x}\mathbf{B}) - \nabla \cdot [\mathbf{A}\mathbf{x}(\nabla\mathbf{x}\mathbf{B})] \qquad (107.6)$$

which when applied to eq. (107.4) yields the result,

$$\nabla \cdot [\mathbf{G}_i^*\mathbf{x}(\nabla\mathbf{x}\mathbf{E})] - \nabla \cdot [\mathbf{E}\mathbf{x}(\nabla\mathbf{x}\mathbf{G}_i^*)] + k_0^2[(\epsilon_{kj}^* - \epsilon_{jk})G_{ik}^*E_j]$$

$$= i\mu_0\omega[\mathbf{E}_i\delta(\mathbf{r} - \mathbf{r}') + \mathbf{J} \cdot \mathbf{G}_i^*] \quad . \qquad (107.7)$$

We integrate this equation over a volume which is bounded by a system of surfaces enclosing the scatterers and by a large sphere which encloses the entire source scattering system. We denote by $\mathbf{n}'$ the unit normal pointing out of the volume and by ∇' the operator with respect to $\mathbf{r}'$; since the medium is lossy the integrals over the surface of the infinite sphere vanishes. The use of the divergence theorem and the property of the delta function then yields,

$$i\mu_0\omega E_i(\mathbf{r}) = \int_S \mathbf{n}' \cdot \{[\mathbf{G}_i^*\mathbf{x}(\nabla'\mathbf{x}\mathbf{E})] - [\mathbf{E}\mathbf{x}(\nabla'\mathbf{x}\mathbf{G}_i^*)]\}dS'$$

$$+ k_0^2\int_V (\epsilon_{kj}^* - \epsilon_{jk})G_{ik}^*E_j d\mathbf{r}' - i\mu_0\omega E_i(\mathbf{r}) \int_V \mathbf{J} \cdot \mathbf{G}_i^* d\mathbf{r}' \quad . \qquad (107.8)$$

The integrals over S refer to the scattering surfaces, the volume integral involving **J** gives the incident field at **r**. The resulting equation is an integral equation for **E**.

If the tangential component of **E** vanishes (*e.g.* when the scattering surfaces have large conductivity compared to the medium in which they are embedded) then from the identity

$$\mathbf{n}' \cdot \{\mathbf{E}(\mathbf{r}')\mathbf{x}[\nabla'\mathbf{x}\mathbf{G}_i^*(\mathbf{r},\mathbf{r}')]\} = [\nabla'\mathbf{x}\mathbf{G}_i^*(\mathbf{r},\mathbf{r}')] \cdot \mathbf{n}'\mathbf{x}\mathbf{E}(\mathbf{r}') \quad , \qquad (107.9)$$

which expresses the condition on the tangential component, the integral involving this term vanishes. If besides, the tensor ϵ is Hermitian then the final Green's formula gives the resultant **E** field as the sum of the incident plus the scattered field. The above formulation permits us to treat problems in which the properties defining the reflecting surface vary slowly over a radiation wave length, and also the class of problems in which the scatterers are small compared to a wave length (*e.g.*, Rayleigh scattering, reflection of very low frequency waves from ionized trails, etc.).

108. RADIATION FROM A SLOT

It is useful to consider the problem of radiation from certain source distributions which arise in practical applications. The problem of a slot radiator in a magneto-ionic medium provides such an example. In this case we consider a coordinate system (x_1, x_2, x_3) in which the applied magnetic field is not co-directional with the x_3-axis but rather is arbitrarily oriented. The configuration is shown in Fig. 29.

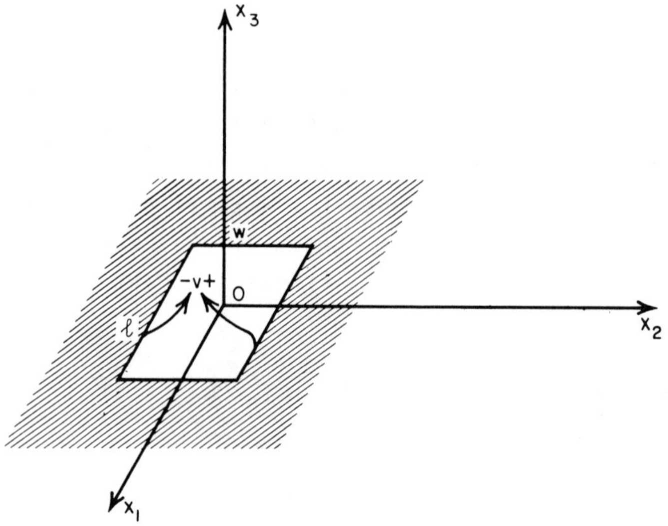

FIG. 29

The technique which is used for this problem is to write the radiation field in terms of two upgoing and two downgoing waves. If we denote by subscripts *uo*, *ue*, *do*, and *de*, these are respectively the upgoing ordinary and extraordinary waves, and similarly for the downgoing waves. Since these modes are independent of each other we can form a spectrum and hence write for the resultant field

$$\mathbf{E}_u = \int_{-\infty}^{\infty}\int_{-\infty}^{\infty} A_{uo}(E_{1,uo}\ E_{2,uo}\ E_{3,uo}) \exp\left[-ik_o(\mathbf{s}\cdot\mathbf{r})\right] ds_1 ds_2$$

$$+ \int_{-\infty}^{\infty}\int_{-\infty}^{\infty} A_{ue}(E_{1,ue}, \ \ldots, \ ) \exp\left[-ik_o(\mathbf{s}\cdot\mathbf{r})\right] ds_1 ds_2 \qquad (108.1)$$

with a similar expression for the **H** field. Here $\mathbf{s} \equiv (s_1, s_2, s_3)$ is the normalized phase propagation vector $\mathbf{k}/k_0$, and s_3 is considered to be a function of s_1, s_2 through a relation equivalent to the Appleton-Hartree equation which will be discussed later. The parameters A_{uo} and A_{ue} are arbitrary functions of s_1, s_2 and will be used to determine the magnitude of each wave in the angular spectrum above. These will be determined from the boundary conditions on the aperture plane $x_3 = 0$. The field for the downgoing waves has the same structure.

We now assume that the boundary conditions over the entire plane $x_3 = 0$ are given by

$$\left.\begin{aligned} E_1(x_1, x_2, 0) &= 0 , \\ E_2(x_1, x_2, 0) &= -p\delta(x_1)\delta(x_2), \end{aligned}\right\} \tag{108.2}$$

where p is a constant, whose significance will be established.

Since the preceding boundary values are known over the entire plane it is sufficient to consider only the upper space $x_3 \gtreqless 0$, the lower space ($x_3 \lesseqgtr 0$) problem will follow from symmetry considerations. Therefore on the boundary, equation (108.1) reduces to

$$\left.\begin{aligned} E_{1u}(x_1, x_2, 0) &= \int_{-\infty}^{\infty}\!\!\int (A_{uo}E_{1,uo} + A_{ue}E_{1,ue}) \exp[-ik_0(s_1x_1 + s_2x_2]ds_1ds_2 , \\ E_{2u}(x_1, x_2 \; 0) &= \int_{-\infty}^{\infty}\!\!\int (A_{uo}E_{2,uo} + A_{ue}E_{2,ue}) \exp[-ik_0(s_1x_1 + s_2x_2)]ds_1ds_2 , \end{aligned}\right\} \tag{108.3}$$

Considering this relation as a Fourier transform, then under the usual restrictions for its existence, we can write the inverse transform as

$$\left.\begin{aligned} A_{uo}E_{1,uo} + A_{ue}E_{1,ue} &= \frac{k_0^2}{4\pi^2}\int_{-\infty}^{\infty}\!\!\int E_{1u}(x_1, x_2, 0) \exp[ik_0(s_1x_1 + s_2x_2)]dx_1dx_2 , \\ A_{uo}E_{2,uo} + A_{ue}E_{2,ue} &= \frac{k_0^2}{4\pi^2}\int_{-\infty}^{\infty}\!\!\int E_{2u}(x_1, x_2, 0) \exp[ik_0(s_1x_1 + s_2x_2)]dx_1dx_2 , \end{aligned}\right\} \tag{108.4}$$

and by substituting into these equations the boundary conditions (108.2), and using the property of the delta function, we find

$$\left.\begin{aligned} A_{uo}E_{1,uo} + A_{ue}E_{1,ue} &= 0 \quad , \\ A_{uo}E_{2,uo} + A_{ue}E_{2,ue} &= -\frac{k}{\lambda_0^2} \quad . \end{aligned}\right\} \tag{108.5}$$

The solution of this pair is,

$$\left.\begin{aligned} A_{uo} &= \frac{1}{\lambda_0^2}\frac{pE_{1,ue}}{\Delta} \quad , \\ A_{ue} &= \frac{1}{\lambda_0^2}\frac{pE_{1,uo}}{\Delta} \quad , \end{aligned}\right\} \tag{108.6}$$

where

$$\Delta = (E_{1,uo}E_{2,ue} - E_{1,ue}E_{2,uo}) \quad , \tag{108.7}$$

Thus, from the above eauations for the A_u we have a complete knowledge of $\mathbf{E}_u$ as given by eq. (108.1), which contains both the near and far field zones. The $\mathbf{H}_u$ is obtained also from the A_u, the structure is the same as eq. (108.1).

Regarding now the lower space problem, the arguments leading to expressions for A_{do} and A_{de} are exactly the same as for the upgoing waves. The resulting equations for them are identical with eqs. (108.5). If we express the s_3 component of the $\mathbf{s}$ vector as a function of s_1, s_2, it will follow from symmetry considerations that $s_{3uo}(s_1\ s_2) = -s_{3do}(-s_1, -s_2)$ and similarly for the extraordinary waves, and from this also $\mathbf{E}_{uo}(s_1, s_2) = \mathbf{E}_{do}(-s_1, -s_2)$ and $\mathbf{E}_{ue}(s_1, s_2) = \mathbf{E}_{de}(-s_1, -s_2)$. From the equations defining A_{do}, A_{de}, A_{uo} and A_{ue} and the symmetry results we conclude that

$$\left.\begin{aligned} A_{do}(-s_1, -s_2) &= A_{uo}(s_1, s_2) \quad , \\ A_{de}(-s_1, -s_2) &= A_{ue}(s_1, s_2) \quad . \end{aligned}\right\} \tag{108.8}$$

The equation defining s_3 as a function of s_1 and s_2 follows from section 10 of Chapter II. In fact for an arbitrary direction of the applied magnetic field referred to a right-handed rectangular cartesian system x_1, x_2, x_3, the dispersion equation is given by eq. (10.7) which takes the form

$$(\mathbf{K} \cdot \mathbf{K})\mathbf{E} - (\mathbf{K} \cdot \mathbf{E})\mathbf{K} - \epsilon_0\mu_0\omega^2\epsilon\mathbf{E} = 0 \quad . \tag{108.9}$$

Now by taking $\mathbf{K} = k_0\mathbf{s}$, we have

$$k_0^2(\mathbf{s} \cdot \mathbf{s})\mathbf{E} - k_0^2(\mathbf{s} \cdot \mathbf{E})\mathbf{s} - \epsilon_0\mu_0\omega^2\epsilon\mathbf{E} = 0 \quad , \tag{108.10}$$

or in tensor form,

$$k_0^2 s^2 E_i - k_0^2 s_j E_j s_i - \epsilon_0\mu_0\omega^2\epsilon_{ij}E_j = 0$$

so that

$$(k_0^2 s^2 \delta_{ij} - k_0^2 s_i s_j - \epsilon_0\mu_0\omega^2\epsilon_{ij})E_j = 0, \quad (i = 1,2,3) \quad , \tag{108.11}$$

and the condition for non-trivial E_i is the vanishing of the determinant

$$|k_0^2 s^2 \delta_{ij} - k_0^2 s_i s_j - \epsilon_0\mu_0\omega^2\epsilon_{ij}| = 0 \quad . \tag{108.12}$$

For this case we must recall that the dielectric tensor does not have the form given by eq. (102.2) of the present chapter. For the above determinental equation we can write it in the form

$$\alpha_1 s_3^4 + \alpha_2 s_3^3 + \alpha_3 s_3^2 + \alpha_4 s_3 + \alpha_5 = 0 \quad , \tag{108.13}$$

where for the case of an electron plasma,

$$\left.\begin{aligned}
\alpha_1 &= \beta(\beta^2 - \Omega^2) - (\beta^2 - \Omega_3^2)a \\
\alpha_2 &= 2(s_1\Omega_1 + s_2\Omega_2)\Omega_3 a \\
\alpha_3 &= -2c^2\beta(\beta^2 - \Omega^2) + \{2(1 + c^2)\beta^2 + (s_1\Omega_1 + s_2\Omega_2)^2 - c^2\Omega_3^2 - \Omega^2\}a - 2\beta a^2 \\
\alpha_4 &= -2c^2(s_1\Omega_1 + s_2\Omega_2)\Omega_3 a \\
\alpha_5 &= c^4\beta(\beta^2 - \Omega^2) - c^2\{(2 + c^2)\beta^2 + (s_1\Omega_1 + s_2\Omega_2)^2 - \Omega^2\}a + (1 + 2c^2)\beta a^2 - a^3 \\
c^2 &= 1 - s_1^2 - s_2^2
\end{aligned}\right\} , \tag{108.14}$$

with $\beta = 1 - i(\nu/\omega)$, $\mathbf{\Omega} = (\Omega_1, \Omega_2, \Omega_3) \equiv \mathbf{B}_0 e/m\omega$ and $a = Ne^2/\epsilon_0 m\omega^2$ (see Chapter II). Consequently, the coefficients α_i are functions of only s_1, s_2 and thus we can regard s_3 also as functions of s_1, s_2 *i.e.*, s_1 and s_2 completely determine the four waves. It is easily verified that if $s_3(s_1, s_2)$ is a root of the quartic eq. (108.13) then also $-s_3(-s_1, -s_2)$ is a root.

The boundary conditions (108.2) can be realized physically if the slot is formed in a perfectly conducting material and is excited across its width by a voltage of magnitude v volts and such that the phase variations across the slot are negligible. The significance of the constant p is that it defines the voltage moment of the elementary slot dipole, therefore, $p = vl$ where l is the length of the slot as shown.

To evaluate the far field one can use the various asymptotic methods for integrals of the type defining $\mathbf{E}_u$, etc, in particular the method of stationary phase extended to the two-dimensional case.*

109. RADIATION FROM AN ELEMENTARY CURRENT-SHEET DIPOLE

We consider now briefly the formulation of the problem of radiation from a current element in a homogeneous magneto-ionic medium as in the previous example. Such a radiating element is realized physically as a current sheet of width w, length l and negligible thickness. The maximum current in the sheet is denoted by I which is uniformly distributed over the dipole surface. Here too we assume that the phase variations over the dipole surface are negligible (see Fig. 30). Because of the negligible dimensions of the current sheet we take the current moment to be $pm = Il$. This problem differs from the previous one in that the boundary conditions are not as simple. In fact the boundary conditions must be stated in terms of the discontinuities of the tangential components of the $\mathbf{H}$ field, at the aperture plane. Because the current is localized at the origin of the aperture it becomes necessary to connect in a continuous manner the upgoing and downgoing spectrums in the remaining parts of the aperture. Thus, at the origin the tangential components of $\mathbf{H}$ are discontinuous transverse to the aperture plane. The magnitude of this discontinuity is equal to the current per unit

---

* G. Toraldo Di Francia, Electromagnetic Waves, Interscience Pub. Inc., pp. 36-39, (1953). See also, G. Braun, Zur Methode der stationären Phase, Acta Physica Austriaca. Vol. 10, pp. 8-33, (1957).

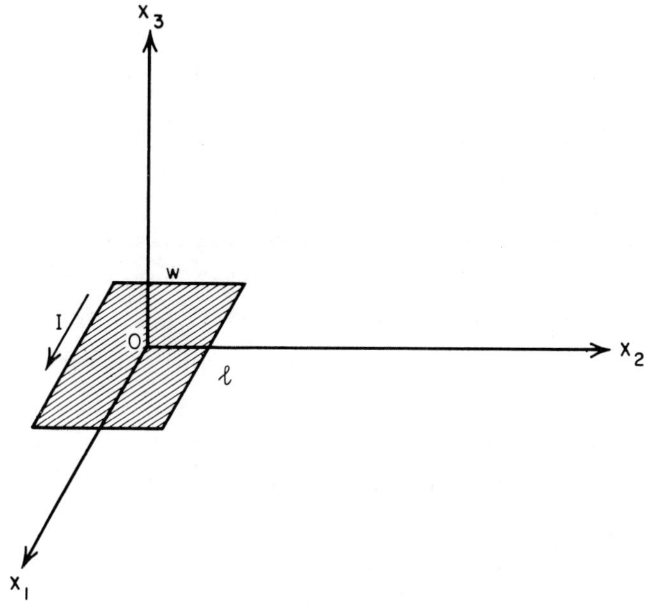

FIG. 30

width. The problem reduces to the determination of four rather than two parameters, *i.e.*, the A's. The boundary conditions are for this case,

$$\left.\begin{aligned} H_{1u}(x_1,x_2,0) - H_{1d}(x_1,x_2,0) &= 0 \quad , \\ H_{2u}(x_1,x_2,0) - H_{2d}(x_1,x_2,0) &= -Il\delta(x_1)\delta(x_2) \quad . \end{aligned}\right\} \quad (109.1)$$

The upgoing and downgoing spectrums are respectively,

$$\left.\begin{aligned} \mathbf{H}_u = & \int_{-\infty}^{\infty}\!\!\int A_{uo}[H_{1,uo},H_{2,uo},H_{3,uo}] \exp[-ik_0(s_1x_1+s_2x_2+s_{3,uo}x_3)]ds_1ds_2 \\ & + \int_{-\infty}^{\infty}\!\!\int A_{ue}[H_{1,ue}, \ldots,] \exp[-ik_0(s_1x_1+s_2x_2+s_{3,ue}x_3)]ds_1ds_2 \quad , \end{aligned}\right\}$$

and (109.2)

$$\left.\begin{aligned} \mathbf{H}_d = & \int_{-\infty}^{\infty}\!\!\int A_{do}[H_{1,do}, \ldots,] \exp[-ik_0(s_1x_1+s_2x_2+s_{3,do}x_3)]ds_1ds_2 \\ & + \int_{-\infty}^{\infty}\!\!\int A_{de}[H_{1,de}, \ldots,] \exp[-ik_0(s_1x_1+s_2x_2+s_{3,de}x_3)]ds_1ds_2 \end{aligned}\right\}$$

(109.3)

Now if we assume that the amplitude parameters are related as follows,

$$\left.\begin{aligned} A_{uo}(s_1,s_2) &= A_{do}(-s_1,-s_2) \quad , \\ A_{ue}(s_1,s_2) &= A_{de}(-s_1,-s_2) \quad , \end{aligned}\right\} \tag{109.4}$$

we shall demonstrate that the boundary conditions are satisfied. As in the electric dipole case it is not difficult to verify that since $s_{3u}(s_1,s_2) = -s_{3,d}(-s_1,-s_2)$ then $\mathbf{E}_u(s_1,s_2) = \mathbf{E}_d(-s_1,-s_2)$ and also $\mathbf{H}_u(s_1,s_2) = -\mathbf{H}_d(-s_1,-s_2)$. These relations simply assert respectively that the phase propagation vector is symmetric about the magnetic field and the remaining conditions relate the wave polarizations. These relations and those of eqs. (109.4) permit us to write in place of eq. (109.3) the following

$$\begin{aligned} \mathbf{H}_d = &- \int_{-\infty}^{\infty}\!\!\int A_{uo}[H_{1,uo}, \; \ldots, \;] \exp[ik_0(s_1x_1 + s_2x_2 + s_{3,uo}x_3)]ds_1ds_2 \\ &- \int_{-\infty}^{\infty}\!\!\int A_{ue}[H_{1,ue}, \; \ldots, \;] \exp[ik_0(s_1x_1 + s_2x_2 + s_{3,ue}x_3)]ds_1ds_2 \end{aligned} \tag{109.5}$$

Using the boundary conditions on the aperture plane $x_3 = 0$, we find

$$\left.\begin{aligned} \int_{-\infty}^{\infty}\!\!\int (A_{uo}H_{1,uo} + A_{ue}H_{1,ue}) \cos[k_0(s_1x_1 + s_2x_2)]ds_1ds_2 &= 0 \quad , \\ \int_{-\infty}^{\infty}\!\!\int (A_{uo}H_{2,uo} + A_{ue}H_{2,ue}) \cos[k_0(s_1x_1 + s_2x_2)]ds_1ds_2 &= \frac{-Il}{2}\,\delta(x_1)\delta(x_2) \end{aligned}\right\} \tag{109.6}$$

The structure of these two equations suggests the use of the Fourier Transform for even functions. Moreover the delta function properties imply that the right side of eqs. (109.6) are even functions of their arguments. Consequently we can replace the $\cos(s_1x_1 + s_2x_2)$ by $\exp[-ik_0(s_1x_1 + s_2x_2)]$ which is justified on the basis of the uniqueness of Fourier Transforms. With this understanding the application of the Fourier Transform to eqs. (109.6) leads to

$$\left.\begin{aligned} A_{uo}H_{1,uo} + A_{ue}H_{1,ue} &= 0 \quad , \\ A_{uo}H_{2,uo} + A_{ue}H_{2,ue} &= -\frac{Il}{2\lambda_0^2} \quad , \end{aligned}\right\} \tag{109.7}$$

whose solution yields,

$$\left.\begin{aligned} A_{uo} &= \frac{(-Il)H_{1,ue}}{2\lambda_0^2\Delta} , \\ A_{ue} &= \frac{(-Il)H_{1,uo}}{2\lambda_0^2\Delta} , \end{aligned}\right\} \tag{109.8}$$

where,

$$\Delta = H_{1,uo}H_{2,ue} - H_{1,ue}H_{2,uo} . \tag{109.9}$$

We see from the results of both the electric dipole case and the preceding magnetic case that there exists a formal equivalence with the E_i replaced by H_i and the replacement of vl by $Il/2$.

In this case also the problem is reduced to the evaluation of integrals which can be effected (at least for the far field zone) by the method of stationary phase as mentioned previously.

BIBLIOGRAPHIES

1. Abraham, L. G., Extensions of the Magneto-ionic theory for radio-wave propagation in the ionosphere including antenna radiation and plane wave scattering, School of Electrical Engr., Cornell Univ., Studies on Propagation in the Ionosphere, Tech. Report No. 13 (August 1, 1953).

2. Barsukov, K. A., On the Doppler effect in an anisotropic and gyrotropic medium, J.E.T.P. (USSR) 36 (1959).

3. Barsukov, K. A. and A. A. Kolomenskii, Doppler effect in an electron plasma in a magnetic field, J. Tech. Phys. (USSR) 29 (1960).

4. Beard, D. B., Microwave emission from high temperature plasmas, Phys. Rev. Letters, Vol. 2, No. 3, pp. 81-82 (Feb. 1, 1959).

5. Beard, D. B., Cyclotron Radiation from magnetically confined plasmas, The Physics of Fluids, Vol. 2, No. 4, pp. 379-389 (July-August 1959).

6. G. A. Begiashvili and E. V. Gedalin, Motion of a charged particle in an anisotropic medium, J.E.T.P. (USSR) 35 (1958)

7. Begiashvili, G. A. and E. V. Gedalin, Cerenkov radiation of a magnetic dipole in an anisotropic medium, J.E.T.P. (USSR) 36 (1959).

8. Bekefi, G, Hirshfield, J. L., and Brown, S. C., Incoherent microwave radiation from plasmas, Phys. Rev. Vol. 116, No. 5, p. 1051 (Dec. 1, 1959).

9. Born, M. and E. Wolf, Principles of Optics, London (1959).

10. Bresler, A. D. and Marcuvitz, N., Operator methods in electromagnetic field theory, Polytechnic Inst. Brookly, Res. Report R-495-56, PIB-425 (1956) and Res. Report R-565-57, PIB-493 (1957).

11. Brown, S. C., The interaction of microwaves with gas discharge plasmas, Trans. IRE, MTT-7 (1959).

12. Bunkin, F. V., On radiation in anisotropic media, J.E.T.P. (USSR) 32 (1957).

13. Clarricoats, P. J., et al., A survey of the theory and applications of ferrites at microwave frequencies, PIEE B 104, Suppl. 6 (1957) 267-82 (with further references).

14. Cohen, M. H., Radiation in a plasma, I, Phys. Rev., Vol. 123, No. 3, pp. 711-721 (Aug. 1, 1961).

15. Collin, R. E., A simple artificial anisotropic dielectric medium, Trans. IRE MTT-6 (1958)

16. Didenko, A. N., Interaction between a charged current carrying jet moving in a circle and a magneto-dielectric medium, Zh. eksper. teor. Fiz. Vol. 35, No. 3 (9), pp. 655-661 (1958).

17. Drummond, J. E., Basic microwave properties of hot magneto-plasmas, Phys. Rev. 110 (1958).

18. Drummond, J. E., Microwave propagation in hot magneto-plasmas, Phys. Rev. 112 (1958).

19. Epstein, P. S., Theory of wave propagation in a gyromagnetic medium, Rev. Mod. Phys. 28 (1956).

20. Fox, A. G., et al., Behaviour and applications of ferrites in the microwave region, B.S.T.J. 34 (1955) 5-103 (with further references)

21. Gershman, B. N., Ginzburg, V. L., Denisov, N. G., The propagation of electromagnetic waves in plasma (ionosphere), Uspekhi fiz Nauk (USSR) 61 (1957) 561-612 (with further references)

22. Ginzburg, V. L., On the electrodynamics of anisotropic medium, J.E.T.P. (USSR) 10 (1940).

23. Ginzburg, V. L., Radiation of an electron moving in a crystal with a constant velocity exceeding that of light, J.E.T.P. (USSR) 10 (1940)

24. Ginzburg, V. L. and Eidman, V. Y., The radiation reaction in the motion of a charge in a medium, J.E.T.P. (USSR) 36 (1959)

25. Gurevich, A. G., Quadratic relationships for media with tensor parameter, Radio Engineering and Electronics (USSR) 2 (1957).

26. Hayakawa, S. and Hokkyo, N., Electromagnetic radiation from electron plasma, Progr. Theor. Phys., Vol. 15, p. 193 (1956).

27. Hazlehurst, J. and Sargent, W.L.W., Hydrodynamics in a radiation field, a covariant treatment, Astrophys. J., p. 276 (July 1959).

28. Kaganov, M. I., J. Techn. Phys. (USSR) 23 (1953).

29. Kaprielian, Z. A., Dielectric properties of a lattice of anisotropic particles, J.A.P. 27 (1956).

30. Kaprielian, Z. A., Anisotropic effects in geometrically isotropic lattices, J.A.P. 29 (1958).

31. Karplus, R., Radiation of hydromagnetic waves, The Physics of Fluids, Vol. 3, No. 5, pp. 800-805 (Sept.-Oct. 1960).

32. Khizkuyak, N. A., Artificial anisotropic dielectrics formed from two dimensional lattices of infinite bars and rods, J. Tech. Phys. (USSR) 29 (1959).

33. Klinger, M. I., The question of the Faraday effect in semi-conductors, J. Tech. Phys. USSR, Vol. 26, pp. 927-937 (1956).

34. Kogelnik, H., On electromagnetic radiation in magneto-ionic media, J. Res. N.B.S., Vol. 64D, No. 5, pp. 515-523 (Sept.-Oct. 1960).

35. Kogelnik, H., The radiation resistance of an elementary dipole in anisotropic plasmas, Univ. of Oxford, Engr. Lab. Tech. Note, No. 3 (1960).

36. Kolomenskii, A. A., J.E.T.P. (USSR) 24 (1953).

37. Kolomenskii, A. A., Doklady Akad. Nauk (USSR) 86 (1952).

38. Kolomenskii, A. A., Radiation from a plasma electron in uniform motion in a magnetic field, Doklady Akad, Nauk (USSR) 106 (1956).

39. Kuehl, H. H., Radiation from an electric dipole in an anisotropic cold plasma, Calif. Inst. Tech., Antenna Laboratory, Tech. Report No. 24 (Oct. 1960).

40. Mikaelyan, A. L., Methods for calculating the dielectric and magnetic permeabilities of artificial media, Radiotechnika (USSR) 10 (1955).

41. Nichols, H. W., Schelling, J. C.

42. Nisbeth, A., Electromagnetic potentials in a heterogeneous nonconducting medium, Proc. Roy. Soc. A, 240 (1957).

43. Oster, L., The continuous absorption coefficient for free-emission in the radio frequency spectral range, z. fur. Astrophysik., Vol. 47, pp. 169-190 (1959).

44. Pafamov, V. E., Cerenkov radiation in anisotropic ferrites, J.E.T.P. (USSR) 30 (1956).

45. Parker, E. N. and Tidman, D. A., Radio emission from plasma shocks, The Physics of Fluids, Vol. 3, No. 3, pp. 369-372 (May-June 1960).

46. Polder, D., On the theory of ferromagnetic resonance, Phil. Mag., 40 (1949), and Physica 15 (1949).

47. Reiche, F. and Ludloff, H. F., Electromagnetic Radiation in an atmosphere of arbitrary electric conductivity, The Physics of Fluids, Vol. 4, No. 5, pp. 618-621 (May 1961).

48. Schwinger, J., On the classical radiation of accelerated electrons, Phys. Rev., Vol. 75, No. 12, pp. 1912-1925 (June 15, 1949).

49. Scott, J. W., The Poynting vector in the ionosphere, P.I.R.E. 38 (1950).

50. Seidel, H., The character of waveguide modes in gyromagnetic media, B.S.T.J. 26 (1957).

51. Sitenko, A. G. and Kolomenskii, A. A., Motion of a charged particle in an optically active anisotropic medium, J.E.T.P. (USSR) 30 (1956).

52. Smerd, S. F. and Westfold, K. C., The characteristics of radio-frequency radiation in an ionized gas with applications to the transfer of radiation in the solar atmosphere, Phil. Mag. Vol. 10, pp. 831-848 (1949).

53. Tanaka, K., Cerenkov radiation, Phys. Rev. 93 (1954).

54. Tidman, D. A., Radio emission by plasma oscillations in non-uniform plasmas, Phys. Rev., Vol. 117, No. 2, pp. 366-374 (Jan. 15, 1960).

55. Tidman, D. A. and Weiss, G. H., Radiation by large-amplitude plasma oscillations, The Physics of Fluids, Vol. 4, No. 7, pp. 866-868 (July 1961).

56. Tikhonov, A. N., The propagation of a continuous electromagnetic wave in a laminary anisotropic medium, Doklady Akad. Nauk (USSR) 126 (1959).

57. Trubnikov, B. A., Plasma Radiation in a Magnetic Field, Soviet Physics, J.E.T.P. USSR, pp. 136-140 (Jan.-Feb. 1958).

58. Twiss, R. Q., Radiation transfer and the possibility of negative absorption in radio astronomy, Austral. J. of Physics, Vol. 11, pp. 564-579 (1958).

59. van Trier, A. A., Guided electromagnetic waves in anisotropic media, Apple. Sci. Res. B 3 (1953).

60. Volterra, V., Sur les vibrations lumineuses dan les milieux birefringents, Acta mathematica 16 (1892).

61. Watkins, D. A., Topics in electromagnetic theory, chapter 4, New York, ((1958).

62. Westfold, K. C., The polarization of synchotron radiation, Astrophys. J. Vols. 129-130, pp. 241-258 (1959).

63. Westfold, K. C., On Kramers' formula for the frequency distribution of the radiation emitted by an electron in a parabolic orbit, Phil. Mag. Vol. 40, pp. 698-703 (1949).

64. Westfold, K. C., The refractive index and classical radiative processes in an ionized gas, ibid, Vol. 41, pp. 509-516 (1950).

65. Woolley, R.v.d.R., The Solar Corona, Supplement to the Austral. Jour. of Science, Vol. 10, No. 2, pp. 63-72 (Oct. 21, 1947).

66. Wyld, H. W., Radiation by plasma oscillations in a bounded plasma in a magnetic field, ibid, Vol. 3, No. 3, pp. 408-415 (May-June 1960).

GENERAL BIBLIOGRAPHIES

1. Born, M, and Wolf, E.

2. Clauser, F.

3. Drummond, J. (Ed.), Plasma Physics.

4. Friedman, B., Principles and Techniques of Applied Mathematics, John Wiley & Sons, N.Y. (1956).

5. Heitler, W., Quantum Theory of Radiation, Oxford (1954).

6. Jelley, J. V., Cerenkov Radiation, Pergamon Press, N.Y. (1958).

7. Landau and Lifshitz, Classical Theory of Fields.

8. Landau and Lifshitz, Electrodynamics ..., .

9. Morse and Feshbach.

10. Poschl, K., Mathematical methods in high frequency technique, Berlin (1956).

11. Ratcliffe, J. A.

12. Schott, G. A., Electromagnetic Radiation, Cambridge Univ. Press (1912).

13. Silver, S.

14. Sommerfeld, A., Electrodynamics.

15. Stratton, J. A.

16. Sneddon, I. N., Fourier Transforms, McGraw-Hill, N.Y. (1951).

17. Sneddon, I. N., Elements of Partial Differential Equations, ibid (1957).

18. Titchmarsh, E. C., The Theory of Fourier Integrals, Oxford (1937).

PROBLEMS FOR CHAPTER 1

(1) In an isotropic medium the equation of geometrical optics is

$$\nabla\phi(\mathbf{r}) = C\boldsymbol{\mu},$$

where C is some constant and $\boldsymbol{\mu}$ is the vector index of refraction. If we write $\boldsymbol{\mu} = \mu(\mathbf{r})\alpha$, where α is a unit vector along a ray, show that the above equation can also be written in the form,

$$\mu(\nabla \mathbf{x} \mathbf{u}) = \mu \mathbf{x} (\nabla\mu) \quad .$$

(2) If ds is an element of arc length along a ray, show that the vector curvature at any point on the ray is given by

$$\frac{d\mathbf{u}}{ds} = - \mathbf{u}\mathbf{x}(\nabla \mathbf{x} \mathbf{u}) \quad ,$$

where $\mathbf{u}$ is defined in the previous problem. Deduce from this expression that in a homogeneous medium

$$\nabla \mathbf{x} \mathbf{u} = 0 \quad .$$

In a nonhomogeneous medium what is the relative orientation of the three vectors $\mathbf{u}$, $d\mathbf{u}$ and $\nabla\mathbf{x}\mathbf{u}$?

(3) Prove that in passing from one homogeneous medium to another that the tangential component of $\boldsymbol{\mu}$ is continuous. [Hint: From problem (1) deduce the result $\nabla\mathbf{x}\mu = 0$, and then apply Stokes' theorem to an appropriate contour of the surface separating the two media.)

What is the relation between the indices of refraction which results from the continuity of the tangential component?

(4) Consider two distinct homogeneous media characterized by vector indices μ_1 and μ_2. Let $\mathbf{n}$ be a vector normal to the surface of separation. Starting with the relation

$$\mu_1 - \mu_2 = \mathbf{n} \quad ,$$

show that if the rays in one medium form a normal congruence, the rays in the second medium also form a normal congruence. This is the theorem of Malus.

(5) Let μ be expressed in a spherical coordinate system (r,ϕ,θ) with arc length defined by

$$ds^2 = dr^2 + r^2 d\phi^2 + r^2 \sin^2 \phi d\theta^2 \quad .$$

Fermat's principle now reads

$$\delta \int_{P_1}^{P_2} \mu(r,\phi,\theta)[(r')^2 + r^2(\phi')^2 + r^2 \sin^2 \phi(\theta')^2]^{1/2} ds = 0 \quad ,$$

with, $r' \equiv dr/ds$, etc. Assume that μ depends only on r; from the Euler-Lagrange equations show that

$$\mu r^2 \phi' = \text{constant} \quad ,$$

and if we define $\sin i$ by the formula

$$ds \sin i = r d\phi \quad ,$$

the above relation takes the form

$$\mu r \sin i = \text{const.}$$

Interpret this formula geometrically. (This formula has practical application in the theory of atmospheric refraction.) Show that all of the rays lie in a plane passing through the center of coordinate system. Can the formula be generalized for a medium which exhibits anisotropy?

(6) Starting with eq. (3.27b), let σ denote the cross-section of a thin tube of rays, show that along a ray the amplitude A satisfies the equation

$$2\sigma\mu d(\log A) + d(\sigma\mu) = 0 \quad ,$$

and hence that A is proportional to $(\sigma\mu)^{-1/2}$ at each point of the ray.

(7) Consider a medium whose properties vary slightly over a wave length. Let the spatial part of the wave be defined by the equation

$$\frac{d^2\psi}{dx^2} + K^2(x)\psi = 0 ,$$

where $K(x)$ is in general complex. Assume a solution of the form

$$\psi(x) = A(x)e^{-i\psi(x)}$$

and show that

(*a*) $A'' - 2iA'\psi' - iA\psi'' + [K^2 - (\psi')^2]A = 0$.

(*b*) If λ is the wave length and D is the distance over which both $A(x)$ and $\psi'(x)$ vary significantly, put $K = 2\pi/\lambda$ and show that

$$A'' \approx \frac{A}{D^2} ,$$

$$-2iA'\psi' - iA\psi'' \approx \frac{A\psi'}{D} ,$$

$$\{K^2(x) - [\psi'(x)]^2\}A \approx \frac{A}{\lambda^2} .$$

(*c*) From these results show that

$$(\psi')^2 = K^2(x) ,$$

$$2A'\psi' + A\psi'' = 0 ,$$

and hence

$$A(x) = \text{const.}\ [K(x)]^{-1/2} .$$

(*d*) Show that

$$\Psi(x) = [K(x)]^{-1/2}\left\{A_1 \exp\left[i\int_{x_0}^{x} K(x)dx\right] + A_2 \exp\left[-i\int_{x_0}^{x} K(x)dx\right]\right\}$$

is a solution of the given differential equation for Ψ under the above hypothesis.

(*e*) In the geometrical optics approximation show that $\Psi^*(d\Psi/dx)$ is independent of x and interpret the result in terms of energy flux.

(8) Show that if the differential equation in problem (7) is modified by replacing $K^2(x)$ by $K^2(x) - a^2$, where a^2 is a constant, then under the hypothesis as in (7), the solution in (*d*) replaces $K(x)$ everywhere by $K(x)\cos\theta(x)$, where $K^2(x)\cos^2\theta(x) = K^2(x) - a^2$.

(*a*) Interpret the geometrical meaning of a.

(9) Let $\Psi = A(\omega)\exp[i\omega t - i(K\cosh\alpha)x_1 - (K\sinh\alpha)x_3]$ represent a plane wave, where $K_1 = K\cosh\alpha$, $K_3 = iK\sinh\alpha$ and K is real.

(*a*) Is this an inhomogeneous plane wave? Describe the surfaces of constant phase and amplitude and find their relative orientation.

(*b*) Find the velocity of propagation and show that it is less than that of an ordinary plane wave. Calculate also the wave length.

(*c*) If K is complex, what is the relative orientation of the surfaces of constant phase and amplitude?

PROBLEMS FOR CHAPTER II

(1) In the absence of a magnetic field show that the skin depth or penetration depth, $d \approx V_0/\omega_c$ if $\omega \ll \omega_c$. Calculate the depth for a medium with electron density of 10^{12} electrons per cubic centimeter for some typical low frequency incident waves.

(2) Assume that the wave frequency ω is very much greater than both the plasma frequency and the gyro-frequency. Show, by using the equation relating $\mathbf{D}_e$ and $\mathbf{E}$ that the medium can be considered as essentially isotropic. Is the index of refraction real, complex or purely imaginary?

(3) Find the conditions on ω, ω_c, the gyro-frequency, and the collision frequency which cause the medium to behave strongly anisotropic. Does this occur at high, intermediate or low frequencies? Derive the relation between $\mathbf{D}_e$ and $\mathbf{E}$ when this occurs.

(4) By neglecting collisions and considering those wave frequencies for which the square of the refractive index is positive, calculate, for a plane wave structure:

(*a*) The energy density in the wave in the presence of a magnetic field and in the absence of such a field.

(*b*) The time average energy density with and without magnetic field.

(*c*) The same for the Poynting vector.

(*d*) The same for the time average Poynting vector.

In (*d*), with magnetic field present, is the time average Poynting vector in the same direction as the wave normal? In what plane does it lie?

(5) Starting with the equation for the index of refraction but neglecting collisions and the factor

$$\frac{a\Omega^2 \sin\theta}{(a-1)[(a-1)^2 - \Omega^2]},$$

(this yields the so-called quasi-longitudinal approximation for the index), find the resulting expression for the index. If the wave frequency is very much greater than both the plasma and gyro-frequencies, show that the neglected factor is equivalent to neglecting terms of order ω^{-4}. If ω is very much less than both the plasma and gyro-frequencies, the neglected factor is equivalent to neglecting terms of order ω^2. In both cases find the resulting expressions for the above neglected factor.

(6) In the above approximation find the real fields of $\mathbf{D}_e$, $\mathbf{E}$ and $\mathbf{B}$ and show that for each mode, the $\mathbf{D}_e$ field and $\mathbf{B}$ precess about the wave normal with precession frequency ω. Is the same true for the real field of $\mathbf{E}$?

(7) In the quasi-longitudinal approximation, compute the time averaged Poynting vector. Is it in the direction of the wave normal? Calculate the angle between the time averaged Poynting vector and the external magnetic field.

(*a*) Find the angle in the high frequency limit and show that for the two modes of propagation the Poynting vector lies in the plane containing the external magnetic field and the wave normal.

(*b*) What is the angle between the Poynting vectors for each mode?

(8) In the same approximation as in problem (7), show that in the low frequency limit, the index is given by

$$M^2 = \pm\left(\frac{a}{\Omega \cos\theta}\right).$$

(*a*) Which mode is a propagating mode?

(*b*) What is the phase velocity of the propagating mode at low frequencies? Is it a slow, fast, intermediate wave mode?

(*c*) Show that the angle between the time averaged Poynting vector and the magnetic field is given by

$$\mathrm{Cos}^{-1}\left\{\frac{(1+\cos^2\theta)\cos\theta}{|\cos\theta|\,[1+3\cos^2\theta]^{1/2}}\right\}$$

for the propagating mode.

(*d*) Plot the graph of this angle as a function of θ. What can you conclude about the direction of the Poynting vector for small values of θ? For large θ?

(*e*) Find the maximum value of this angle and show that it occurs when $\cos\theta = \sqrt{3}/3$. Do the results of this problem indicate the strong influence of the earth's magnetic field in the guiding of low frequency waves in the ionosphere? Why?

(9) At what angle(s) and frequencies is the quasi-longitudinal approximation invalid? Why?

(10) The quasi-transverse approximation is defined by the condition, $4(1 - a)^2 \cos^2\theta \ll \Omega^2 \sin^4\theta$. What are the resulting expressions for the index of refraction for both modes?

(*a*) At very high frequencies and neglecting terms of order ω^{-4} show that the indices are identical and become

$$M^2 = 1 - a \quad .$$

How does the medium behave in this case?

(*b*) Under what conditions does the same result obtain in the quasi-longitudinal approximation?

(11) In the quasi-transverse approximation show that for low frequencies, the indices for the two modes reduce to

$$M^2 = -a \quad ,$$

and

$$M^2 = -\frac{a^2}{a + \Omega^2 \cos^2\theta} \quad ,$$

so that neither mode propagates.

(12) Using formula (14.1a), assume $a \gg 1$ and $\Omega \gg 1$, (low frequency approximation), but θ is as yet unrestricted.

(*a*) Find the resulting expression for M^2.

(*b*) Which mode is non-propagating for all θ?

(*c*) For the remaining mode, what is the range of θ which yields a propagating wave; a non-propagating wave?

(*d*) Show that the transition from propagating to non-propagating wave takes place when

$$\theta' = \cos^{-1}\left\{\frac{a + \Omega^2}{\Omega^2\ (a + 1)}\right\} .$$

(*e*) Show that under the given assumptions, $\theta' \approx \pi/2$.

(*f*) For what values of θ is the quasi-longitudinal approximation valid?

(*g*) Show that if the collision frequency vanishes at θ', the index becomes infinite.

(*h*) Is the Poynting vector (time averaged) parallel to the magnetic field at θ'?

(13) Let the external magnetic field direction and the wave normal $\mathbf{n}$ define a plane. Let $\mathbf{m}$ be a unit vector perpendicular to $\mathbf{n}$ but coplanar with the magnetic field and $\mathbf{n}$ and such that $\mathbf{m}$ rotates into $\mathbf{n}$ in a positive sense. Show that in the absence of collisions, the group velocity of a wave packet is given by

$$\mathbf{V}_g = V_0 \left[\mathbf{n} - \left(\frac{1}{M}\frac{\partial M}{\partial \theta}\right)\mathbf{m}\right]\frac{\partial(\omega M)}{\partial \omega}.$$

(*a*) What can you infer about the relative orientation of the time averaged Poynting vector of a plane wave of frequency ω and the group velocity of a packet centered about ω and $\mathbf{n}$? Are they parallel?

(*b*) Show that the ratio of the time averaged Poynting vector to the time averaged energy density in a plane wave is given by

$$\frac{V_0}{M}\frac{\partial(\omega M)}{\partial M}\mathbf{V}_g .$$

(*c*) Using the quasi-longitudinal approximation and the low frequency approximation deduce that

$$\mathbf{V}_g = V_0[2\mathbf{n} - \mathbf{m} \tan\theta]\left[\frac{\Omega}{a}|\cos\theta|\right]^{1/2}$$

for the propagating mode. If V_0 is the speed of light is it possible for $|\mathbf{V}_g| > V_0$ in the quasi-longitudinal approximation? If so, explain the paradox.

PROBLEMS FOR CHAPTER III

(1) Prove the relation (22.1).

(2) Show that the velocity of an element near a reference particle P_0 is the vector sum of a translation $\mathbf{v}_0$ equal to the velocity of P_0, a rigid body rotation about an axis through P_0 with angular velocity $(1/2)\nabla\mathbf{x}\mathbf{v}$ and a deformation of the element given by $\mathbf{e}\Delta\mathbf{x}$ where $\mathbf{e}$ is the strain rate tensor and $\Delta\mathbf{x}$ is the position vector from P_0 to the particle, *i.e.*,

$$\mathbf{v} = \mathbf{v}_0 + \frac{1}{2}(\nabla\mathbf{x}\mathbf{v})\mathbf{x}\Delta\mathbf{x} + \mathbf{e}\Delta\mathbf{x} \quad .$$

(3) Let $f(\mathbf{r},t) = 0$ define a surface in space and suppose that no fluid ever crosses the surface, show that $df/dt = 0$ everywhere on the surface.

(4) Prove that if div $\mathbf{v} = 0$, then the Jacobian

$$J \equiv \frac{\partial(\mathbf{r})}{\partial(\alpha)} = 1$$

(5) Let

$$v_1 = -\frac{2x_1x_2x_3}{(x_1^2+x_2^2)^2}, \quad v_2 = \frac{(x_1^2-x_2^2)x_3}{(x_1^2+x_2^2)^2}, \quad v_3 = \frac{x_2}{(x_1^2+x_2^2)^2} .$$

(*a*) Calculate div $\mathbf{v}$.

(*b*) Calculate $\nabla\mathbf{x}\mathbf{v}$, (the vorticity).

(*c*) Describe the flow.

(6) Show that a velocity field defined by

$$v_1 = -k\frac{x_2}{(x_1^2+x_2^2)^2}, \quad v_2 = k\frac{x_1}{(x_1^2+x_2^2)^2}$$

describes an irrotational vortex motion, where k is a constant.

(7) Derive relation (24.1) by considering a tetrahedron as stated in the text. Why is a tetrahedron used? Can other geometric figures be used?

(8) Let $x^i = x^i(\overline{x}^1, \overline{x}^2, \overline{x}^3)$ define a transformation of coordinates and suppose the inverse transformation exists. An absolute scalar is defined by $\phi(x^i) = \overline{\phi}(\overline{x}^i)$. Consider the relation

$$\delta^i_j \frac{\partial x^j}{\partial \overline{x}^\alpha} \frac{\partial \overline{x}^\beta}{\partial x^i} = \frac{\partial x^i}{\partial \overline{x}^\alpha} \frac{\partial \overline{x}^\beta}{\partial x^i} = \frac{\partial \overline{x}^\beta}{\partial \overline{x}^\alpha} = \delta^\beta_\alpha .$$

An isotropic tensor $A^i_j(x)$ is one for which $\overline{A}^i_j[\overline{x}(x)] = A^i_j(x)$. The A^i_j transforms according to the rule

$$A^i_j(x) = A^\alpha_\beta \frac{\partial \overline{x}^i}{\partial x^\beta} \frac{\partial x^\beta}{\partial \overline{x}^j} ;$$

(*a*) Show that

$$\frac{\partial \overline{x}^j}{\partial x^\alpha} (\delta^\alpha_\sigma A^i_j - \delta^i_j A^\alpha_\sigma) = 0 .$$

(*b*) If $\partial \overline{x}^j / \partial x^\alpha$ can be chosen arbitrarily prove that $\delta^\alpha_\sigma A^i_j = \delta^i_j A^\alpha_\sigma$, for all i, j, α, σ.

(*c*) Choose $i \neq j$, and $\alpha = \sigma$ and deduce that $A^i_j = 0$, if $i \neq j$.

(*d*) Choose $i = j$, $\alpha = \sigma$, deduce that $A^\alpha_\alpha = A^i_i$, no sum on α or i.

(*e*) Show that the diagonal elements of A^i_j are equal to some scalar $\phi(x)$ such that $A^i_j = \phi \delta^i_j$, (which is the structure of an isotropic tensor of rank two).

(9) If A^{ij}_{Kl} is an isotropic tensor (of rank four) prove that

$$A^{ij}_{Kl} = \phi(x) \delta^i_K \delta^j_l + f(x) \delta^i_l \delta^j_K .$$

(10) Use this last result to show that

$$C_{ijKl} = \lambda \delta_{ij} \delta_{Kl} + \mu(\delta_{iK}\delta_{jl} + \delta_{jK}\delta_{il}) .$$

(11) A fluid is called barotropic if the pressure and density surfaces coincide at every point and at all times, *i.e.*, $\rho = \rho(p)$. Prove that if a frictionless barotropic fluid has zero vorticity at some initial time then the vorticity is zero for all time.

(12) Let μ/ρ define the kinematic coefficient of viscosity and prove that for an incompressible fluid acted upon by conservative body forces the vorticity satisfies the following equation,

$$\frac{d}{dt} \nabla \mathbf{x} \mathbf{v} = (\nabla \mathbf{x} \mathbf{v} \cdot \nabla)\mathbf{v} + \frac{\mu}{\rho} \nabla^2 (\nabla \mathbf{x} \mathbf{v}) .$$

(13) Consider a one-dimensional real fluid flow which is governed by the mass and momentum conservation equations

$$\frac{\partial \rho}{\partial t} + \frac{\partial}{\partial x} (\rho v) = 0 ,$$

$$\rho \frac{\partial v}{\partial t} + \rho v \frac{\partial v}{\partial x} + \frac{\partial P}{\partial x} - \frac{\partial}{\partial x} \left(\mu_2 \frac{\partial v}{\partial x} \right) = 0 ,$$

where $v = v(x)$ is the velocity of the fluid in the x-direction, ρ is the fluid density, P the thermodynamic pressure and μ_2 is the longitudinal viscosity

$$\left[\mu_2 = \frac{4}{3} \mu + \frac{1}{3} (2\mu + 3\lambda) \right] .$$

(*a*) Define a mass coordinate M by the formula

$$dM \equiv \rho dx - \rho v dt$$

and show that the two conservation equations can be written respectively, as

$$\frac{\partial}{\partial t} \rho^{-1} - \frac{\partial v}{\partial M} = 0 ,$$

$$\frac{\partial v}{\partial t} + \frac{\partial P}{\partial M} - \frac{\partial}{\partial M} \left(\mu_2 \rho \frac{\partial v}{\partial M} \right) = 0 .$$

(*b*) Prove that the equation of continuity implies the existence of the mass coordinate. Is the first equation of (*a*) an integrability condition for x in the definition of M?

(*c*) Derive the following equation;

$$\frac{\partial^2}{\partial t^2}\rho^{-1} + \frac{\partial^2 P}{\partial M^2} - \frac{\partial^2}{\partial M^2}\left[\mu_2 \rho \frac{\partial}{\partial t}\rho^{-1}\right] = 0 .$$

(*d*) Let S be the entropy per unit mass of fluid, T the absolute temperature and k the thermal conductivity, assume the validity of the following relation (uniform composition)

$$\rho T \frac{\partial S}{\partial t} + \rho v T \frac{\partial S}{\partial x} - \frac{\partial}{\partial x}\left(k \frac{\partial T}{\partial x}\right) - \mu_2 \left(\frac{\partial v}{\partial x}\right)^2 = 0 ,$$

transform this equation into the following

$$T \frac{\partial S}{\partial t} - \frac{\partial}{\partial M}\left(k\rho \frac{\partial T}{\partial M}\right) - \mu_2 \rho \left[\frac{\partial}{\partial t}(\rho^{-1})\right]^2 = 0 .$$

(*e*) Suppose this last equation and that of (*c*) are given. How many relations must exist between $(\rho, P, T, S, \mu_2, k)$ to completely describe the exact one-dimensional fluid flow?

(14) Assume a polytropic process of the form

$$P = P_0\left(\frac{\rho}{\rho_0}\right)^{\gamma} ,$$

where P_0, ρ_0 are constants, and let the longitudinal viscosity be given by

$$\mu_2 = \mu_{2,0}\left(\frac{P}{P_0}\frac{\rho_0}{\rho}\right)^{1/2} ,$$

where $\mu_{2,0}$ is a constant.

(*a*) Using the above relations and (13c) find the partial differential equation satisfied by P.

(*b*) Show that for a perfect gas μ_2 is proportional to $T^{1/2}$.

(*c*) Let α be an arbitrary positive constant, prove that if t is replaced by αt and P by $(\alpha)^{-2\gamma/(\gamma+1)}P$ the partial differential equation derived in (*a*) remains invariant, and solutions of the form

$$P = P_0 \left[\frac{\gamma(\gamma+1)P_0}{(\gamma-1)\mu_{2,0}} t\phi(\xi)\right]^{-2\gamma/(\gamma+1)}$$

are also invariant, where

$$\xi = \frac{(\gamma+1)}{(\gamma-1)\mu_{2,0}}\left(\frac{\gamma P_0}{\rho_0}\right)^{1/2} M \ .$$

(*d*) Find the ordinary differential equation satisfied by $\phi(\xi)$ and hence the integral form of ξ.

(*e*) Discuss the solution for $\gamma = 5/3$ and interpret physically.

(15) Assume a "tangent gas" description

$$P - P_0 = C^2(\rho_0^{-1} - \rho^{-1}) \ , \quad P_0 > 0 \ , \quad \rho_0 > 0 \ , \quad C > 0 \ ,$$

such that

$$|P - P_0| \leq \frac{1}{4} P_0 \quad \text{and} \quad \mu_2\rho = 2\beta = \text{constant}, \ \beta > 0 \ .$$

(*a*) Show that eq. (13c) reduces to the linear partial differential equation

$$\frac{\partial^2 P}{\partial t^2} - C^2 \frac{\partial^2 P}{\partial M^2} - 2\beta \frac{\partial^3 P}{\partial M^2 \partial t} = 0 \ .$$

(*b*) Prove that this equation has the general solution

$$P - P_0 = \int_{-\infty}^{\infty} [A(K) \exp(iKM - \nu_1 t) + B(K) \exp(iKM - \nu_2 t)]\, dK \ ,$$

where

$$\nu_{1,2} = \beta K^2 \pm iCK \left[1 - \left(\frac{\beta K}{C}\right)^2\right]^{1/2} \quad \text{for } |K| \leq \frac{C}{\beta} ,$$

$$\nu_{1,2} = \beta K^2 \left\{1 \pm \left[1 - \left(\frac{C}{\beta K}\right)^2\right]^{1/2}\right\} \quad \text{for } |K| \geq \frac{C}{\beta} .$$

(*c*) How are $A(K)$, $B(K)$ determined?

(*d*) Define the critical wave number $K_c = C/\beta$ and show that if $|K| \geq K_c$, propagation of a spectral component is not possible mathematically. What is the physical significance of K_c?

(*e*) Show that for weak shocks a pressure wave will eventually increase its width proportional to $t^{1/2}$, *i.e.*, consider the viscous dispersion of a pressure pulse at $t = 0$.

PROBLEMS FOR CHAPTER IV

(1) Assume that thermal motion of electrons is neglected and the ions are at rest, the collision free system is over-all neutral and there is no external magnetic field. With the usual assumptions, show that the equations of motion are

(*a*)
$$\frac{\partial n}{\partial t} + N_0 \nabla \cdot \mathbf{v} = 0 \ ,$$

$$m \frac{\partial \mathbf{v}}{\partial t} + e\mathbf{E} = 0 \ ,$$

(b) For longitudinal oscillations **E** satisfies Poisson's equation

$$.\nabla \cdot \epsilon_0 \mathbf{E} = - en \ ,$$

show that density fluctuations exhibit sinusoidal oscillations with a frequency equal to the plasma frequency.

(*c*) Can a wave packet propagate through such a plasma?

(*d*) What is the group velocity of the waves obtained in (*b*)?

(2) With the same assumptions as in the above problem show that the transverse plasma oscillations are governed by the following set of equations

(*a*)
$$\frac{\partial n}{\partial t} + N_0 \nabla \cdot \mathbf{v} = 0 \ ,$$

$$m \frac{\partial \mathbf{v}}{\partial t} + e\mathbf{E} = 0 \ ,$$

$$\nabla \mathbf{x} \mathbf{E} + \mu_0 \frac{\partial \mathbf{h}}{\partial t} = 0 \ ,$$

$$\nabla \mathbf{x} \mathbf{h} = - N_0 e \mathbf{v} + \epsilon_0 \frac{\partial \mathbf{E}}{\partial t} \ ;$$

(*b*) Show that the equation governing the electric field is

$$\frac{\partial^2 \mathbf{E}}{\partial t^2} + \omega_c^2 \mathbf{E} + (\mu_0 \epsilon_0)^{-1} \nabla \mathbf{x} \nabla \mathbf{x} \mathbf{E} \quad ;$$

(*c*) Assume **E** has a plane wave structure, derive the dispersion relation for transverse oscillations from the requirement that

$$\mathbf{K} \mathbf{x} \mathbf{E} \neq 0 \quad .$$

(*d*) Show that a wave packet propagates through such a medium with a group velocity given by

$$\mathbf{V}_g = \frac{\mathbf{K}}{K\left[\mu_0 \epsilon_0 \left(1 + \dfrac{\mu_0 \epsilon_0 \omega_c^2}{K^2}\right)\right]^{1/2}} \quad .$$

(3) By taking into account the thermal motions of the electrons but assuming the low temperature approximation, that is, $\omega^2/K^2 >> kT/m$, and with the same assumptions as in the previous problems, show that if we use the adiabatic relation $d/dt(p\rho^{-\gamma}) = 0$ for the electrons, where γ is the ratio of specific heats, the dispersion relation for longitudinal oscillations is given by

$$\omega^2 = \omega_c^2 + \gamma \frac{kT}{m} K^2 \quad .$$

(4) If in the previous problem we define the displacement of the electron by

$$\mathbf{v} = \frac{\partial \mathbf{u}}{\partial t} \quad ,$$

and replace the adiabatic law by the tensor equation

$$p_{ij} = -p(\nabla \cdot \mathbf{u})\delta_{ij} - p\left[\frac{\partial u_i}{\partial x_j} + \frac{\partial u_j}{\partial x_i}\right] \quad ,$$

and assume a plane wave structure for all quantities, the dispersion relation for longitudinal oscillations is now given by

$$\omega^2 = \omega_c^2 + 3 \frac{kT}{m} K^2 \quad ,$$

while for the transverse modes there results

$$\omega^2 = \omega_c^2 + \frac{K^2}{\mu_0 \epsilon_0} + K^2 \frac{(kT)}{m} \left[\frac{\omega_c^2}{\omega_c^2 + \dfrac{K^2}{\mu_0 \epsilon_0}} \right] \quad .$$

What is the physical significance of the perturbed tensor relation?

(5) Assume a collision free neutral ion-electron plasma in the absence of an external magnetic field. Let p_{ij} now denote the perturbation tensor of the ions, and m_i the mass of an ion. Show that the linearized equations of motion are

(*a*) $$\frac{\partial n_i}{\partial t} + N_i \nabla \cdot \mathbf{v} = 0 \quad ,$$

$$m_i N_i \frac{\partial \mathbf{v}}{\partial t} = - \operatorname{div} p_{ij} + N_i e \mathbf{E} \quad ,$$

$$\frac{\partial}{\partial t} p_{ij} = - p(\nabla \cdot \mathbf{v}) \delta_{ij} - p\left[(\nabla \mathbf{v})_{ij} + (\nabla \mathbf{v})_{ji}\right] \quad ,$$

$$\nabla \cdot \epsilon_0 \mathbf{E} = e(n_i - n_e) \quad ,$$

where $(\nabla \mathbf{v})_{ij}$ is a dyadic and $(\nabla \mathbf{v})_{ji}$ its transpose, N_i is the ion density.

(*b*) Let $\mathbf{E} = - \nabla \phi$, where ϕ is the electrostatic potential, and assume

$$n_e = N_i \left[\exp \frac{e\phi}{kT_e} - 1 \right] \quad ,$$

where T_e is the electron temperature. Derive the dispersion relation for longitudinal oscillations,

$$\omega^2 = \frac{1}{1 + (K\lambda_d)^{-2}}\,\omega^2_{c,i} + 3K^2\,\frac{kT_i}{m_i} ,$$

where

$$\omega^2_{c,i} = \frac{N_i e^2}{\epsilon_0 m_i}$$ and T_i is the ion temperature,

$$\lambda_d^2 = \frac{kT_e}{N_i e^2}$$ is the square of the Debye shielding distance.

(*c*) What is the physical significance of λ_d?

(*d*) If $K\lambda_d << 1$, what is the form of the dispersion relation?

(*e*) When can the thermal motions of the ions be neglected?

(*f*) If $T_i < T_e$ but not very much smaller than T_e, what can be inferred about the ion oscillations? Strongly damped? Weakly damped?

(6) Consider a uniform collisionless, two species plasma of electrons and ions in the presence of a uniform external magnetic field $\mathbf{B}_0$. Assume further that the plasma is cold. If in the equilibrium state each constituent has a constant velocity $\mathbf{V}_0$, and if all quantities have a plane wave structure, show from the linearized equations of motion that the perturbed densities are given by

(*a*) $$n = \frac{N_0}{(\omega - \mathbf{K}\cdot\mathbf{V}_0)}\,(\mathbf{K}\cdot\mathbf{v}) \;;$$

and

$$i(\omega - \mathbf{K}\cdot\mathbf{V}_0)\mathbf{v} = \frac{e}{m}\,[\mathbf{E} + \mathbf{V}_0\mathbf{x}\mathbf{B}_0] - \frac{e}{m}\,\mathbf{B}_0\mathbf{x}\mathbf{V}_0 \quad .$$

(*b*) Interpret the term $\omega - \mathbf{K}\cdot\mathbf{V}_0$. Is $\mathbf{K}\cdot\mathbf{V}_0$ the Doppler shift? To what is it due?

(*c*) From Maxwell's equations and the results from (*a*), find an expression for $\mathbf{v}$.

(*d*) Using the results of part (*a*), show that the current density arising from the oscillations is

$$\mathbf{J} = \Sigma\, e_r N_r \left(\mathbf{v}_r + \frac{\mathbf{K} \cdot \mathbf{v}_r}{\omega - \mathbf{K} \cdot \mathbf{V}_0} \mathbf{V}_0 \right) ,$$

where the sum is over ions and electrons.

(*e*) Using Maxwell's equations again and (*d*) show that

$$[\omega^2 - (\mu_0 \epsilon_0)^{-1} K^2] \epsilon_0 \mathbf{E} + (\mu_0 \epsilon_0)^{-1} \mathbf{K}(\mathbf{K} \cdot \epsilon_0 \mathbf{E}) - i\omega\, \Sigma\, e_r N_r \left(\mathbf{v}_r + \frac{\mathbf{K} \cdot \mathbf{v}_r}{\omega - \mathbf{K} \cdot \mathbf{V}_0} \mathbf{V}_0 \right) = 0 .$$

(*f*) Use the results from (*c*) and (*e*) to establish the homogeneous system of equations

$$\mathbf{AE} = 0 ,$$

and show that **A** is an Hermitian matrix.

(*g*) The dispersion relation is obtained by setting the det **A** = 0, why?

(7) Consider a static plasma by setting $\mathbf{V}_0 = 0$ in the previous problems.

(*a*) Let **K** be directed along the positive x_3-axis of a rectangular Cartesian system, choose $\mathbf{B}_0$ in the $x_1 x_3$ plane and denote by θ the angle between $\mathbf{B}_0$ and the x_3-axis. Show, under these conditions, that the matrix **A** is defined by

$$A_{11} = \omega^2 - (\mu_0 \epsilon_0)^{-1} K^2 - \Sigma\, \omega_{c,r}^2 + \sum \frac{\omega_{c,r}^2 \Omega_r^2 \cos^2 \theta}{\Omega_r^2 - 1} ,$$

$$A_{12} = - A_{21} = - \Sigma\, i\omega_{c,r}^2 \frac{\Omega_r \cos \theta}{\Omega_r^2 - 1} ,$$

$$A_{13} = A_{31} = - \Sigma\, \omega_{c,r}^2 \frac{\Omega_r^2}{\Omega_r^2 - 1} \sin \theta \cos \theta ,$$

$$A_{22} = \omega^2 - (\mu_0\epsilon_0)^{-1}K^2 - \Sigma\,\omega_{c,r}^2 + \Sigma\,\omega_{c,r}^2 \frac{\Omega_r^2}{\Omega_r^2 - 1} ,$$

$$A_{23} = -A_{32} = -i\,\Sigma\,\omega_{c,r}^2 \frac{\Omega_r \sin\theta}{\Omega_r^2 - 1} ,$$

$$A_{33} = \omega^2 - \Sigma\,\omega_{c,r}^2 + \Sigma\,\omega_{c,r}^2 \frac{\Omega_r^2 \sin^2\theta}{\Omega_r^2 - 1} .$$

(*b*) Put $\theta = 0$ and obtain the dispersion relation for longitudinal oscillations,

$$\omega^2 = \Sigma\,\omega_{c,r}^2$$

and show that this is approximately equal to the square of the electron plasma frequency.

(*c*) Show that the transverse oscillations are circularly polarized and defined by

$$\left[\omega^2 - (\mu_0\epsilon_0)^{-1}K^2 - \Sigma\,\omega_{c,r}^2 \frac{1}{1 \mp \Omega_r}\right](E_1 \pm iE_2) = 0 .$$

(*d*) If Ω_i denotes the normalized ion gyro-frequency and Ω_e for electrons, show that for high frequency oscillations, that is, $\Omega_i << 1$, the dispersion relation obtained from part (*c*) above, becomes

$$\omega^2 - (\mu_0\epsilon_0)^{-1}K^2 - \omega_{c,e}^2\left(\frac{1}{1 + \Omega_e}\right)\omega^2_{c,i} \approx 0 .$$

What does this become if also $\Omega_e << 1$?

(*e*) Let $\Omega_e \approx 1$, show that the relation given in (*d*) becomes

$$-\Omega_e\left[1 - \frac{a_e}{\Omega_e^2 - (1 + a_e)}\right] \approx 1 ,$$

where

$$a_e = \frac{\omega_{c,e}^2}{\omega^2} .$$

Find the necessary condition for the above relation to hold.

(f) Let $\Omega_i > 1$, (low frequency case), show that the dispersion relation from (c) becomes,

$$\omega^2 - (\mu_0\epsilon_0)^{-1}K^2 + \omega_{c,i}^2\Omega_i^{-1}(1 + \Omega_i^{-1}) - \omega_{c,e}^2\Omega_e^{-1} \approx 0 .$$

(g) Show from the condition of neutrality of the plasma that the above equation gives

$$\omega^2 = \frac{\mu_0\epsilon_0 K^2}{1 + \dfrac{1}{\mu_0\epsilon_0 V_A^2}}$$

where V_A is the Alfvén speed.

(h) Assume $1/\mu_0\epsilon_0 V_A^2 >> 1$, find $(\omega/K)^2$. If $1/\mu_0\epsilon V_A^2 << 1$, find $(\omega/K)^2$.

(i) Let $\Omega_i \approx 1$, then $\Omega_e > 1$, show in this case that the dispersion relation in part (c) now reduces to

$$\omega^2 - (\mu_0\epsilon_0)^{-1}K^2 - \omega_{c,i}^2 - \omega_{c,i}^2\frac{\Omega_i}{1 - \Omega_i} \approx 0 ,$$

if

$$\Omega_i^2 >> a_i + (\mu_0\epsilon_0)^{-1}\left(\frac{K}{\omega}\right)^2 ,$$

find an expression for ω.

(8) Take the plasma as in problem (6), but now set $\theta = \pi/2$ and $\mathbf{V}_0 = 0$.

(a) If the $\mathbf{E}$ field is parallel to $\mathbf{B}_0$, show that the dispersion relation obtained from det $\mathbf{A} = 0$ for this case is

$$\omega^2 \approx (\mu_0\epsilon_0)^{-1}K^2 + \omega_{c,e}^2 .$$

(*b*) For the remaining two modes, determine the dispersion equation.

(*c*) In (*b*), suppose $\omega \ll (\mu_0 \epsilon_0)^{-\frac{1}{2}} K$. Show that the dispersion relation reduces to

$$1 + \frac{a_i}{\Omega_i^2 - 1} + \frac{a_e}{\Omega_e^2 - 1} \approx 0 \quad .$$

Now assume, $\Omega_i \ll 1 \ll \Omega_e \ll \sqrt{a_e}$, and show that

$$(\Omega_e \Omega_i)^{\frac{1}{2}} \approx 1 \quad .$$

Interpret this result.

(*d*) Using (*b*), now let $\Omega_i^2 \ll 1$, and $a_i \ll 1$. Show that

$$(\Omega_e^2 + a_e)^{\frac{1}{2}} \approx 1 \quad .$$

Interpret this equation.

(*e*) Using (*b*) again, discuss the high frequency case, $\Omega_i \ll 1$ and $a_i \ll 1$.

(9) Using the results of 6(*f*) and 7(*a*) discuss the weak magnetic field case $\Omega_e \ll 1$.

(*a*) Assume $\Omega_r \approx 0$, derive the conclusion that $E_3 = 0$.

(*b*) What does this imply about the coupling of the longitudinal and transverse modes?

(*c*) Neglecting terms of order Ω_e^2 and higher, derive the elements of the matrix in

$$\mathbf{B}\mathbf{E}_t = 0$$

where

$$\mathbf{E}_t = \begin{pmatrix} E_1 \\ E_2 \end{pmatrix} \quad ,$$

and discuss the polarization.

(*d*) Using the results from (*c*) in the weak field approximation find the dispersion equation neglecting terms of Ω_e^3 and higher.

(*e*) Evaluate the relation for $\theta = 0$ and $\theta = \pi/2$.

(*f*) Discuss the coupling of the longitudinal and transverse waves and their polarization.

(10) Now consider the case of strong magnetic field, $\Omega_i >> 1$, neglect terms of order Ω_r^3 and higher, find the dispersion equation from 6(*f*) and 7(*a*).

(*a*) Using the neutrality condition, show that one root of the dispersion equation is

$$\omega = \left[\frac{(\mu_0\epsilon_0)^{-1}K^2}{1 + \dfrac{1}{\mu_0\epsilon_0 V_A^2}}\right]^{1/2},$$

which is the dispersion relation for the extraordinary hydro-magnetic wave and shows the influence of a strong magnetic field which gives rise to it.

(*b*) Assume $\mu_0\epsilon_0 V_A^2 << 1$, find the roots of the remaining two modes.

(*c*) Under what conditions does a pure Alfvén mode, $\omega^2 = K^2V_A^2$, occur?

PROBLEMS FOR CHAPTER V

(1) Prove that for an isotropic, non-conducting, compressible fluid in an electromagnetic field, the Helmholtz free energy per unit mass $A(\rho, T, \mathbf{B}, \mathbf{D})$ must have the form

$$A = A(\rho, T, B^2, D^2, \mathbf{B} \cdot \mathbf{D}) \quad .$$

(2) From the fact that the state function $A(\rho, T, \mathbf{B}, \mathbf{D})$ yields an exact differential dA, deduce the relations (52.10 – 52.13).

(3) Consider a fluid whose electrical properties are defined by $\mathbf{D} = \epsilon(\rho, T)$, $\mathbf{B} = \mu(\rho, T)\mathbf{H}$. Use the results of problem (2) to obtain

$$A = \frac{1}{2\rho}\left[\frac{D^2}{\epsilon} + \frac{B^2}{\mu}\right] + A^{(m)}(\rho, T)$$

where $A^{(m)}(\rho, T)$ is an arbitrary function of (ρ, T), and is strictly the mechanical part of A.

(4) If $A^{(m)}(\rho, T)$ is the free energy of a perfect gas, find

$$A = A^{(e)} + A^{(m)} \quad .$$

(5) Use eq. (52.13) together with the results of problem (4) to find

$$p = \rho RT + \frac{1}{2}(\mathbf{B} \cdot \mathbf{H} + \mathbf{D} \cdot \mathbf{E}) - \frac{1}{2}\left(\rho H^2 \frac{\partial \mu}{\partial \rho} + \rho E^2 \frac{\partial \epsilon}{\partial \rho}\right)$$

and interpret the terms.

(6) For the perfect gas, calculate:

(*a*) Entropy, internal energy and enthalpy per unit mass.

(*b*) Separate in each of the above, the terms of mechanical and electromagnetic origin.

(7) For the perfect gas show that

$$\tau_{ij}^{(e)} = -\frac{1}{2}\left[\mathbf{D}\cdot\mathbf{E} + \mathbf{B}\cdot\mathbf{H} - \rho E^2 \frac{\partial\epsilon}{\partial\rho} - \rho H^2 \frac{\partial\mu}{\partial\rho}\right]\delta_{ij} + D_i E_j + B_i H_j$$

(8) Derive completely eq. (51.21).

(9) For the perfect gas, derive the expression for the ponderomotive force.

(10) Consider a parallel plate condenser such that the distance between the plates is very much smaller than all other dimensions. Let the space between the plates be filled with a compressible fluid with a dielectric constant ϵ. Now apply a voltage across the plates and maintain the voltage difference by moving a certain amount of charge from one plate to the other. Suppose also that the distance between the plates is changed by a differential amount. Show that the total stress due to both mechanical and electromagnetic effects is

(a) $\tau_{ij} = -p\delta_{ij} + D_i E_j$, and that the work done per unit mass of the medium is

(b) $dW = -pd(1/\rho) + Ed(D/\rho)$.

(11) Consider a non-viscous, perfect, compressible plasma undergoing isentropic motion in an electromagnetic field. As in Chapter III, let $\mathbf{r} = \mathbf{r}(\alpha_1,\alpha_2,\alpha_3,t) \approx \mathbf{r}(\alpha,t)$ define the particle paths of the fluid, and let $J(\mathbf{r};\alpha) = (\partial\mathbf{r}/\partial\alpha)$ denote the Jacobian of the transformation from $\alpha \rightarrow \mathbf{r}$, so that volume elements in both spaces are related by $d^3\mathbf{r} = Jd^3\alpha$. Show that the Lagrangian density function which describes the system consists of three terms, a mechanical, an electromagnetic and an interaction term, where

(a) $$L^{(m)} = \frac{1}{2}\rho(\alpha)\mathbf{v}\cdot\mathbf{v} - \rho(\alpha)A(\rho,T) \quad ,$$

$$L^{(e)} = J(\mathbf{r},\alpha)\left[\frac{1}{2}\epsilon\left(-\nabla\phi - \frac{\partial\mathbf{A}}{\partial t}\right)^2 - \frac{1}{2}\mu^{-1}(\nabla\mathbf{x}\mathbf{A})^2\right]$$

$$L^{(i)} = -\rho_e(\alpha)[\phi - \mathbf{v}(\alpha,t)\cdot\mathbf{A}] \quad ;$$

ϕ and $\mathbf{A}$ are respectively the scalar and vector potentials of the electromagnetic field, $\mathbf{v}$ is the velocity of the fluid referred to the stationary observer's inertial frame. Both ϕ and $\mathbf{A}$ are also functions of (α, t). From the kinematic constraints,

$$J\rho(\mathbf{r}, t) = \rho(\alpha, t) \;;\quad J\rho_e(\mathbf{r}, t) = \rho_e(\alpha, t)$$

prove that

$$(b) \qquad \frac{dJ}{dt} = J\nabla \cdot \mathbf{v}$$

(12) In the preceding problem, let $\lambda_i(\alpha, t)$, $i = 1, 2$, be Lagrange multipliers and construct the functional

$$I = \int_{t_1}^{t_2} dt \int d^3\alpha \left\{ L + \lambda_1 \left[J - \frac{\rho(\alpha, t)}{\rho} \right] + \lambda_2 \left[J - \frac{\rho_e(\alpha, t)}{\rho_e} \right] \right\} .$$

Take the first variation of I with respect to ϕ, and by imposing the proper boundary conditions in space and time deduce that

(a) $\delta I = 0$ for arbitrary $\delta\phi$ implies

$$\epsilon J\nabla \cdot \left(-\nabla\phi - \frac{\partial \mathbf{A}}{\partial t} \right) = \rho_e(\alpha, t)$$

or,

$$\rho(\mathbf{r}, t) = \epsilon\nabla \cdot \mathbf{E} \quad ,$$

where

$$\mathbf{E} = -\nabla\phi - \frac{\partial \mathbf{A}}{\partial t} .$$

(b) $\delta I = 0$ for arbitrary $\delta\mathbf{A}$ implies

$$\nabla \mathbf{x} \nabla \mathbf{x} \mathbf{A} = \mu\epsilon \frac{\partial \mathbf{E}}{\partial t} + \mu\rho_e \mathbf{v} .$$

(c) By setting $\mathbf{B} = \nabla \mathbf{x} \mathbf{A}$ show that the results of (a) and (b) yield Maxwell's equations.

(*d*) Show that the λ_2 multiplier can be omitted from the functional I in the sense that it yields no new result other than the continuity equation for the fluid charge density.

(13) In problem (11) define a new parameter "a" such that the free energy

$$A(\rho,T) \equiv A\left(\rho, \frac{da}{dt}\right) .$$

Using eqs. (52.10) and (52.13) and setting the electromagnetic field quantities to zero in the latter, show that

(*a*) $\delta I = 0$ for arbitrary δa implies

$$\frac{dS}{dt} = 0 .$$

(*b*) What does a variation in λ_1 yield?

(*c*) Prove first that

$$\delta J = J\,\frac{\partial(\delta\mathbf{r})}{\partial\mathbf{r}} , \quad \delta\rho = -\rho\,\frac{\partial(\delta\mathbf{r})}{\partial\mathbf{r}} , \quad \delta T = \frac{d}{dt}\left(\frac{\partial a}{\partial\mathbf{r}} \cdot \delta\mathbf{r}\right) ,$$

and

$$\delta \iint dt\,d^3\alpha\, J\left[\frac{1}{2}\,\epsilon\mathbf{E}\cdot\mathbf{E} - \frac{1}{2}\,\mu^{-1}\mathbf{B}\cdot\mathbf{B}\right] = 0$$

for variations $\delta\mathbf{r}$, hence, deduce that $\delta I = 0$ for arbitrary $\delta\mathbf{r}$ implies

$$\rho\,\frac{d\mathbf{v}}{dt} + \nabla p = \rho_e(\mathbf{E} + \mathbf{v}\mathrm{x}\mathbf{B}) .$$

(14) The results of problems (11), (12), and (13) show that there exists a variational principle for the fluid and field equations of the above stated plasma when the Lagrangian density is given by 11a. Is the Lagrangian unique, that is, do there exist other Lagrangian densities which yield the same equations? Compare this situation with Poynting's Theorem.

PROBLEMS FOR CHAPTER VI

(1) Let a plane wave whose electric vector is perpendicular to the plane of incidence be incident obliquely from a homogeneous medium characterized by (ϵ_0,μ) on to the plane surface of a semi-infinite medium characterized by (ϵ,μ) in which ϵ varies in a direction perpendicular to the surface. Choose the interface between the media as the $x_1 - x_2$ plane; take the x_3-axis which is perpendicular to the plane as positive for points in the homogeneous medium and negative for points in the inhomogeneous medium.

(*a*) If the electric vector of the incident wave is parallel to the surface, with amplitude $\mathbf{E}_0$, varying as $e^{i\omega t}$, and if θ is the angle of incidence show that the resultant electric field in the homogeneous medium has only an x_2-component and has the form

$$E_{0,2} = E_0(e^{ik_0x_3 \cos\theta} + Re^{-ik_0x_3 \cos\theta}) \exp(i\omega t - ik_0x_1 \sin\theta)$$

where $k_0^2 = \epsilon_0\mu\omega^2$, and R is the reflection coefficient.

(*b*) Show that the electric vector in the inhomogeneous medium has only an x_2-component and can be written as

$$E_2 = E(x_3)e^{i\omega t - ik_0x \sin\theta} .$$

(*c*) Show that Maxwell's equations in the inhomogeneous medium are given by

$$i\mu\omega H_1 = -\frac{\partial E_2}{\partial x_3}$$

$$i\mu\omega H_3 = -ik_0E_2 \sin\theta$$

$$-i\omega\epsilon(x_3)E_2 = \frac{\partial H_1}{\partial x_3} + ik_0H_3 \sin\theta$$

and that E_2 satisfies

$$\frac{\partial^2 E_2}{\partial x_3^2} + [k^2(x_3) - k_0^2 \sin^2\theta]E_2 = 0 ,$$

where

$$k^2(x_3) = \epsilon(x_3)\mu\omega^2 .$$

(*d*) Assume that

$$\epsilon(0) = \epsilon_1 , \ \epsilon(-\infty) = \epsilon_2$$

such that

$$\epsilon(x_3) = (\epsilon_1 - \epsilon_2)e^{\beta x_3} + \epsilon_2 , \quad x_3 \leq 0 , \quad \beta > 0 ,$$

and find the equation satisfied by $E(x_3)$.

(*e*) Define a new variable,

$$u = \left(\frac{2}{\beta}\right) e^{\beta x_3 / 2} (k_1^2 - k_2^2)^{1/2} ,$$

where

$$k_1^2 = \epsilon_1\mu\omega^2, \quad k_2^2 = \epsilon_2\mu\omega^2 ,$$

and deduce that E satisfies

$$u^2 \frac{d^2E}{du^2} + u \frac{dE}{du} + \left[u^2 + \left(\frac{2}{\beta}\right)^2 (k_2^2 - k_0^2 \sin^2 \theta)\right]E = 0 .$$

(*f*) Assume a solution of the form $E = E_0 T J_\nu(u)$, where T is an arbitrary constant, $J_\nu(u)$ is a Bessel function of the first kind,

$$\nu = [k_0^2 \sin^2 \theta - k_2^2]^{1/2} ,$$

and apply the boundary conditions:

E_{02}, E_2, H_{01}, H_1 are continuous at $x_3 = 0$ to find

$$1 + R = TJ_\nu(u_0) = \frac{2ik_0 J_\nu(u_0) \cos\theta}{J_\nu(u_0) ik_0 \cos\theta + (k_1^2 - k_2^2)^{1/2} J_\nu'(u_0)}$$

where,

$$u_0 = \frac{2(k_1^2 - k_2^2)^{1/2}}{\beta} ,$$

and the prime means differentiation with respect to the argument of the Bessel function. Why is the Bessel function of the second kind not permitted?

(g) Show that if

$$\frac{(k_1^2 - k_2^2)^{1/2}}{\beta} << 1 ,$$

then

$$1 + R = \frac{2k_0 \cos\theta}{k_0 \cos\theta + (k_2^2 - k_0^2 \sin^2\theta)^{1/2}} .$$

Interpret this Fresnel equation.

(2) Consider the same problem as in (1) but now let the electric vector be parallel to the plane of incidence. In this case, obtain the solution for the magnetic field vectors in both regions. For simplicity, assume normal incidence and that the *WKB* approximation is valid, find the reflection and transmission coefficients.

(3) Consider a stationary, almost homogeneous medium characterized by a refractive index $M = M_1[1 + n(\mathbf{r})]$, where M_1 is a dimensionless constant and slightly greater than unity and $|n(\mathbf{r})| << 1$. The permeability of the medium is μ_1 and is constant. Let the permittivity be given by

$$\epsilon(\mathbf{r}) = \epsilon_1[1 + 2n(\mathbf{r})] ,$$

where

$$\epsilon_1 = \frac{M_1^2 \mu_0 \epsilon_0}{\mu_1} .$$

(*a*) By starting with the wave equation for **E** in a linear, isotropic, charge free medium of zero conductivity and assuming that

$$\text{div } \mathbf{E} \approx -2\mathbf{E} \cdot \text{grad } n$$

find the equation satisfied by **E**.

(*b*) If **E** has a sinusoidal time dependence

$$\mathbf{E}(\mathbf{r}, t) = \mathbf{E}_0(\mathbf{r}) \sin \omega t$$

show that $\mathbf{E}_0$ satisfies the equation

$$\nabla^2 \mathbf{E}_0 + \text{grad } (\mathbf{E}_0 \cdot \text{grad } n) + \left(\frac{2\pi}{\lambda_1}\right)^2 (1 + 2n)\mathbf{E}_0 = 0 ,$$

where,

$$\lambda_1 = \frac{2\pi}{\omega\sqrt{\mu_1 \epsilon_1}} .$$

(*c*) Let $\mathbf{E}_0$ denote the total field which consists of a weak scattered field $\mathbf{E}_s$ and a dominant homogeneous field $\overline{\mathbf{E}}$ such that

$$\nabla^2 \overline{\mathbf{E}} + \left(\frac{2\pi}{\lambda_1}\right)^2 \overline{\mathbf{E}} = 0 ,$$

show that if secondary scattering of the scattered field is neglected then

$$\nabla^2 \mathbf{E}_s + \left(\frac{2\pi}{\lambda_1}\right)^2 \mathbf{E}_s = -\left(\frac{8\pi^2}{\lambda_1^2}\right) n\overline{\mathbf{E}} - 2\text{grad}(\overline{\mathbf{E}} \cdot \text{grad } n)$$

so that $\overline{\mathbf{E}}$ is a source for the scattered field. Note that if n is arbitrary then the source field is arbitrary in direction and magnitude.

(*d*) Now choose

$$n(\mathbf{r}) = n_0 \exp\left(-\frac{r^2}{s^2}\right)$$

where n_0 is the maximum value of n and $r^2 = x_1^2 + x_2^2 + x_3^2$; s is called the anomaly radius, and let the incident direct field be a uniform plane wave with electric intensity parallel to the x_1-axis and propagating in the x_3-direction so that

$$\bar{\mathbf{E}} = A_0 \exp\left(-\frac{i2\pi x_3}{\lambda_1}\right)\mathbf{e}_1 ,$$

where $\mathbf{e}_1$ is a unit vector in the x_1-direction and A_0 is the constant amplitude. Using this form for the source field in (c) and from the theory of retarded potentials deduce that the components of the scattered field are given by

$$E_{s,1} = \frac{n_0 A_0}{4\pi}\int_{-\infty}^{\infty} d^3\xi \, \frac{4}{R}\left[\frac{2\pi^2}{\lambda_1^2} + \frac{2\xi_1^2 - s^2}{s^4}\right]\rho(\xi)$$

$$E_{s,2} = \frac{n_0 A_0}{4\pi}\int_{-\infty}^{\infty} d^3\xi \, \frac{8}{R}\,\frac{\xi_1\xi_2}{s^4}\,\rho(\xi)$$

$$E_{s,3} = \frac{n_0 A_0}{4\pi}\int_{-\infty}^{\infty} d^3\xi \, \frac{8}{R}\left[\frac{\xi_1\xi_3}{s^4} + \frac{i\pi}{\lambda_1}\,\frac{\xi_1}{s^2}\right]\rho(\xi)$$

where $\xi \equiv (\xi_1, \xi_2, \xi_3)$ denotes the variables of integration, $d^3\xi = d\xi_1 d\xi_2 d\xi_3$,

$$\rho(\xi) = \exp\left[-\frac{(\xi_1^2 + \xi_2^2 + \xi_3^2)}{s^2} - \frac{i2\pi(\xi_3 + R)}{\lambda_1}\right] ,$$

and

$$R^2 = |\mathbf{r} - \xi|^2 .$$

(*e*) Evaluate the integrals above in the far field region by using the approximation $R \approx r - [(\mathbf{r} \cdot \xi)/r]$ in the expression for $\rho(\xi)$, and show that

$$E_{s,1} \approx C \left(1 - \frac{x_1^2}{r^2}\right) \exp\ (D) \quad ,$$

$$E_{s,2} \approx - C \frac{x_1 x_2}{r^2} \exp\ (D) \quad ,$$

$$E_{s,3} \approx - C \frac{x_1 x_3}{r^2} \exp\ (D) \ ,$$

where

$$C = n_0 A_0 \frac{\sqrt{\pi}}{2} \frac{s}{r} \left(\frac{2\pi s}{\lambda_1}\right)^2$$

and

$$D = - \frac{2\pi^2 s^2}{\lambda_1^2}\left(1 - \frac{x_3}{r}\right) - \frac{i\,2\pi}{\lambda_1} r \quad ,$$

provided $R \approx r$ in the denominators of the integrands.

(*f*) Find the magnitude q of the ratio of the scattered field strength to the incident field strength.

(*g*) Let σ be the scattering cross section defined by

$$\sigma = \int_0^{2\pi}\int_0^{\pi} q^2 r^2 \sin\theta d\theta d\phi$$

and calculate the ratio of σ to the "geometrical cross section" πs^2 and show that in the limit as $s \to \infty$,

$$\frac{\sigma}{\pi s^2} \to \left(32\pi^5 \frac{n_0^2}{3}\right)\left(\frac{s}{\lambda_1}\right)^4 \quad .$$

(*h*) Describe the class of physical processes for which the above treatment can be considered as applicable.

(4) In a plane stratified medium, the energy attenuation is defined by eq. (65.19). Assume that the relation (65.21) is satisfied and derive Martyn's theorem

$$\Delta(\phi_0, \omega, \nu) \approx \cos\phi_0 \Delta(0, \omega\cos\phi_0, \nu)$$

and interpret the result.

(5) In formula (65.1), the Eikonal equation, replace M^2 by the dielectric constant $\epsilon(\mathbf{r})$, using also eqs. (65.2) and (65.13) with $\mu_0 \neq 1$ deduce that

$$(a) \quad \left.\begin{array}{l} 2\mu^2\cos^2\phi \\ 2\chi^2 \end{array}\right\} = \pm\,(Re\epsilon - \mu_0^2\sin^2\phi_0) + [(Re\epsilon - \mu_0^2\sin^2\phi_0)^2 + (Im\epsilon)^2]^{1/2} .$$

(*b*) From eqs. (65.22) we have $Re\epsilon = p$, $Im\epsilon = q$, if either ν/ω or ω_c^2/ω^2 is sufficiently small, show that

$$\chi \approx \frac{Im\epsilon}{2[Re\epsilon - \mu_0^2\sin^2\phi_0]^{1/2}} = \frac{q}{2[p - \mu_0^2\sin^2\phi_0]^{1/2}} .$$

(*c*) The decrement of attenuation is defined by

$$\Delta = 2\frac{\omega}{V_0}\int \chi(x_3)dx_3 \quad ;$$

show that under the conditions stated in (b),

$$\Delta(\phi_0, \omega, \nu) = \frac{1}{V_0}\int \frac{\nu}{\omega}\frac{\omega^2 q}{[\omega^2(p - \mu_0^2\sin^2\phi_0)]^{1/2}}dx_3$$

$$= \Delta(0, \omega\cos\phi_0, \nu\cos\phi_0)$$

thus only for $(\nu/\omega)^2 << 1$ is the decrement simply proportional to the collision frequency and therefore

$$\Delta(\phi_0, \omega, \nu) = \cos\phi_0 \Delta(0, \omega\cos\phi_0, \nu)$$

which is Martyn's equivalence theorem.

(*d*) Show that if the expression on the right side of (a) is generalized to take into account the earth's curvature by replacing μ_0 with (μ_0/r), where r is the distance from the center of the earth, then no such equivalence theorems result. Note, we are thinking here that the stratified plasma region is the ionosphere.

(6) Consider a horizontally stratified plasma in which the magnetic field is not parallel with the x_3-axis. Starting with Maxwell's equations in the form

$$\nabla\mathbf{x}\mathbf{E} = -i\mu\omega\mathbf{H} \ ,$$

$$\nabla\mathbf{x}\mathbf{H} = -i\omega\epsilon_0\epsilon(x_3)\mathbf{E} \ ,$$

(*a*) Assume solutions of the form

$$\mathbf{E}(\mathbf{r}) = \mathbf{V}(x_3) \exp\left[-i\omega(p_1x_1 + p_2x_2)\right]$$

$$\mathbf{H}(\mathbf{r}) \quad \mathbf{I}(x_3) \exp\left[-i\omega(p_1x_1 + p_2x_2)\right]$$

and find $V_3(x_3)$ as a linear combination of $I_1(x_3), I_2(x_3), V_1(x_3)$ and $V_2(x_3)$; similarly for $I_3(x_3)$. Define the vector

$$\mathbf{W}(x_3) = \begin{pmatrix} V_1(x_3) \\ I_2(x_3) \\ I_1(x_3) \\ V_2(x_3) \end{pmatrix}$$

and show that $\mathbf{W}$ satisfies an equation of the form

$$\frac{d\mathbf{W}(x_3)}{dx_3} = -i\omega\mathbf{A}(x_3)\mathbf{W}(x_3) \ .$$

(*b*) Exhibit the structure of the complex matrix $\mathbf{A}(x_3)$ and show that it contains no zero elements in general.

(*c*) Let $\mathbf{P}(x_3)$ be a non-singular 4×4 matrix and define a new vector $\mathbf{u}(x_3)$ by the relation

$$\mathbf{W} = \mathbf{P}\mathbf{u} \quad ,$$

hence show that $\mathbf{u}$ satisfies the equation

$$\frac{d\mathbf{u}(x_3)}{dx_3} = -\left[i\omega \mathbf{P}^{-1}\mathbf{A}\mathbf{P} + \mathbf{P}^{-1}\frac{d\mathbf{P}}{dx_3}\right]\mathbf{u}(x_3) \; .$$

(*d*) If we put $p_1 = p_2 = 0$ (normal incidence), and rotate the x_1, x_2-plane about the x_3-axis so that the magnetic field lies in the x_2, x_3-plane, show that the matrix $\mathbf{A}(x_3)$ has the following structure

$$\mathbf{A}(x_3) = \begin{pmatrix} 0 & 1 & 0 & 0 \\ \alpha & 0 & 0 & \gamma \\ \gamma & 0 & 0 & -\beta \\ 0 & 0 & -1 & 0 \end{pmatrix}$$

also show that if $\gamma = 0$, then the matrix equation for $\mathbf{W}$ reduces to two independent systems of two equations each, so that γ is a measure of the coupling between waves defined by the orthogonal pairs (V_1, I_2) and (I_1, V_2) of the field components. In particular show that $I_3(x_3) = 0$ and that $V_3(x_3)$ is a linear combination of only V_1 and V_2. What is the advantage of this form of the equations? What is the disadvantage?

(7) In the previous problem, introduce a (formal) variable Lorentz transformation (rotation through a complex angle) of the electric and magnetic field components separately as follows

$$\mathbf{P}(x_3) = [1 - \mu^2(x_3)]^{-1/2} \begin{pmatrix} u & 0 & 0 & 1 \\ 0 & -u & 1 & 0 \\ 0 & 1 & -u & 0 \\ 1 & 0 & 0 & u \end{pmatrix}$$

$$\mathbf{P}(x_3) = [1 - u^2(x_3)]^{-½} \begin{pmatrix} -u & 0 & 0 & 1 \\ 0 & u & 1 & 0 \\ 0 & 1 & u & 0 \\ 1 & 0 & 0 & -u \end{pmatrix}$$

where $u(x_3)$ is to be determined. Let the new components which are to form two orthogonal pairs be denoted by $[\pi_1(x_3),\psi_1(x_3)]$ and $[\psi_2(x_3),\pi_2(x_3)]$ and put

$$\mathbf{u}(x_3) = \begin{pmatrix} \pi_1 \\ \psi_1 \\ \psi_2 \\ \pi_2 \end{pmatrix},$$

(*a*) Show that the scalar function $u(x_3)$ must satisfy the equation

$$u^2 + \left[\frac{\alpha - \beta}{\gamma}\right]u + 1 = 0 ,$$

if $\mathbf{P}^{-1}\mathbf{A}\mathbf{P}$ is to have zero off-diagonal blocks. Show that the equation for u has reciprocal roots and find them.

(*b*) Show that

$$\mathbf{P}^{-1}\mathbf{A}\mathbf{P} = \begin{pmatrix} 0 & -1 & 0 & 0 \\ -\lambda_1^2 & 0 & 0 & 0 \\ 0 & 0 & 0 & \lambda_2^2 \\ 0 & 0 & 1 & 0 \end{pmatrix}$$

and

$$-\mathbf{P}^{-1}\frac{d\mathbf{P}}{dx_3} = \frac{\left(\dfrac{du}{dx_3}\right)}{(1 - u^2)} \begin{pmatrix} 0 & 0 & 0 & -1 \\ 0 & 0 & 1 & 0 \\ 0 & 1 & 0 & 0 \\ -1 & 0 & 0 & 0 \end{pmatrix}$$

where

$$\lambda_1^2(x_3) = \alpha + \frac{\gamma}{u} = \beta - \gamma u \quad ,$$

$$\lambda_2^2(x_3) = \alpha + \gamma u = \beta - \frac{\gamma}{u} \quad .$$

(*c*) Prove that $\pm\lambda_1^2(x_3)$ and $\pm\lambda_2^2(x_3)$ are the eigenvalues of $\mathbf{A}(x_3)$.

(*d*) Eliminate ψ_1 and ψ_2, hence obtain Rydbeck's equations,

$$\pi_1''(x_3) + \left[\omega_1^2\lambda_1^2(x_3) + \left(\frac{u'}{1 - u^2}\right)^2\right]\pi_1(x_3)$$

$$= -2\left(\frac{u'}{1 - u^2}\right)\pi_2'(x_3) - \left(\frac{u'}{1 - u^2}\right)'\pi_2(x_3) \quad ,$$

$$\pi_2''(x_3) + \left[\omega^2\lambda_2^2(x_3) + \left(\frac{u'}{1 - u^2}\right)^2\right]\pi_2(x_3)$$

$$= -2\left(\frac{u'}{1 - u^2}\right)\pi_1'(x_3) - \left(\frac{u'}{1 - u^2}\right)'\pi_1(x_3) \quad ,$$

where the prime indicates differentiation with respect to x_3. Show that if the magnetic field is horizontal, the system of equations becomes uncoupled, and if the magnetic field approaches the vertical direction, the system also becomes uncoupled. What does u approach in the latter case?

(8) Using eq. (69.13) find the form of δ for an electron plasma at low and very low frequencies, $\omega \ll \nu$.

(9) Show that for an isotropic medium eqs. (69.17) and (69.18) are identical.

(10) Prove the statements at the end of section 69.

(11) Deduce the form of eqs (70.19) and (70.20) as the magnetic field approaches zero and also as it approaches infinity. Consider the low and very low frequency cases.

(12) Interpret the numerator and denominator of eq. (70.27).

(13) How can the results for the **E**-parallel polarization be obtained from those of the **H**-parallel polarization without solving the boundary value problem again for the cylindrically stratified medium? Show that the dielectric tensor reduces to a scalar for this case. Why?

(14) Consider an infinitely long circular cylinder of radius $r = a$ and let a line source of unit strength be placed at $(r_0, 0)$, $r_0 > a$. Suppose the refractive index of the cylinder is given by $M(r)$, and that the spatial part of a scalar wave is defined by

$$\nabla^2\psi + K^2M^2(r)\psi = -\left(\frac{2\pi}{r_0}\right)\delta(r - r_0)\delta(\theta)$$

in the region $r \geq a$, $-\infty < \theta < \infty$ (an infinitely sheeted Riemann surface), with boundary conditions $\psi(a,\theta) = 0$ and the radiation condition at infinity. The Laplacian ∇^2 is expressed in polar coordinates.

(*a*) Show that a solution of the problem, periodic in θ is of the form

$$\Phi(r,\theta) = \sum_{n=-\infty}^{\infty} \psi(r,\theta + 2\pi n)$$

and interpret the solution.

(*b*) Let Z be a complex variable and introduce the conformal transformation

$$W = ln\, Z = ln\, r + i\theta\ , \quad |W'| = \frac{1}{|Z|} = \frac{1}{r}\ ,$$

show that the Riemann surface is mapped onto the half-plane $u \geq ln\, a$, $-\infty < v < \infty$, and that $\psi(r,\theta)$ now satisfies the equation

$$\frac{\partial^2\psi}{\partial u^2} + \frac{\partial^2\psi}{\partial v^2} + K^2[M^2(e^u)]e^{2u}\psi = r_0\delta(e^u - r_0)\delta(v) = \delta(u - u_0)\delta(v)$$

where $u_0 = ln\, r_0$, with boundary condition $\psi|_{u=ln\, a} = 0$. This technique shows that a wave propagation problem in a cylindrically stratified medium is reduced to a problem in a plane stratified medium with refractive index $N(u) = e^u M(e^u)$.

(*c*) Calculate $(d/du) ln\, N(u)$ at $u = ln\, a$.

(*d*) Let $M(r) = 1/r$, and show that $\psi(u,v)$ satisfies

$$\nabla^2\psi + K^2\psi = \delta(u - u_0)\delta(v) \; ; \quad \psi(ln\, a, v) = 0,$$

with solution

$$\psi = \frac{i\pi}{2} [H_0^{(1)}(KR) - H_0^{(1)}(KR')] \quad ,$$

where

$$R = [(u - u_0)^2 + v^2]^{1/2} \; , \quad R' = [(u + u_0 - 2 ln\, a)^2 + v^2]^{1/2} \; .$$

How does this solution compare with that obtained by the geometrical optics solution? What part of the solution represents the direct ray? The reflected ray?

(*e*) Show that lines in the (u,v)-plane are mapped into hyperbolic spirals in the (x_1, x_2)-plane, and that this whole plane is covered by one system of spiral rays starting from the source and another system of spiral rays starting at the reciprocal point.

(*f*) Show that the solution to the original problem, the cylindrically stratified medium with $M(r) = 1/r$ is given by

$$\psi(r,\theta) = \frac{i\pi}{2} \sum_{n=-\infty}^{\infty} [H_0^{(1)}(KR_n) - H_0^{(1)}(KR_n')] \quad ,$$

where,

$$R_n = \left[2 ln\, \frac{r}{r_0} + (\theta + 2\pi n)^2\right]^{1/2} \; , \quad R_n' = \left[2 ln\, \frac{r r_0}{a^2} + (\theta + 2\pi n)^2\right]^{1/2}$$

and interpret the result.

(15) Consider the half-space, $x_2 \geq a$; and a unit line source at $(0,h)$. Let the index be defined by $M(x_2) = \exp(x_2/a)$ so that

$$\nabla^2\psi + K^2 \exp\left(\frac{x_2}{a}\right)\psi = -2\pi\delta(x_1)\delta(x_2 - h) .$$

(a) Show that $W(Z) = u + iv = re^{i\theta} = ae^{iZ/a}$ maps conformally the upper half-plane onto $r \geq a$, $-\infty < \theta < \infty$ if $a > 0$, or onto $r \leq |a|$, $-\infty < \theta < \infty$, if $a < 0$, and that the wave equation in (u,v) coordinates becomes

$$\nabla^2\psi + K^2\psi = -\frac{2\pi}{\left(\frac{r}{a}\right)^2}\delta(a\theta)\delta\left(a\ln\frac{r}{a} - h\right) = -\frac{2\pi}{r_0}\delta(\theta)\delta(r - r_0)$$

where

$$r_0 = ae^{h/a} .$$

(b) Let $a > 0$, and put

$$\psi = \int_{-\infty}^{\infty} G_\nu(r)e^{i\nu\theta}d\nu ,$$

and show that

$$\int_{-\infty}^{\infty}\left[G_\nu'' + \frac{1}{r}G_\nu' + \left(K^2 - \frac{\nu^2}{r^2}\right)G_\nu\right]e^{i\nu\theta}d\nu = -\frac{2\pi}{r_0}\delta(r - r_0)\delta(\theta) .$$

(c) Invert the Fourier integral and show that the Green's function satisfies the equation,

$$G_\nu'' + \frac{1}{r}G_\nu' + \left(K^2 - \frac{\nu^2}{r^2}\right)G_\nu = -\frac{1}{r_0}\delta(r - r_0) ,$$

and can be represented in the form,

$$G_\nu(r) = \begin{cases} \dfrac{i\pi}{4} H_\nu^{(1)}(Kr_0)\left[H_\nu^{(2)}(Kr) - \dfrac{H_\nu^{(2)}(Ka)}{H_\nu^{(1)}(Ka)} H_\nu^{(1)}(Kr)\right], & a \le r \le r_0 , \\ \dfrac{i\pi}{4} H_\nu^{(1)}(Kr)\left[H_\nu^{(2)}(Kr_0) - \dfrac{H_\nu^{(2)}(Ka)}{H_\nu^{(1)}(Ka)} H_\nu^{(1)}(Kr_0)\right], & r \ge r_0 . \end{cases}$$

where $H_\nu^{(1)}$, $H_\nu^{(2)}$ are Hankel functions of the first and second kind of order ν. What is $G_\nu(a)$, $G_\nu(\infty)$? Evaluate $\lim_{\epsilon\to 0} G'_\nu\Big|_{r_0-\epsilon}^{r_0+\epsilon}$.

(*d*) Suppose the solution ψ is given for $r \le r_0$, how is it found for $r > r_0$?

(*e*) Perform the inverse conformal transformation and show that the rays

$$|\theta| = \cos^{-1}\left(\frac{a}{r_0}\right) + \cos^{-1}\left(\frac{a}{r}\right)$$

are mapped into the curve

$$\left|\frac{x_1}{a}\right| = \cos^{-1}\left[\exp\left(-\frac{x_2}{a}\right)\right] + \cos^{-1}\left[\exp\left(\frac{x_2}{a}\right)\right] .$$

(*f*) Define $ds = |W'(Z)dZ| = M|dZ|$, prove that the minimum value of the functional

$$\int_{(0,h)}^{(x_1,x_2)} ds$$

is given by

$$L = a[(e^{2h/a} - 1)^{1/2} + (e^{2x_2/a} - 1)^{1/2}] - a[\cos^{-1}(e^{-h/a}) + \cos^{-1}(e^{-x_2/a})] + |x_1|$$

so that L is the optical length of the curve of the least optical path from the source to the observation point which lies in the upper half-plane. What is the significance of L in the (r,θ) space?

(16) Reduce the problem of wave propagation in a cylindrically stratified medium, where $M(r) = (r/a)^k$ for $p \neq -1$, to a problem for a homogeneous medium by using the transformation

$$W(Z) = Re^{i\phi} = \frac{a}{p+1}\left(\frac{Z}{a}\right)^{p+1} .$$

(a) For $p > -1$, show that the infinitely sheeted Riemann surface $r \geq a$, $-\infty < \theta < \infty$ is mapped onto the infinite-sheeted surface $R \geq a/p + 1$, $-\infty < \phi < \infty$, which is the region exterior to a cylinder of radius $a/p + 1$.

(b) What is the relation between the above mapping and those of (14b) and (15a).

(17) Consider an absorbing slab, bounded on the left by free space and in contact on the right with a perfectly conducting plane. Let the x_3-axis be perpendicular to the plane of the slab and let "a" be the thickness of the slab, which is characterized by $\epsilon(x_3)$ and $\mu(x_3)$. The slab is excited from the left by a plane wave normally incident on it. Suppose the polarization of the wave is such that

$$\mathbf{E} = E(x_3)\mathbf{e}_2 , \quad \mathbf{H} = -H(x_3)\mathbf{e}_1 ,$$

where $\mathbf{e}_1$, $\mathbf{e}_2$ are unit vectors along the x_1 and x_2 axis.

(a) Write Maxwell's equations for the fields in the slab.

(b) Define the reflection coefficient R in terms of the input impedance $Z(x_3)$ at $x_3 = 0$ by

$$R = \frac{Z(0) - 1}{Z(0) + 1} ,$$

and

$$\overline{Z}(x_3) = \frac{E(x_3)}{H(x_3)} ;$$

show that $Z(x_3)$ satisfies the Riccati equation

$$Z'(x_3) - ik_0\epsilon(x_3)[Z(x_3)]^2 + ik_0\mu(x_3) = 0 .$$

(*c*) Show that

$$E(x_3) = E(x_{3,0}) \exp\left\{- ik_0 \int_{x_{3,0}}^{x_3} \mu(x_3)[Z(x_3)]^{-1}dx_3\right\}$$

$$H(x_3) = H(x_{3,0}) \exp\left[- ik_0 \int_{x_{3,0}}^{x_3} \epsilon(x_3)Z(x_3)dx_3\right].$$

(*d*) Assume

$$\epsilon(x_3) = \frac{\alpha_1}{(\alpha_2 + x_3)^2} \quad ; \quad \mu(x_3) = \alpha_3 \quad ,$$

where $\alpha_1, \alpha_2, \alpha_3$ are complex constants, solve the Riccati equation and find $Z(0)$.

(*e*) Assume

$$\frac{\mu(x_3)}{\epsilon(x_3)} = \alpha^2 \quad ;$$

α is a complex constant, carry out the solution as indicated in (d).

(*f*) Analyze the problem for

$$\epsilon(x_3) = \frac{A - iBx_3}{(1 - cx_3)^2} \quad ,$$

$\mu(x_3)$ = complex constant, A, B, C are complex constants.

(18) Prove that there always exists at least one vector function $\pi(\mathbf{r})$ satisfying eq. (71.13) and such that eqs. (71.9) and (71.10) are satisfied, where $\mathbf{E},\mathbf{H}$ are solutions of eqs. (71.7) and (71.8).

(19) Prove that if $\mathbf{E}'_i$ satisfies the adjoint eq. (72.35), $\mathbf{E}'^*_i$ satisfies the complex conjugate of the adjoint equation.

(20) Compare the original integral equation for $\mathbf{E}_j$ with the equation satisfied by $\mathbf{E}'^*_i$ and show that the susceptibility matrix $\mathbf{B}$ of the latter is the transpose of the former or original medium.

(a) Show further that the **A** matrix of the complex conjugate equation is obtained from the original equation by replacing angle ϕ with $-\phi$.

(b) Call $\mathbf{B}'^*$ the susceptibility matrix of the "transposed" medium and define

$$R'_{ji} = \frac{-iK_0}{2\cos\phi}\int_0^a \exp(-iK_0x_3\cos\phi)\mathbf{u}_j\mathbf{B}'^*(x_3)\mathbf{E}'^*_i(x_3)dx_3 ,$$

prove that $R_{ij} = R'_{ji}$ so that (R'_{ji}) is the reflection matrix of the "transposed" medium. This is a reciprocity theorem.

(c) Prove in an analogous way that $S_{ij} = S'_{ji}$ and $T_{ij} = T'_{ji}$.

(d) Interpret the results of (a), (b), and (c) physically.

(21) Write the susceptibility matrix for a magneto-ionic medium for arbitrary orientation of the magnetic field and show that the susceptibility matrix of the transposed medium differs from the original in that the direction of the magnetic field is reversed at every point.

PROBLEMS FOR CHAPTER VII

(1) Show that the system of equations given below yields the ray path.

$$V\alpha = \frac{\partial H}{\partial \sigma},$$

$$V \frac{\partial}{\partial \mathbf{r}}\left(\frac{1}{V}\right) = -\frac{\partial H}{\partial \mathbf{r}},$$

$$\frac{d\sigma}{ds} = \frac{\partial}{\partial \mathbf{r}}\left(\frac{1}{V}\right).$$

(2) Using the concept that the polar planes are the envelope of the surface $V(\mathbf{r},\xi) = 1$, derive the fact that $H(\mathbf{r},\sigma) = 1$ is the reciprocal surface of $V(\mathbf{r},\xi) = 1$.

(3) If $\lambda_i^2\xi_i^2 = 1$, and all λ_i are positive, show that $\sigma_i^2\lambda_i^{-2} = 1$ is the reciprocal surface.

(4) Let $\xi'\mathbf{A}\xi = 1$ be the equation of a convex quadric, where $\mathbf{A}$ is a 3×3 matrix. Let $\mathbf{n}$ be any point not on the quadric, show that the equation of the polar plane with respect to the quadric is given by $\mathbf{n}'\mathbf{A}\xi = 1$.

(*a*) Find the polar plane with respect to the quadric, $3\xi_1^2 + 2\xi_1\xi_2 + \xi_2^2 = 1$.

(*b*) Show that any straight line from the point $\mathbf{n}$ intersecting the quadric is cut harmonically by the surface and the polar plane of $\mathbf{n}$. That is, if P and Q are the points of intersection of the line and the quadric, and if R is the point of intersection of this line with the line joining the tangents from $\mathbf{n}$ to the quadric; show that

$$\frac{1}{\overline{\overline{nP}}} + \frac{1}{\overline{\overline{nQ}}} = \frac{2}{\overline{\overline{nR}}}.$$

(5) If $\sigma = \mathbf{A}\xi$, where

$$\mathbf{A} = \begin{pmatrix} 2 & 1 \\ 1 & 1 \end{pmatrix},$$

show that the locus of σ lies on the reciprocal ellipse $\sigma'\mathbf{A}^{-1}\sigma = 1$ when ξ lies on $\xi'\mathbf{A}\xi = 1$. Find the equations of the polar planes of both ellipses.

(6) If the index of a medium is given by $M(\mathbf{r},\alpha) = (\alpha \cdot \alpha)^{1/2}$, find

(a) $\mathbf{H}(\mathbf{r},\sigma) = 1$.

(b) Find the Euler equations and integrate them.

(c) Find the ray path equations, and also the rays.

(7) Suppose we are given the following system of equations

$$d\mathbf{r} = \frac{\partial H}{\partial \sigma} du, \quad \frac{1}{V(\mathbf{r},\mathbf{r}')} = \sigma \cdot \frac{\partial H}{\partial \sigma}, \quad H(\mathbf{r},\sigma) = 1,$$

where

$$\mathbf{r}' \equiv \frac{d\mathbf{r}}{du}$$

and u is some parameter along a ray.

(a) How can V be determined from this system?

(b) Does the integral of $\sigma \cdot d\mathbf{r}$ having a meaning for a curve other than a ray? Why?

(c) If V can be determined from the above system of equations, show that $1/V$ is a positive homogeneous function of degree one in $\mathbf{r}'$.

(8) If $M(\mathbf{r},\alpha)$ is invariant under a rotation of axis whose origin is at $\mathbf{r}$, prove that M is a function of position alone, and hence defines an isotropic medium.

(9) If

$$\frac{\partial M(\mathbf{r},\alpha)}{\partial \mathbf{r}} = 0,$$

prove that M is a function of direction only.

(10) Find the ray path when

$$M(\mathbf{r},\alpha) = \frac{(\alpha \cdot \alpha)^{1/2}}{V(\mathbf{r})} .$$

(*a*) Find σ.

(*b*) Find $H(\mathbf{r},\sigma)$.

(*c*) Calculate the curvature of the rays.

(11) If $M(\mathbf{r},\alpha) = M(\alpha)$, show that the rays are straight lines, and find their equation.

(12) If $M(\mathbf{r},\alpha) = f(x_3)(\alpha \cdot \alpha)^{1/2}$, find the ray path equations.

(13) If $M(\mathbf{r},\alpha) = f(r)(\alpha \cdot \alpha)^{1/2}$, where $r^2 = x_i x_i$, find the equation of the rays.

(14) Let $M_1(\mathbf{r},\alpha) = C_1(\alpha \cdot \alpha)^{1/2}$ and $M_2(\mathbf{r},\alpha) = C_2(\alpha \cdot \alpha)^{1/2}$, where $C_1 \neq C_2$ are constants. Examine the conditions for reflection, refraction, either, neither, or both.

(15) Prove that the second of Hamilton's equations transforms as a covariant vector.

(16) Show that Euler's equations transform covariantly.

(17) Verify that eqs. (88.28) hold for arbitrary curvilinear coordinate systems x^i and y^i.

(18) Let the vector index of refraction be given in the form (as in section 86), $\mu = \mu_1\mathbf{e}_1 + \mu_2\mathbf{e}_2 + \mu_3\mathbf{e}_3$, where $\mathbf{e}_i \cdot \mathbf{e}_j = \delta_{ij}$. Suppose further that μ_3 can be expressed explicitly by $\mu_3 = \mu_3(\mu_1,\mu_2,\omega)$ or implicitly by $\mu(\mu_1,\mu_2,\mu_3,\omega) = 0$, and that the phase of a wave in an inhomogeneous, anisotropic medium is

$$P(\mu_1,\mu_2,\omega) = \omega V_0 t - \int_0^s \omega(\mu \cdot \alpha)\,ds$$

where s is the arc length along a ray path and ω is the angular frequency of the wave. The incident direction of the wave is defined by μ_1 and μ_2, and ω, μ_1 and μ_2 are independent parameters. Invoke the principle of stationary phase in the form $dP = 0$ and show that it yields

(*a*) $$\int_0^s \left(\frac{\partial\mu}{\partial\mu_1}\cdot\alpha\right)ds = 0\,, \quad \int_0^s \left(\frac{\partial\mu}{\partial\mu_2}\cdot\alpha\right)ds = 0\,,$$

$$V_0 t - \int_0^s \frac{\partial}{\partial\omega}[\omega(\mu\cdot\alpha)]_{\alpha=\text{constant}}\,ds = 0\,.$$

(*b*) Show that the first two equations define the ray path position, and the last equation defines the equivalent path length of the ray and the group refractive index along the ray, namely

$$\frac{\partial}{\partial\omega}[\omega(\mu\cdot\alpha)]_{\alpha=\text{constant}}$$

(*c*) Does it give the group velocity?

(*d*) If $\mathbf{r}$ is the position vector from the point of transmission of the wave to a point on the ray, define $\alpha = d\mathbf{r}/ds$, and obtain $dx_3/ds = \alpha\cdot\mathbf{e}_3$, and

$$\frac{\partial\mu}{\partial\omega} = \frac{\partial\mu_3}{\partial\omega}\mathbf{e}_3$$

and hence show that

$$\frac{\partial}{\partial\omega}(\mu\cdot\alpha)_{\alpha=\text{constant}} = \frac{\partial\mu}{\partial\omega}\cdot\alpha = \frac{\partial\mu_3}{\partial\omega}\alpha\cdot\mathbf{e}_3\,.$$

(*e*) Using the results above and eq. (86.12) deduce that

$$V_0 t = \int_0^{x_3}\left(\frac{\mu\cdot\alpha}{\alpha\cdot\mathbf{e}_3} + \omega\frac{\partial\mu_3}{\partial\omega}\right)dx_3\,.$$

(*f*) What is the expression for the phase path in terms of the parameter x_3?

(19) Answer the following questions.

(*a*) For a general medium, are Huygen's Principle and Fermat's Principle equivalent?

(*b*) Is the correspondence between ray and normal in a point always unique? Consider a biaxial crystal.

(20) Prove that at a point on a surface of discontinuity of two media, the normals to the incident, the reflected and the refracted wave fronts, and the normal to the surface of discontinuity all lie in the same plane.

(21) Consider an infinitely long cylindrically stratified plasma column surrounded by free space. Let a bundle of straight parallel rays be incident on the plasma column. If the dielectric constant of the plasma is a function only of the radial distance r from the center of the cylinder, show that Snell's Law is of the form,

(*a*)
$$\left[\frac{\epsilon(r)}{\epsilon_0}\right]^{1/2} r \sin\alpha = \text{constant} ,$$

where α is the angle between the ray direction and the radial direction.

(*b*) Assume that for large r, $\epsilon \to \epsilon_0$ and $r \sin\alpha \to b$; show that

$$r\left(\frac{d\theta}{dr}\right)^2 = \tan^2\alpha ,$$

where (r,θ) are polar coordinates of any point.

(*c*) Derive the differential equation of the rays in the medium,

$$\left(r\frac{d\theta}{dr}\right)^2 = \left(r^2\frac{\epsilon}{b^2\epsilon_0} - 1\right)^{-1} .$$

(*d*) The dielectric constant is given by

$$\frac{\epsilon}{\epsilon_0} = 1 - \frac{N(r)e^2}{\epsilon_0 m\omega^2} ,$$

where $N(r)$ is the variable electron density. Put

$$a(r) = \frac{N(r)e^2}{\epsilon_0 m\omega^2} ,$$

and show that

$$\left|\frac{d\theta}{dr}\right| = r^{-2}[b^{-2} - r^{-2} - b^{-2}a(r)]^{-1/2}$$

defines the ray with parameter b.

(e) Show that the angle between the direction along which the ray comes in from infinity and the direction along which it goes out to infinity again is given by,

$$2\int_{r_0}^{\infty} \left|\frac{d\theta}{dr}\right| dr \quad .$$

(f) Show that the limiting value of the angular coordinate (the deflection angle of the ray) as $r \to \infty$ is

$$\theta(b) = \pi - 2\int_{r_0}^{\infty} r^{-2}[b^{-2} - r^{-2} - b^{-2}a(r)]^{-1/2}dr \quad ,$$

where r_0 is the distance of closest approach for this ray and is such that $dr/d\theta = 0$ at $r = r_0$.

(22) In the previous problem consider $\theta(b)$ as given so that (21f) is an integral equation for $a(r)$. Put $x = b^{-2}$, $u = r^{-1}$, $v(u) = 1 - a$, $W = u^2v^{-1}$, show that (21f) becomes,

$$(a) \qquad \frac{\pi - \theta(x)}{2} = \int_0^x \frac{v^{-1/2}\left(\frac{du}{dW}\right)}{(x - W)^{1/2}} dW \quad .$$

(b) Put

$$g(W) = v^{-1/2}\frac{du}{dW} ,$$

prove that

$$g(W) = \frac{d}{dW}\left[\frac{1}{2\pi}\int_0^W \frac{\pi - \theta(x)}{(W - x)^{1/2}}\,dx\right] = \frac{1}{2}W^{-1/2} - \frac{1}{2\pi}\frac{d}{dW}\int_0^W \frac{\theta(x)dx}{(W - x)^{1/2}}$$

(c) From $W = u^2v^{-1}$ derive,

$$g(W) = \frac{1}{2}W^{-1/2} + \frac{1}{2}W^{1/2}v^{-1}\left(\frac{dv}{dW}\right),$$

and use the condition that $v = 1$ at $W = 0$ to deduce

$$v(W) = \exp\left\{\int_0^W [2(W')^{-1/2}g(W') - (W')^{-1}]\,dW'\right\}.$$

(d) From the expressions given in (c), obtain the result

$$v(W) = \exp\left[\frac{-1}{\pi}\int_0^W \frac{1}{(W')^{1/2}}\frac{d}{dW'}\int_0^W \frac{\theta(x)dx}{(W' - x)^{1/2}}\right].$$

(e) How is $a(r)$ finally obtained?

(23) In the previous problem, discuss the conditions for which a ray is

(a) Penetrable,

(b) Impenetrable.

(c) Let

$$\frac{\theta}{\theta_0} = \frac{\dfrac{2b}{b_0}}{1 + \left(\dfrac{b}{b_0}\right)^2}$$

find $a(W)$ and $r(W)$.

(d) Show that if $r \approx W^{-1/2}$, and as $W \to 0$, $a \approx 2\theta_0(b_0/r)$.

(24) An observer at a point on the earth's surface at sunset sees the coming tangential rays as horizontal along the straight line path, but due to atmospheric refraction, the sun has already set and has an angular position other than horizontal at a very large distance from the observer. Assuming that the index of refraction for the earth's atmosphere is given by

$$M(r) = \left(1 + \frac{K^2}{r^2}\right)^{1/2} ,$$

where r is the distance measured from the center of the earth, find an expression for the deflection of the sun's rays from the horizon.

(25) Starting with Maxwell's equations,

$$\text{curl } \mathbf{H} - \frac{\partial \mathbf{D}}{\partial t} = \mathbf{J} ,$$

and

$$\text{curl } \mathbf{E} + \frac{\partial \mathbf{B}}{\partial t} = 0 ,$$

and the constitutive equations $\mathbf{B} = \mu_0 \mathbf{H}$, $\mathbf{D} = \epsilon_0 \mathbf{E} + \mathbf{P}$, $\mathbf{J} = \sigma \mathbf{E}$, $\mathbf{P} = \epsilon_0 \mathbf{S} \mathbf{E}$, where μ_0 is constant, σ and $\mathbf{S}$ are tensors, which are in general complex. Assume the medium is inhomogeneous so that the tensors depend on position. The time dependence is of the form $e^{i\omega t}$.

(*a*) Find the vector wave equation satisfied by $\mathbf{E}$.

(*b*) Choose an arbitrary orthogonal curvilinear coordinate system (u_1, u_2, u_3) and unit vectors $(\mathbf{e}_1, \mathbf{e}_2, \mathbf{e}_3)$ to express the vector line element in the form $d\mathbf{s} = \sum_i \mathbf{e}_i g_i du_i$, with $\mathbf{e}_i \cdot \mathbf{e}_j = \delta_{ij}$. Put

$$\nabla = \sum_{i=1}^{3} \frac{\mathbf{e}_i}{g_i} \frac{\partial}{\partial u_i}$$

and

$$\mathbf{E} = \sum_{i=1}^{3} \mathbf{e}_i E_i$$

and expand the vector wave equation in (a).

(*c*) Examine the terms in the expansion which must be neglected in order to transform $\nabla\mathbf{x}(\nabla\mathbf{x}\mathbf{E})$ into $\nabla(\nabla \cdot \mathbf{E}) - \nabla^2\mathbf{E}$ and show that the sufficient conditions for it to hold impose a condition on the curvature of the coordinate lines.

(*d*) Show that the conditions are exactly satisfied by a rectangular cartesian system.

(26) In the previous problem, consider the equation satisfied by the spatial part of $\mathbf{E}$ after neglecting the terms stated above. Put

$$\mathbf{E}(\mathbf{r}) = \sum_{i=1}^{3} \mathbf{e}_i \mathbf{E}_0 \exp\,[-ik_0\psi_i(\mathbf{r})] \quad ,$$

where $\mathbf{E}_0$ is constant and each ψ_i is complex, into the resulting equation satisfied by $\mathbf{E}(\mathbf{r})$.

(*a*) Find the equation satisfied by $\mathbf{E}(\mathbf{r})$ and show that it leads to a homogeneous linear system of equations for the $E_i(\mathbf{r})$.

(*b*) Show that the coefficients of this system involve the partial derivatives of all ψ_i.

(*c*) The matrix of this system is called the "Eikonal Matrix." Show that the necessary and sufficient condition for the existence of non-trivial $\mathbf{E}(\mathbf{r})$ is that the determinant of the "Eikonal Matrix" vanish identically. Hence show that this leads to a non-linear partial differential equation of the second order for the three dependent variables ψ_i.

(*d*) How can the polarization be introduced?

(*e*) Discuss how to determine an index of refraction.

(27) A canonical transformation is one which preserves the canonical form of the equations of the rays. Define the following

$$\mathbf{y} = \begin{pmatrix} \mathbf{r} \\ \sigma \end{pmatrix}, \quad d\mathbf{y} = \begin{pmatrix} d\mathbf{r} \\ d\sigma \end{pmatrix}, \quad \mathbf{W} = \begin{pmatrix} \dfrac{\partial H}{\partial \mathbf{r}} \\[2ex] \dfrac{\partial H}{\partial \sigma} \end{pmatrix}, \quad \Gamma = \begin{pmatrix} \mathbf{0} & \mathbf{I} \\ -\mathbf{I} & \mathbf{0} \end{pmatrix},$$

show that the canonical eqs. can be written in the form,

(*a*)
$$d\mathbf{y} = dt\,\boldsymbol{\Gamma}\mathbf{W} \quad .$$

(*b*) If $\mathbf{J}$ denotes the Jacobian of the transformation from $(\mathbf{r},\sigma) \rightarrow (\mathbf{r}',\sigma')$, prove that a necessary and sufficient condition on $\mathbf{J}$ in order that the transformation having $\mathbf{J}$ for Jacobian should be a canonical transformation is

$$\mathbf{J}^{-1}\boldsymbol{\Gamma}(\mathbf{J}^{-1})' = \boldsymbol{\Gamma} \quad .$$

(*c*) Prove that det $\mathbf{J} = \pm 1$.

PROBLEMS FOR CHAPTER VIII

(1) Let Q_i denote new position variables with P_i the corresponding canonical conjugate momentum. The extension in phase of an ensemble of states measured in the old and new spaces is the same

$$\int dq_1 dq_2 \ldots dq_n dp_1 \ldots dp_n = \int dQ_1 \ldots dQ_n dP_1 \ldots dP_n .$$

Establish this property by showing that

$$\frac{\partial(P_1, P_2, \ldots, P_n)}{\partial(p_1, \ldots, p_n)} = \frac{\partial(q_1, \ldots, q_n)}{\partial(Q_1, \ldots, Q_n)} ,$$

and hence,

$$J \equiv \frac{\partial(P_1, \ldots, P_n, Q_1, \ldots, Q_n)}{\partial(p_1, \ldots, p_n, q_1, \ldots, q_n)} = \frac{\partial(p_1, \ldots, p_n)}{\partial(P_1, \ldots, P_n)} \cdot \frac{\partial(q_1, \ldots, q_n)}{\partial(Q_1, \ldots, Q_n)} = 1 .$$

[Hint: Write $P_i = p_i + \dot{p}_i dt + \ldots$, $Q_i = q_i + \dot{q}_i dt + \ldots$, and show that

$$J = 1 + \left(\frac{\partial}{\partial p_i} \dot{p}_i + \frac{\partial}{\partial q_i} \dot{q}_i\right) dt + \ldots,]$$

(2) Let $\dot{q}_i$ be the set of velocity coordinates obtained from the q_i. Show that in velocity space the following integrals have an invariant property:

(*a*) $$\int \left[\frac{\partial(p_1, \ldots, p_n)}{\partial(q_1', \ldots, q_n')}\right]^{\frac{1}{2}} d\dot{q}_1, \ldots, d\dot{q}_n ;$$

(*b*) $$\int \left[\frac{\partial(q_1, \ldots, q_n')}{\partial(p_1, \ldots, p_n)}\right]^{\frac{1}{2}} dp_1, \ldots, dp_n .$$

(*c*) Are these integrals conserved in the course of motion?

(3) Consider a single point in a space (x_1, x_2, x_3) with distance defined by

$$ds^2 = g_{iK}(x_1, x_2, x_3)\,dx_i\,dx_K$$

and kinetic energy by

$$T = \frac{m}{2} g_{iK}\dot{x}_i\dot{x}_K \quad .$$

(a) Calculate

$$p_i = \frac{\partial T}{\partial \dot{x}_i} \quad \text{and} \quad \frac{\partial p_i}{\partial \dot{x}_K} \, ,$$

and show that

$$\frac{\partial(\mathbf{p})}{\partial(\dot{\mathbf{q}})} \equiv A \equiv \left(\frac{g_{iK} + g_{Ki}}{2}\right) , \quad (i, K = 1, 2, 3) \quad .$$

(b) Now consider n point masses (equal mass m) whose positions are given by $x_{i,j}$, $j = 1, 2, \ldots, n$. Define new coordinates $(q_1, q_2, q_3) \equiv (x_{1,1}, x_{2,1}, x_{3,1})$, $(q_4, q_5, q_6) \equiv (x_{1,2}, x_{2,2}, x_{3,2})$, etc., so that we have $(q_1, \ldots, q_{3n})$ a point in $3n$-dimensional space. The kinetic energy of the system is now given by

$$T = \frac{m}{2} \sum_{j=1}^{n} g_{iK}(x_{1,j}, x_{2,j}, x_{3,j})\dot{x}_{i,j}\dot{x}_{K,j} \quad ,$$

calculate

$$p_{i,j} = \frac{\partial T}{\partial \dot{x}_{i,j}} \quad \text{and} \quad \frac{\partial p_{i,j}}{\partial \dot{x}_{K,j}}$$

and show that the determinant

$$\frac{\partial(\mathbf{p})}{\partial(\mathbf{q})} = m^{3n}\begin{vmatrix} |\Delta| & 0 & 0 & & 0 \\ 0 & |\Delta| & 0 & & 0 \\ 0 & & & & 0 \\ & 0 & 0 & 0 & |\Delta| \end{vmatrix} = m^{3n}\Delta^n ,$$

where Δ is a 3×3 determinant and the zeros also represent 3×3 null determinants.

(*c*) Show that the integral in (2b) can now be written as

$$m^{3n/2}\int \Delta^{n/2} d\dot{q}_1 \ldots, d\dot{q}_{3n} .$$

(4) Consider a collection of n-homogeneous, rigid, spherical molecules with masses $m_1, m_2, \ldots m_n$ in a certain volume of space. Denote the center of mass of each molecule by $(x_{1,1}, x_{2,1}, x_{3,1})$, $(x_{1,2}, x_{2,2}, x_{3,2})$, etc. Define generalized coordinates by $q_1 = \sqrt{m_1}x_{1,1}$, $q_2 = \sqrt{m_1}x_{2,1}$, $q_3 = \sqrt{m_1}x_{3,1}$, $q_4 = \sqrt{m_2}x_{1,2}$, etc., then the kinetic energy of the system is

$$T = \frac{1}{2}\sum_{j=1}^{n} \dot{q}_j^2 .$$

(*a*) Show that the elementary probability can be written in the form

$$dP = f(E)dq_1, \ldots, dq_n dp_1, \ldots, dp_n$$

where E is a first integral of the motion of the system.

(*b*) Put $F_n(E) = (m_1, \ldots, m_n)^{3/2} f(E)[V]^n$ where V is the volume occupied by the molecules, and denote by dP' the elementary probability in the momentum space, show that

$$dP' = F_n(E)dp_1, \ldots, dp_n .$$

(*c*) Consider only distributions in which we know that the energy lies between E and $E + dE$, where $E \equiv T$. Let the representative points of the system lie between two hyperspheres of radii $R = \sqrt{2E}$ and $R + dR = \sqrt{2(E + dE)}$, and introduce the parametric representation,

$$\begin{cases} p_1 = R\cos\theta_1 \\ p_2 = R\sin\theta_1\cos\theta_2 \\ p_3 = R\sin\theta_1\sin\theta_2\cos\theta_3 \\ \vdots \\ p_{n-1} = R\sin\theta_1\sin\theta_2\ldots,\sin\theta_{n-2}\cos\theta_{n-1} \\ p_n = R\sin\theta_1\sin\theta_2\ldots,\sin\theta_{n-1}\cos\theta_n \end{cases}$$

where $(\theta_1,\theta_2,\ldots,\theta_{n-2})$ vary between 0 and π; θ_{n-1} varies between 0 and 2π. Verify that the distance between two neighboring points is expressed by

$$ds^2 = dR^2 + R^2[d\theta_1^2 + \sin^2\theta_1 d\theta_1^2 + \ldots, + (\sin\theta_1\sin\theta_2\ldots,\sin\theta_{n-2})^2 d\theta_{n-1}^2] ,$$

and hence the coordinates R and θ_i are rectangular. From this, prove that the element of volume in velocity space can therefore be written in the form

$$R^{n-1}dR(\sin\theta_1)^{n-2}(\sin\theta_2)^{n-3}\ldots,\sin\theta_{n-2}d\theta_1 d\theta_2\ldots,d\theta_{n-1} .$$

(*d*) From the above considerations, prove that

$$dP' = F_n(E)(2E)^{(n-1)/2}dR(\sin\theta_1)^{n-2}(\sin\theta_2)^{n-1}\ldots,\sin\theta_{n-2}d\theta_1\ldots,d\theta_{n-1},$$

or

$$dP' = \frac{(\sin\theta_1)^{n-2}(\sin\theta_2)^{n-3}\ldots,\sin\theta_{n-2}d\theta_1\ldots,d\theta_{n-1}}{\left[\int_0^\pi(\sin\theta_1)^{n-2}d\theta_1\int_0^\pi(\sin\theta_2)^{n-3}d\theta_2\ldots,\int_0^\pi(\sin\theta_{n-2})d\theta\right]2\pi} .$$

(*e*) Deduce from (d) the probability that a molecule say M_1 has simultaneously three momentum components lying between $p_1, p_1 + dp_1$;

$p_2, p_2 + dp_2$; $p_3, p_3 + dp_3$; the other molecules having arbitrary momentum and show that it is defined by

$$dP_3 \equiv \frac{dp_1 dp_2 dp_3}{R^3} \frac{(\sin\theta_1 \sin\theta_2 \sin\theta_3)^{n-5} \int_0^{\pi} (\sin\theta)^{n-5} d\theta \ldots, \int_0^{2\pi} d\theta}{\int_0^{\pi} (\sin\theta)^{n-2} d\theta \ldots, \int_0^{2\pi} d\theta};$$

(in the integrals, θ acts as a dummy variable of integration).

$$dP_3 \equiv \frac{(\sin\theta_1 \sin\theta_2 \sin\theta_3)^{n-5} dp_1 dp_2 dp_3}{R^3 \int_0^{\pi} (\sin\theta)^{n-2} d\theta \int_0^{\pi} (\sin\theta)^{n-3} d\theta \int_0^{\pi} (\sin\theta)^{n-4} d\theta}.$$

(*f*) Introduce

$$\sin^2\theta_1 = 1 - \frac{p_1^2}{R^2},$$

$$\sin^2\theta_2 = 1 - \frac{p_2^2}{R^2 \sin^2\theta_1},$$

$$\sin^2\theta_3 = 1 - \frac{p_3^2}{R^2 \sin^2\theta_1 \sin^2\theta_2},$$

show that

$$(\sin\theta_1 \sin\theta_2 \sin\theta_3)^2 = 1 - \frac{p_1^2 + p_2^2 + p_3^2}{R^2}$$

and that the numerator in (e) can be written as

$$\left(1 - \frac{p_1^2 + p_2^2 + p_3^2}{2E}\right)^{(n-5)/2} dp_1 dp_2 dp_3 \quad .$$

Use the fact that if n is large

$$\int_0^{\pi} (\sin\theta)^n \, d\theta \doteq \left(\frac{2\pi}{n}\right)^{1/2}$$

and therefore show

$$dP_3 = \frac{\left(1 - \frac{p_1^2 + p_2^2 + p_3^2}{2E}\right)^{(n-5)/2} [(n-2)(n-3)(n-4)]^{1/2} \, dp_1 dp_2 dp_3}{(2E)^{3/2}(2\pi)^{3/2}} \, .$$

(g) Assume the energy of M_1 is very small compared with E, and n is large, show that

$$dP_3 = \left(\frac{n}{4\pi E}\right)^{3/2} \exp\left[-\frac{n}{4E}(p_1^2 + p_2^2 + p_3^2)\right] dp_1 dp_2 dp_2 \quad .$$

Generalize this formula for any number of components, say ν, but still assuming $\nu \ll n$ and obtain

$$dP_\nu = \left(\frac{n}{4\pi E}\right)^{\nu/2} \exp\left(-\frac{n}{4E}\sum_{i=1}^{\nu} p_i^2\right) dp_1, \ldots, dp_\nu \quad .$$

(5) (*a*) Suppose the potential energy of the previous system is not negligible, assume that

$$T = \frac{1}{2}\sum_{i=1}^{n} p_i^2$$

and the potential energy is given by

$$u = \frac{1}{2}\sum_{j=1}^{n'} Q_j^2, \ldots, Q_j = Q_j(q_1, \ldots, q_n) \quad ,$$

with $n' \leq n$, show that now

$$dP_\nu = Af(E)dp_1, \ldots, dp_\nu \int dQ_1, \ldots, dQ_n dp_{\nu+1}, \ldots, dp_n$$

where

$$E = \frac{1}{2}\left(\sum_{i=1}^{n} p_i^2 + \sum_{j=1}^{n'} Q_j^2 \right),$$

A is the functional determinant obtained by changing $q \to Q$ and is constant.

(*b*) By reasoning analogous to (4), deduce that

$$dP_\nu = \left(\frac{n + n'}{4\pi E}\right)^{\nu/2} \exp\left[- \frac{(n + n')}{4E} \sum_{i=1}^{n} p_i^2 \right] dp_1, \ldots, dp_\nu \ .$$

(6) Prove that the pressure tensor as defined by eq. (97.38) is indeed a tensor of the type indicated.

(7) What is the form of the Boltzmann equation in cylindrical coordinates? In an arbitrary orthogonal curvilinear coordinate system?

(8) Let $f(\mathbf{r}, v) = f(x_1, v)$ be a one dimensional time independent constant of motion and let ϕ denote the potential field of a charged particle, show that

$$f = \left(f \, \frac{1}{2} mv^2 + e\phi \right)$$

is a stationary solution of the Boltzmann equation.

(9) What is the form of eq. (97.88) in a cylindrical system with only radial symmetry?

(10) Write the Boltzmann equation in the form

$$\frac{\partial f}{\partial t} + \mathbf{v} \cdot \frac{\partial f}{\partial \mathbf{r}} + \mathbf{F} \cdot \frac{\partial f}{\partial \mathbf{v}} - \left(\frac{\partial f}{\partial t}\right)_{\text{coll.}} = 0 \ ;$$

associated with this form is the set of equations

$$\frac{dt}{1} = \frac{d\mathbf{r}}{\mathbf{v}} = \frac{d\mathbf{v}}{\mathbf{F}} = \frac{df}{\left(\frac{\partial f}{\partial t}\right)_{\text{coll.}}} .$$

(*a*) Suppose $\mathbf{r}(t_0)$ and $\mathbf{v}(t_0)$ are prescribed, show that if

$$\mathbf{r} = \mathbf{r}(\mathbf{r}_0, \mathbf{v}_0, t_0, t) ,$$

$$\mathbf{v} = \mathbf{v}(\mathbf{r}_0, \mathbf{v}_0, t_0, t) ,$$

$$f(\mathbf{r}, \mathbf{v}, t) - f(\mathbf{r}_0, \mathbf{v}_0, t_0) = \int_{t_0}^{t} \left(\frac{\partial f}{\partial t}\right)_{\text{coll.}} dt$$

and interpret the result.

(*b*) How could this technique be applied to one-dimensional stationary shock waves?

(11) If (r, θ, z) are the usual cylindrical coordinates and if $\mathbf{A}$ is a vector potential, prove that

$$f\left(\frac{1}{2} mv^2, mr^2\dot{\theta} + erA_\theta\right)$$

is a stationary solution of the Boltzmann equation when the magnetic field is azimuthally symmetric.

(12) Assume that the force density term for a plasma can be written in the form

$$\mathbf{f} = \epsilon_0(\nabla \cdot \mathbf{E})\mathbf{E} + (\epsilon - \epsilon_0)\left[\frac{\partial}{\partial t}(\mathbf{E}\text{x}\mathbf{B}) + \frac{1}{2}\nabla\mathbf{E}^2 - (\mathbf{E} \cdot \nabla)\mathbf{E}\right]$$

where ϵ is a scalar function of position.

(*a*) Show that

$$\int_V \mathbf{f} \cdot \mathbf{r} dV = \int_T \Big[\epsilon(\nabla \cdot \mathbf{E})(\mathbf{E} \cdot \mathbf{r}) - \frac{1}{2}(\epsilon - \epsilon_0)E^2$$

$$+ (\mathbf{E} \cdot \mathbf{r})(\mathbf{E} \cdot \nabla\epsilon) - \frac{1}{2} E^2(\mathbf{r} \cdot \nabla\epsilon) \Big] dV$$

$$+ \int_V (\epsilon - \epsilon_0)\mathbf{r} \cdot \frac{\partial}{\partial t}(\mathbf{E}\mathrm{x}\mathbf{B}) dV$$

$$+ \int_S \left[\frac{1}{2} E^2(\epsilon - \epsilon_0)\mathbf{r} - (\mathbf{E} \cdot \mathbf{r})(\epsilon - \epsilon_0)\mathbf{E} \right] \cdot d\mathbf{S}$$

where V and S are respectively the volume and surface of a plasmoid.

(*b*) Assume $\nabla \cdot \mathbf{E} = \mathbf{E} \cdot \nabla\epsilon = 0$ (transverse waves) and reduce the expression in (a).

(*c*) Let $\epsilon - \epsilon_0 = -C_1 \exp[-C_2\langle E^2\rangle]$, $C_1 > 0$, $C_2 > 0$; assume that if a plasmoid exists, $\langle E^2\rangle$ is a minimum at the center and becomes a maximum on an outer surface. Using this outer surface as the bounding surface S integrate the result of (b) and note that since this surface is also a surface of constant ϵ, $\mathbf{E} \cdot d\mathbf{S} = 0$; ignoring the radiation energy and assuming the plasmoid lasts longer than the time for the wave to have extended beyond the integration surface, show that

$$\int_V (\epsilon - \epsilon_0)\mathbf{r} \cdot \frac{\partial}{\partial t}(\mathbf{E}\mathrm{x}\mathbf{B}) dV$$

can be neglected, so that

$$\int_V f \cdot \mathbf{r} dV = \int_V (\epsilon - \epsilon_0)\left(\frac{1}{2}\mathbf{r} \cdot \nabla E^2 + E^2\right) dV$$

(*d*) Prove that if E^2 is monotone increasing from the interior of the plasmoid to the surface of integration, the integral in (c) is negative..

(*e*) Identify

$$\int_V \mathbf{f} \cdot \mathbf{r} dV \quad \text{with} \quad \int_V x_i \sum_s N_s \langle F_i \rangle dV$$

and use the preceding results to show that self-confinement of a plasmoid is possible.

(*f*) Does this result contradict the conclusion obtained from the virial theorem? Discuss the conclusion in both cases.

(*g*) If the permittivity varies as in (c), can transverse field standing waves exist in a simply connected plasmoid? In multiply connected plasmoids, *e.g.*, a torus?

(13) Show that if the collisionless Boltzmann equation is satisfied then $dS/dt = 0$, where S is the entropy defined by eq. (99.2).

(14) By reasoning as in the two and three dimensional cases, deduce the adiabatic equation of state for a one-dimensional collisionless gas.

(15) The existence of longitudinal waves in a non-homogeneous plasma (variable electron density) can be studied in a simple way by using the following system of equations.

$$\text{curl } \mathbf{E} = -\frac{\partial \mathbf{B}}{\partial t},$$

$$\text{curl } \mathbf{H} = q \int_V \mathbf{V} f(\mathbf{r}, \mathbf{v}, t) d^3\mathbf{V} + \epsilon_0 \frac{\partial \mathbf{E}}{\partial t}$$

$$\frac{\partial f}{\partial t} + \text{div } (\mathbf{V} f) = 0$$

$$\frac{\partial \mathbf{V}}{\partial t} + \mathbf{V} \cdot \text{grad } \mathbf{V} = \frac{q}{m} [\mathbf{E} + \mathbf{V} \mathbf{x} \mathbf{B}],$$

where q is the electronic charge.

The distribution function is defined through the relation

$$\rho(\mathbf{r}, t) = \int_V f(\mathbf{r}, \mathbf{V}, t) d^3\mathbf{V} \quad .$$

(*a*) If subscript zero denotes the undisturbed state and lower case letters denote the perturbations from the undisturbed state, show that the linearized form of the system of equations above is

$$\text{curl } \mathbf{e} = -\mu_0 \frac{\partial \mathbf{h}}{\partial t} \quad ,$$

$$\text{curl } \mathbf{h} = q \int_{V_0} (\mathbf{V}_0 f_1 + \mathbf{v} f_0) d^3\mathbf{V}_0 + \epsilon_0 \frac{\partial \mathbf{e}}{\partial t} \quad ,$$

$$\frac{\partial f_1}{\partial t} + f_0 \text{ div } (\mathbf{v}) + \mathbf{V}_0 \cdot \text{grad } f_1 + \mathbf{v} \cdot \text{grad } f_0 = 0 \quad ,$$

$$\frac{\partial \mathbf{v}}{\partial t} + \mathbf{V}_0 \cdot \text{grad } \mathbf{v} = \frac{q}{m} (\mathbf{e} + \mu_0 \mathbf{V}_0 \mathbf{x} \mathbf{h}) \quad ,$$

where,

$$f = f_0(\mathbf{r}, \mathbf{V}_0) + f_1(\mathbf{r}, \mathbf{V}_0, \mathbf{v}, t) \quad ,$$

$$\mathbf{V}(\mathbf{r}, t) = \mathbf{V}_0(\mathbf{r}) + \mathbf{v}(\mathbf{r}, \mathbf{V}_0, t) \quad .$$

(*b*) Consider an inhomogeneity only in the x_1-direction so that

$$|\text{grad } f_0| = \left| \frac{\partial f_0}{\partial x} \right| \quad ,$$

(dropping subscript for convenience) and assume that $\mathbf{e}, \mathbf{h}, \mathbf{v}$ and f_1 are all of the form (Eikonal ansatz),

$$\exp \left\{ i \left[\omega t + \int_0^{\mathbf{r}} \mathbf{K}(x) \cdot d\mathbf{r} \right] \right\}$$

and restrict $\mathbf{K}(x)$ so that

$$|\mathbf{K}| = K_x \equiv k(x) \quad .$$

Show that for pure longitudinal wave fields, $\mathbf{K}$ is parallel to $\mathbf{e}, \mathbf{h}$ and $\mathbf{v}$, and that the above system of equations becomes

$$i\epsilon_0 \omega e_x + q \int_{V_0} (V_{0x} f_1 + v_x f_0) d^3\mathbf{V}_0 = 0 \quad ,$$

$$i\omega f_1 + v_x \frac{\partial f_0}{\partial x} + i(V_{0x} f_1 + v_x f_0)k = 0 \quad ,$$

$$i\omega v_x + iV_{0x} v_x k = \frac{q}{m} e_x \quad .$$

(c) Show that for a non-trivial solution to exist it is necessary to satisfy the dispersion equation

$$\omega = \frac{q^2}{\epsilon_0 m} \int_{V_0} \frac{iV_{0x} \dfrac{\partial f_0}{\partial x} + \omega f_0}{(\omega + V_{0x} k)^2} d^3\mathbf{V}_0 \quad .$$

(d) Assume f_0 varies only in the x-direction and that $V_{0x} = V =$ constant, deduce that

$$k = -\frac{\omega}{V} \pm \left(\frac{\omega_c^2}{V^2} + \frac{i}{V} \frac{\omega_c^2}{\omega} \frac{\rho'}{\rho} \right)^{1/2} \quad ,$$

where

$$\omega_c^2 = \frac{\rho q^2}{\epsilon_0 m} \,, \quad \rho(x) = \int_{V_0} f_0 d^3\mathbf{V}_0 \,, \quad \rho' = \frac{\partial \rho}{\partial x} \,.$$

(e) Find the real and imaginary parts of k and show that as $\rho' \to 0$ (the uniform plasma),

$$Re(k) \to -\frac{\omega}{V} \pm \frac{\omega_c}{V_0} \quad ,$$

and $Im(k) \to 0$.

(*f*) In the system of equations in (b), replace $i\omega$ by $\partial/\partial t$ and ik by $\partial/\partial x$. Describe a method by which the resulting system can be used as the basis of an iteration procedure to find the longitudinal waves in an inhomogeneous medium.

(16) Consider a magneto-plasma with magnetic field applied in the x_3-direction. Assume that the radio frequency magnetic field is neglected and that an electron is brought to rest at each collision. Let the propagation of a very high frequency circularly polarized wave be restricted in direction along the applied magnetic field and consider only the extraordinary ray.

(*a*) Assume the following conditions for an electron:

$$v_1 = v_2 = 0 , \quad \dot{v}_1 = -\frac{eE_0}{m} \sin \omega t' , \quad \dot{v}_2 = -\frac{eE_0}{m} \cos \omega t' ,$$

where t' is the time at which an electron makes a collision. Show that

$$v_1 - iv_2 = \frac{eE_0}{m(\omega - \omega_L)} \left\{ e^{i\omega t} - e^{i[\omega_L t + (\omega - \omega_L)t']} \right\}$$

where ω_L is the electron gyro-frequency.

(*b*) If n is the electron density, define the collision frequency ν by the formula

$$dn = n\nu e^{-\nu(t-t')} dt' ,$$

show that the current density is given by

$$J_1 - iJ_2 = \frac{-n\nu e^2 E_0}{m(\omega - \omega_L)} \int_{-\infty}^{t} \left\{ e^{i\omega t} - e^{i[\omega_L t + (\omega - \omega_L)t']} \right\} e^{-\nu(t-t')} dt'$$

and find the integrated forms of J_1 and J_2.

(*c*) Prove that if the electric field is moving in the direction of increasing x_3 with phase constant β and wave frequency ω_0 then an electron moving in the same direction with velocity $v_3 = v$ is subjected to an angular frequency $\omega_0 - \beta v$. Interpret as a Doppler shift.

(*d*) Suppose dn_0 electrons per unit volume have an x_3-component of velocity between v and $v + dv$ and if the velocity distribution is given by

$$dn_0 = n_0 \left(\frac{m}{2\pi kT}\right)^{1/2} \exp\left(-\frac{mv^2}{2kT}\right) dv \quad ,$$

show that the contribution to J_1 and J_2 in a coordinate system moving with velocity v in the x_3 direction is

$$dJ_1 = \frac{n_0 e^2 E_0}{m} \left(\frac{m}{2\pi kT}\right)^{1/2} \exp\left(-\frac{mv^2}{2kT}\right)\left[\frac{\nu \sin \omega t - (\omega - \omega_L) \cos \omega t}{\nu^2 + (\omega - \omega_L)^2}\right] dv \quad ,$$

$$dJ_2 = \frac{n_0 e^2 E_0}{m} \left(\frac{m}{2\pi kT}\right)^{1/2} \exp\left(-\frac{mv^2}{2kT}\right)\left[\frac{\nu \cos \omega t + (\omega - \omega_L) \sin \omega t}{\nu^2 + (\omega - \omega_L)^2}\right] dv \quad ,$$

where $\omega = \omega_0 - \beta v$.

(*e*) Prove that by transforming back to the original reference frame the amplitude of dJ_1 and dJ_2 is unchanged but the frequency becomes ω_0, and that

$$\begin{pmatrix} J_1 \\ J_2 \end{pmatrix} = \frac{n_0 e^2 E_0}{m} \left(\frac{m}{2\pi kT}\right)^{1/2} \int_{-\infty}^{\infty} \exp\left(-\frac{mv^2}{2kT}\right) \begin{pmatrix} \nu \sin \omega_0 t - (\omega - \omega_L) \cos \omega_0 t \\ \nu \cos \omega_0 t + (\omega - \omega_L) \sin \omega_0 t \end{pmatrix} \left[\nu^2 + (\omega - \omega_L)^2\right]^{-1} dv \ .$$

(*f*) Show that the parts of J_1 and J_2 which are in phase with E_1 and E_2 are equal and correspond to a transverse conductivity,

$$\sigma_T = \frac{n_0 e^2}{m} \left(\frac{m}{2kT}\right)^{1/2} \int_{-\infty}^{\infty} \exp\left(-\frac{mv^2}{2kT}\right)\left[\frac{\nu}{\nu^2 + (\omega_0 - \omega_L - \beta v)^2}\right] dv \quad ,$$

and a transverse permittivity,

$$\epsilon_T = \epsilon_0 - \frac{n_0 e^2}{\omega_0 m} \left(\frac{m}{2\pi kT}\right)^{1/2} \int_{-\infty}^{\infty} \exp\left(-\frac{mv^2}{2kT}\right)\left[\frac{\omega_0 - \omega_L - \beta v}{\nu^2 + (\omega_0 - \omega_L - \beta v)^2}\right] dv \ .$$

(17) In the previous problem let T denote the effective temperature corresponding to the thermal motion of the electrons parallel to the applied magnetic field lines. Assume that this temperature T is large and that the collision frequency is small in the sense that

$$\nu \ll \beta \left(\frac{kT}{m}\right)^{1/2} .$$

(a) Prove that unless $\omega_0 - \omega_L - \beta v < \nu$, then

$$\left[\frac{\nu}{\nu^2 + (\omega_0 - \omega_L - \beta v)^2}\right]$$

is a small quantity.

(b) Show that within this narrow range of values of v, the conductivity σ is given by

$$\sigma \approx \frac{\pi n_0 e^2}{\beta m}\left(\frac{m}{2\pi kT}\right)^{1/2} \exp\left\{-\frac{m}{2kT}\left[\frac{(\omega_0 - \omega_L)}{\beta}\right]^2\right\}.$$

(c) Consider the integral in (16f) for ϵ_T. Make the following transformations;

$$t = \left(\frac{m}{2kT}\right)^{1/2} v , \quad t_0 = \left(\frac{m}{2kT}\right)^{1/2}\left[\frac{(\omega_0 - \omega_L)}{\beta}\right] , \quad z = t - t_0 ,$$

and set $\nu = 0$. Show that the integral becomes

$$I = -\beta^{-1}\int_{-\infty}^{\infty}\frac{e^{-(z+t_0)^2}}{z}\,dz .$$

Define the integral by

$$-\beta I = e^{-t_0^2}\lim_{\epsilon\to 0}\left[\int_{-\infty}^{-\epsilon}\exp\left(-z^2 - 2t_0 z\right)\frac{dz}{z} + \int_{+\epsilon}^{+\infty}\exp\left(-z^2 - 2t_0 z\right)\frac{dz}{z}\right],$$

replace z by $-z$ in the first integral, hence show that

$$\frac{\beta I}{2} = e^{-t_0^2} \int_0^\infty \frac{e^{-z^2/2}}{z} \sinh 2t_0 z \, dz \ .$$

Evaluate the above integral by expanding $\sinh 2t_0 z$ and integrate term-wise.

(*d*) Using the results of (e) above; assume that the conductivity is small, show that the absorption coefficient can be calculated from the formula

$$\kappa = \frac{\sigma_T}{2\omega\epsilon_T} = \frac{\sigma_T}{2\omega\epsilon_0 p^2} \ ,$$

where,

$$p^2 = 1 - \frac{2V_0}{v_L} \frac{\omega_c^2}{\omega_0^2 p} \exp\left\{-\frac{V_0^2}{v_L^2 p^2}\left[\frac{(\omega_0 - \omega_L)}{\omega_0}\right]^2\right\}\left[\frac{V_0}{v_L p}\left(\frac{\omega_0 - \omega_L}{\omega_0}\right)\right.$$

$$\left. - \frac{1}{3}\frac{V_0^3}{v_L^3 p^3}\left(\frac{\omega_0 - \omega_L}{\omega_0}\right)^3 + \ldots,\right]$$

and

$$v_L = \left(\frac{2kT}{m}\right)^{1/2} \ ;$$

note that p is the real part of the refractive index, $V_0^2 = (\mu_0 \epsilon_0)^{-1}$.

(*e*) Put

$$\omega_c^2 = \frac{n_0 e^2}{m\epsilon_0}$$

and hence show that

$$\kappa = \frac{\sqrt{\pi}}{2} \frac{V_0}{v_L} \frac{\omega_c^2}{\omega_0^2 p^3} \exp\left[-\frac{V_0^2}{v_L^2 p^2}\left(\frac{\omega_0 - \omega_L}{\omega_0}\right)^2\right].$$

(18) (*a*) If $f(v)$ is a velocity distribution function parallel to the magnetic field defined by

$$dn_0 = n_0 f(v) dv \quad ,$$

$$\int_{-\infty}^{\infty} f(v) dv = 1 \quad ;$$

show that the transverse conductivity of the plasma can be written in the form

$$\sigma_T = \frac{\pi n_0 e^2}{\beta m} f\left(\frac{\omega_0 - \omega_L}{\beta}\right) ,$$

and the attenuation coefficient takes the form

$$\alpha = \frac{\pi e^2 \mu_0}{2m} \frac{\omega_0}{\beta^2} n_0 f\left(\frac{\omega_0 - \omega_L}{\beta}\right) .$$

(*b*) Describe how the electron velocity distribution parallel to the magnetic field can be obtained from the experimentally observable quantities.

(*c*) Suppose that the distribution function also depends on x_3 and that the rate of change of attenuation per wavelength is not too large, then along the transmission path $\int \alpha dx_3$ measures the total attenuation approximately. Describe how the "average" distribution function can be determined.

(19) (*a*) Using (16f) and assuming ν is independent of v, show that if

$$\nu >> \beta \left(\frac{kT}{m}\right)^{1/2} ,$$

(the cold plasma),

$$\sigma_T = \frac{ne^2}{m} \frac{\nu}{\nu^2 + (\omega_0 - \omega_L)^2} ,$$

$$\frac{\epsilon_T}{\epsilon_0} = 1 - \omega_c^2 \frac{(\omega_0 - \omega_L)}{\nu^2 + (\omega_0 - \omega_L)^2} .$$

(*b*) If $(\omega_0 - \omega_L) << \nu$ find σ_T; also if $\nu << (\omega_0 - \omega_L)$ find σ_T.

(20) (*a*) Show, by using the results of (16a), that if no collisions take place, an electron starting from rest at $t = 0$ acquires a kinetic energy in a time t equal to

$$\frac{1}{2}\frac{e^2E_0}{m}\left\{\frac{\sin\left[\left(\frac{\omega - \omega_L}{2}\right)\right]t}{\frac{\omega - \omega_L}{2}}\right\}^2 .$$

(*b*) For a cold plasma, assume as in (19b), $\nu >> (\omega_0 - \omega_L)$, show that the time rate of change of the kinetic energy [as given in (a)] reduces to $(e^2E_0^2/m)t$, and that the average rate of absorption per electron is $(e^2E_0^2/m)\nu^{-1}$.

(*c*) Assume $\nu << \omega_0 - \omega_L$, show that the kinetic energy acquired by an electron when averaged over a long time between collisions is

$$\frac{e^2E_0^2}{m(\omega_0 - \omega_L)^2} .$$

Prove that if on the average this amount of energy is given up by an electron at each collision, the average rate of absorption of energy per electron is

$$\frac{e^2E_0^2}{m(\omega_0 - \omega_L)^2}\nu .$$

(*d*) Compare the results of (b) and (c) with those obtained from (19b) and interpret.

(21) Consider a "hot" plasma such that

$$\nu << \beta\left(\frac{kT}{m}\right)^{1/2} .$$

(*a*) Integrate over all frequencies

$$\frac{ne^2}{m}\int_{-\infty}^{\infty}\frac{\nu}{\nu^2+(\omega-\omega_L)^2}\,d\omega$$

and show that the absorption is independent of ν to first order if ν is sufficiently small. Explain why this is so physically.

(*b*) If ν is a function of v, under what conditions is the foregoing analysis valid?

(22) Let $\mathbf{v}_0$ be the equilibrium velocity of an electron in a uniform electron plasma with distribution function $f(\mathbf{v}_0)$. In the absence of an applied magnetic field show that the velocity of the electron in the perturbed state is given by

$$\mathbf{v} = \mathbf{v}_0 - \frac{ie}{m}\,\frac{\mathbf{E}(\mathbf{r},t)}{(\omega-\mathbf{K}\cdot\mathbf{v})}$$

provided $\mathbf{E}(\mathbf{r},t) = \mathbf{E}\exp[i(\omega t - \mathbf{K}\cdot\mathbf{r})]$ and $e\mathbf{v}_0\mathbf{x}\mathbf{B}$ are neglected.

(*a*) Assume that the equilibrium distribution $f(\mathbf{v}_0)$ is an even function of $\mathbf{v}_0$ and that the current distribution is defined by

$$\mathbf{J} = e\int \mathbf{v}f(\mathbf{v}_0)\,d^3\mathbf{v}_0 ,$$

show that

$$\mathbf{J} = \frac{-ie^2}{m}\,\mathbf{E}(\mathbf{r},t)\int\frac{f(\mathbf{v}_0)}{(\omega-\mathbf{K}\cdot\mathbf{v}_0)}\,d^3\mathbf{v}_0 .$$

(*b*) Assume that at the singular point defined by $\omega - \mathbf{K}\cdot\mathbf{v}_0 = 0$, the distribution function is approximately zero and write

$$\frac{1}{\omega-\mathbf{K}\cdot\mathbf{v}_0} = \frac{1}{\omega}+\frac{1}{\omega^2}\,\mathbf{K}\cdot\mathbf{v}_0 + \frac{1}{\omega^3}\,(\mathbf{K}\cdot\mathbf{v}_0)^2 + \ldots,$$

deduce the result

$$\mathbf{J} = \frac{-ie^2n_0}{m\omega}\left(1+\frac{1}{3}\frac{K^2}{\omega^2}\,\langle v_0^2\rangle + \ldots,\right)\mathbf{E}(\mathbf{r},t) .$$

(*c*) If $\mathbf{H}$ denotes the perturbation in the magnetic field then

$$\nabla \mathbf{x} \mathbf{H} = \mathbf{J} + \epsilon_0 \frac{\partial \mathbf{E}}{\partial t} .$$

Use the result of (b) for $\mathbf{J}$ and show that the dielectric constant is given by

$$\epsilon = \epsilon_0 \left[1 - a\left(1 + \frac{1}{3}\frac{K^2}{\omega^2} \langle v_0^2 \rangle + \ldots,\right)\right] ,$$

where

$$a = \frac{\omega_c^2}{\omega^2} , \ \omega_c \text{ is the plasma frequency.}$$

(*d*) Show that the electrostatic modes of oscillation are governed by the dispersion relation

$$\omega^2 = \omega_c^2 + \frac{1}{3} K^2 \langle v_0^2 \rangle + \ldots, \quad .$$

Interpret the result in terms of the temperature of the electrons.

(23) Consider a low density collisionless electron plasma and denote by $f_0(\mathbf{r},\mathbf{v})$ the equilibrium distribution function which is normalized to unity. Let

$$f(\mathbf{r},\mathbf{v},t) = n_0 f_0(\mathbf{r},\mathbf{v}) + f_1(\mathbf{r},\mathbf{v},t) ,$$

where f_1 is a small perturbation from the equilibrium distribution. In the absence of an applied magnetic field and with the following definition of $\mathbf{E}$,

$$\mathbf{E}(\mathbf{r}, t) = e \iint \frac{(\mathbf{r} - \mathbf{r}')}{|\mathbf{r} - \mathbf{r}'|^3} f_1(\mathbf{r}',\mathbf{v}',t) d^3\mathbf{r}' d^3\mathbf{v}' ,$$

(*a*) Show by using the linearized form of the collisionless Boltzmann equation that

$$\frac{\partial f_1}{\partial t} = i\mathbf{L} f_1 ,$$

where $\mathbf{L}$ is a linear integro-differential operator.

(*b*) Exhibit the form of the operator and prove that it is Hermitian.

(*c*) Put $f_n(\mathbf{r},\mathbf{v},t) = e^{i\omega_n t} f_n(\mathbf{r},\mathbf{v})$, where ω_n is real, and prove that the operator $i(\partial/\partial\mathbf{r})$ commutes with the operator $\mathbf{L}$.

(*d*) Set $f_n(\mathbf{r},\mathbf{v}) = g_n(\mathbf{v})e^{-iK\cdot r}$ in the equation $\omega_n f_n = \mathbf{L}f_n$ and use the result

$$\int d^3\mathbf{r}' \frac{\mathbf{r}-\mathbf{r}'}{|\mathbf{r}-\mathbf{r}'|^3} e^{-iK\cdot(r'-r)} = 4\pi i \frac{\mathrm{K}}{K^2}$$

to show that

$$g_n(\mathbf{v}) = \frac{\omega_c^2}{K^2}\left(\mathbf{K}\cdot\frac{\partial}{\partial\mathbf{v}}\right)f_0 \frac{1}{(\mathbf{K}\cdot\mathbf{v}-\omega)}\int d^3\mathbf{v} g_n(\mathbf{v}) .$$

(*e*) Normalize $g_n(\mathbf{v})$ such that $\int g_n(\mathbf{v})d^3\mathbf{v} = 1$ and find from (d) that

$$g_n(\mathbf{v}) = \frac{\omega_c^2}{K^2}\left(\mathbf{K}\cdot\frac{\partial}{\partial\mathbf{r}}\right)f_0 \frac{1}{(\mathbf{K}\cdot\mathbf{v}-\omega)} ,$$

and hence,

$$\frac{\omega_c^2}{K^2}\mathbf{K}\cdot\int d^3\mathbf{v}\frac{\partial f_0}{\partial\mathbf{v}}\frac{1}{(\mathbf{K}\,.\,\mathbf{v}-\omega)} = 1 .$$

(*f*) Integrate the above expression by parts, assume f_0 is an even function of $\mathbf{v}$ and expand the denominator in the expression

$$\omega_c^2\int\frac{f_0(\mathbf{v})}{(\mathbf{K}\cdot\mathbf{v}-\omega)^2}d^3\mathbf{v} = 1$$

to find the dispersion equation

$$\left(\frac{\omega}{\omega_c}\right)^2 = 1 + \frac{K^2}{\omega_c^2}\langle v^2\rangle + \ldots, .$$

What condition must be imposed on f_0 so that the above integral is meaningful?

(24) In the collisionless Boltzmann equation for a particle species (not necessarily electrons) assume that both $\partial f_0/\partial t$ and $\mathbf{v} \cdot (\partial f_0/\partial \mathbf{r})$ can be neglected so that

$$\frac{q}{m}(\mathbf{E} + \mathbf{v}\mathrm{x}\mathbf{B}) \cdot \frac{\partial f_0}{\partial \mathbf{v}} = 0$$

is valid where $\mathbf{B}$ is the total magnetic field.

(*a*) Define the vector

$$\mathbf{u} = \mathbf{v} - \frac{\mathbf{E}\mathrm{x}\mathbf{B}}{E^2}$$

and first show that $\mathbf{u}\mathrm{x}\mathbf{B} = (\mathbf{E} + \mathbf{v}\mathrm{x}\mathbf{B}) - \mathbf{E}_B$, where $\mathbf{E}_B$ is the projection of $\mathbf{E}$ in the direction of $\mathbf{B}$.

(*b*) Assume $\mathbf{E}_B = 0$, show that $\partial f_0/\partial \mathbf{v}$ has no component in the direction of $\mathbf{u}\mathrm{x}\mathbf{B}$ and hence f_0 must be constant on the circles u = constant, and therefore the distribution is isotropic.

(*c*) From the above result prove that $f_0(\mathbf{r}, \mathbf{v}, t)$ must have the structure $f_0(u, v_B, \mathbf{r}, t)$ where v_B is the magnitude of $\mathbf{v}_B$.

(*d*) Argue that a sufficient condition for the neglecting of $\partial f/\partial t$ and $\mathbf{v} \cdot (\partial f/\partial \mathbf{r})$ is that the gyro-frequency $(q/m)B$ is very much larger than both of the neglected terms. Use a dimensional argument.

(*e*) Show that the pressure tensor p_{iK} in a local coordinate system with the x_3-axis along $\mathbf{B}$ has the form

$$p_{iK} = \begin{pmatrix} p_\perp & 0 & 0 \\ 0 & p_\perp & 0 \\ 0 & 0 & p_B \end{pmatrix},$$

where $p_\perp$ is the component perpendicular to $\mathbf{B}$.

(*f*) If $(q/m) \gg 1$ is used as a parameter in a series expansion of f show that the first order equation for f_1 is

$$\frac{\partial f_0}{\partial t} + \mathbf{v} \cdot \frac{\partial f_0}{\partial \mathbf{r}} + \frac{q}{m}(\mathbf{E}_0 + \mathbf{v}\mathrm{x}\mathbf{B}_0) \cdot \frac{\partial f_1}{\partial \mathbf{v}} = 0 .$$

(25) Consider a fluid vacuum interface such that inside the fluid the following equations are valid.

$$(i) \quad \frac{\partial \rho}{\partial t} + \text{div } (\rho \mathbf{v}) = 0 \,, \quad (\rho \text{ is the fluid mass density})$$

$$(ii) \quad \frac{d}{dt} (p\rho^{-\gamma}) = 0 \,, \quad (p \text{ is the pressure, } \gamma \text{ is ratio of specific heats})$$

$$(iii) \quad \rho \frac{d\mathbf{v}}{dt} = - \text{grad } p + \frac{1}{\mu_0} \text{curl } \mathbf{BxB} \,,$$

$$(iv) \quad \frac{\partial \mathbf{B}}{\partial t} = \text{curl } (\mathbf{vxB}) + \frac{1}{\mu_0 \sigma} \nabla^2 \mathbf{B} \,, \quad (\sigma \text{ is the conductivity}),$$

and inside the vacuum Maxwell's equations are satisfied. Neglect the displacement current in the fluid and assume infinite conductivity so that $\mathbf{E} + \mathbf{vxB} = 0$. Let $\mathbf{n}$ be the unit normal to the interface and denote by Δ the jump in any quantity across the interface.

(*a*) Show first that $\mathbf{nx} \, \Delta\mathbf{E} = (\mathbf{n} \cdot \mathbf{v})\Delta \mathbf{B}$.

(*b*) Assuming surface currents exist show that on the surface $\mathbf{nx} \, \Delta \mathbf{B} = \mu_0 \mathbf{J}_s$, where $\mathbf{J}_s$ is the surface current density.

(*c*) Let $\delta \mathbf{r}$ be a virtual displacement from one side of the boundary to the other, using (*iii*) above deduce that as $\delta \mathbf{r} \to 0$,

$$\delta\left(p + \frac{B^2}{2\mu_0}\right) = \Delta\left(p + \frac{B^2}{2\mu_0}\right) .$$

(*d*) Prove that if $\mathbf{n} \cdot \mathbf{B} = 0$ then infinite force densities can not arise at the boundary.

(*e*) Show that if the interface is a boundary between two fluids $\mathbf{n} \cdot \Delta\mathbf{v} = 0$ is a necessary boundary condition.

(*f*) Suppose the fluid is in contact with a rigid perfectly conductive boundary, prove that (a) and (e) become respectively $\mathbf{nxE} = 0$ and $\mathbf{n} \cdot \mathbf{v} = 0$, and therefore $\mathbf{n} \cdot (\partial \mathbf{B}/\partial t) = 0$.

(26) Deduce that for an infinitely conducting medium which satisfies an adiabatic equation of state, the system of hydromagnetic equations has an energy integral given by

$$\int_R \left(\frac{1}{2}\rho v^2 + \frac{p}{\gamma - 1} + \frac{B^2}{2\mu_0} \right) d\tau = \text{constant} ,$$

where R is the complete fluid vacuum volume, and interpret the terms separately.

(27) Prove by direct substitution that in an infinitely conducting unbounded and incompressible fluid, $\mathbf{B} = \mathbf{B}_0 + \mathbf{b}(x_1, x_2, x_3 \pm Vt)$

$$\left(\text{with } \mathbf{v} = \mp \frac{\mathbf{b}}{\sqrt{\mu_0 \rho_0}} , \quad V = \frac{B_0}{\sqrt{\mu_0 \rho_0}} \right)$$

is a solution of the non-linear hydromagnetic equations, where subscript zero denotes the equilibrium values of the variables shown. Contrast this with the plane wave solutions of the linearized system. Is the above true in a compressible fluid?

(28) Discuss the propagation of Alvén waves in a medium with an anisotropic pressure tensor.

(29) Discuss qualitatively the validity of the hydromagnetic equations starting from the Boltzmann equation with collision term.

PROBLEMS FOR CHAPTER IX

(1) If the field quantity $\mathbf{F}(t)$ varies sinusoidally with time it can be written in the form

$$\mathbf{F}(t) = \frac{1}{2}\left[\mathbf{F}e^{i\omega t} + \mathbf{F}^* e^{-i\omega t}\right] \quad .$$

Denote by $\mathbf{F}_1$ and $\mathbf{F}_2$ the real and imaginary parts of the complex amplitude $\mathbf{F}$ so that

$$\mathbf{F} = \mathbf{F}_1 + i\mathbf{F}_2 \ .$$

(*a*) Show that $\mathbf{F}(t)$ can be written in the form

$$\mathbf{F}(t) = \mathbf{F}_1 \cos \omega t - i\mathbf{F}_2 \sin \omega t \quad .$$

(*b*) Show that

$$\mathbf{F}_2 \mathbf{x} \mathbf{F}_1 = \frac{1}{2i} \mathbf{F} \mathbf{x} \mathbf{F}^*$$

is perpendicular to the plane of the ellipse defined by (a).

(*c*) Show that the modulus of $\mathbf{F}_2\mathbf{x}\mathbf{F}_1$ is equal to the area of the ellipse divided by π.

(2) From eq. (102.22) derive first the relation

(*a*) $$\left(\epsilon_1^2 - \epsilon_2^2 - \epsilon_1 \frac{K_1^2}{k_0^2}\right)\left[\epsilon_3 - (n_1^2 + n_2^2)\frac{K_1^2}{k_0^2}\right]$$

$$= \epsilon_3 n_3^2 \left(\epsilon_1 - \frac{K_1^2}{k_0^2}\right)\frac{K_1^2}{k_0^2}$$

where K_1 satisfies eq. (102.22) and $\mathbf{n} = (n_1, n_2, n_3)$ is the unit wave normal.

(b) Denote the electric field with propagation constant K_1 by $\mathbf{E}_{(1)}$. Using the relation (a) and eq. (102.13) with $\mu = \mathbf{I}$ show that

$$\mathbf{E}_{(1)} = \frac{\epsilon_3 n_3 E_3}{(n_1^2 + n_2^2)\left(\epsilon_2^2 - \epsilon_1^2 + \epsilon_1 \dfrac{K_1^2}{k_0^2}\right)} \mathbf{e}_{(1)} ,$$

where

$$\mathbf{e}_{(1)} = \begin{pmatrix} n_1\left(\epsilon_1 - \dfrac{K_1^2}{k_0^2}\right) + i n_2 \epsilon_2 \\ n_2\left(\epsilon_1 - \dfrac{K_1^2}{k_0^2}\right) - i n_1 \epsilon_2 \\ \dfrac{n_1^2 + n_2^2}{\epsilon_3 n_3}\left(\epsilon_2^2 - \epsilon_1^2 + \epsilon_1 \dfrac{K_1^2}{k_0^2}\right) \end{pmatrix}$$

Why does this vector define the polarization of $\mathbf{E}_{(1)}$? How is the polarization of $\mathbf{H}_{(1)}$ defined? If K_1 is replaced by K_2 how are the above results changed?

(3) Let the direction of propagation of a plane wave be in the direction of $\mathbf{B}_0$ so that $\mathbf{n} = (0,0,1)$. Show that

$$(a) \qquad \frac{K_1^2}{k_0^2} = \epsilon_1 + \epsilon_2 \; ; \quad \frac{K_2^2}{k_0^2} = \epsilon_1 - \epsilon_2 ,$$

and hence

$$\mathbf{E}_{(1)} = E_1 \begin{pmatrix} 1 \\ i \\ 0 \end{pmatrix}, \quad \mathbf{H}_{(1)} = H_1 \begin{pmatrix} 1 \\ i \\ 0 \end{pmatrix} ;$$

$$\mathbf{E}_{(2)} = E_1^* \begin{pmatrix} 1 \\ -i \\ 0 \end{pmatrix}, \quad \mathbf{H}_{(2)} = H_1^* \begin{pmatrix} 1 \\ -i \\ 0 \end{pmatrix}$$

(*b*) For $\mathbf{n} = (1,0,0)$, show that

$$\frac{K_1^2}{k_0^2} = \frac{\epsilon_1^2 - \epsilon_2^2}{\epsilon_1} \quad , \quad \frac{K_2^2}{k_0^2} = \epsilon_3 \quad ,$$

$$\mathbf{E}_{(1)} = E_2 \begin{bmatrix} i(\epsilon_2/\epsilon_1) \\ 1 \\ 0 \end{bmatrix} , \quad \mathbf{H}_{(1)} = H_3 \begin{pmatrix} 0 \\ 0 \\ 1 \end{pmatrix} ;$$

$$\mathbf{E}_{(2)} = E_3^* \begin{pmatrix} 0 \\ 0 \\ 1 \end{pmatrix} , \quad \mathbf{H}_{(2)} = H_2^* \begin{pmatrix} 0 \\ 1 \\ 0 \end{pmatrix} .$$

(4) Establish the identities in eqs. (104.8).

(5) Starting from eq. (106.1), set $\mathbf{M} = 0$, and consider the power radiated per unit length along the x_3-axis. Using the two dimensional Fourier Transform (Partial Transform),

$$\mathbf{J}(\mathbf{r}) = \iint_{-\infty}^{\infty} \mathbf{J}(K_1, K_2, x_3) e^{-i(K_1 x_1 + K_2 x_2)} dK_1 dK_2 \quad ,$$

and its inverse

$$\mathbf{J}(K_1, K_2, x_3) = \frac{1}{(2\pi)^2} \iint_{-\infty}^{\infty} \mathbf{J}(\mathbf{r}) e^{i(K_1 x_1 + K_2 x_2)} dx_1 dx_2 \quad ,$$

(*a*) Derive the result for the power radiated per unit length,

$$\frac{dP}{dx_3} = -\pi \int d\mathbf{K} \int_{-\infty}^{\infty} dx_3' \; \mathbf{J}^{*\prime}(K_1, K_2, x_3) \mathbf{g}_{EJ} \mathbf{J}(K_1, K_2, x_3') e^{-iK_3(x_3 - x_3')} \quad .$$

(*b*) Find tha analogous expression for the case of a magnetic current density. The above formula is useful in the study of Cerenkov radiation.

(6) Consider a cylinder parallel to the x_3-axis whose cross-sectional area is unity. To calculate the power radiated by a current distribution within the cylinder eq. (106.1) is used again. For $\mathbf{M} = 0$,

$$\frac{dP}{dA_{12}} \equiv -\frac{1}{2}\int_{-\infty}^{\infty} \mathbf{J}^{*\prime}\mathbf{E}\, dx_3 \quad ,$$

where $dA_{12} \equiv dx_1 dx_2$. Show, by using the partial Fourier Transform

$$\mathbf{J}(\mathbf{r}) = \int_{-\infty}^{\infty} dK_3 \mathbf{J}(x_1, x_2, K_3) e^{\neg K_3 x_3} \quad ,$$

and its inverse

$$\mathbf{J}(x_1, x_2, K_3) = \frac{1}{2\pi}\int_{-\infty}^{\infty} dx_3\, \mathbf{J}(\mathbf{r}) e^{iK_3 x_3} \quad ,$$

show that

(*a*)

$$\frac{dP}{dA_{12}} = -\frac{1}{4\pi}\int d\mathbf{K} \iint_{-\infty}^{\infty} dx_1' dx_2' \mathbf{J}^{*\prime}(x_1, x_2, K_3) \mathbf{g}_{EJ} \mathbf{J}(x_1', x_2', K_3) e^{-i[K_1(x_1 - x_1') + K_2(x_2 - x_2')]}$$

(*b*) Find the analogous expression for magnetic current distributions.

(7) Take a current distribution of the form

$$J_1 = I e^{-i(\omega/v)x_1} \delta(x_3) \quad ,$$

where I is the charge per unit length (amps/meter) in the x_2-direction.

(*a*) Apply the partial transform in problem (7) and find

$$J_1(x_1, x_2, K_3) = \frac{I}{2\pi} e^{-i(\omega/v)x_1}$$

(*b*) Show that the complex power radiated per unit area is

$$\frac{dP}{dA_{12}} = \frac{I^2}{16\pi^3} \int d\mathbf{K} \iint_{-\infty}^{\infty} dx_1' dx_2' g_{11}(\mathbf{K}) e^{-i\{(x_1 - x_1')[K_1 - (\omega/v)] + K_2(x_2 - x_2')\}} ,$$

where g_{11} is the element in the first row and first column of $\mathbf{g}_{EJ}$.

(*c*) Calculate the spatial integrations and obtain,

$$\frac{dP}{dA_{12}} = -\frac{I^2}{4\pi} \int d\mathbf{K} g_{11}(\mathbf{K}) \left(K_1 - \frac{\omega}{v}\right) \delta(K_2) e^{-i\{x_1[K_1 - (\omega/v)] + K_2 x_2\}}$$

$$= -\frac{I^2}{4\pi} \int_{-\infty}^{\infty} dK_3 g_{11}\left(\frac{\omega}{v}, 0, K_3\right) .$$

(*d*) From the definition of the wave matrix $\mathbf{W}_E$ and also det $\mathbf{W}_E$, find

$$g_{11}\left(\frac{\omega}{v}, 0, K_3\right) .$$

(*e*) Show that

$$\frac{dP}{dA_{12}} = i\omega\mu_0 \frac{I^2}{4\pi} \left[1 - \frac{(V_0/v)^2}{\epsilon_3}\right] \int_{-\infty}^{\infty} dK_3 \frac{K_3^2 + \frac{\omega^2}{v^2} - k_0^2 \epsilon_1}{\left[K_3^2 - K_{(1)}^2\right]\left[K_3^2 - K_{(2)}^2\right]}$$

where $V_0^2 = (\mu_0 \epsilon_0)^{-1}$ and $K_{(1)}$, $K_{(2)}$ are roots of the eq. (102.22).

(*f*) Assuming the medium as lossy so that $ImK_{(1)} < 0$, $ImK_{(2)} < 0$, apply the residue theorem to find

$$\frac{dP}{dA_{12}} = I^2 \left(\frac{\mu_0}{\epsilon_0}\right)^{1/2} \frac{\left[1 - \frac{(V_0^2/v)^2}{\epsilon_3}\right]}{\frac{4\left[K_{(1)} + K_{(2)}\right]}{k_0}} \left[1 + \frac{\left(\epsilon_1 - \frac{V_0^2}{v^2}\right)}{\frac{K_{(1)}K_{(2)}}{k_0^2}}\right]$$

(*g*) Let the medium be isotropic and lossless. Find the conditions under which real power can be radiated. Are the results similar to Cerenkov radiation?

(8) In section 105 an expression was obtained for the waves excited by a planar distribution of dipoles.

(*a*) What is the significance of the delta function term?

(*b*) Show that, with the aid of the identity in (2a) and the vector $\mathbf{e}_{(1)}$ in (2b), the matrix $\mathbf{D}_{EJ}$ can be put in the form

$$\mathbf{D}_{EJ}(K_{m1}\mathbf{m}) = \frac{k_0^4}{m_1^2 + m_2^2} \frac{\epsilon_3 - (m_1^2 + m_2^2)\dfrac{K_{m1}^2}{k_0^2}}{\epsilon_1 - \dfrac{K_{m1}^2}{k_0^2}} \mathbf{e}_{(1)}(\mathbf{m})\bar{\mathbf{e}}'_{(1)}(\mathbf{m}) \quad ,$$

where $\bar{\mathbf{e}}_{(1)}$ is obtained from $\mathbf{e}_{(1)}$ by replacing ϵ_2 with $-\epsilon_2$ and the prime indicates transpose. A similar result obtains for Km_2.

(*c*) Denote by P_r the real power. Show that the real power radiated per unit volume of the source is

$$\frac{dP_r}{dV} = -\frac{1}{2} Re\mathbf{J}^{*\prime}\mathbf{E}(0) \quad ,$$

where $\mathbf{E}(0)$ is found from eq. (105.13). Assume the medium is lossless, and consider a coordinate in the direction of $\mathbf{m}$. By integrating along this coordinate obtain the real power radiated per unit area of the current distribution;

(*d*)

$$\frac{dP_r}{dA} = -\frac{1}{4\omega\epsilon_0 \mathbf{m}'\epsilon\mathbf{m}(K_{m1}^2 - K_{m2}^2)} Re\left\{\mathbf{I}'\left[\frac{\mathbf{D}_{EJ}(K_{m1}\mathbf{m})}{K_{m1}} - \frac{\mathbf{D}_{EJ}(K_{m2}\mathbf{m})}{K_{m2}}\right]\mathbf{I}\right\} .$$

(*e*) In a lossless plasma, $\bar{\mathbf{e}}'_{(1)} = \mathbf{e}^*_{(1)}$. If P_{r1} is the power delivered to the wave defined by K_{m1}, and similarly for P_{r2}. Show that

$$\frac{P_{r1}}{P_{r2}} = \frac{ReK_{m1}}{ReK_{m2}} \left|\frac{\mathbf{e}^{*\prime}_{(1)}\mathbf{I}}{\mathbf{e}^{*\prime}_{(2)}\mathbf{I}}\right|^2 \frac{\epsilon_1^2 - \epsilon_2^2 - \epsilon_1\dfrac{K_{m2}^2}{k_0^2}}{\epsilon_1^2 - \epsilon_2^2 - \epsilon_1\dfrac{K_{m1}^2}{k_0^2}}$$

(*f*) Calculate the above ratio when $\mathbf{m} = (0,0,1)$.

(9) Consider a linearly polarized dipole moment $\mathbf{p}$. Show that the real power is given by

$$(a) \qquad P_r = \frac{\omega^2}{1} \mathbf{p}^{*\prime} \begin{pmatrix} R_1 & 0 & 0 \\ 0 & R_1 & 0 \\ 0 & 0 & R_1 \end{pmatrix} \mathbf{p} \quad .$$

(*b*) Plot this in a polar diagram. What is the figure of $(P_r)^{-1/2}$?

(*c*) Find P_r when $\mathbf{p}$ is parallel to $\mathbf{B}_0$, and perpendicular to $\mathbf{B}_0$.

(*d*) Calculate P_r for a circularly polarized dipole moment.

(10) Evaluate R_1, R_2, R_3 when

(*a*) $\epsilon_1 = \epsilon_3$, $\epsilon_2 = 0$

(*b*) $\epsilon_2 = 0$, $\epsilon_1 = \epsilon_3 > 0$

(*c*) $\epsilon_2 = 0$, $\epsilon_1 = \epsilon_3 < 0$

(*d*) $\epsilon_1 < 0$, $\epsilon_3 < 0$, $\epsilon_2^2 \leq \epsilon_1^2$, what is P_r?

(11) Consider the wave equation in the form

$$\mathbf{K}\mathbf{x}(\mathbf{K}\mathbf{x}\mathbf{E}) + k_0^2 \epsilon \mathbf{E} = 0 \quad .$$

To find the eigenfunctions and eigenvalues of this equation we replace $\mathbf{E}$ by $\mathbf{E}_\lambda$ and k_0 by K_λ. Suppose the medium is lossless then ϵ is Hermitian. Two distinct vectors are called ϵ-orthogonal if they satisfy the condition, $\mathbf{A}'\epsilon^*\mathbf{B}^* = 0$.

(*a*) Find the characteristic or secular equation satisfied by K_λ^2.

(*b*) Find the eigenvectors of the above wave equation.

(*c*) Show that, if K_λ^2 is real, the corresponding eigenvectors are ϵ-orthogonal.

(*d*) If K_λ^2 is not real, show that the eigenvectors are self orthogonal, that is, they satisfy $\mathbf{E}_\lambda'\epsilon^*\mathbf{E}_\lambda^* = 0$.

(*e*) If the medium is a lossless plasma, show that for very low frequency waves, K_λ^2 is real.

(*f*) Show that the eigenvectors do not form a basis for three-dimensional space; construct such a basis from them.

(*g*) How could the Green's tensor be represented in terms of this basis?

(12) Show that the Green's tensor defined by eq. (105.1) reduces to the free-space Green's tensor.

(*a*) Where are the poles located in this case?

(*b*) Show that the free-space Green's tensor takes the form

$$G_{ij}(\mathbf{r},\mathbf{r}') = \frac{i\omega\mu_0}{4\pi}\left(\frac{1}{k_0^2}\frac{\partial^2}{\partial x_i \partial x_j} + \delta_{ij}\right)\frac{e^{-ik_0 r}}{r} .$$

(13) Consider Maxwell's equations for time harmonic varying fields for a medium characterized by $\boldsymbol{\epsilon}$. Suppose that only electrical current distributions are given. Introduce scalar and vector potentials $\phi(\mathbf{r})$ and $\mathbf{A}(\mathbf{r})$ such that $\mathbf{E} = -i\omega\mu_0\mathbf{A} - \nabla\phi$.

(*a*) Derive the equation satisfied by $\mathbf{A}$.

(*b*) Show that $\mathbf{A}$ and ϕ are related by

$$\nabla^2\mathbf{A} + k_0^2\boldsymbol{\epsilon}\mathbf{A} + \mathbf{J} = \nabla(\nabla\cdot\mathbf{A}) + i\omega\epsilon_0\boldsymbol{\epsilon}\nabla\phi .$$

(*c*) Is it possible to satisfy the Lorentz condition, $\nabla(\nabla\cdot\mathbf{A}) + i\omega\epsilon_0\boldsymbol{\epsilon}\nabla\phi = 0$, with a single scalar function ϕ as in the isotropic case?

(*d*) Verify whether the following tensor with components

$$G_{11}(\mathbf{r},\mathbf{r}') = \frac{1}{8\pi}\left(\frac{e^{-iK_1R}}{R} + \frac{e^{-iK_2R}}{R}\right)$$

$$G_{22} = G_{11}, \quad G_{12} = \frac{-i}{8\pi}\left(\frac{e^{-iK_1R}}{R} - \frac{e^{-iK_2R}}{R}\right) = -G_{21} ,$$

$$G_{33} = \frac{1}{4\pi}\frac{e^{-iK_3R}}{R}, \quad G_{13} = G_{31} = G_{23} = G_{32} = 0 ,$$

where, $R = |\mathbf{r} - \mathbf{r}'|$, and $K_1^2 = k_0^2(\epsilon_1 + \epsilon_2)$, $K_2^2 = k_0^2(\epsilon_1 - \epsilon_3)$, $K_3^2 = k_0^2\epsilon_3$, is the Green's tensor of the equation,

$$(\nabla^2\mathbf{I} + k_0^2\epsilon)\mathbf{G}(\mathbf{r},\mathbf{r}') = -\delta(\mathbf{r} - \mathbf{r}')\mathbf{I} \ , \quad \mathbf{I} \equiv \delta_{ij} \ .$$

(*e*) Suppose that the Lorentz condition is satisfied, how are **A**, **G** and **J** related?

(*f*) Suppose an **A** has been found which satisfies all conditions of (b) and (c), show that

$$\mathbf{E} = \frac{-i}{\omega\epsilon_0}\left(k_0^2\mathbf{I} + \epsilon^{-1}\nabla\nabla'\right)\mathbf{A} \ ,$$

where ∇ is a row vector, ∇' its transpose, so that $\nabla\nabla'$ is a dyadic operator.

(*g*) With the Green's tensor as given in (d) calculate a vector potential defined by $\mathbf{A} = \int\mathbf{G}(\mathbf{r},\mathbf{r}')\mathbf{J}(\mathbf{r}')d^3\mathbf{r}'$ for a dipole $\mathbf{J} = (Idl)\delta(\mathbf{r}')\mathbf{e}$ placed at the origin, where **e** is a unit vector.

(*h*) From **A** as calculated in (g), calculate the field **E** defined in part (f).

(14) Find the Fourier transform of the tensor **G** defined in (13d) and call it **g**.

(*a*) Calculate the difference between **g** and $\mathbf{g}_{EJ}$ defined by eq. (104.13) and estimate the maximum error of $|\mathbf{g} - \mathbf{g}_{EJ}|$.

(*b*) Find the differential equation satisfied by $\mathbf{G} - \mathbf{G}_{EJ}$.

(*c*) Describe how **G** can be used for the approximate solution of radiation problems.

(15) Consider a magneto-ionic medium in which the effect of the heavy ions are included in the description of the permittivity tensor. Derive the conditions under which this tensor becomes diagonal.

(16) Suppose a current density of the form

$$Qv\frac{\mathbf{r}}{r^3}\delta(r - vt)$$

is prescribed in a magneto-ionic medium, where Q is the total charge, $\mathbf{v}$ is its radial velocity (*e.g.*, an expanding spherical shell).

(*a*) Can such a distribution radiate in an isotropic medium?

(*b*) Describe qualitatively the general features of the low frequency radiation of such a distribution in the presence of a magnetic field.

AUTHOR INDEX

SUBJECT INDEX